A GOLDEN TREASURY OF JEWISH LITERATURE

Books by Leo W. Schwarz

THE JEWISH CARAVAN:
GREAT STORIES OF TWENTY-FIVE CENTURIES

A GOLDEN TREASURY OF JEWISH LITERATURE

MEMOIRS OF MY PEOPLE

A Golden Treasury
of
Jewish Literature

SELECTED AND EDITED BY

LEO W. SCHWARZ

ILLUSTRATIONS BY

LIONEL S. REISS

RINEHART & COMPANY, INC.
NEW YORK   TORONTO

PREFACE

WHEREVER Jews have lived they have enriched society. Their contribution to the history of religion has been amply recognized but other equally significant contributions in the domain of social relations, thought and literature have been obscured or neglected. The Bible and Apocrypha, for example, are generally regarded as part of the Christian tradition of the West, and one is hardly surprised by a recently reported query of a Sunday School teacher: "Is the Hebrew Bible a good translation of the King James version?" Philo of Alexandria was for a considerable period accepted as a church father, and until less than a century ago students of philosophy considered *The Fountain of Life* by the poet-philosopher Ibn Gabirol, the work of a medieval Christian thinker. The utterance of Judah Maccabee's valiant father is still pertinent, "What nation hath not had a part in Israel's kingdom, and gotten of her spoils?"

Probably no other aspect of Jewish life has been so persistently misjudged and underestimated, both by Jews and non-Jews, as Jewish literature. That it is totally omitted from literary manuals is in itself significant. That it has been given scant and grudging appreciation by Jewish interpreters leads us to the root cause of this curious paradox. For modern society (the period, let us say, from September 28, 1791, when the National Assembly issued a decree granting French Jewry complete civil rights to September 15, 1935, when by the promulgation of the Nuremberg laws the German Jews were relegated to a juridical ghetto) almost destroyed the organic character of Jewish life and in Western countries made religion, sharply revised and modified, the axis of the community. The central interests of the theologian were liturgy and history. Literature became, not the occupation of men of letters, but the servant of the scholar and the rabbi. And because what was written in the two native Jewish tongues, Hebrew and Yiddish, was a sealed well to the outside world, it was inevitably concluded, despite the outcries of apologists, that there was no Jewish literature. Only during recent years has there been an unmistakable change in viewpoint. It has been due, in large measure, to the popularity of the novels of Sholem Asch and I. J. Singer and the translated works of other Hebrew and Yiddish authors. It is not surprising that one of Mark Van Doren's most valuable compilations, *An Anthology of World Poetry,* contains a considerable section devoted to Hebrew poetry.

What, then, is Jewish literature? Some commentators assert that it comprises everything written about Jews. Obviously, this definition extends the boundaries too far; we should have to include the harsh jibes of Horace and Meleager and the fulminations of Apion and Houston Stewart Chamberlain. Another view is that whatever Jews have written belongs to the realm of Jewish letters. But here the gauge is indiscriminate and confusing. What justification can one find for including Spinoza's *The Improvement of the Understanding,* Marx's *Das Kapital,* Bergson's *Creative Evolution* or Heine's *Buch der Lieder?* A third definition confines Jewish literature to writings in the Hebrew and Yiddish languages only. It is true that the bulk of Jewish classics were written in these tongues. It is also true, however, that the limitations of this linguistic norm would compel us to omit the larger part of the book of *Daniel* which was written in Aramaic, Halevi's masterful *Kuzari* and Maimonides' brilliant *Guide to the Perplexed,* both of which were written in Arabic, and the writings of Mendelssohn, Heine, Zangwill, Fleg, Lewisohn and numerous others who have expressed themselves in European languages. By the same logic, only the authors who have written in Celtic would be included in an anthology of Irish literature.

These considerations have led the editor to utilize a sociological approach to the subject. The Jews are a unique minority. They have never been bound together by allegiance to a sovereign state or even by the expectation of one in Palestine. Their chief basis of unity has been a loyalty to the traditions of history and religion and experience. That is why their literature, like their religion and history, is complicated by a strong mixture of the elements of nationality and universality. It is for the same reason that their literature is more properly understood as the expression of a group with a common history and problems and aspirations. It is our view therefore that Jewish literature is what Jews have written about themselves and their life in any language as well as their creations, whatever the subject matter, in the Hebrew and Yiddish tongues.

Before touching upon the specific aim of this volume, we must glance at the character and scope of Jewish literature. It is the oldest of literatures with an unbroken tradition of three thousand years or more. The earliest poem in the book, *The Song of Deborah and Barak,* belongs to the twelfth century before the common era and the latest one to the thirties of the twentieth century. It is as prodigious as it is ancient. Nor has any other literature portrayed so consistently and so graphically the essential triumph of the spirit of a people over the tragedy of its body. But it is a curious fact that whereas other literatures have one great representative who towers above all others—Spain her Cervantes, Germany her Goethe and England her Shakespeare—it is doubtful whether literary historians can discover a Jewish writer who is as representative. It has been brilliantly written: "It is possible to question whether the books of great Jews always belonged to the great books of the world. There may have been, and there were, greater legalists than Rashi, greater poets than Judah Halevi, greater philosophers than Maimonides, greater moralists than Bahya. But there has been no greater literature than that which these and numerous other Jews represent. . . . Rabbinism was a sequel to the Bible, and if like all sequels it was unequal to its original, it nevertheless shared its greatness. The works of all Jews up to the modern period were the sequel to this sequel. Through them all may be detected the unifying principle that literature in its truest sense includes life itself; that intellect is the handmaid to conscience; and that the best books are those which best teach men how to live. This underlying unity gave more harmony to Jewish literature than is possessed by many literatures more distinctively national. The maxim, 'Righteousness delivers from death,' applies to books as well as to men. A literature whose consistent theme is Righteousness is immortal." (Israel Abrahams)

It is the aim of this compilation to present, especially for our young adults, a literary autobiography of the Jewish people. The Jewish inheritance has meant little to the younger generation, it has meant less than nothing to non-Jews. The present educational setup has succeeded in severing rather than illuming the past. It is our belief that the live coal of Jewish literature can still touch the lips of its dispirited heirs and reveal a dignity, a vitality, and a beauty which may fortify all who love liberty and justice and peace.

This objective has led to a fresh arrangement of the literary materials. The conventional presentation of literature, according to countries and epochs and movements, might help to fix chronologically authors and their works; it would hardly serve the needs and tastes of a modern mind that wishes to look into its past in terms of its own present experience. This can be done, if progressive educational theory be correct, by beginning with contemporary times and turning the sleeve of history inside out. Hence the first section of the book, "Our Native Land," comprises a collection of stories by American writers, which indicate the problems and paradoxes of the present generation of American Jews. The second section, "Four Corners of the Earth," extends the picture to the four other continents where the remainder of the Jewish family is scattered. The selections in the third section, "Our Fathers That Begat Us," have been arranged to mirror the social and cultural roots of the modern Jew, as they reflect themselves in stories of atmosphere and character. The remaining four sections will take the reader back and forth over the seven seas of Jewish literature on galleons of humor, poetry, drama and prose.

The special design of the book and the exigencies of space have severely curtailed the number of selections. It has not been easy to exclude great bodies of ancient or medieval literature or masterful writings of modern and contemporary writers. Any one volume would be too small a vessel to hold so mighty a literary stream, but, however inadequate, the majesty and inspiration of a great literature should shine through it.

I am indebted to many authors, translators and publishers, particularly The Jewish Publication Society of America, The Menorah Journal and The Viking Press, for their generous co-operation. I wish to record my gratitude to Miss Kathryn Mansell of Sarah Lawrence College for reading the entire manuscript and for many invaluable suggestions. And I must also acknowledge the continual helpfulness of Miss Elizabeth L Gilman of the editorial staff of Farrar & Rinehart.

L. W. S.

New York City
May 20th, 1937

CONTENTS

PREFACE v

I. OUR NATIVE LAND

FOREWORD 2
A HERRING FOR MY UNCLE .... Albert Halper 3
HOW MANY ANGELS . . . . Irving Fineman 12
THE SAINT OF THE UMBRELLA STORE .... Michael Gold 20
MANASSEH .... S. Lieben 28
EGYPT, 1937 .... Meyer Levin 31
HEDER .... Henry Roth 38
RACHEL AND HER CHILD .... Myron Brinig 44
AARONS .... Edwin Seaver 54
THE FAST .... Edna Ferber 57
HOLY LAND .... Ludwig Lewisohn 69
OUR FATHERS THAT BEGAT US .... Marvin Lowenthal 76

II. FOUR CORNERS OF THE EARTH

FOREWORD 116
THE HAUNTED CINEMA .... Louis Golding 117
SAFE HARBOUR .... G. B. Stern 120
THE APPARITION .... Arnold Zweig 126
THE CASE OF AGATHON GEYER .... Jakob Wassermann 129
THE POOR JEWS .... André Maurois 135
THE OUTING .... Jean-Richard Bloch 138
MENDEL HERTZ .... Meir Aron Goldschmidt 150
THE ZADDIK .... Ilya Ehrenbourg 156
FROM BODANA'S DIARY .... I. Kipnis 159
MY PIGEON-HOUSE .... Isaac Babel 168
THE ACCOUNT .... Hayyim Hazaz 178
THE GRAVES OF THE MACCABEES .... David Shiminowitz 187
LATIFA .... Moses Smilansky 191
THE DECISION .... Sarah Gertrude Millin 195
BITTER MATÉ .... Samuel Glusberg 203

ix

III. OUR FATHERS THAT BEGAT US

FOREWORD 216
THREE GIFTS ....Isaac Loeb Perez............ 217
MALKAH ....I. J. Singer................ 225
A PASSOVER EVE ....Heinrich Heine.............. 233
JOSEPH CARO ....J. Opatoshu................ 237
A LETTER FROM AMERICA ....Leon Kobrin................ 240
THEY'RE LEAVING . . . .Simeon Yushkevitch......... 246
THE KISS ....L. Shapiro................. 251
GLASS ....I. D. Berkowitz............ 254
MILITARY SERVICE ....Judah Steinberg............ 260
A TALE OF BARNOW ....Karl Emil Franzos.......... 267
ESCAPADE ....Max Brod................... 271
ON TO BERLIN ....Solomon Maimon............. 278
KABBALISTS ....Lion Feuchtwanger.......... 283
ZIPPORAH'S WEDDING ....Glückel of Hameln.......... 290
QUEST FOR GOD ....Uriel Acosta............... 293
AMONG THE MARRANOS ....David Reubeni.............. 303

IV. LAUGHTER THROUGH TEARS

FOREWORD 318
THE KING OF SCHNORRERS............Israel Zangwill............ 319
BENJAMIN'S FIRST JOURNEY ....Mendele Mocher Seforim..... 332
PASSOVER FUGUE ....Sholem Aleichem............ 342
BEFORE I WAS BORN ....Joseph Cotler.............. 350
A POT STORY ....S. J. Agnon................ 355
MENDEL MARANTZ—HOUSEWIFE ....David Freedman............. 359
BABY MILLY AND THE PHARAOH ....Ben Hecht.................. 376
MRS. GROSS REMEMBERS ....Arthur Kober............... 389
MR. KAPLAN'S SO-AND-SO............Leonard Q. Ross............ 392

V. PLAYS OF A CHANGING WORLD

FOREWORD 400
MICHAL ....David Pinski............... 401
THE EVERLASTING ROAD ....Stefan Zweig............... 411
PAUL AND GAMALIEL ....Franz Werfel............... 426
SHYLOCK'S CHOICE ....John Cournos............... 436
URIEL ACOSTA ....Charles Reznikoff.......... 441
THE TRIAL ....S. Ansky................... 457
PROFESSOR BERNHARDI ....Arthur Schnitzler.......... 468
IN THE DARK ....Perez Hirschbein........... 504
THE SEER LOOKS AT HIS BRIDE ....Harry Sackler.............. 514

THE SINNER .... Sholem Asch 528
THAT SPECK .... S. N. Behrman 537

VI. RIPE POMEGRANATES

FOREWORD 544
THE SONG OF DEBORAH AND BARAK ..... Anonymous 545
LAMENT .... David ben Jesse.............. 547
SPRING SONG .... Anonymous ....:...... 548
LOVE .... Anonymous 549
TWO VISIONS .... Isaiah ben Amoz........... 550
TRAVAIL .... Jeremiah ben Hilkiah....... 552
HO, EVERY ONE THAT THIRSTETH ...... Anonymous 553
BEYOND KNOWLEDGE .... Anonymous 555
GO TO THE ANT, THOU SLUGGARD ...... Anonymous 555
DIVINE CHALLENGE .... Anonymous 556
GOD IN NATURE .... Anonymous 559
AS A SIGNET OF CARBUNCLE .... Simeon ben Sira........... 561
POEMS .... Eleazar ben Kalir........... 561
POEMS .... Solomon ibn Gabirol........ 564
POEMS .... Moses ibn Ezra............. 572
POEMS .... Judah Halevi............... 577
POEMS .... Abraham ibn Ezra........... 582
LOVE SONG .... Judah Alharizi............. 585
THE BURNING OF THE LAW .... Meir of Rothenburg........ 586
SPRING SONG .... Nahum 590
COME, MY BELOVED .... Solomon Halevi Alkabez..... 592
LOVED OF MY SOUL .... Israel Najara.............. 594
SONG .... Rachel Morpurgo........... 595
DONNA CLARA .... Heinrich Heine............ 595
WINE .... Micah Joseph Lebensohn...... 598
HORSE AND RIDER .... J. L. Gordon.............. 599
VENUS OF THE LOUVRE .... Emma Lazarus.............. 599
THE MESSIAH .... David Frishman............ 600
THE GOLDEN KEY .... S. Frug.................. 603
THE JEWISH MAY .... Morris Rosenfeld.......... 604
HEAR, O ISRAEL! .... André Spire.............. 607
POEMS .... Yehoash.................. 609
POEMS .... Hayyim Nahman Bialik...... 611
THE END OF SORROW .... Edmond Fleg.............. 618
POEMS .... Saul Tchernihowsky........ 619
MY PEOPLE .... Else Lasker-Schüler........ 625
SONGS .... Abraham Raisen............ 626
POEMS .... Jacob Kahan.............. 627
ROAST LEVIATHAN .... Louis Untermeyer......... 630
TWILIGHT .... Mane Layb............... 636
POEMS .... Zalman Schnaiur.......... 636

These Are the Chosen People .... Robert Nathan 639
Psalm: 1933 .... Babette Deutsch 639
For All that Ever Has Been Ours . . . Sicha Landau 640
The Jew .... Isaac Rosenberg 641
From a Zionist in the Trenches ..... Martin Feinstein 641
Poems .... Uri Zwi Greenberg 642
Poems .... Abraham Shlonsky 643
Lyrics .... Rachel 644
Joy of Knowledge .... Isidor Schneider 646
Süsskind of Trimberg .... Harry Alan Potamkin 647
Exile Consumed .... I. M. Lask 648
Haggadah .... Abraham M. Klein 649

VII. THE WELL OF WISDOM

Foreword 654
Divine Manifesto .... Deuteronomy 655
Of Wisdom and Love .... The Wisdom of Solomon 656
Meditations of a Sceptic .... Ecclesiastes 658
Of God and Man .... Philo of Alexandria 664
The Sciences and the Aim of Life .... Abraham ibn Daud 669
The Unity of God .... Bahya ibn Pakuda 670
Of the First and the Last Things ..... Zohar 672
Israel and the World .... Judah Halevi 679
Of Prophecy .... Moses ben Maimon 686
In Defense of Republics .... Isaac Abravanel 690
In Defense of the Torah .... Joseph Albo 693
Of Race Superiority .... Baruch Spinoza 698
Atticism and Judaism .... S. D. Luzzatto 702
Civil and Religious Autonomy .... Moses Mendelssohn 703
Emancipation and Judaism .... Samson Raphael Hirsch 710
The Emancipation of the Jew .... Karl Marx 714
Judaism and Nationality .... Moses Hess 718
The Interpretation of Judaism .... Abraham Geiger 722
The Law in Judaism .... Solomon Schechter 726
Some Comfort .... Ahad Haam 730
The Jewish Question .... Theodor Herzl 735
Socialism and Zionism .... Nahman Syrkin 741
The Teaching of Jewish History ...... S. M. Dubnow 749
Work and Culture .... Aaron David Gordon 752
The Solution of the Jewish Problem .. Louis D. Brandeis 755
The Tenets of Zionism .... Max Nordau 761
The Spiritual Pattern of Judaism ..... Martin Buber 763
The Jewish Religion .... C. G. Montefiore 767
Of the Jewish Religion .... Albert Einstein 773
Torah as a Way of Life .... Mordecai M. Kaplan 775

CONTENTS

BIOGRAPHICAL NOTES 781
SELECTED BIBLIOGRAPHY 807
INDEX OF AUTHORS 809
INDEX OF TITLES 811
INDEX OF FIRST LINES OF POETRY 813
ACKNOWLEDGMENTS 817

OurNative Land

While this great continent still swarmed with forests and was in possession of primitive natives, Jews joined other persecuted and adventurous colonists in their search for land, freedom and security. Waves of Jewish immigrants from all parts of Europe rolled out in circle after circle for hundreds of years. Their communities dotted the coast in colonial times; they fought boldly in the War of Independence; they pioneered in the South and the West; their fiber was knitted to the growing civilization of America. "After an absence of three years," wrote Mordecai M. Noah, the first American consul to Tunis, as far back as 1815, "I landed in my native country, more attached to the soil, to the character of the people and national institutions, from the opportunity of contrasting their advantages with those of foreign nations." His faith and loyalty are a marked characteristic of the increased progeny of his people in America.

These qualities comprised the bulk of the baggage that the Jewish settler brought with him. A long and bitter and glorious past bulked large in his consciousness, and even when history and tradition receded in an atmosphere that was unfavorable to its flowering, their impact still was alive. Historians, literary critics and psychologists differ in their attempted appraisals of the nature of the impact, but all have observed an agile adaptability, a perennial vitality and a smoldering passion as constant elements in it. The flood of industrialism has washed away much, but the mountains and valleys of the Jewish character remain. The process is evident in the streamlined Passover ceremony at Lil's in Chicago, in Manasseh's pathetic search for beauty in the squalor of the ghetto and in the fierce family passion for Rachel's child in Montana.

The younger generation of American Jews regard their country as "their own, their native land." They are part and parcel of our stalwart and perplexing American Leviathan, prominent in the seething urban centers and not absent in the expansive rural areas. They form a series of colorful strands, stretching to the four or more corners of the country, in which the feeling, thought and strivings of the people are imprinted. Thus their expression in literature, as evidenced in several stories in this section and the unincluded writings of younger authors like Benedict, Bragin, Fuchs, Godin and Vogel, have all been American in their inspiration. The sentimentality and ghetto fixation of the prewar years have yielded to solid realism and widening horizons.

Here, then, is a portrait of the American Jew. The artists have portrayed vividly his struggles and dilemmas in a rapidly changing society. The figures on the canvas are not always pleasant, but human and recognizable; the colors are rarely bright and lyrical, but real and striking. Those who wish to study the subject with broader and deeper understanding will find aid in two of the most significant interpretations of our scene published in recent decades: Van Wyck Brooks' *America's Coming of Age* and Waldo Frank's *The Re-Discovery of America*.

A HERRING FOR MY UNCLE

by ALBERT HALPER

My father came from a family of many sons, but only two of them reached America. Of the others, one took root in faraway New Zealand, another was swallowed up in British South Africa, and two or three more settled down somewhere in Northern and Western Europe. There were sisters, too, but my father lost track of them.

Twenty-two years ago, when I was a very small boy, a letter was forwarded from the Census Bureau at Washington to our home, and, when my father opened it, he found it came from his brother Herman, whom he had not seen since they had separated as young men in Europe. The letter came all the way from Wellington, New Zealand, to Chicago, and I remember the excitement it caused in the flat. We looked at the post-mark and saw it had taken six weeks to make the trip.

Uncle Herman wrote that he had arrived in New Zealand a long time ago, after wandering about for a while in Eastern Europe. He said he had married early and now had a large family, mostly girls. He was in the butcher business and was doing fairly well.

He wrote in a large, strong hand and he must have used a pen with a stub point, for the lettering was firm and flowing and fairly marched across the page. All of us crowded around; I jumped up on my oldest brother's back to get a peep at the postage stamps, and the letter was read over many times.

Then something fell out of the envelope, and when we picked it up we found it was Uncle Herman's photograph—a small picture about the size of a post-card, showing his head and shoulders. My father stood looking at the photograph for a long time, then passed it quietly among us. We saw the likeness of a man of fifty, a wide-shouldered fellow with a big, square head, iron-gray hair, and a heavy moustache. He was a fine-looking man, he looked straight at us from the photograph.

"That's Herman," said my father, and took the photograph in his hands again and stared and stared at it. After a while, because he knew

3

all of us were watching, he turned sharply, blew his nose violently, and wanted to know why we weren't eating our supper.

Just before we went to bed, when my father returned from the store, he took the letter out once more and sat in the old rocker in the front room. He was a man who rarely showed his feelings (I speak of his younger days), but the arrival of this letter broke down all his barriers. I slept in a big, hard bed between my youngest and an older brother, and as I lay I could see, by lifting the upper part of my body, that my father was still sitting in the chair; he was rocking gently, holding the post-card in his hands and staring at the picture. The gaslight in the front room flared, making a hissing sound, and my father had to frown a bit because his eyes were just beginning to go back on him.

The next day, after the first excitement died down, my oldest brother was told to take out pen and paper and answer Uncle Herman. My oldest brother, about seventeen then, had just finished an evening course at a business college, and he sat down and wrote a letter to our relatives far away in New Zealand.

At first, my father told him what to write, but after a while he found himself dictating the same words over and over, so at last my oldest brother tore the sheet up and started on another. We sat around in a circle quietly until the letter was finished; then my brother read it over, we all listened, and my father insisted on putting ten cents in stamps on it, so it would be sure to reach New Zealand.

The next day I heard my mother talking to my father. "Why don't you tell Gustav?" she asked. "You haven't seen him for a long time now."

My father started; he had forgotten all about telling his older brother about it, the other one who had also come to America.

So my mother stood in the store while my father got ready to call upon his brother. At the last minute he took me along; I had been wearing a hand-me-down from my bigger brothers, and my trousers were patched on the seat and at the knees. I was about five years old and was very small for my age then, and my pants were always dragging around my ankles. My older brothers once made up a little rhyme about my sloppy appearance, but this has nothing to do with the story.

"All right," said my father, looking at my mother's pleading eyes. "I'll get him a suit, but even an iron one won't last on him."

So I followed him out of the store, keeping a pace behind. We rode the Lake Street trolley to Halsted and transferred south to Maxwell Street. The big outdoor market was there and for two dollars my father picked out a suit for me. A tall, skinny merchant argued hotly for a long time and finally, placing the garment against my body to show what a perfect fit it was, he at last convinced my father, who handed over the money.

Then we walked off and I had a hard time carrying the package, because the string was thin and cut into my fingers. I kept thinking of the nickel-plated buttons on the new jacket and made up my mind to spit on them, and then rub, thus working up a better shine.

When we came to a busy crossing I reached up and took my father's hand. Car tracks cut across in all directions, the iron rims of wagon wheels struck the cobbles with a jarring bang. Running southwest was a crowded diagonal street, one of the old Indian trails, which I learned later was Blue Island Avenue. But though the streets were heavy with traffic, the neighborhood had a dead and desolate appearance. There were plenty of buildings about—it was an old settlement—but many stores were empty and there were old chalk marks on the filmy windows.

At the corner we went into a fish store where my father bought a herring, and when we came out he handed it to me. Now both hands were full and I didn't know what to do. The string cut into one palm while I felt the juice from the herring soaking through the newspaper into the other. Besides this, my nose had just started running. I kept walking fast, my pants dragging, and tried to keep up with my father.

My uncle Gustav, every time I saw him after that, was fond of telling me how I looked when I came up with the new suit and the herring.

In the middle of the next block we approached a small cigar factory. I stopped to watch two Cuban men rolling tobacco in the front window, but was called away.

"Downstairs," said my father, and we went down a flight of old wooden steps.

At the bottom, inside, hung long rows of tobacco leaves. There was a small gaslight burning because of the darkness, and the cellar had a damp and musty smell. From a table in a corner someone stood up and smiled our way. It was Uncle Gustav. I put down the package and the herring and wiped my juicy palm against my trousers.

"Shake hands with Uncle Gustav," my father said and I stuck out my dampish hand.

I was glad to see my uncle, but I turned my eyes aside. He held my hand for a long time and, when I looked up, I saw him smiling at my father. His palm was soft and had a gentle sort of pressure to it. Then he smelt the herring and chuckled softly; he knew my father had brought it especially for him.

"You carried it?" he asked.

I rubbed my palm against my pants and nodded.

"Ech, ech," he said and opened up the package.

Uncle Gustav was my favorite relative. He was smaller than my father and did not have my father's broad and robust build, and many times I heard my parents talking together, saying that Uncle Gustav was a very sickly man. He had a short, brown beard and always wore a low, black hat, and now when I recall him I think of a little Jewish rabbi going meekly through a field.

We all sat down at the small tobacco table and Uncle Gustav cut the herring equally into three parts. He watched me with a smile as I tore into it with my fingers and when I turned to look at him I saw him nibbling gently like a rabbit.

My father cleared his throat, felt his inner pocket, but did not come directly to the matter. He asked his brother how he felt, if he was making more by working piece-work, and when Uncle Gustav started coughing my father looked the other way. He was younger than Uncle Gustav, but because he owned a little grocery and was a healthy fellow he treated Gustav like a younger brother.

"And how is Selma?" asked my father. "Does she still plague you, does she still think I'm hoarding all your savings?"

My uncle began coughing again, placed his handkerchief to his lips, and slowly shook his head. Then he turned to me and his little, mild, brown eyes began twinkling. For the hundredth time he asked me how old I was, what I wanted to be when I grew up, and he also inquired if I still ran after laundry-wagons. Every time I saw him he asked the same questions, yet they did not bore or grate upon me.

My father cleared his throat again, and frowned. "Herman—I've got a letter from Herman."

Uncle Gustav gave a queer gurgle and for a while could not talk; he began coughing, clutched at his mouth, and finally fought the fit down. Looking important, sitting strong and stocky on a packing case, my father brought out the letter, showed the photograph, and told his brother all about it. While they talked I wandered around the basement, poking into dark places. I heard the talking and saw that Uncle Gustav was excited and liked the way he sat there meekly near the gaslight. He called to me and began telling me about his brother Herman, how Herman was a devil of a fellow but not so bad at that.

Before we left he pressed a coin into my hand, when my father wasn't watching, and gave my head a pat. He stood there smiling at the bottom of the stairs as we climbed up into the light and for some reason or other I had the feeling that he was crying; he crinkled up his eyes so strangely.

We rode back to the store in silence. Every time my father saw his brother he would feel sad for days afterward. He used to tell my mother that Gustav was the best of all his brothers and yet was weak and ailing and married to a witch.

Later on, when I grew older, I learned my uncle's story.

In Europe Gustav was a student, the scholar of the family. When the break-up came, he remained home alone while all the others went their ways. My father went to England and struggled on in London for three years, and because he was having a hard time of it wrote to Gustav to stay at home and finish up his studies.

Then my father came to America, lived in a few cities, tried his hand at several jobs, and at last settled down in Chicago just before the Columbian Exposition. He did not hear from Gustav for seven years.

Then one day he received word from him—Gustav was coming to America too. He had been tricked into a marriage, but of course made no mention of it in his letter, and when my father, who knew nothing about it, met Gustav at the railroad station, he found his brother accompanied by a small, wiry woman and two children. Gustav stood there smiling meekly. I can picture every detail of the scene: I know the way my father frowns, how he wrinkles up his brows. I know the way my uncle used to smile, the goodness shining from his little eyes. There they stood, my father short and stocky, my uncle small and slight.

My father clears his throat, I know that rumble.

"Gustav," he says, and stands there frowning, scowling at his older brother.

"Ech, Isak," says my uncle, surrounded by his family and the baggage. He still smiles faintly, standing meek and mild.

The immigrants arrived over the Baltimore & Ohio, pulling in at the old Polk Street depot. I know that station. It has a wide, smooth floor, old-fashioned arches, and the draft from off the railroad yards whistles into the waiting room.

There they stand, the little woman hard and tight-faced. She knows my father, she was already a widow with two babies when my father left the town. "Selma?" he says and still he stands there frowning.

Then, without another word, he picks up my uncle's bag, turns around darkly, and is followed by the woman and her kids. They carry their own bundles; my father will have nothing to do with them.

Later on, the truth came out—slowly. One of the woman's relatives gave a small dowry, another promised to take the children, and so a bargain was struck. In the end the relatives of the bride took up a further collection, bought steerage tickets, and shipped the whole family over. Selma was older than my uncle and was known as the village shrew, and everybody was glad to be rid of her.

And so my uncle married, and so he came to America. He took a flat a mile away from my father's place and stumbled about the brawling city, trying to learn the language. My father, through a friend, got him a job in a stock-room, but the hours were long and, besides, Uncle Gustav was not a muscular man. Then Selma stepped in. She went sniffing about the city and finally found a relative who was a cigar-maker, and so Uncle Gustav learned a trade. The hours were long, but there was no heavy lifting to do; he had small, quick hands and in a short time was firmly settled.

All this happened just before the turn of the century, about six years before I was born. My father rarely talks about his brother Gustav now. His hate for Selma was a long time in dying; he never could stand the sight of her. She had the small, sharp head of an alert weasel. She never came over to visit us, but went about the town, telling everybody Gustav was giving a part of the wages he earned at the cigar factory to his brother, stinting his own children, hoarding money in secret. When Gustav came home from work, all tired out, fatigue etched deeply in his face, she used to shrill at him, then stick her bony hands in all his pockets. She bore him no children.

Sometimes, in the long summer evenings, Uncle Gustav used to come over to my father's store before going home. He worked on a piece-work basis, and if he labored especially hard was able to get off an hour earlier now and then. I remember how they used to stand in the rear of the store, where my father used to keep the big kerosene barrel, their hands clasped behind their backs, not talking much, staring toward the front windows and the street. The structure of the Lake Street elevated threw thick shadows into the store and across the way; if one looked through the first row of shelves, one could see the tops of the swaying trees over in Union Park.

Business was always quiet in the evening, and if a customer came in my father used to wait on her, ring up the sale, then go back to stand near Uncle Gustav, his face heavy, his short, strong arms behind his back again. I was too small to understand a lot of things, but I sensed the tragic mood of both of them. It must have been apparent, to an older person, that my father's brother was slowly dying.

And each time, before he left, he'd call me over and shake my hand, giving it a gentle pressure.

"How about the herring?" he would ask me, chuckling softly. "Ech, ech, have you got a little herring in your pocket?"

My father, unmoving in the rear, would stand frowning toward the windows as his brother gave my head a pat and left the store. Working in the cigar-shop, down in the damp of the basement, was the worst thing in the world for Uncle Gustav. To save money he used to bring his lunch along and at noon would go out for a five-cent bottle of pop to wash the dry sandwiches down. The carbonated water caused him to belch for hours, little belches which relieved him but left him weakened. My mother talked to my father about him late at night, but there was nothing my father could do. He himself was a poor man, with a big family on his hands. He couldn't go over to visit Uncle Gustav in the evenings because of Selma, and he was unable to see his brother very often because of the grocery. But my mother used to stand there crying, and in the end, leaving her cooking and her washing, she said she'd mind the store and wait on the trade.

So every few months or so my father went over to Blue Island Avenue, and after a while he began taking me along. I believe his brother told him to. We would cross the tangle of car tracks and I would reach up for my father's hand, and at the corner fish-store we would stop to buy a herring. Walking along, keeping a pace behind, the juice would go soaking through the newspaper, until my palm was wet.

"You carried it?" Uncle Gustav would say.

And I'd rub my palm against my pants and nod.

"Ech, ech," he'd whisper and then would open up the package.

Each time I saw him I had grown a little taller. Each time I left him I had the feeling, as we climbed up the stairs into the daylight, that he stood there smiling and crying to himself. My father's face was always set as he climbed the stairs. We came outside, out upon that dead, desolate section near Blue Island Avenue, and as we reached the car tracks we had to stop until a line of wagons drew away. The thoroughfare was used by the farmers on their way to the great Randolph Street markets and I remember how the horses had prairie flowers in their manes, because coming to market with a great load was something of a festive event. And there were small, barefooted kids, who sat on top of the heaped vegetables and fruit, and if I hollered one or two of them would throw an apple or a peach my way.

All this while we had been exchanging letters with Uncle Herman in New Zealand. He had some grown-up daughters and they too wrote, sending photographs and asking for ours. So one Sunday afternoon we all went over to a studio on Madison Street and had our pictures taken. My father acted strangely about it. He went over to Blue Island Avenue a day before and talked to Gustav, and when we were ready to go to the studio, the door opened and Gustav came in, his low, black hat upon his head.

"Gustav wants to send Herman his picture too," my father said, and we all walked the six blocks to Madison Street.

In the studio we were posed by the photographer, my father sitting in the front row beside my mother, one fist on his knee, the other out of sight. My kid brother sat upon my mother's lap, and the photographer had to talk soothingly a long time to make him sit quiet and reserved.

When it was all over, my father went up to Uncle Gustav. "You sit alone," he said. "You get a picture taken by yourself."

"Ech, Isak. Why should I do it?"

"I'll pay for it," my father said, and so my uncle posed. He sat there with his low, black hat on and meekly stared toward the camera.

Then we all went from the shop and walked the six blocks home.

A few months after the photographs were sent away, we received a letter from New Zealand, a letter with a black border around it. My oldest brother was the first to read it, and did not want to give it to my father. Uncle Herman had passed away while undergoing an operation for appendicitis.

As soon as my father learned the news, he closed the store early and came over to the flat. It was winter time, and both coal stoves were going. When he reached the flat, we were already finished with our supper, and our mother had warned us beforehand not to talk or move around.

My father came home and didn't eat the meal. He stood with his back toward the flat in the kitchen, staring out at the snow in the back-yard and the alley, and cracked his fingers, one by one. His face was heavy, his eyes were clouded. Later on, he read the letter over and over, slowly and in a quiet way, his lips moved a little, forming the words to himself as he read. Then he took out his brother's photograph and stared and stared at it.

"He was the strongest of us all," he told my mother, and that was all he said.

In the night, once again in the big, hard bed, I raised myself and through the bedroom doorway had a view of the parlor. I was seven years old then. My father rocked gently, working up a sort of rhythm, and as he rocked he whimpered quietly to himself. I could hardly hear it. He sat rocking like that for a long time.

Months later he told Uncle Gustav about their brother's death, but Uncle Gustav had noticed my father's mood and was prepared for the worst of news. They stood at the rear of the store near the big kerosene barrel, not talking much, and when Uncle Gustav left he asked me, so as not to break the habit, if I had a little herring in my pocket; but now I saw that he was really crying, he did not try to hide it as he gave my head a pat.

And three years later Uncle Gustav died. My mother cried the hardest. She cried so much that my father put on a stern and surly look and acted sharp around the flat.

We sat about all evening, my mother with her puffy, reddened face, my father staring dully at the stove.

Then we went to bed, everyone except my father.

And once more, for the third time, I raised my body and turned to look through the doorway toward the parlor. My father was rocking there. His face was stern and heavy, I could see the set muscles in his jaw. He rocked up and back, working up a sort of rhythm, his feet firm upon the floor.

How long he rocked I do not know. I grew tired holding my body rigid and had to rest a couple of times. But I did not go to sleep. I lay stiffened in the dark, listening to the flare of the gas flame in the front room. And pretty soon I heard my father, his whimpering sounded like a kind of humming. I raised my body more.

Now his face was slack and flabby. He was holding Gustav's photograph in his hands and stared and stared at it. The tears were pouring down his face. He moaned softly, one fist holding the picture, the other resting heavy on his knee. I sat up rigid in the dark, between my two sleeping and unstirring brothers, and heard my uncle's voice.

"You carried it?"

I rubbed my thigh under the quilt and nodded.

"Ech, ech," he chuckled and opened up the package.

HOW MANY ANGELS . . .

by IRVING FINEMAN

IT was always in the kitchen that my father took his ease. The kitchen was as large a room as the parlor (for those were the days when there were parlors), and warmer. And it was less encumbered than the parlor, where, suited to the needs of neither mind nor body, were many pieces of carved mahogany—a sofa with uncomfortably curving back and legs, and chairs stiffly upholstered in tufted apple-green velours, a music stand, and a lamp with a stained-glass dome by the draped, gleaming length of the piano, a what-not in the corner surmounted by the bronze figure of a handsome harvester nude to the waist and sharpening his scythe. Thus it was that my father took his ease in the kitchen and that it was always in the kitchen that we had those memorable nocturnal meetings, my father and I.

Memorable, I say, for when we sat, my father and I, on opposite sides of the square kitchen table (and kitchen tables in those days were generously large) whose white oilcloth cover, stamped in blue with a florid design of an intricacy endlessly tempting to explore, shone under the soft brilliance of a Welsbach mantle glowing in the gaslight, those meetings appear to have been informed with a high significance that, it seems now, could then have been only deliberately ignored; as one comes to the theater prepared to see a play but willing to forget it is a play. To me now it seems as if we came, my father and I, deliberately, to sit in the bare brilliance of that austere room, with its bright central light and diffused reflections—from white crockery ranged behind glass doors, from the scrubbed linoleum on the floor checkered in endless diagonals of blue and white, from the nickel trim on the black polished stove, from the pale buff-tinted walls and the spread of oilcloth on the table between us —as surgeons come to a chamber, brightly lit and isolated (for the rest of the household would be fast asleep in the darkness of the bedrooms), to conduct a clinic, to dissect, to examine something laid before them. It seems so to me now, I say; at the time there seemed never anything deliberate, anything anticipated about our meetings. Never on departing from some rowdy, boyish party, walking home along the dark canyons of city streets, or, as I was fond of doing, crossing the Brooklyn Bridge, slung like a huge web of vines between the tops of monstrous trees high over a black jungle river, or returning in the noisy, swaying progress of a belated street car from a long evening's work at some distant library, never would it occur to me to look forward to one of those meetings.

I would enter and, from the dark hall while I put up my hat and coat and glanced as of habit toward the bright rectangle of the kitchen door, I would hear perhaps the clink of glass against saucer as my father reached for them in the cupboard and closed the door with a familiar click of the latch. Setting these and the sugar bowl by an open book he had been reading on the shining expanse of the table, he would peer at me, stooping a little from under the bright light that shone on the fringe of his hair around the black skull cap he wore on the back of his head; and, after exchanging a few words of greeting or inquiry with me, he would continue his customary pacing back and forth, back and forth, around two sides of the table, stopping now and then as he passed the stove in his progress to lift the lid of the white enameled teakettle and peer down into the cloud of steam that rose from it. By limiting somewhat the extent of his pacing, he would leave me free to repair to the ice box by the sink. While I stood leisurely examining its chill, fragrant contents, I could hear behind me the measured tread of his walk, the comfortable creaking of the floor under his feet, and the first murmurings of the kettle that would soon, with a rushing plume of steam from its spout, bring him to a halt. And as I made my choice from the left-overs—a remnant of fish, or a wing of chicken with, perhaps, a saucer of stewed prunes—I must have heard without listening (for why should one listen for such things, and yet I can hear them now) the opening and closing of a drawer, the clink of a spoon in the glass (which, he believed, prevented the glass from cracking), the trickle of the essence, and, at last, the hot gasp with which the water rushed from the steaming spout.

Then he would sit and wait for me, his hands folded to catch the warm cloud that rose from the ruddy glass in which the silver spoon appeared curiously orange-tinted and bent. He sat there thinking; indeed he had been thinking all the time, I always knew, of something he wanted to discuss, and very soon we should begin to talk. But as I brought myself bread and a knife and, cutting a crisp slice, enjoyed in advance the seasoned tang of the frozen amber sauce clotted about the edges of the fish, or the delicate flavor of the tender white meat on the wing bones under their yellow skin, or stood gazing as if fascinated at the light reflected from the black pool of prune juice from which the prunes rose wrinkled and glistening like islands of worn and polished basalt, never once (and I should remember, if I had, as I remember the rest) did I wonder what he and I were about to say, or why it was that we should meet to talk as we were bound to. I should remember, if I had, as I remember the sensual delight it was to sit down then in the bright silence of that room after the evening's fatigue, to feel the radiant warmth of the stove at my back, and smell the delicate odors rising into the air as if reflected from the shining table—the cool fragrance of the food before me, the warm fragrance of my father's tea, and the musty fragrance of the old Hebrew book before him (that smell of an old Hebrew book which is like that of no other old book) that rose in an unforgettable cloud as he turned its yellow leaves and examined the lines of heavy black characters that, I could see clearly across the table, lay swimming like islands in the middle of a sea of commentaries in fine print. . . .

It was the Talmud. My father sipped his tea as he turned the pages, and nibbled at a lump of sugar between sips. "Tomorrow night," he may have begun, "is the first night of Hanukkah." My mind and senses, curiously intermingled and playing like a vague phosphorescence successively over the chicken wing I was gnawing and the problem in dynamics I had been studying all evening, floated off and, as if alighting at his words, came to rest on the Maccabees—on a picture of lusty men, fighting, not like shrewd Jewish lawyers with their wits, but like gladiators with broken swords in their fists. I liked the Maccabees. . . . "Now the Gemara says," he continued, looking over my head at the stove, "What is Hanukkah!"

The Gemara, I understood, was not asking a question. "What is Hanukkah" was a ball tossed into the air, as in a game, between eager waiting minds. "When the Syrians—that is to say, the Greeks" (my father had picked up the ball and was carrying it to me; and, finding it at the moment difficult to recall the history of that period, I wondered as I picked at the delicious chicken bones if he was justified in that archaeological assumption) "took Jerusalem, they sacked the Temple and desecrated all the holy utensils including the holy oil for the lighting of the Menorah. Afterwards, when the Maccabees re-took the city and put them to flight, but one container of the holy oil was to be found, a single small cruse with the seal of the high priest upon it intact, a quantity ordinarily sufficient for but one day's lighting of the Menorah. Then, it is said, occurred the miracle that, during the eight days required for the manufacture of a new supply of the holy oil, the one small undesecrated cruse provided sufficient to keep the holy flame alight. It is for this reason that the victory is celebrated for eight days and candles are lit." I pushed away the plate with its remnant bones, listening as it were with one ear. For this seemed a childish game, this speculation concerning a miracle and a monopoly of holy oil manufactured by canting, white-robed high priests. Doughty old Mattathias battling on the Sabbath, and Judas Maccabeus, "the Hammer," with his followers, fighting like gladiators with their hard fists, desperately, against superior numbers, would, I was sure, have had none of that nonsense.

I considered simultaneously going ahead with the dish of prunes and sending the ball back to my father. But he was turning the pages searching some particular reference, wetting a finger-tip now and then to grasp one of the thick yellow leaves, and I, for the moment, lost myself in consideration of a pretty question in hydro-statics, namely, to what extent the viscosity of prune juice affected its buoyant action on the prune which it surrounded: was it then transmitting an upward pressure through a thin film seeping in under the prune as water would? . . .

"Ah!" said my father; he had found the place. "Now with reference to the lights, one Tanna says here that each family should have at least one light for each member of the family. And those still more informed should, says Shammai, have eight lights the first night, seven the second, and so on down to one light on the eighth night. But the great Hillel says precisely the contrary: one light the first night, two the second, and so on to eight on the eighth night. Now come the Tannaim attempting in their commentaries to interpret these two contrary opinions, in this manner: Shammai, one says, tells us to light each evening as many candles as there are days of Hanukkah still coming, while Hillel instructs us to number them as the passing of the days. Again another Tanna points out that Shammai's plan parallels and probably takes as a precedent the ancient system of burnt offerings sacrificed on the altar at Succoth: fourteen oxen the first day, thirteen the second, and so on down to seven on the seventh day; but Hillel, he says, was always of the opinion that holy things should be increased rather than decreased." My father bit a hard corner from a lump of sugar and took a sip from his steaming glass as he turned the page. "Then follows," he continued, his eyes running down the page, "a dispute as to whether it is permissible to perform any work by the light of these Hanukkah candles." (I considered that there were, of course, no candles in those days; but I forbore to interrupt.) "One says yes, and another no. Then in the name of the Tanna Rab it is laid down that above all it is not permissible to count money by the light of the Hanukkah candles. . . ." My father's voice descended into a studious sing-song murmur and his lips moved as he searched again the finely printed commentaries on the page. "And that argument just about fills this page of Gemara," he said at last, taking another sip of tea and looking up at me.

I swallowed the last of the prune juice and, still savoring its heavy sweetness, looked at my father and said: "How many angels can dance on the head of a pin? . . ."

He smiled indulgently; for my father knew what I meant by that signal of scoffing criticism. I had used it before. He smiled indulgently and shook his head. "Surely," he answered, "you do not believe that such minds, such authorities as Hillel and Shammai, would stoop to controversies over literally worthless matters. Hillel, who said: 'The uncultivated man is not innocent; the ignorant man is not devout . . .' was himself neither uncultivated nor ignorant; would he, you think, concern himself unworthily with discussions which are indeed (and my father's eyes twinkled) only as meaningless superficially as the pages of mathematical symbols in your book on mechanics are to the uninitiate like myself?"

"The symbolism in my book on mechanics is a necessary mathematical convention for convenience in elaborate but logical discussions. But why should presumably intelligent men have resorted to far-fetched, apparently meaningless metaphors when they were speaking of things of the spirit?" I was warming up; feeling no longer tired, and a little belligerent after the food. "It looks to me as if they had so far removed themselves from life that . . ." My father's nod of comprehension saved me the end of that sentence.

"There is no accounting reasonably for the particular forms in which the men choose to express themselves. I have seen," said my father mildly, and thoughtfully wiping his brow as he pushed the black skull-cap still further back on his head (for the tea had warmed him too), "I have seen Chinese pictures in which ladies are shown stepping into boats which, in proportion to their bodies, are about the size of teacups. These pictures are, I suppose, not ridiculous to the Chinese. They must be seen with the eyes of one trained or accustomed to that peculiar convention to be understood and appreciated. Now, I have, I think, been in my early days in a yeshibah very close to the spirit of these controversies of the Tannaim. Let me try to give you," he said and, as if to reinforce his wish and to hold my attention with a gesture, he handed me as I rose his empty glass, tinkling precariously on the saucer whose round it did not quite fit, so that in pouring myself a cup of tea I might give him another, "let me try to give you what I think is the real significance of all this discussion. To begin with the miracle itself: the Menorah, and its modern representative the Hanukkah light, is the symbol for Torah, for learning and culture, for civilization. The Temple was the one light-house in a world of spiritual darkness, and it drew toward it the animosity of the rules of the Greeks who hated it for its moral significance and desired to destroy it, and to reduce the Jewish folk to living in the state of darkness in which they themselves then existed."

To have destroyed my father's metaphorical lighthouse (it was one of long standing) would, it occurred to me, have been for him a personal disaster as dire as the one he was describing. I was myself tempted to shake it by calling his attention to the arts, the philosophy, the science of the ancient Greeks (thinking vaguely of the pure marmoreal beauties of Praxiteles and Phidias, of the clarities of Plato and the geometricians —darkness indeed!) but having always had a weak head for historical dates, and being uncertain of the chronological relation between the time of the Maccabees and the heights of Greek culture, I held my peace. In all likelihood, my father would, I knew, have countered with an irrefutable reference to their moral decadence, to nameless and indescribable practices . . . irrefutable because those were matters not to be carefully examined between father and son. And I should then have been prompted to retort with a demand for the riches of art, of philosophy, of science, bequeathed to mankind by that ancient, austere, Jewish morality, which had shone uniquely, like a lighthouse. A lighthouse, I might have said, is usually founded upon a barren rock . . . But I held my peace.

"And so successful were they in their determination to destroy the detested Jewish morality, to undermine the fundamentals of the irritating Jewish religion that it appeared that neither would last more than a brief day, a single generation." My father looked at me then and smiled, assuring himself that I was grasping the parable. "But then, when the Maccabees succeeded in overpowering and dispersing the barbarians, occurred the miracle that the light of Judaism, very nearly extinguished as the barbarians had thought, continued to burn, has continued even to this day to illumine the world despite all the adverse winds and storms which, from time to time, have blown so frightfully upon it. That," and my father's face glowed as if in the light of his own poetic concept, "that, then, is the significance of our Hanukkah lights. And if every Jew obeyed this injunction and, following this ancient and significant custom, placed a little light in his window, it would make the loveliest illumination in all the world as well as the most powerful demonstration against those barbarians in spirit who, to this day, hate Jewish morality and law —it would be the beautiful sign of the persistent miracle of their survival . . ."

I sipped my tea in silence, fixing my eyes as he paused on the colorful package of Quaker Oats on the lowermost shelf of the cupboard behind my father's head. For had I looked at my father then, I should have been impelled to ask him: "What is this miraculous light of Judaism of which you speak; where is it now, in these times, to be seen other than in the poetic imagery you have evoked? Let us," I should have had to say, "have done with metaphors and talk fact. And as for illuminations—in another month or so you will be seeing again as pretty and as insignificant a lighting of windows as ever warms lyric souls to singing 'peace on earth, good will to men' and betrays the optimistic into rhapsodies over the progress of human kind." But not wanting to say such things to my father's face, glowing triumphantly over the steaming glass in his hand, I waited for him to continue, diverting myself the while with an ancient boyish speculation as to how far, working with the aid of a powerful magnifying glass, the engraver of the design on the box of oatmeal might have carried his ingenious conceit—a scroll inscribed with the words Quaker Oats and the trademark, a reproduction of the figure of William Penn holding in his extended hand a scroll, similarly inscribed and carrying in miniature another William Penn extending his smaller scroll with its minuscular inscription whereon the eye, infinitely intrigued, searched a minute spot for yet further glimpses of progressively infinitesimal reproductions of William Penn extending his cosmic scroll. . . .

"When the Tanna says that each family should burn at least the one light, he means it for those who have conserved the spirit of the old days when the father's Torah was also the children's Torah, when the one light of learning sufficed for all the family Now, however, in more advanced times, says the Tanna, each member of the family should burn his own light; for the concepts of ancient days must not be forced upon the newer generation; the Torah, he means to say, must be adapted to the new spirit of the times." My father looked across at me now with an earnest benevolence shining from his eyes, and the bright light overhead reflected from his forehead. He wanted me to understand him. I listened now, attentive only to his words. "Now," he continued, "come Shammai and Hillel, teaching the new generation, each according to his lights. And Shammai, it appears, was a very strict teacher, a hard master. He says: Young man—your future lies before you; but make haste. Burn all your lights now: learn all you can now, for as time passes the lights become fewer and one cannot recapture them. But Hillel, gentler, more liberal, says: Be thorough; learn one thing today and tomorrow add another to what you have learned and thus steadily increase the light of your wisdom. Thus only, in time, shall you learn all. Another Tanna"—my father set down his glass to consult again the finely printed commentaries—"suggests that Hillel and Shammai had still other meanings hidden among their various ideas. Shammai interprets the reduction in the number of oxen sacrificed at Succoth as the symbol of the failing powers of man as he grows older, and as his strength grows less in his later days so too does his ability to study, hence his injunction to study in the fullest extent in youth. But Hillel replies that though it is true of physical power that it decreases with age, with Torah, that is, learning, it is quite the contrary. A learned man becomes wiser with age. . . ."

I perceived suddenly that the Maccabees had, alas, disappeared from view; and even the Hanukkah lights were no longer substantial tapers but ideas that danced in the heads of men—firm Shammai and gentle Hillel, those vague anonymous Tannaim, and my father—lighting their faces. . . .

"Then comes the question whether study is permissible for the purpose of making a living from it. One Tanna says no; one must study solely for the purpose of knowing. Another says it does not matter why, so long as one studies; one may even draw sustenance from it. But the last word comes from the great teacher: that one may not count money by the light of the Hanukkah candles, which means simply, that one should not draw back from a course of study which does not pay as well as another."

Ah! There were still the candles after all; though the hard-fisted Maccabees, I perceived, were indeed hopelessly lost.

"You see?" said my father, and he swallowed the last of his tea. "These men were in their field as scrupulous, as unselfish, as your scientist who today spends his time in the laboratory speculating on—say, how many atoms can dance on the head of a pin"; and, holding up the book so that I could see its mottled brown leather binding, worn and broken, looked keenly over its edge at me, and, curiously, in that glance he seemed to be setting me inexorably between himself and the leaf of Gemara as between two mirrors where each was reflected in the other—

my father in the printed page and it in him—and where I beheld myself reflected endlessly in both. . . .

"And now," he said, "let us see if we shall have enough lights for this Hanukkah." So I went to one of the deep drawers under the cupboard and after tugging at it (it always stuck because of the hammer, the ice pick or a screw driver lodged in it) and displacing tins of tacks, odd nails and screws, bits of discarded hardware and twine found at last the box of Christmas candles (there was a green tree and a red-clad Santa Claus on the box) left from the year before. This I brought to the table and, disclosing the colored layers of spiraled as if twisted candles, bright red and pure white, translucent cream, pale green, dark blue and yellow, removed the broken ones. "We shall need," I said, "one, and two and three and . . ." adding it quickly in my head, for I was proud of my arithmetical prowess, "thirty-six."

"And eight more for the Shammes," added my father, "makes forty-four; and, after all, the amount of light is the same whether you follow Hillel or Shammai."

But these were not metaphorical lights I was counting. The brittle, greasy feel of them and their bright colors recalled the childish delight it used to be to be permitted to hold the Shammes, to communicate that soft yellow flame, to make, as if magically, two flames out of one. There were just about enough. I poured them back into the box.

"Next year," said my father, "we shall need new lights." He rose and, as I passed into the hall, reached up and slowly turned down the gas light that first glowed red in the mantle and then vanished.

THE SAINT OF THE UMBRELLA STORE

by MICHAEL GOLD

REB SAMUEL hummed hasidic hymns as he worked at his machines in the umbrella store. He was trying to forget America. But who can do that? It roared in the street outside, it fought against him from the lips of his own children. It even reached into his synagogue, and struck at his God.

It finally defeated him, this America; it broke the old man, because he could not bend.

Tall, frail, austere, there was a dignity about Reb Samuel that made everyone respect him. His face, white as Siberian snow, with beard as white, was pure and solemn as a child's. It was transparent as if he never ate. His large blue eyes were calm with spiritual certainties. He had that air of grandeur that surrounds so many old pious Jews. The world can move them no longer; they have seen and suffered all.

Reb Samuel never hurried; he was never angry. He walked through the filth and chaos of our street leaning on his staff, a stately Prince of Zion in exile. Talmudic texts interpolated his ordinary talk. When one of his children cried, he soothed it with quotations from the great rabbis. Even as he sat in his miserable shop, sewing umbrella tops all day, an eternal dignity rested on him.

He liked to have me come into the store and talk to him while he worked. My mother's father in Hungary had been a hasid like Reb Samuel. The old man would remind me of my tradition, and urge me to be true to it.

The hasidim are a sect who revolted some three hundred years ago against the dry formalism into which Judaism had sunk. They were mystics whose exaltation bordered on hysteria. In their synagogues today they still leap, dance, and sing like Holy Rollers, seeking the *dveikuss,* the ecstasy in which man is united with God.

Hasidim look down on other orthodox Jews, and call them the "Misnagdim," the worldly ones, the outsiders. And these others sneer in turn at the hasidim, and call them madmen and drunkards.

"But we are not drunkards," Reb Samuel would say quietly. "It is true we use wine and food to show our joy in God. Food is holy; wine is holy; God is everywhere, even among these umbrellas that I am sewing. Do you understand, Mechel?"

"Yes, Reb Samuel."

"You must learn to do good deeds, for every good deed hastens the coming of the Messiah. You want Him to look like Buffalo Bill. I tell you, He will not look like Buffalo Bill, nor will He kill anyone. He will come to save the world, not to destroy it, like the false Messiah of the Christians. First He will redeem the Jews, then the other nations. This is why we now must suffer more than the rest of humanity. This is why hasidim rejoice in the midst of suffering. We Jews have been chosen; we are fortunate. Do you understand what I am teaching you, my child?"

"Yes, Reb Samuel."

"And now repeat after me these words. I believe—"

"I believe," I chanted in the rich Hebrew vowels:

"In the coming of the Messiah—"

"In the coming of the Messiah—"

"And though He tarry, I will wait daily for His coming."

"And though He tarry, I will wait daily for His coming," I chanted in the ancient singsong.

Reb Samuel patted my head gently.

"Good," he said. "You will make a better Jew than my own stubborn children. You have a Jewish heart. Tomorrow I will teach you the rest of the Credo."

Reb Samuel was the spiritual leader of a small congregation of hasidim. Often they would come to his home and talk and sing, and I would sit quietly and listen.

They fascinated me. They were as mysterious as the folk in my father's fairy-tales. They were not pale East Side carpenters, tailors and peddlers, but sorcerers and spirits. They drank tiny glasses of brandy, and then danced in a circle, clapping their hands. Their beards wagged, their eyes were shut in ecstasy, the big veins throbbed in their throats as they wailed the hypnotic desert melodies. It was weird; and something deep inside of me responded to it.

At first Reb Samuel had tried to manage the umbrella business. But he had no mind for figures; he believed in everyone's honesty; he was above the petty things. The business was being destroyed, and so his wife had to take it over. We went on working at the machine. Reb Samuel was glad of this arrangement. It left his mind free for religion.

But it was hard on little Mrs. Ashkenazi, his wife. She was a tiny, gray woman, weighing not more than ninety pounds, and sapped dry as a herring by work. Her eyelids were inflamed with loss of sleep. She slaved from dawn till midnight, cooking and cleaning at home, then working in the umbrella store. At forty she was wrinkled like a woman of seventy. She was always tired, but was a sweet, kindly, uncomplaining soul, who worshiped her family, and revered her impractical husband.

The shop was a dreary hole. It stank like a sewer of glue, dyes, damp cloth and human bodies. Three girls worked at machines alongside of Reb Samuel, sewing umbrella tops. His oldest child, Rachel, a girl of fifteen, drilled holes into umbrella handles at another machine. His little wife steamed umbrellas onto the ribs at a big copper kettle.

The machines clattered; steam hissed; the girls talked or coughed; peddlers and customers came in and out arguing, bargaining. It was a bedlam at all times, a place of petty tragedy, petty slavery; just another of those thousand cockroach businesses that are scattered over the East

Side, and that have but a single point in their favor; each keeps a family alive.

On rainy days the peddlers crowded in. They took bundles of umbrellas on credit, to be sold at elevated stations and street corners. Reb Samuel's wife had to check the bundles in and out. The peddlers were young semi-vagabond Jews, loud blusterers and liars who thought it clever to cheat her. And so the timid little woman had learned to argue brazenly, to fight back, to be bold in defending her family.

Reb Samuel was calm in the midst of the bedlam. He never interfered with his wife's management. He never worried when a week passed and there was no rain. All this was of the world, and for his wife to worry about; Reb Samuel had more serious cares.

His hasidic congregation had no synagogue to worship in. They met in each other's homes for worship; on holidays they rented a dance hall or lodge room for the services. And they had no rabbi.

"Ach, everything is falling to pieces," Reb Samuel would sigh. Things were happening such as were never heard of in Jewry. America was conquering even the hasidim. The last fort of God in this country was falling before the enemy.

Reb Samuel was patient with America. He submitted to it as once he had submitted to the pogrom. He saw Jews working on the Sabbath, Jews eating pork, and practicing other abominations. He learned to shrug his shoulders and be silent.

But a member of his own sect went so far as to shave his orthodox beard, because in America beards are laughed at. This was going too far. At this point the dreamy Reb Samuel made a stand.

He demanded that the criminal be expelled from the congregation. The man, a shrewd dry goods merchant, rose boldly at the meeting and advanced the following arguments:

"Brother hasidim," he said, "I have not broken the Mosaic law by taking off my beard, and I can prove it. What says the Law on this point, brothers? It says plainly: Thou shalt not trim or cut the corners of thy beard. What does this mean? How does one trim or cut a beard? With a scissors or razor. Our holy law-giver Moses had these in mind when he uttered his commandment.

"But, brothers, do I use a scissors or a razor on my beard? No; I use a white powder that eats away the beard without cutting or shaving. It is this powder that I use. A famous rabbi in the Bronx uses it. Many pious Jews and hasidim are using it. It is not forbidden, brothers. I am as good a hasid as Reb Samuel! May God smite my children if I use razor or scissors!"

This bold, plausible defense made a great impression on the congregation of mystics. Others of them had found the long orthodox beard a handicap in America and were secretly attracted by any legal way out. The dry goods merchant was not expelled. And a week later two other members of the congregation appeared without beards. They, too, were using the depilatory. Reb Samuel's soul was shaken to its core. The fervent, simple old man could not sleep nights for worry.

With other ultra-orthodox factionalists he discussed the matter. They reached the conclusion that a synagogue was needed at once, and a rabbi —a leader—a general in the war against America. So for the next five years these poor carpenters, umbrella-makers and sweatshop slaves deprived themselves of food, and their children of food, that a permanent synagogue might be leased and a rabbi brought from Europe—a real rabbi, not one of these American compromisers.

They fetched over the great-great-great-grandson of a zaddik who had been famous all through Poland, Lithuania and Russia.

These zaddikim were reputed to be descended from the thirty-six Wise Men of Israel; the thirty-six who were the last remnant of the Lost Tribes. Unknown, unheralded, in rags and humility, they wandered over the world and appeared at crucial moments when the Jewish nation needed them most.

The famous zaddik had performed his miracles around the year 1810. Such virtue is considered hereditary, and his descendants had lived in the same region for two hundred years, working the same miracles. Reb Samuel and his congregation brothers learned that the present vessel of the original zaddik's virtues was anxious to come to America. Times were bad; his congregation was starving; he, too, was living lean.

They sent him a steamship ticket and some money, and waited for him as for the Messiah.

"Ach, when the Rabbi Schmarya comes, how different everything will be!" Reb Samuel would say.

At last the dream came true. It was a summer morning. A strange medieval parade walked down our street. The new rabbi was being escorted to the new synagogue.

I have seen pictures of religious processions in India. Theatrical, exotic and fierce with unaccountable passions, they remind me of that summer parade on my street. A hundred bearded Jews wrapped like

Bedouins in white praying shawls were marching slowly. The tenement windows and sidewalks were lined with spectators. The hasidim were mad with holy joy. They skipped like children, they sang, they clapped their hands, they kissed each other with naked ecstasy. Reb Samuel led the ecstatic mob of bearded men. He was pale with emotion, and carried the synagogue Torah in his arms. It was ponderous, this huge scroll of parchment dressed like a king's child in precious silk and gold. But it was the Holy Law, and the old man hugged it tenderly in his arms, and sang in a high, trembling voice.

At last, at last! Hope had arrived to the East Side. God was looking down on Chrystie Street! Some of the older hasidim wept. They flung themselves about in grotesque pinwheels, and shouted, and ignored the smiles and jeers of the more cynical onlookers. What mattered dignity now? God was to dwell in America!

In the center of the parade, reposing on the plush cushions of an open barouche drawn by four white horses, appeared the descendant of the miracle-working zaddik and the thirty-six Wise Men; the Rabbi Schmarya himself.

I was disappointed. I had caught some of Reb Samuel's exaltation and had imagined some rabbi like a shining angel in white, all beautiful with a golden aureole. But I saw a fat, dull-faced man in a frock coat and high hat. He was obviously pleased with the new silk hat, and fiddled with it. His face held no ecstasy but beefy smugness.

He leaned back, blasé as a fat African king. His heavy eyelids blinked, as without emotion he regarded the whores, peddlers, saloon riffraff, graybeards, and tearful Jewish men and women around him. These were his subjects, and one could guess he knew how to rule them. His royal calm was broken only by noisy children who broke through the parade and tried to shake his hand. He pushed the children away, and squeaked ridiculously. He slapped the face of one boy bolder than the rest. The rabbi did not seem to like children.

I followed the procession into the synagogue on Forsythe Street, in the basement of a tenement. Here I watched, with a child's cruel intelligence, the rabbi in the midst of his flock.

The hasidim were still chattering, laughing, kissing each other. Some wept with emotion; a large group formed a circle at one end of the synagogue, and danced a sacred rondo to their own singing. At rhythmic intervals they flung their arms to the ceiling, and uttered a howl of primeval joy and pain: then danced again, whipping themselves into a state of delirium.

But the new rabbi was not abandoning himself to the sacred rage. He was busy eating. He had immediately sat down at the refreshment table, and was stuffing himself with herring, sponge-cake, *apfelstrudel*, *gefulte fish*, and raisins. He devoured platters of food until his eyes popped, and sweat covered his face.

I was disturbed by his gorging, not for esthetic or religious reasons, but because I was hoping to eat some of the food myself. With a host of other small boys of hasidic connection, I was waiting until the ceremonies were over, and the refreshments served. But the rabbi was definitely eating up all those refreshments.

I found Reb Samuel leaping solemnly with a group of the mystics, and plucked at his *talith*.

"Reb Samuel," I said anxiously, "the new rabbi is eating up all the food. There will be nothing left!"

Reb Samuel broke off his ecstasy to glare at me. He walked me into a quiet corner, and shook his finger at me, while his face twitched with anger. I had never seen Reb Samuel so angry before.

"Go home!" he said. "You have committed a sin in talking so stupidly about our Rabbi Schmarya. For this I want you to go home!"

"But, Reb Samuel," I pleaded, "I didn't mean to say anything bad."

"Go home!" he repeated, and stalked away. I felt mean. I hadn't meant to make Reb Samuel angry; I liked him too well. But I didn't want to go without tasting some of the nuts, raisins, apples and cakes that were heaped so high on the tables. Yet what apologies could I offer to Reb Samuel? Wasn't it true that the rabbi was eating up all the food?

I lingered at the fringes of the crowd for some minutes. Reb Samuel saw me again. He motioned sternly for me to go. So home I went, furious at the new rabbi who had cheated me out of food and experience.

Alas for Reb Samuel. He should have been warned by a child's truthful impressions. I was right about the new rabbi, and he was wrong.

The rabbi, who had been such a saint and miracle-worker in Europe, changed in the electric air of America.

For one thing, his scale of living went up by leaps and bounds. He made many demands on his little flock. Reb Samuel neglected his umbrella shop entirely, and spent weeks and months raising money to buy the rabbi a home in Brooklyn. The rabbi demanded that his wife and children be sent for from Europe. That took more money-raising. The rabbi's family needed a servant. More money.

Reb Samuel did not begrudge the rabbi these luxuries: they were due the great man. What made Reb Samuel paler, gaunter, and melancholy as months passed was that the rabbi took no firm stand on the heresy of beards. Reb Samuel was too loyal to say it, but other hasidim whispered that the new rabbi was friendly to the Depilatory faction. They were the richer group in the synagogue, and he seemed to prefer the rich.

The climax came a year after his arrival. One day the rabbi deserted his congregation. He had been offered a better-paying job by a wealthy and un-hasidic congregation in the Bronx. He wrote a brief announcement to his flock, and simply never appeared again.

The blow crushed my teacher, Reb Samuel. He rarely spoke at home, or in the umbrella shop; he brooded within himself. His eyes lost their peace; his face no longer reflected the eternities. He became a tired, bewildered, lonely old Jew.

He returned one night from one of the many bitter meetings at the congregation, where the factions now quarreled endlessly. He opened the door of his home and stood at the threshold. His face was ghastly with suffering. His wife looked up from the kitchen stove in amazement. She waited for him to walk into the room.

But he lingered strangely. Then a look of unspeakable surprise passed over his face. His stick clattered to the ground; he clutched at his heart.

In a strangled voice he exclaimed:

"What's the matter? What's the matter? What's the matter?"

Before his wife could reach him, he collapsed to the floor. He tried to talk to her, but his tongue strangled. Queer, terrible, animal sounds came forth. He wept and wept as he made the vain effort to communicate with her. He could not get up from the floor. He could not move his arms and legs. Dr. Axelrod, after examining him, announced that Reb Samuel was paralyzed and needed a long rest.

For the next ten years, while I was growing up, Reb Samuel lay in bed and rested. He could not stir, he could not speak above a painful whisper. He lived on crackers and milk and faded to a white, mournful skeleton.

His little wife arose now an hour earlier each morning to sponge him, to spoon-feed him like a child, to fix his bedpan and other needs. Then she worked in the umbrella store and returned at noon to care for him again.

He lay by the window. My father arranged three mirrors in such a fashion that everything below reflected into a mirror hung from the ceiling. Without turning his eyes, Reb Samuel could see everything in the street. He was a man at a never-ending play. He was a spectator, a ghost watching our crazy world.

He was still gentle. He would smile and whisper, "Ach, America! Who can understand America?" Every night his wife talked to him about their children, and about the problems of the umbrella store. He gently gave her comfort and advice.

When he died, everyone on the street was sad and went to his funeral. *"Ai,"* the people said, shaking their heads, "Reb Samuel was such a good man and so truly pious! Men like this do not grow on every bush in America! He lived by umbrella-making, but in his heart he was a saint!"

MANASSEH

by S. LIEBEN

I T was a stifling summer evening. I had just come home from work, taken off my coat, unbuttoned my waistcoat, and sat down panting by the window of my little room.

There was a knock at the door, and without waiting for my reply, in came a woman with yellow hair, and very untidy in her dress.

I judged from her appearance that she had not come from a distance. She had nothing on her head, her sleeves were tucked up, she held a ladle in her hand, and she was chewing something or other.

"I am Manasseh's wife," said she.

"Manasseh Gricklin's?" I asked.

"Yes," said my visitor, "Gricklin's, Gricklin's."

I hastily slipped on a coat, and begged her to be seated.

Manasseh was an old friend of mine, he was a capmaker, and we worked together in one shop.

And I knew that he lived somewhere in the same tenement as myself, but it was the first time I had the honor of seeing his wife.

"Look here," began the woman, "don't you work in the same shop as my husband?"

"Yes, yes," I said.

"Well, tell me," and the yellow-haired woman gave a bound like a hyena, "how is it I see you come home from work with all other respectable people, and my husband not? And it isn't the first time, either, that he's gone, goodness knows where, and come home two hours after everyone else. Where's he loitering about?"

"I don't know," I replied gravely.

The woman brandished her ladle in such a way that I began to think she meant murder.

"You don't know?" she exclaimed with a sinister flash in her eyes. "What do you mean by that? Don't you two leave the shop together? How can you help seeing what becomes of him?"

Then I remembered that when Manasseh and I left the shop, he walked with me a few blocks, and then went off in another direction; and that one day, when I asked him where he was going, he had replied, "To see some friends."

"He must go to some friends," I said to the woman.

"To some friends?" she repeated, and burst into strange laughter. "Who? Whose? Ours? We're greeners, we are, we have no friends. What friends should he have, poor miserable wretch?"

"I don't know," I said, "but that is what he told me."

"All right!" said Manasseh's wife. "I'll teach him a lesson he won't forget in a hurry."

With these words she departed.

When she had left the room, I pictured to myself poor consumptive Manasseh being taught a "lesson" by his yellow-haired wife, and I pitied him.

Manasseh was a man of about thirty. His yellowish-white face was set in a black beard; he was very thin, always ailing and coughing, had never learnt to write and he read only Yiddish—a quiet, respectable man, I might almost say the only hand in the shop who never grudged a fellow-worker his livelihood. He had been only a year in the country, and the others made sport of him, but I always stood up for him, because I liked him very much.

Wherever does he go, now? I wondered to myself. I resolved to find out.

Next morning I met Manasseh as usual, and at first I intended to tell him of his wife's visit to me the day before; but the poor operative looked so low-spirited, so thoroughly unhappy, that I felt sure his wife had already given him the promised "lesson," and I hadn't the courage to mention her to him just then.

In the evening, as we were going home from the workshop, Manasseh said to me:

"Did my wife come to see you yesterday?"

"Yes, brother Manasseh," I answered. "She seemed annoyed with you."

"She has a dreadful temper," observed the workman. "When she is really angry, she's fit to kill a man. But it's her bitter heart, poor thing —she's had so many troubles! We're so poor, and she's far away from her family."

Manasseh gave a deep sigh.

"She asked you where I go other days after work?" he continued.

"Yes."

"Would you like to know?"

"Why not, Mister Gricklin!"

"Come along a few blocks further," said Manasseh, "and I'll show you."

I agreed, and we walked on together.

A few more blocks and Manasseh led me into a narrow street, not yet entirely built in with houses.

Presently he stopped, with a contented smile. I looked round in some astonishment. We were standing alongside a piece of waste ground, with a meagre fencing of stones and burnt wire, and utilized as a garden.

"Just look," said the workman, pointing at the garden, "how delightful it is! One so seldom sees anything of the kind in New York."

Manasseh went nearer to the fence, and his eyes wandered thirstily over the green, flowering plants, just then in full beauty. I also looked at the garden. The things that grew there were unknown to me, and I was ignorant of their names. Only one thing had a familiar look—a few tall, graceful "moons" were scattered here and there over the place, and stood like absent-minded dreamers, or beautiful sentinels. And the roses were in bloom, and their fragrance came in wafts over the fencing.

"You see the 'moons'?" asked Manasseh, in rapt tones, but more to himself than to me. "Look how beautiful they are! I can't take my eyes off them. I am capable of standing and looking at them for hours. They make me feel happy, almost as if I were at home again. There were a lot of them at home!"

The operative sighed, lost himself a moment in thought, and then said:

"When I smell the roses, I think of old days. We had quite a large garden, and I was so fond of it! When the flowers began to come out, I used to sit there for hours, and could never look at it enough. The roses appeared to be dreaming with their great golden eyes wide open. The cucumbers lay along the ground like pussy-cats, and the stalks and leaves spread ever so far across the beds. The beans fought for room like street urchins, and the pumpkins and the potatoes—you should have seen them! And the flowers were all colors, pink, and blue and yellow, and I felt as if everything were alive, as if the whole garden were alive— I fancied I heard them talking together, the roses, the potatoes, the beans. I spent whole evenings in my garden. It was dear to me as my own soul. Look, look, don't the roses seem as if they were alive?"

But I looked at Manasseh, and thought the consumptive workman had grown younger and healthier. His face was less livid, and his eyes shone with happiness.

"Do you know," said Manasseh to me, as we walked away from the garden, "I had some cuttings of rosetrees at home, in a basket out on the fire-escape, and they had begun to bud."

There was a pause.

"Well," I inquired, "and what happened?"

"My wife laid out the mattress to air on the top of the basket, and they were all crushed."

Manasseh made an outward gesture with his hand, and I asked no more questions.

The poky, stuffy shop in which he worked came into my mind, and my heart was sore for him.

EGYPT, 1937

by MEYER LEVIN

"I DON'T understand what makes you so religious all of a sudden!" Lil exclaimed sarcastically. "Why don't you grow a beard and go to *shul* while you're at it!"

"Religion has nothing to do with it," he responded patiently. "You know perfectly well, all that stuff means nothing to me. It's just the— the social side of it. I mean—"

"That's the whole point! Socially, it means something to us to go to Ev's."

"Listen, Lil," he said with hopeless restraint. "You know perfectly well that, if your own mother was having a *seder,* we would have to go there. But since your mother and father are in Rochester, my folks naturally expect us to come to them. It would be like a slap in the face not to come."

"Oh, mygod, do I have to sit like a prisoner till twelve o'clock while your grandfather mumbles the whatyacall it through his beard? We were there year before last and that ought to hold them for a while!"

"It was three years ago."

"Whenever it was, once was enough! Mygod, you'd think that, with all your uncles and aunts, your family would have enough customers for their *seder* without dragging me into it!"

"That isn't the point," Sam said. "It doesn't hurt us, and it makes them feel good to see their son and their grandchild at the table."

"Listen, Sam. We're young, we're modern. For three years we were tied down to the house with the kid and everything, but now at least we can begin to go out and see people, so why we do have to get stuck with a bunch of old dodoes? I think Ev's idea is wonderful. Why not have a *seder* for young couples only! I wish I had thought of the idea myself! A *seder* is supposed to be a celebration, isn't it! Why not have a good time!"

"If you're so keen on going there, go on," Sam said. "I'll take Jackie to my folks."

Lil gave him a burning look; her hand went to her mouth, stifling a sob. "Oh, so that's it! So you want to show them what a terrible mother he's got!" She rushed into the bedroom.

Sam sank into a chair and clutched the arms, tight. Gradually, his anger eased. He decided to laugh the whole thing off. That he should quarrel about religion—he, the agnostic!

He found her lying face down on the bed, sobbing.

"I'm sorry, Lil." He stroked her hair. "I don't know what's the matter with me lately, I'm getting so nervous I get contrary on the slightest provocation." He wanted to tell her, to tell someone, about the times in court or in his office when he felt himself getting all tense in knots, as though he were a rope being twisted tighter and tighter; to tell her of the disgust and loss he felt in his daily work, in his getting out of politics, in having to curry favors from a louse like Judge Horowitz.

"It was my fault, Sammy. I aggravate you when you're tired," she said, sitting up and drawing his head to her. "I shouldn't even have mentioned Ev. We ought to go to your family this year. It's only right."

"Oh, it doesn't matter, they probably won't even notice we're missing. We can go there for the second night, anyway. They're used to having us come then."

"Of course!" she exclaimed. The second night was a *seder,* too!

"C-o-n

S-t-a-n-t-i-n . . ."

the radio was going, as they entered. Thelma was dancing with Manny Kassell, and there was a strange couple dancing. Ev, who looked ravishing in a flowing white gown that completely concealed her condition—though there was nothing as yet to conceal—came rushing toward them.

"Oh, darling, look at me! Does it show?" she whispered quite audibly, to Lil.

"It doesn't show a bit!" Lil whispered back.

"She just wanted an excuse to wear that gown," Phil remarked, with a loving proud sophisticated kidding glance at his wife.

"Oh, it's cute," Lil said. "It's darling."

"Oh, Jackie! Isn't he cute!" Ev swooped.

"Say hello to Aunt Ev, Jackie."

"Hi, toots," Jackie said, and they all roared.

Phil introduced them to the strangers, Mr. and Mrs. McIlwain, who were dying to see a Jewish Passover ceremony.

The maid passed around cocktails, and little caviar canapés on matzoth.

"Aren't they wonderful!" Mrs. McIlwain cried, examining the canapés. "Passover or no Passover, I think that's an awfully smart way to serve caviar."

"They're awfully cute," Lil agreed.

"Darling, you must tell me where to buy this—what do you call it?" Mrs. McIlwain said.

"Matt-zote," Ev carefully mispronounced the word, and giggled.

"Say, this don't taste like bathtub gin to me," Manny comically complained of his drink.

"That's real prescription stuff," Phil admitted. "I'm afraid you'll have to put up with it, as Ev has been using our bathtub lately."

They laughed.

"One of the saddest things about Prohibition," McIlwain said, "is we don't know good liquor when we get it. I always used my old man as a tester-in-chief. Boy, he used to sozzle the real stuff!"

They looked at him, envious of his being the son of a real drunken Irishman.

"Well, Sam, I hear you have deserted the sinking ship," Phil remarked.

"Yah, with the rest of the rats," Sam caught him up.

"Oh," Phil laughed appreciatively. "Well, I guess Big Bill is through, in this town."

"I don't know," Sam said. "He's still mayor."

"He must be kind of lonesome, in the city hall these days." McIlwain referred to the defeat of Thompson's candidates.

"Anyway, he might as well get out," Phil said. "His pals've grabbed everything there was to be grabbed."

"I guess that's so," Sam agreed. "They've about scraped the bottom of the till."

"I hear he has presidential aspirations," McIlwain remarked.

"With him, it's a case of I do choose to run," Manny cracked.

"Will you men stop talking politics!" Ev laughed, and steered them into the dining room.

"Oh, Ev, it's just too cute for words!" Lil screamed, seeing the table. In the center was a layer cake, and atop it was a doll in a flowing robe, with a long white cotton-batting beard stuck to its cherubic chin. Moses!

"Do you get it?" Thelma tittered. "What's it supposed to be?"

"Moses on the Mountain?" Mrs. McIlwain ventured.

"Uh-uh."

"I got it! If you can't eat bread, eat cake!" Manny roared.

"No fair, you knew!" Ev cried.

They all laughed, and Ev modestly said: "It was Phil's idea."

The place cards were the cleverest things! Each card was a cut-out of a biblical character, only Ev had fixed devilish little short skirts over the long gowns of the women characters, and put derby hats on the men. But the most comical thing she had done was to get pictures of movie stars and paste their faces on the biblical figures.

"Who is this supposed to be?" Lil screeched, and they all piled around a picture of Adolphe Menjou, in a silk hat, on the body of an Egyptian taskmaster who wielded a whip.

First they thought it was McIlwain because he was a Gentile (get it, Egyptian) and, besides, he was an engineer; but it turned out to be Manny Kassell on account of his Menjou mustache, and the whip was because he was a dentist. Next to him was a picture of Lillian Gish as Queen Esther playing a harp, and naturally that was Thelma, on account of the harp. Phil and Ev were Doug Fairbanks and Mary Pickford, the perfect couple, as Samson and Delilah! Sam was Groucho Marx as Adam, and Lil was Vilma Banky as Eve, and Jackie was Jackie

Cooper as David. Immediately, he yelled: "Mother, I wanna slingshot!"

"Hush, Jackie, mother will buy you one tomorrow."

"Naw, I wan' it now!"

"Where on earth did you get all those pictures of the movie stars?" Lil said, trying to ignore him.

"Oh, Phil has a friend in Lubliner and Trinz," Ev said, "and he got them out of their advertising department, special."

"Wanna!" Jackie tugged at Lil.

"Look, Jackie," Phil said, and picked up the favor on Jackie's plate. It unfolded into an Indian headdress. "Nize beby," he quoted Milt Gross.

Jackie stopped bawling and put the paper feathers on his head. "Yay, I'm an Indian!" he yelled, happily.

"You know, Phil really has a way with children," Ev said. "I guess he'll make a good papa after all."

The others were discovering their favors. On each plate was a comical hat of the sort worn at New Year's parties.

"You see, good Jews always wear skull caps or some kind of hat at the table on Passover," Ev explained to the Gentiles.

"Don't get the idea this is a real service," Phil said. "We just decided to do this our own way for a change."

The McIlwains put on their hats. Mr. McIlwain had drawn a red-white-and-blue fez with a tassel on the top. His young, round, pink-massaged face beamed good will. Sam's hat was yellow and green, and shaped like an overseas cap. Manny had a dunce cap! The girls had hats, too.

"You know who would appreciate this? Alvin Fox!" Thelma exclaimed. "Remember he trained to be a rabbi and gave it up."

"I was going to ask him," Ev said, "but they just went to Europe on a late honeymoon."

"He married a Gentile girl," Thelma said to the McIlwains, beaming.

"He was ruining the business putting out those modernistic chairs," Phil laughed, "so the old man said it was cheaper to send him to Europe."

They all laughed good-naturedly.

Now the wine went around. Phil had secured some real Chianti, with the straw basket around the bottle.

"Just like a regular *seder!*" Lil cried as the maid served the first dish, consisting of hardboiled eggs cut up in salt water.

"What do you call this?" Mrs. McIlwain inquired.

"*Charokis,*" Ev promptly responded, anglicizing the word beyond recognition.

"How did you ever know about all this stuff?" Lil said, awed. "My mother used to make a kind of a *seder* but I would never dream of trying it myself!"

"Kid, you'll never guess where I got the directions," Ev said. "There was a complete Passover menu in Prudence Penny's column!"

"No!"

"I'll prove it to you!" And Ev produced the clipping. "I just gave it to the girl and told her to follow it religiously."

"Religiously, that's good," Manny repeated.

"What kind of bread would you like, rye or white?" Phil jested, passing the plate of matzoth.

"I'm really going to eat this, it's good for you, I'm on a diet!" Ev said. "My gynecologist said it was the best thing."

The maid brought in a plate of hot biscuits, which most of them accepted, though the McIlwains insisted on eating matzoth.

"Isn't there supposed to be a glass of wine for somebody?" Lil prompted.

"Oh, yah! *Eli hanoveh!*" Thelma supplied.

"What's that?"

"Elijah," Phil translated.

"Yah. That's cute," Lil said. "You're supposed to fill a glass with wine, and Elijah comes and drinks it up."

"How about giving Elijah a real treat, for a change?" Phil said, and filled a glass with gin. "Where you are, old boy old boy! Open the door for Elijah!"

"Who is Elijah?" Jackie said.

"He comes and drinks it up," Lil explained.

"When?"

"Right away. You can't see him. He's invisible."

"Aw," Jackie watched her face. "You're kidding me."

"It's a fact," Lil said. "He goes into every house, and drinks the wine."

"Yah? Then I bet he gets pie-eyed!" Jackie piped.

They roared.

"Isn't he the cutest thing!"

Ev leaned intimately to Phil.

"Oh, Lil, make him ask the four questions!" suggested Thelma.

"That's right, that's what he's here for!"

Philip explained to the McIlwains. "Of course we're not doing this in proper order or anything, but at a real *seder* they follow the *Haggada*, that's a sort of book of procedure, and the youngest son of the house asks the traditional four questions, and the head of the household, usually the grandfather, reads the responses."

"Surprise!" Ev said, and produced a *Haggada,* printed in both Hebrew and English. This curiosity was passed around, everybody explaining to the McIlwains that the Hebrew was read backwards instead of up and down, like Chinese. They studied the booklet respectfully.

"Oh, you know what I want to sing!" Thelma cried. *"Chad gadyo!* We always used to sing that when I was a kid!" She turned the pages. "One kid, one kid for two *zuzim!"* she began. The wine was affecting her noticeably, her cheeks were flaming. *"Chad gadyo! Chad gadyo!"*

"Doesn't that come at the end of the meal?" Ev said.

"What's the difference!"

Manny began to sing with her: *"Chad gadyo! Chad gadyo!"*

The maid brought in an immense, sugar-baked ham.

Squeals and titters.

Manny picked up a curled streamer that lay near his plate and blew noisily. The red crape paper shot across the table, and dropped over Sam's ear.

"The four questions, the four questions!" Lil insisted.

"All right, you read them for Jackie, and Phil will answer them!" Ev said.

"Now, Jackie, look." Lil showed him the lines in the book. "You say what I say—ready?"

Jackie nodded eagerly.

"Why . . ."

"Why."

"Is this night . . ."

"Is this night."

"Different . . ."

"Diffrunt."

Sam heard his son piping and, glancing across at the book in Lil's hand, suddenly remembered the Hebrew words: *"Mah nishtonah halaylah hazeh . . . ?"* as he had used to say them, awed, and the grave answering intonation of his grandfather.

"From all other nights?"

"Fmallothnights." Jackie stuck out his hand, for a reward.

"Because this is April 4," Phil answered, "and every other night is another night."

Their guffaws rattled the glassware.

Sam got up.

"You'll have to excuse me," he managed to mumble, as he made for the door.

Lil rushed after him. "What's the matter, are you sick?" Her first look at him was worried. Then: "Are you crazy? Disgracing me before my best friends!"

Ev rushed up to them.

"This is the end!" Lil sputtered hotly, collapsing in tears into Evelyn's arms.

In Sam's mind, these words were flashing, as though he were reading them on an electric sign, on and off, on and off: "This is where I get off. This is where I get off."

HEDER

by HENRY ROTH

ONE edge shining in the vanishing sunlight, the little white-washed house of the heder lay before them. It was only one story high, the windows quite close to the ground. Its bulkier neighbors, the tall tenements that surrounded it, seemed to puff out their littered fire-escapes in scorn. Smoke curled from a little, black chimney in the middle of its roof, and overhead myriads of wash-lines criss-crossed intricately, snaring the sky in a dark net. Most of the lines were bare, but here and there was one sagging with white and colored wash, from which now and again a flurry of rinsings splashed into the yard or drummed on the heder roof.

"I hope," said his mother, as they went down the wooden stairs that led into the yard, "that you'll prove more gifted in the ancient tongue than I was. When I went to heder, my rabbi was always wagging his head at me and swearing I had a calf's brain." And she laughed. "But I think the reason I was such a dunce was that I could never wrench my nose far enough away to escape his breath. Pray this one is not so fond of onions!"

They crossed the short space of the yard and his mother opened the heder door. A billow of drowsy air rolled out at them. It seemed dark inside. On their entrance, the hum of voices ceased.

The rabbi, a man in a skull cap, who had been sitting near the window beside one of his pupils, looked up when he saw them and rose. Against the window, he looked short and bulbous, oddly round beneath the square outline of the skull cap.

"Good day," he ambled toward them. "I'm Reb Yidel Pankower. You wish—?" He ran large, hairy fingers through a glossy, crinkled beard.

David's mother introduced herself and then went on to explain her mission.

"And this is he?"

"Yes. The only one I have."

"Only one such pretty star?" He chuckled and reaching out, caught David's cheek in a tobacco-reeking pinch. David shied slightly.

While his mother and the rabbi were discussing the hours and the price and the manner of David's tuition, David scanned his future teacher more closely. He was not at all like the teachers at school, but David had seen rabbis before and knew he wouldn't be. He appeared old and was certainly untidy. He wore soft leather shoes like house-slippers, that had no place for either laces or buttons. His trousers were baggy and stained, a great area of striped and crumpled shirt intervened between his belt and his bulging vest. The knot of his tie, which was nearer one ear than the other, hung away from his soiled collar. What features were visible were large and had an oily gleam. Beneath his skull cap, his black hair was closely cropped. Though full of misgivings about his future relations with the rabbi, David felt that he must accept his fate. Was it not his father's decree that he attend a heder?

From the rabbi his eyes wandered about the room. Bare walls, the brown paint on it full of long wavering cracks. Against one wall, stood a round-bellied stove whose shape reminded him of his rabbi, except that it was heated a dull red and his rabbi's apparel was black. Against the other wall a long line of benches ran to the rabbi's table. Boys of varying ages were seated upon them, jabbering, disputing, gambling for various things, scuffling over what looked to David like a few sticks. Seated upon the bench before the rabbi's table were several others obviously waiting their turn at the book lying open in front of the rabbi's cushioned chair.

What had been, when he and his mother had entered, a low hum of voices, had now swollen to a roar. It looked as though half of the boys in the room had engaged the other half in some verbal or physical conflict. The rabbi, excusing himself to David's mother, turned toward them, and with a thunderous rap of his fist against the door, uttered a ferocious, "Shah!" The noise subsided somewhat. He swept the room with angry glittering eyes, then softening into a smile again returned to David's mother.

At last it was arranged and the rabbi wrote down his new pupil's name and address. David gathered that he was to receive his instruction somewhere between the hours of three and six, that he was to come to the heder shortly after three, and that the fee for his education would be twenty-five cents a week. Moreover he was to begin that afternoon. This was something of an unpleasant surprise and at first he protested, but when his mother urged him and the rabbi assured him that his first lesson would not take long, he consented, and mournfully received his mother's parting kiss.

"Sit down over there," said the rabbi curtly as soon as his mother had left. "And don't forget," he brought a crooked knuckle to his lips. "In a heder one must be quiet."

David sat down, and the rabbi walked back to his seat beside the window. Instead of sitting down however, he reached under his chair, and bringing out a short-thonged cat-o'-nine-tails, struck the table loudly with the butt-end and pronounced in a menacing voice: "Let there be a hush among you!" And a scared silence instantly locking all mouths, he seated himself. He then picked up a little stick lying on the table and pointed to the book, whereupon a boy sitting next to him began droning out sounds in a strange and secret tongue.

For a while, David listened intently to the sound of the words. It was Hebrew, he knew, the same mysterious language his mother used before the candles, the same his father used when he read from a book during the holidays—and that time before drinking wine. Not Yiddish, Hebrew. God's tongue, the rabbi had said. If you knew it, then you could talk to God. Who was He? He would learn about Him now—

The boy sitting nearest David, slid along the bench to his side. "Yuh jost stottin' heder?"

"Uhh!" he groaned, indicating the rabbi with his eyes. "He's a louser! He hits!"

David regarded the rabbi with panicky eyes. He had seen boys slapped by teachers in school for disobedience, although he himself had never been struck. The thought of being flogged with that vicious scourge he had seen the rabbi produce sealed his lips. He even refused to answer when next the boy asked him whether he had any match-pictures to match, and hastily shook his head. With a shrug, the boy slid back along the bench to the place he had come from.

Presently, with the arrival of several late-comers, older boys, tongues once more began to wag and a hum of voices filled the room. When David saw that the rabbi brandished his scourge several times without wielding it, his fear abated somewhat. However, he did not venture to join in the conversation, but cautiously watched the rabbi.

The boy who had been reading when David had come in had finished, and his place was taken by a second who seemed less able to maintain the rapid drone of his predecessor. At first, when he faltered, the rabbi corrected him by uttering what was apparently the right sound, for the boy always repeated it. But gradually, as his pupil continued in his error, a harsh note of warning crept into the rabbi's voice. After awhile he began to yank the boy by the arm whenever he corrected him, then to slap him smartly on the thigh, and finally, just before the boy had finished, the rabbi cuffed him on the ear.

As time went by, David saw this procedure repeated in part or whole in the case of almost every other boy who read. There were several exceptions, and these, as far as David could observe, gained their exemption from punishment because the drone that issued from their lips was as breathless and uninterrupted as the roll of a drum. He also noticed that whenever the rabbi administered one of these manual corrections, he first dropped from his hand the little stick with which he seemed to set the pace on the page, and an instant later reached out or struck out, as the case might demand. So that, whenever he dropped the stick, whether to scratch his beard or adjust his skull cap or fish out a half-burned cigarette from a box, the pupil before him invariably jerked up an arm or ducked his head defensively. The dropping of that little stick, seemed to have become a warning to his pupils that a blow was on the way.

The light in the windows was waning to a blank pallor. The room was warm; the stagnant air had lulled even the most restive. Drowsily, David wondered when his turn would come.

"Aha!" he heard the rabbi sarcastically exclaim. "Is it you, Hershele, scholar from the land of scholars?"

This was addressed to the boy who had just slid into the vacant place before the book. David had observed him before, a fat boy with a dull face and an open mouth. By the cowed, sullen stoop of his shoulders, it was clear that he was not in good standing with the rabbi.

"Herry is gonna loin," giggled one of the boys at David's side.

"Perhaps, today, you can glitter a little," suggested the rabbi with a freezing smile. "Come!" He picked up the stick and pointed to the page.

The boy began to read. Though a big boy, as big as any that pre-ceded him, he read more slowly and faltered more often than any of the others. It was evident that the rabbi was restraining his impatience, for instead of actually striking his pupil, he grimaced violently when he corrected him, groaned frequently, stamped his foot under the table and gnawed his under-lip. The other students had grown quiet and were listening. From their strained silence—their faces were by now half ob-scured in shadow—David was sure they were expecting some catastrophe any instant. The boy fumbled on. As far as David could tell, he seemed to be making the same error over and over again, for the rabbi kept repeating the same sound. At last, the rabbi's patience gave out. He dropped the pointer; the boy ducked, but not soon enough. The speed-ing plane of the rabbi's palm rang against his ear like a clapper on a gong.

"You plaster dunce!" he roared, "when will you learn a byse is a byse and not a vyse. Head of filth, where are your eyes?" He shook a menacing hand at the cringing boy and picked up the pointer.

But a few moments later, again the same error and again the same correction.

"May a demon fly off with your father's father! Won't blows help you? A byse, Esau, pig! A byse! Remember, a byse, even though you die of convulsions!"

The boy whimpered and went on. He had not uttered more than a few sounds, when again he paused on the awful brink, and as if out of sheer malice, again repeated his error. The last stroke of the bastinado! The effect on the rabbi was terrific. A frightful bellow clove his beard. In a moment he had fastened the pincers of his fingers on the cheeks of his howling pupil, and wrenching the boy's head from side to side roared out—

"A byse! A byse! A byse! All buttocks have only one eye. A byse! May your brains boil over! A byse! Creator of earth and firmament, ten thousand heders are in this land and me you single out for torment! A byse! Most abject of God's fools! A byse!"

While he raved and dragged the boy's head from side to side with one hand, with the other he hammered the pointer with such fury against the table that David expected at any moment to see the slender stick buried in the wood. It snapped instead!

"He busted it!" gleefully announced the boy sitting near.

"He busted it!" the suppressed giggle went round.

Horrified himself by what he saw, David wondered what the rest could possibly be so amused about.

"I couldn't see," the boy at the table was blubbering. "I couldn't see! It's dark in here!"

"May your skull be dark!" the rabbi intoned in short frenzied yelps, "and your eyes be dark and your fate be of such dearth and darkness that you will call a poppy-seed the sun and a caraway the moon. Get up! Away! Or I'll empty my bitter heart upon you!"

Tears streaming down his cheeks, and wailing loudly, the boy slid off the bench and slunk away.

"Stay here till I give you leave to go," the rabbi called after him. "Wipe your muddy nose. Hurry, I say! If you could read as easily as your eyes can piss, you were a fine scholar indeed!"

The boy sat down, wiped his nose and eyes with his coat-sleeve and quieted to a suppressed snuffling.

Glancing at the window, the rabbi fished in his pockets, drew out a match and lit the low gas jet sticking out from the wall over head. While he watched the visibility of the open book on the table, he frugally shaved down the light to a haggard leaf. Then he seated himself again, unlocked a drawer in the table and drew out a fresh stick which looked exactly like the one he had just broken. David wondered whether the rabbi whittled a large supply of sticks for himself, knowing what would happen to them.

"Move back!" He waved the boy away who had reluctantly slipped into the place just vacated before the table. "David Schearl!" he called out, tempering the harshness of his voice. "Come here, my gold."

Quailing with fright, David drew near.

"Sit down, my child," he was still breathing hard with exertion. "Don't be alarmed." He drew out of his pocket a package of cigarette-papers and a tobacco pouch, carefully rolled a cigarette, took a few puffs, then snuffed it out and put it into an empty cigarette box. David's heart pounded with fear. "Now then," he turned the leaves of a book beside him to the last page. "Show me how blessed is your understanding." He drew David's tense shoulder down toward the table, and picking up the new stick, pointed to a large hieroglyph at the top of the page. "This is called Komitz. You see? Komitz. And this an Aleph. Now, whenever one sees a Komitz under an Aleph, one says, Aw." His hot tobacco-laden breath swirled about David's face.

His mother's words about her rabbi flashed through his mind. He thrust them aside and riveted his gaze to the indicated letter as if he would seal it on with his eyes.

"Say after me," continued the rabbi, "Komitz-Aleph—Aw.!"

David repeated the sounds.

"So!" commanded the rabbi. "Once more! Komitz-Aleph—Aw!"

And after David had repeated it several times. "And this," continued the rabbi pointing to the next character, "is called Bais, and a Komitz under a Bais—Baw! Say it! Komitz-Bais—Baw!"

"Komitz-Bais—Baw!" said David.

"Well done! Again."

And so the lesson progressed with repetition upon repetition. Whether out of fear or aptitude, David went through these first steps with hardly a single error. And when he was dismissed, the rabbi pinched his cheek in praise and said:

"Go home. You have an iron head!"

RACHEL AND HER CHILD

by MYRON BRINIG

THE child lay beside her in the bed where it had been born a week before. Her eyes were wide open and she looked at Rachel and smiled. There had been long days of pain and nausea and thoughts about life not being worth a candle, and why did a woman have to go through all this? Rachel would gaze into the mirror and see herself hideous, a caricature, her body of a girl turned into the ugliness of a monster. She hated the sight of her body like that and shut herself up in a dark room and wouldn't come out. "I won't come out!" She had screamed when the family had begged her eat something. She had stayed in the dark room and Rebecca had brought in food. "I had seven and I never acted so foolish," Rebecca said. "Nowadays, a woman has a child and it's like she was carrying a bushel of snakes. Look at me who had seven and worked all the time over the stove in the kitchen. But there ain't no more women like me to have seven and burn myself over a hot stove all day."

The dark room had been a cave under the world. Long days were endless ladders that Rachel climbed, each rung jagged with dagger points. She had carried the volcano of her body up the ladder. And one horrible night, Rachel had reached the top of the ladder, and there was nothing to do but jump off. She had jumped into black space, screaming, and that was the end of the ladder of days. When light came, the baby was beside her in the bed and it smiled. Is this smiling baby the same monster that was inside of me, weighing me down, stabbing me with the horns of red devils? wondered Rachel. She touched the child's forehead with the tip of her finger, and it was as though she touched the petal of a delicate flower.

And now, a week later, she was telling her baby a story. "Once upon a time there was a girl, that's me, and the girl met a prince, that's Boris, and they loved. He was—let me tell you about your father, my darling. You may never see him, no more, no more. He was tall and straight and he looked as if he were about to jump off the world into a divine blue space. We made our days, Boris and I. We gathered the days close to our lips and breathed on them and they came to life. We breathed the sun into our days, the clouds and the snow. You're the only one who understands me, my darling. I can tell you stories about Boris and myself and you won't close your ears. You won't make other stories on top of my story. Once upon a time there was a girl named Rachel and a prince named Boris, and they met and loved. What, do you want my breast? Here, my darling, take me, take me. Eat me up. Drink me into your body. You are the girl I was and the boy he was. Our blood is mingled in you." And when Rachel touched the tip of her finger to the child's forehead she touched the petal of a rose.

Louis came into the room where Rachel lay with her baby. "This is Uncle Louis, darling. He was away for a long time, but now he's back again. Look, Louis, who's smiling at you. I lie here and tell her stories about a princess and a prince. You belong in the story, Louis. You're the good brother who was away in a far-off country, and we didn't hear from you for a long time, and then you came back."

Louis sat very close to the bed and his black hair fell over his forehead. "When she smiles she looks like Boris," said Louis, "but when she's sad, she's a Singermann. What are you going to call her, Rachel?"

"Gloria."

"Well, that's a pretty name. Let me take her, Rachel. Aw, I won't hurt her. Want to come to your uncle? Come, come to your damn fool uncle."

"Sh! Louis! Such language before a young lady!"

"Say, she's a heavyweight, she is. Hey, what you smiling at? Hey, who you laughing at? Don't you laugh at me. When she laughs, she looks like Boris. This little piggy went to market, this little piggy stayed at home. But when she's sad, she's a Singermann."

Louis thought of himself in his room at Mrs. Shaner's, the coldness, the emptiness of that room; and here he was back home again, holding Rachel's baby in his arms. This child would grow up some day and go out and have a lover. Her life would assume all kinds of shapes, take on many colors, some as lovely and delicate as a flower's colors, some harsh and ugly. Here she was in his arms, this baby, and she was something new, anything you chose to think her. She was snow newly fallen that you hold in your hands and press into many shapes. Louis lost himself in the child. He would like to shape her into beauty. He would strive to create perfection of her. He would take her by the hand and lead her along a country road and their feet would be bare and the warm sand would trickle between their toes. He would paint her, and her soul would emerge from inanimate canvas, aspiring and immortal. Oh, if he were God! He would shield her away from bitterness and cruelty. Together they would go to far-off places, tramp through art galleries. This is La Gioconda, and does she not seem cryptic and alive? And this is Corot. Observe the branches above the road and the shadows beneath. And here is El Greco praying to a God above God. And if you are bored by paintings, we will read Shakespeare. *To me, fair friend, you never can be old,* thin scented paper in a black leather book. Oh, if I were a power that could work miracles! I'd lead Gloria along a road away from drudgery and meanness, away from Mrs. Shaner and the department store and the baseball coming down with a merciless swiftness and slipping through my fingers.

Louis placed Gloria in her mother's arms. "She's anything," he said. "If you call her a queen, isn't she one? What does she see, I wonder? What were the things we saw when we were a week old? And where did the pictures go, the sounds, the smells, the feels? Back there, when we were too young to remember, what happened to those sounds and pictures and feelings?"

"But she is the only one who understands my stories," said Rachel, and snuggled in close to her baby, away from Louis, away from the world. In there, under the covers, close to her child, Rachel was safe and nothing could touch her.

Louis went away still thinking about the pictures unseen, the sounds unheard, the sensations unrealized.

They were all glad of the baby, the Singermanns. Moses would come home and allow the child to pull his beard. He melted beside the child and made himself a plaything, a great, astounding toy. The child was not frightened of him and laughed and begged him to take her. Sometimes, Moses would get in his bed and ask that the baby be brought to him so that he could fall asleep beside her. But Rachel said it was bad for an old man and a baby to be in bed together. The man took the baby's breath. The baby was weakened and drawn out of herself into the man.

One Friday evening, Moses took the baby to the synagogue and made up a prayer in music. "Look down, O Lord, and behold my grandchild. Is she not beautiful? When Moses ruled in the young days of the world, was ever a child so firm, so fine to look upon? In the land of Judea, in the great days when Solomon ruled, was there such a girl child to enrapture the hearts of the old men? I bring you my grandchild, and she was not born in wedlock, but you are a merciful God and you will forgive, for is she not an armful to hold, weighing strong in my arms, with such health in her cheeks? And I, Moses Singermann, pass along the street where my brothers see me. And they whisper to one another, 'Look, there is Moses Singermann and the child that was born of a sinner who had two wives before he took a third.' But is the child less pleasing in your eyes, O Lord?" And Moses brought the child into the synagogue and sang to God so that she would be acceptable in His eyes and blessed. And Moses beat his breast, under the holy Torah, under the swimming flames of the candles. "Wilt Thou smile upon a little child? Hear, O Israel, the Lord our God, the Lord is One."

And in the house on West Granite Street, David would carry the child from one room to another and bury his black hair in her breast. "I'll eat you! I'll eat you for supper!" he would cry, and his voice was everywhere, rich, resounding, golden, and magnetic to the ear. "Whose kid d'ya think you are, huh?" asked David, holding the child aloft over his head. "Are you my kid? Are you Sol's brat? Are you Harry's kid? Maybe Michael is your papa? Where did you come from? What are you doing here? You're my supper, and I'll eat you!"

Harry and Sol viewed the child tolerantly. But Michael was jealous. He and Rachel had been close together and had told one another stories. But now that Rachel had Gloria everything was different. Everyone was absorbed in the baby, and when Michael showed his face, a great derisive cry arose. "Your nose is out of joint! Mike's nose is out of joint!" Michael presented a brave face while the others were looking at him. But just as soon as they took their eyes off him, he ran to a mirror, but his nose looked just the same as it had before Gloria arrived.

Rebecca was greatly concerned for the baby. "Eat!" she would call to Rachel. "The baby must have good milk, and so you must eat. When a baby has good milk in its stomach, it is happy, and the mother should eat hearty. When the baby cries, it is because the milk you give it is poisoned. So you should keep yourself full of good food and laugh all day. When your head is free from worry then your baby gets rich milk, but when you are sad, the baby gets sick. Eat, Rachel. Eat and laugh."

Sam Straller came to the house one day. He had not been there since Rachel had gone away with Boris, but now he came to look at the baby. Rachel did not want to see him. Her days were full of the child who made her remember Boris. She was feeding the baby when Sam came and she covered her breasts and turned her head away from him. She knew why Sam had come. She could see the reason in his eyes. He wanted her back, and she could not bear the thought.

"Well, I must say, Rachel. You're looking fine. You never looked better than you do now. Say, that's a baby. I'd call that a fine lady, you bet."

There was a look of prosperity about Sam. His features had become set and his manner was more assured. But he sent a sharp arrow of repugnance through Rachel. He stood for her days before she met Boris. What was I before I met Boris? Nothing but dull, lifeless earth. Boris was the sun and the rain and the wind. Now I am in bloom. I am blossoms in the wind and there is perfume in the air. And here comes Sam Straller, thinking I am dull, lifeless earth again. Go away! I can have nothing to do with you. Go away!

"I'd like to take you and the baby out some time," Sam invited Rachel. "We could go walking together, and maybe everybody would think I was its father."

"Nobody would think that!" replied Rachel sharply. "Nobody could think such a foolish thing. What do you mean, speaking that way to me? Now you've made the baby cry. She doesn't like you."

There was that awful beaten look that came into Sam's eyes. Here he had come to parade his new prosperity before Rachel, and she was angry with him. He was receiving ten dollars a week more for his salary down at the newspaper office. He had bought a new suit that was more fashionable than any he had ever worn. The shoulders were padded and made him look stronger. The trousers were peg-top, tight about the waist and flaring at the hips. His patent leather shoes had brown cloth uppers and gray buttons. He did not like button shoes, they were such a bother to put on, and they hurt his feet when he used the button-hook. Yet despite all this show, Rachel was angry with him and the baby was screaming. "You've frightened my baby," said Rachel. "Anybody would know that you're not her father. I won't ever forgive you for saying such a thing."

"I didn't mean anything," mumbled Sam. "I only wanted to pay a call and see you and the baby. Why are you mad at me like this? I'd cut my hand off for you."

Rachel looked at him. "You can't do anything for me," she said. "Now go away, for you've frightened my little girl."

"But if I go away I want to come back," he pleaded. "Day after day, I've thought about you. When you married Boris Romanovitch, I thought about you. Do you think I was happy about it? I remember the times we used to be out in Columbia Gardens together, and I used to eat sandwiches there with you. I used to walk with you at Columbia Gardens, and I was a different man. And then you went away with the barber, and do you think I wasn't miserable? I lost all interest in my work. I lost weight. Everybody who looked at me, said, 'Sam, you're looking bad. You're losing weight. You need something to build you up.' My worries were eating me alive."

"Could I help that?" asked Rachel. "I never thought about you. You were not even the wind that blew over my head."

"All the time, I was thinking about you, Rachel, And then he went away from you and—do you think I was glad when he went away? I knew how you'd feel. But he was gone, and so that was over. And then, when you had the baby, I was glad of it. Now she'll feel better. She won't be so lonesome, now that she's got a baby. I felt that way about it. Let me tell you, the other day I saw you passing in the street. I was in my room alone. I was all alone by myself. I saw you wheeling the baby carriage. You picked the baby up in your arms and looked at it. And I saw something come out of your eyes, out of your body, a kind of happiness I never saw before my whole life long. And I got that happy feeling in me, like I was with the baby, like I was holding her up in my arms. Was it wrong for me to feel that way? 'I'll go and see Rachel,' I said to myself. 'Maybe she'll share some of that happiness with me.'"

"How can I?" asked Rachel sadly. "This is not your little girl. She came from his body, not yours. How can I give you happiness? When I knew you I was nothing. See that chair? I was like that. I was nothing.

If you go away, maybe my baby will fall asleep. You scare her. She's only a baby."

He had come to see Rachel with his patent leather, button shoes and his padded shoulders, and he had felt tall and chivalrous. And now he was small again and he thought that he must look ridiculous. "I don't want to go away for good," he murmured. "I'll come back some time, Rachel. Maybe you won't mind so much if I come back some time."

She was sorry for him. "Yes, come back," she said. "Only not tomorrow or the day after. My love is far away. And my love is here in the baby."

When the baby was six months old she began to be a real person, not just a bundle of cotton that saw sights unseen and heard sounds beyond hearing. Her hair was golden brown, long for her age, and Rachel liked to curl it gently over her fingers. My hair is straight and black, and every morning when I get up, I look in the mirror and see my plain hair. So I will make hers curly. Gloria had large golden-brown eyes, too, and concentrating on those eyes, Rachel would sometimes feel that Boris was once more beside her. She would hold the baby close to her, and she would feel Boris' breath on her face. Sometimes, when she kissed Gloria, she was kissing Boris where he lay beside her in the bed. "Get up, you sleepy head," and she used to kiss him, and he would open his eyes and look at her in a daze. He would look at her that early in the morning, and he would be a tightly drawn network of nerves. And she would kiss him again and again until the nerves seemed less tight and his eyes looked less puzzled. Then he was awake. "Aa-ee-oo!" he would yawn. He would open his mouth wide and yawn like a baby, like Gloria.

Rebecca wanted to bathe Gloria. On Sunday mornings, Louis begged the privilege of bathing her. And David would come into the hot kitchen, just before he was going to shave, and watch Gloria splashing about in the small tub. "I'll get in there with you!" David would cry, and in his brown bathrobe he looked like a great bear eager to swallow babies whole. Gloria would laugh until David lifted a leg as if he were about to get in the tub, and then she would scream. But there was a thrilled merriment in her screaming.

"No, darling," Rachel would soothe her daughter. "He's not coming in your tub. This is your own tub and David can't come and have a nice bath." Rachel always bathed Gloria in the kitchen because that was the warmest room in the house, what with the kitchen stove red-hot on winter mornings. The bathroom was cold, and besides, the boys used the tub in the bathroom, and it wasn't safe for Gloria. Sol had that dreadful barber's itch, and Harry was frequently troubled with throat afflictions. The kitchen stove was a fat black Falstaff burning red with merriment. He was full of cherry-colored coals and he let off chuckles of warmth. How comfortable it is to be sitting near Falstaff in the kitchen on a cold winter morning when he's chuckling with warmth! Outdoors, the wind is diving out of the sky, and his long tapering fingers scoop up snow off the drifts and send the dazzling particles flying over the roofs, against the window panes. The snowflakes are lifted by the wind and scattered over the town, over the Flats, the buildings, Br-rr-rrr!— But inside, near the stove, your body purrs with satisfaction and you stretch out your contentment as far as it will go.

Rachel would get down on her knees beside the tub, blue on the outside, white enamel within, and she would pass her hands over the child's silky skin. The water was clear blue, a lake surrounded by steep white cliffs of enamel, and the soap was a white ship that bobbed up and down and wasn't going anywhere. Gloria would reach for the ship. She wanted to hold it in her hands and examine it minutely. She would capture it, but the slippery decks escaped her inadequate fingers. The ship traveled around and around, and behind Gloria's back was another harbor and strange. She followed the ship with her eyes. When she punched the water with her hands, the soap wasn't there. She kicked the water and created waves. She wanted to drink the water and eat the soap but a slight taste was unpleasant. Sometimes she would catch hold of the sides of the tub and try to lift herself, but her mother would always sit her down again. Gloria was determined to rise, and Rachel was just as determined that she should remain seated. They fought one another with a tender and profound love. When Gloria struck at her mother with her small hands, she was striking someone of whom she was assured.

Steam ran down the window panes in the kitchen. The linoleum on the floor was damp and smelled of laundry soap and the bristles of a scrubbing brush. The kettle on the stove whistled a melody of delicate mist. Often, the hired girl would open the small gate of the stove and you could see to the bottom of Falstaff's spirited and chuckling throat. Outdoors, the wind jumped down from the clouds with his long draperies of legs floating behind him, and he shook the snow out of his shanks and wriggled free from the ice that would clamp his toes. He made a long moaning sound, but the teakettle on the stove, squat and impertinent, whistled right back into his fury. Every corner of the kitchen was soothing with a kindly, familiar warmth. The room smelled of Gloria and Rachel and Rebecca and the teakettle and the huge black stove. The world was a kindly, comfortable blur to Gloria. It was something that lay around her, that she could curl up in. But sometimes, when one of the boys entered the kitchen of a Sunday morning, the wind reached one of his icy hands into the room and Gloria shuddered.

"Quick, shut the door!" Rachel would cry. "Can't you see the baby is in the tub?"

"*Vermach die tier!*" cried Rebecca. "*Bist blint? Sehst nisht die kint?*"

"All right. All right. You'd think I was the ice man. There's nothing to get excited about. Hello, there, Snookums. Ain't you 'shamed, bein' in a man's company without any clothes?"

"Tell him you don't care, darling. Tell him if he doesn't like you without any clothes, he doesn't have to look."

Rover, the female water spaniel, would sneak into the kitchen when the door was opened, and she would try to get near the stove. She didn't like the wind outside. She wanted to be in the kitchen near the black bulk of warmth. She liked the tub and the baby, and she liked Rachel on her knees beside the tub. Rover would hide under the table, but she gave herself away when she grunted her lazy pleasure. "*Der hint! Der hint!*" Rebecca would cry, and taking hold of the broom handle she would chase Rover out of the kitchen into the diving, icy wind. Rover would flee from the stiff, yellow straws of the broom, humiliated, with her short tail vanquished and despondent. Rover's nose was out of joint just as the cat's nose was out of joint, just as Michael's nose was out of joint.

All those warm days in the kitchen when you got down on your knees and gave Gloria her bath. What was your life but getting down on your knees? Dressing Gloria and undressing her? A long, lemon-colored dress with white lace edges. Gloria and I are going to a party. A white cap for Gloria with a pink ribbon. You put the cap over Gloria's hair, and this was a different Gloria. Now she was beautiful, and you saw her features refining and becoming strangely wise. New shoes for Gloria, white and black. The shoes weighed an ounce. A lemon-colored dress and a cap with a blue ribbon and red and black shoes. Gloria knows that she has a new dress and a new pair of shoes. She holds out her feet. She looks at her dress. Before, she had looked at things unseen, beyond the beyond. She had become very still; she had listened. Who was speaking there in the beyond the beyond? A smile would turn up the corners of her mouth. The doctor said, "When she smiles, she has the colic." But Rachel thought, Even if it is the colic that makes her smile, why does the doctor have to spoil it by saying so? I'd rather believe that Gloria was listening to something I can't hear, sounds no grown person can hear, voices from beyond the beyond. Now that Gloria has her new clothes, she does not pay so much attention to the beyond the beyond. She is emerging from the bud of infancy into something here, settled, formed. I speak to her and she hears and understands. She sees objects, a bottle, a cake of soap, a dress, a table. Things that are here now, prosaic things. She is discovering the world. Will there come a day when everything will be discovered? The world will be familiar then, and she will turn away and look into herself, her mind, her heart. Will she be tall, will she be fair? Will her voice be high or low? Will she sing old songs? How will she stand? What postures, what graces will she assume? But she's only a baby now. The future is a long time away.

Rachel did not heed anything but her baby. There had been times when she loved to walk through the snow and catch the flakes in her eyes. She had walked under the trees in Columbia Gardens and heard the leaves rustling. She had smelled the wet grass and clover. She would look out of train windows and see brown and white cows in green meadows, and she would think that everything was outside of yourself, and you must search for beauties—the lie of the land; pines against the sky. But now there was only Gloria to see. Gloria was all that Rachel had searched for. She was trees and grass, the animals in the field, the clouds in the sky. Rachel would become transfixed looking at her child. She was looking at the world, through the world. Everything was plain to her. This life was of her body and her spirit, and that was enough to know. The baby's eyes, hands, feet, heartbeats, the baby sitting up, the baby crawling, the baby asleep, just this expression that came into the baby's face—these were the ways that Rachel saw through the world. Is there some secret we do not know? It was in the child. Where do we go when we die? It was in the child. Is there Fate? Is life chance? There were no questions. There were only answers, answers in the texture of Gloria's skin, the color of her eyes, the sounds she made when she cried, the way her small fingers closed about a toy.

AARONS

by EDWIN SEAVER

AFTER Aarons left the office we all felt much better. Not that Aarons was a bad sort. On the contrary we all liked him quite a lot even though he was a Jew. Yet somehow we felt relieved when one day, out of a clear sky, Aarons rose from his desk and slamming a drawer shut with such a bang we all jumped in our chairs, said:

"I'm through."

Then he took his hat and coat and without saying goodbye to anybody closed the door behind him.

We were all so surprised nobody even thought of asking Aarons where he was going. We simply sat there staring at each other. It was so still in the office you could hear the clock on Mr. Mold's desk ticking away patiently.

Suddenly we all began talking and laughing at once. We actually became hilarious and laughed at each other's remarks as if everything that was said was unbearably funny.

"The crazy Jew," Mr. Mold said, his mouth still open in amazement, "now what do you suppose has bitten him?"

"Oh, lord," gasped Miss Childe, throwing up her hands and leaning back in her chair so that her skirt came up way over her knees, "that's the richest yet."

As for Mr. Nash, he was beside himself. Taking a handful of papers from his wastebasket he hurled them into the air and cried:

"Hurrah for Aarons! There's one Jew less in the Company."

It was as if a load had suddenly dropped from our shoulders. The very atmosphere of the office seemed lighter now and when we returned to our typewriters we all felt unusually elated. Nothing so remarkable had happened in the office for years.

When you come right down to it I guess we didn't like Aarons so much after all. He was a strange yid; we could never make him out.

I suppose Aarons was what you might call a Red. I mean he was a born troublemaker. Before he came to the office we all got along together fine. As members of the editorial bureau we felt that we were important factors in the Company. After all it was we who presented the Company to the public; it was we who wrote the bosses' speeches for them. In our way we were, as the vice president-commercial relations once said to us in conference, artists.

As soon as Aarons came all that went by the board. What I mean is he made us all feel kind of foolish and before we knew what had happened we were all playing up to him. It wasn't any one thing in particular that he did. I guess it was just the fact that he was among us upset the whole morale of the office. We began to make fun of our work. We would read aloud to each other the most serious parts of a speech or an article we were preparing just to get a laugh.

"How's that for bunk?" we would say, winking to one another or sticking our tongue in our cheek and pulling a sly face.

Now I ask you, is that right? It seems to me a fellow owes something to the Company that's hiring him. Deuce take it, if we don't like our jobs we know what we can do. A man't got to feel some respect for himself and his work. Aarons robbed us of our self-respect. Every day we took our jobs more and more as a joke. We made out to each other we were getting real reckless and didn't give a hang for anything or anybody but underneath it all I think we were beginning to get scared of ourselves.

You see, it was affecting our work. We no longer could turn out copy the way we used to. It became harder and harder to write inspirationally the way the boss wanted us to and we would sit for hours before our machines tearing up sheet after sheet of paper and cursing ourselves and our jobs. But the more fun Aaron made of his work the better copy he turned out. You had to hand it to him.

"When you're a harlot you have to know how, eh, boys?" he would say, banging away at his machine and talking all the time. And he would grin down his long nose as if we were the big joke.

Now what kind of way is that for a fellow to talk about his work, especially with ladies in the office. That's the trouble with these Jews; they never know when to stop. It used to make me sick to see Miss Childe shining up to Aarons and trying to appear clever just to get him to say something nice about her copy.

But the climax came one day when the boss called us into conference. What do you suppose he said? He said we were all letting up on our jobs except Aarons and that Aarons was the only one that was worth anything to him.

"You could all take a lesson from Aarons," the boss said. "When he writes he puts his whole heart into it. He convinces you in whatever he does because he's convinced before he puts down a word on paper. I want to see more of his conviction in your work hereafter."

And there was Aarons sitting there all the time as cool as you please. It's a wonder we didn't choke on the boss' words. Believe me we felt pretty cheap, I can tell you.

After we got back to our desks Aarons didn't say anything for some time. He sat there holding his head in his hands as if he had a headache. He had never been so quiet before.

"There's no fool like an old fool, eh, Mr. Aarons," Miss Childe said sort of laughing, but you could see she was bursting with envy for what the boss had said to him.

Aarons didn't even answer her. He lifted his head and speaking in a voice we had never heard before, almost as if he were begging Mr. Mold to listen to him, he said:

"Mold, you've got a wife and child, you'll understand me. Suppose you couldn't get a job, suppose no matter how hard you tried you couldn't fit in anywhere, would you let your wife walk the streets for you?"

Mr. Mold was so surprised he actually turned pale.

"Why, what do you mean?" he stammered.

"Don't get angry please," Aarons went on in that strange pleading voice that was so new to us. "Look at it another way. Suppose you didn't want another job, you just couldn't stick it any longer, see, and you knew you could never be satisfied with another job, would you let your wife and child go shift for themselves sooner than go on humiliating yourself?"

Mr. Mold stared at Aarons and then a broad grin broke over his face.

"Say, what are you up to now, Aarons?" he said, and we all laughed with relief to think Aarons was only joking again.

But Aarons didn't laugh at all. He merely shrugged his shoulders and suddenly he looked extraordinarily sad as if he were going to cry. Then he got up, went over to the washstand in the corner of the office and began washing his hands.

Mr. Nash rapped his forehead with his knuckles and nodded to us as much as to say: "I told you so."

And the next thing we knew Aarons had quit.

THE FAST

by EDNA FERBER

MOST families must be described against the background of their homes, but the Brandeis family life was bounded and controlled by the store. Their meals and sleeping hours and amusements were regulated by it. It taught them much, and brought them much, and lost them much. Fanny Brandeis always said she hated it, but it made her wise, and tolerant, and, in the end, famous. I don't know what more one could ask of any institution. It brought her in contact with men and women, taught her how to deal with them. After school she used often to run down to the store to see her mother, while Theodore went home to practice. Perched on a high stool in some corner she heard, and saw, and absorbed. It was a great school for the sensitive, highly-organized, dramatic little Jewish girl, for, to paraphrase a well-known stage line, there are just as many kinds of people in Winnebago as there arc in Washington.

It was about this time that Fanny Brandeis began to realize, actively, that she was different. Of course, other little Winnebago girls' mothers did not work like a man, in a store. And she and Bella Weinberg were the only two in her room at school who stayed out on the Day of Atonement, and on New Year, and the lesser Jewish holidays. Also, she went to temple on Friday night and Saturday morning, when the other girls she knew went to church on Sunday. These things set her apart in the little Middle Western town; but it was not these that constituted the real difference. She played, and slept, and ate, and studied like the other healthy little animals of her age. The real difference was temperamental, or emotional, or dramatic, or historic, or all four. They would be playing tag, perhaps, in one of the cool, green ravines that were the beauty spots of the little Wisconsin town.

They nestled like exquisite emeralds in the embrace of the hills, those ravines, and Winnebago's civic surge had not yet swept them away in a deluge of old tin cans, ashes, dirt and refuse, to be sold later for building lots. The Indians had camped and hunted in them. The one under the Court Street bridge, near the Catholic Church and monastery, was the favorite for play. It lay, a lovely, gracious thing, below the hot little town, all green, and lush, and cool, a tiny stream dimpling through it.

The plump Capuchin Fathers, in their coarse brown robes, knotted about the waist with a cord, their bare feet thrust into sandals, would come out and sun themselves on the stone bench at the side of the monastery on the hill, or would potter about the garden. And suddenly Fanny would stop quite still in the midst of her tag game, struck with the beauty of the picture it called from the past.

Little Oriental that she was, she was able to combine the dry text of her history book with the green of the trees, the gray of the church, and the brown of the monk's robes, and evolve a thrilling mental picture therefrom. The tag game and her noisy little companions vanished. She was peopling the place with stealthy Indians. Stealthy, cunning, yet savagely brave. They bore no relation to the object, contemptible, and rather smelly Oneidas who came to the back door on summer mornings, in calico, and ragged overalls, with baskets of huckleberries on their arm, their pride gone, a broken and conquered people. She saw them wild, free, sovereign, and there were no greasy, berry-peddling Oneidas among them. They were Sioux, and Pottawatomies (that last had the real Indian sound), and Winnebagos, and Menomonees, and Outagamis. She made them taciturn, and beady-eyed, and lithe, and fleet, and every other adjectival thing her imagination and history book could supply. The fat and placid Capuchin Fathers on the hill became Jesuits, sinister, silent, powerful, with France and the Church of Rome behind them. From the shelter of that big oak would step Nicolet, the brave, first among Wisconsin explorers, and last to receive the credit for his hardihood. Jean Nicolet! She loved the sound of it. And with him was La Salle, straight, and slim, and elegant, and surely wearing ruffles and plumes and sword even in a canoe. And Tonty, his Italian friend and fellow adventurer— Tonty of the satins and velvets, graceful, tactful, poised, a shadowy figure; his menacing iron hand, so feared by the ignorant savages, encased always in a glove. Surely a perfumed g—— Slap! A rude shove that jerked her head back sharply and sent her forward, stumbling, and jarred her like a fall.

"Ya-a-a! Tag! You're it! Fanny's it!"

Indians, priests, cavaliers, *coureurs de bois,* all vanished. Fanny would stand a moment, blinking stupidly. The next moment she was running as fleetly as the best of the boys in savage pursuit of one of her companions in the tag game.

She was a strange mixture of tomboy and book-worm, which was a mercifully kind arrangement for both body and mind. The spiritual side of her was groping and staggering, and feeling its way about as does that of any little girl whose mind is exceptionally active, and whose mother is unusually busy. It was on the Day of Atonement, known in the Hebrew as Yom Kippur, in the year following her father's death that that side of her performed a rather interesting handspring.

Fanny Brandeis had never been allowed to fast on this, the greatest and most solemn of Jewish holy days. Molly Brandeis' modern side refused to countenance the practice of withholding food from any child for twenty-four hours. So it was in the face of disapproval that Fanny, making deep inroads into the steak and fried sweet potatoes at supper on the eve of the Day of Atonement, announced her intention of fasting from that meal to supper on the following evening. She had just passed her plate for a third helping of potatoes. Theodore, one lap behind her in the race, had entered his objection.

"Well, for the land's sakes!" he protested. "I guess you're not the only one who likes sweet potatoes."

Fanny applied a generous dab of butter to an already buttery morsel, and chewed it with an air of conscious virtue.

"I've got to eat a lot. This is the last bite I'll have until tomorrow night."

"What's that?" exclaimed Mrs. Brandeis, sharply.

"Yes, it is!" hooted Theodore.

Fanny went on conscientiously eating as she explained.

"Bella Weinberg and I are going to fast all day. We just want to see if we can."

"Betcha can't," Theodore said.

Mrs. Brandeis regarded her small daughter with a thoughtful gaze. "But that isn't the object of fasting, Fanny—just to see if you can. If you're going to think of food all through the Yom Kippur services—"

"I sha'n't!" protested Fanny passionately. "Theodore would, but I won't."

"Wouldn't any such thing," denied Theodore. "But if I'm going to play a violin solo during the memorial service I guess I've got to eat my regular meals."

Theodore sometimes played at temple, on special occasions. The little congregation, listening to the throbbing rise and fall of the fifteen-year-old boy's violin playing, realized, vaguely, that here was something disturbingly, harrowingly beautiful. They did not know that they were listening to genius.

Molly Brandeis, in her second best dress, walked to temple Yom Kippur eve, her son at her right side, her daughter at her left. She had made up her mind that she would not let this next day, with its poignantly beautiful service, move her too deeply. It was the first since her husband's death, and Rabbi Thalmann rather prided himself on his rendition of the memorial service that came at three in the afternoon.

A man of learning, of sweetness, and of gentle wit was Rabbi Thalmann, and unappreciated by his congregation. He stuck to the Scriptures for his texts, finding Moses a greater leader than Roosevelt, and the miracle of the Burning Bush more wonderful than the marvels of twentieth-century wizardry in electricity. A little man, Rabbi Thalmann, with hands and feet as small and delicate as those of a woman. Fanny found him fascinating to look on, in his rabbinical black broadcloth and his two pairs of glasses perched, in reading, upon his small hooked nose. He stood very straight in the pulpit, but on the street you saw that his back was bent just the least bit in the world—or perhaps it was only his student stoop, as he walked along with his eyes on the ground, smoking those slender, dapper, pale brown cigars that looked as if they had been expressly cut and rolled to fit him.

The evening service was at seven. The congregation, rustling in silks, was approaching the little temple from all directions. Inside, there was a low-toned buzz of conversation. The Brandeis' seat was well toward the rear, as befitted a less prosperous member of the rich little congregation. This enabled them to get a complete picture of the room in its holiday splendor. Fanny drank it in eagerly, her dark eyes soft and luminous. The bare, yellow-varnished wooden pews glowed with the reflection from the chandeliers. The seven-branched candlesticks on either side of the pulpit were entwined with smilax. The red plush curtain that hung in front of the Ark on ordinary days, and the red plush pulpit cover too, were replaced by gleaming white satin edged with gold fringe and finished at the corners with heavy gold tassels. How the rich white satin glistened in the light of the electric candles! Fanny Brandeis loved the lights, and the gleam, and the music, so majestic and solemn, and the sight of the little rabbi, sitting so straight and serious in his high-backed chair, or standing to read from the great Bible. There came to this emotional little Jewess a thrill that was not born of religious fervor at all, I am afraid.

The sheer drama of the thing got her. In fact, the thing she had set herself to do today had in it very little of religion. Mrs. Brandeis had been right about that. It was a test of endurance, as planned. Fanny had never fasted in all her healthy life. She would come home from school to eat formidable stacks of bread and butter, enhanced by brown sugar or grape jelly, and topped off with three or four apples from the barrel in the cellar. Two hours later she would attack a supper of fried potatoes, and liver, and tea, and peach preserve, and more stacks of bread and butter. Then there were the cherry trees in the back yard, and the berry bushes, not to speak of sundry bags of small, hard candies of the jelly-bean variety, fitted for quick and secret munching during school. She liked good things to eat, this sturdy little girl, as did her friend, that blonde and creamy person, Bella Weinberg.

The two girls exchanged meaningful glances during the evening service. The Weinbergs, as befitted their station, sat in the third row at the right, and Bella had to turn around to convey her silent messages to Fanny. The evening service was brief, even to the sermon. Rabbi Thalmann and his congregation would need their strength for tomorrow's trial.

The Brandeises walked home through the soft September night, and the children had to use all their Yom Kippur dignity to keep from scuffing through the piled-up drifts of crackling autumn leaves. Theodore went to the cellar and got an apple, which he ate with what Fanny considered an unnecessary amount of scrunching. It was a firm, juicy apple, and it gave forth a cracking sound when his teeth met in its white meat. Fanny, after regarding him with gloomy superiority, went to bed.

She had willed to sleep late, for gastronomic reasons, but the mental command disobeyed itself, and she woke early, with a heavy feeling. Early as it was, Molly Brandeis had tiptoed in still earlier to look at her strange little daughter. She sometimes did that on Saturday mornings when she left early for the store and Fanny slept late. This morning Fanny's black hair was spread over the pillow as she lay on her back, one arm outflung, the other at her breast. She made a rather startling black and white and scarlet picture as she lay there asleep. Fanny did things very much in that way, too, with broad, vivid, unmistakable splashes of color. Mrs. Brandeis, looking at the black-haired, red-lipped child sleeping there, wondered just how much determination lay back of the broad white brow. She had said little to Fanny about this feat of fasting, and she told herself that she disapproved of it. But in her heart she wanted the girl to see it through, once attempted.

Fanny awoke at half past seven, and her nostrils dilated to that most exquisite, tantalizing and fragrant of smells—the aroma of simmering coffee. It permeated the house. It tickled the senses. It carried with it visions of hot, brown breakfast rolls, and eggs, and butter. Fanny loved her breakfast. She turned over now, and decided to go to sleep again.

But she could not. She got up and dressed slowly and carefully. There was no one to hurry her this morning with the call from the foot of the stairs of, "Fanny! Your egg'll get cold!"

She put on clean, crisp underwear, and did her hair expertly. She slipped an all-enveloping pinafore over her head, that the new silk dress might not be crushed before church time. She thought that Theodore would surely have finished his breakfast by this time. But when she came down-stairs he was at the table. Not only that, he had just begun his breakfast. An egg, all golden, and white, and crispy brown at the frilly edges, lay on his plate. Theodore always ate his egg in a mathematical sort of way. He swallowed the white hastily first, because he disliked it, and Mrs. Brandeis insisted that he eat it. Then he would brood a moment over the yolk that lay, unmarred and complete, like an amber jewel in the center of his plate. Then he would suddenly plunge his fork into the very heart of the jewel, and it would flow over his plate, mingling with the butter, and he would catch it deftly with little mops of warm, crisp, buttery roll.

Fanny passed the breakfast table just as Theodore plunged his fork into the egg yolk. She caught her breath sharply, and closed her eyes. Then she turned and fled to the front porch and breathed deeply and windily of the heady September Wisconsin morning air. As she stood there, with her stiff, short black curls still damp and glistening, in her best shoes and stockings, with the all-enveloping apron covering her sturdy little figure, the light of struggle and renunciation in her face, she typified something at once fine and earthy.

But the real struggle was to come later. They went to temple at ten, Theodore with his beloved violin tucked carefully under his arm. Bella Weinberg was waiting at the steps.

"Did you?" she asked eagerly.

"Of course not," replied Fanny disdainfully. "Do you think I'd eat old breakfast when I said I was going to fast all day?" Then, with sudden suspicion, "Did you?"

"No!" stoutly.

And they entered, and took their seats. It was fascinating to watch the other members of the congregation come in, the women rustling, the men subdued in the unaccustomed dignity of black on a week day. One glance at the yellow pews was like reading a complete social and financial register. The seating arrangement of the temple was the *Almanach de Gotha* of Congregation Emmanuel. Old Ben Reitman, patriarch among the Jewish settlers of Winnebago, who had come over an immigrant youth, and who now owned hundreds of rich farm acres, besides houses, mills and banks, kinged it from the front seat of the center section. He was a magnificent old man, with a ruddy face, and a fine head with a shock of heavy iron-gray hair, keen eyes, undimmed by years, and a startling and unexpected dimple in one cheek that gave him a mischievous and boyish look.

Behind this dignitary sat his sons, and their wives, and his daughters and their husbands, and their children, and so on, back to the Brandeis pew, third from the last, behind which sat only a few obscure families branded as Russians, as only the German-born Jew can brand those whose misfortune it is to be born in that region known as hinter-Berlin.

The morning flew by, with its music, its responses, its sermon in German, full of four- and five-syllable German words like *Barmherzigkeit* and *Eigentümlichkeit*. All during the sermon Fanny sat and dreamed and watched the shadow on the window of the pine tree that stood close to the temple, and was vastly amused at the jaundiced look that the square of yellow window glass cast upon the face of the vain and overdressed Mrs. Nathan Pereles. From time to time Bella would turn to bestow upon her a look intended to convey intense suffering and a resolute though dying condition. Fanny stonily ignored these mute messages. They offended something in her, though she could not tell what.

At the noon intermission she did not go home to the tempting dinner smells, but wandered off through the little city park and down to the river, where she sat on the bank and felt very virtuous, and spiritual, and hollow. She was back in her seat when the afternoon service was begun. Some of the more devout members had remained to pray all through the midday. The congregation came straggling in by twos and threes. Many of the women had exchanged the severely corseted discomfort of the morning's splendor for the comparative ease of second-best silks. Mrs. Brandeis, absent from her business throughout this holy day, came hurrying in at two, to look with a rather anxious eye upon her pale and resolute little daughter.

The memorial service was to begin shortly after three, and lasted almost two hours. At quarter to three Bella slipped out through the side aisle, beckoning mysteriously and alluringly to Fanny as she went. Fanny looked at her mother.

"Run along," said Mrs. Brandeis. "The air will be good for you. Come back before the memorial service begins."

Fanny and Bella met, giggling, in the vestibule.

"Come on over to my house for a minute," Bella suggested. "I want to show you something." The Weinberg house, a great, comfortable, well-built home, with encircling veranda, and a well-cared-for-lawn, was just a scant block away. They skipped across the street, down the block, and in at the back door. The big sunny kitchen was deserted. The house seemed very quiet and hushed. Over it hung the delicious fragrance of freshly-baked pastry. Bella, a rather baleful look in her eyes, led the way to the butler's pantry that was as large as the average kitchen. And there, ranged on platters, and baking boards, and on snowy-white napkins, was that which made Tantalus's feast seem a dry and barren snack. The Weinberg's had baked.

It is the custom in the household of Atonement Day fasters of the old school to begin the evening meal, after the twenty-four hours of abstainment, with coffee and freshly-baked coffee cake of every variety. It was a lead-pipe blow at one's digestion, but delicious beyond imagining. Bella's mother was a famous cook, and her two maids followed in the ways of their mistress. There were to be sisters and brothers and out-of-town relations as guests at the evening meal, and Mrs. Weinberg had outdone herself.

"Oh!" exclaimed Fanny in a sort of agony and delight.

"Take some," said Bella, the temptress.

The pantry was fragrant as a garden with spices, and fruit scents, and the melting, delectable perfume of brown, freshly-baked dough, sugar-coated. There was one giant platter devoted wholly to round, plump cakes, with puffy edges, in the center of each a sunken pool that was all plum, bearing on its bosom a snowy sifting of sifted sugar. There were others whose centers were apricot, pure molten gold in the sunlight. There were speckled expanses of cheese kuchen, the golden-brown surface showing rich cracks through which one caught glimpses of the lemon-yellow cheese beneath—cottage cheese that had been beaten up with eggs, and spices, and sugar, and lemon. Flaky crust rose, jaggedly, above this plateau. There were cakes with jelly, and cinnamon kuchen, and cunning cakes with almond slices nestling side by side. And there was freshly-baked bread—twisted loaf, with poppy seed freckling its braid, and its sides glistening with the butter that had been liberally swabbed on it before it had been thrust into the oven.

Fanny Brandeis gazed, hypnotized. As she gazed Bella selected a plum tart and bit into it—bit generously, so that her white little teeth met in the very middle of the oozing red-brown juice and one heard a little squirt as they closed on the luscious fruit. At the sound Fanny quivered all through her plump and starved little body.

"Have one," said Bella generously. "Go on. Nobody'll ever know. Anyway, we've fasted long enough for our age. I could fast till supper time if I wanted to, but I don't want to." She swallowed the last morsel of the plum tart, and selected another—apricot, this time—and opened her moist red lips. But just before she bit into it (the Inquisition could have used Bella's talents) she selected its counterpart and held it out to Fanny. Fanny shook her head slightly. Her hand came up involuntarily. Her eyes were fastened on Bella's face.

"Go on," urged Bella. "Take it. They're grand! M-m-m-m!" The first bite of apricot vanished between her rows of sharp white teeth. Fanny shut her eyes as if in pain. She was fighting the great fight of her life. She was to meet other temptations, and perhaps more glittering ones, in her lifetime, but to her dying day she never forgot that first battle between the flesh and the spirit, there in the sugar-scented pantry—and the spirit won. As Bella's lips closed upon the second bite of apricot tart, the while her eye roved over the almond cakes and her hand still held the sweet out to Fanny, that young lady turned sharply, like a soldier, and marched blindly out of the house, down the back steps, across the street, and so into the temple.

The evening lights had just been turned on. The little congregation, relaxed, weary, weak from hunger, many of them, sat rapt and still except at those times when the prayer book demanded spoken responses. The voice of the little rabbi, rather weak now, had in it a timbre that made it startlingly sweet and clear and resonant. Fanny slid very quietly into the seat beside Mrs. Brandeis, and slipped her moist and cold little hand into her mother's warm, work-roughened palm. The mother's brown eyes, very bright with unshed tears, left their perusal of the prayer book to dwell upon the white little face that was smiling rather wanly up at her. The pages of the prayer book lay two-thirds or more to the left. Just as Fanny remarked this, there was a little moment of hush in the march of the day's long service. The memorial hour had begun.

Little Doctor Thalmann cleared his throat. The congregation stirred a bit, changed its cramped position. Bella, the guilty, came stealing in, a pink-and-gold picture of angelic virtue. Fanny, looking at her, felt very aloof, and clean, and remote.

Molly Brandeis seemed to sense what had happened.

"But you didn't, did you?" she whispered softly.

Fanny shook her head.

Rabbi Thalmann was seated in his great carved chair. His eyes were closed. The wheezy little organ in the choir loft at the rear of the temple began the opening bars of Schumann's Träumerei. And then, above the cracked voice of the organ, rose the clear, poignant wail of a violin. Theodore Brandeis had begun to play. You know the playing of the average boy of fifteen—that nerve-destroying, uninspired scraping. There was nothing of this in the sounds that this boy called forth from the little wooden box and the stick with its taut lines of catgut. Whatever it was— the length of the thin, sensitive fingers, the turn of the wrist, the articulation of the forearm, the something in the brain, or all these combined —Theodore Brandeis possessed that which makes for greatness. You realized that as he crouched over his violin to get his cello tones. As he played today the little congregation sat very still, and each was thinking of his ambitions and his failures; of the lover lost, of the duty left undone, of the hope deferred; of the wrong that was never righted; of the lost one whose memory spells remorse. It felt the salt taste on its lips. It put up a furtive, shamed hand to dab at its cheeks, and saw that the one who sat in the pew just ahead was doing likewise. This is what happened when this boy of fifteen wedded his bow to his violin. And he who makes us feel all this has that indefinable, magic, glorious thing known as Genius.

When it was over, there swept through the room that sigh following tension relieved. Rabbi Thalmann passed a hand over his tired eyes, like one returning from a far mental journey; then rose, and came forward to the pulpit. He began, in Hebrew, the opening words of the memorial service, and so on to the prayers in English, with their words of infinite humility and wisdom.

"Thou hast implanted in us the capacity for sin, but not sin itself!"

Fanny stirred. She had learned that a brief half hour ago. The service marched on, a moving and harrowing thing. The amens rolled out with a new fervor from the listeners. There seemed nothing comic now in the way old Ben Reitman, with his slower eyes, always came out five words behind the rest who tumbled upon the responses and scurried briskly through them, so that his fine old voice, somewhat hoarse and quavering now, rolled out its "Amen!" in solitary majesty. They came to that gem of humility, the mourners' prayer; the ancient and ever-solemn Kaddish prayer. There is nothing in the written language that, for sheer drama and magnificence, can equal it as it is chanted in the Hebrew.

As Rabbi Thalmann began to intone it in its monotonous repetition of praise, there arose certain black-robed figures from their places and stood with heads bowed over their prayer books. These were members of the congregation from whom death had taken a toll during the past year. Fanny rose with her mother and Theodore, who had left the choir loft to join them. The little wheezy organ played very softly. The black-robed figures swayed. Here and there a half-stifled sob rose, and was crushed. Fanny felt a hot haze that blurred her vision. She winked it away, and another burned in its place. Her shoulders shook with a sob. She felt her mother's hand close over her own that held one side of the book. The prayer, that was not of mourning but of praise, ended with a final crescendo from the organ. The silent black-robed figures were seated.

Over the little, spent congregation hung a glorious atmosphere of detachment. These Jews, listening to the words that had come from the lips of the prophets in Israel, had been, on this day, thrown back thousands of years, to the time when the destruction of the temple was as real as the shattered spires and dome of the cathedral at Rheims. Old Ben Reitman, faint with fasting, was far removed from his everyday thoughts of his horses, his lumber mills, his farms, his mortgages. Even Mrs. Nathan Pereles, in her black satin and bugles and jets, her cold, hard face usually unlighted by sympathy or love, seemed to feel something of this emotional wave. Fanny Brandeis was shaken by it. Her head ached (that was hunger) and her hands were icy. The little Russian girl in the seat just behind them had ceased to wriggle and squirm, and slept against her mother's side. Rabbi Thalmann, there on the platform, seemed somehow very far away and vague. The scent of clove apples and ammonia salts filled the air. The atmosphere seemed strangely wavering and luminous. The white satin of the Ark curtain gleamed and shifted.

The long service swept on to its close. Suddenly organ and choir burst into a pæan. Little Doctor Thalmann raised his arms. The congregation swept to its feet with a mighty surge. Fanny rose with them, her face very white in its frame of black curls, her eyes luminous. She raised her face for the words of the ancient benediction that rolled, in its simplicity and grandeur, from the lips of the rabbi:

"May the blessing of the Lord our God rest upon you all. God bless thee and keep thee. May God cause His countenance to shine upon thee and be gracious unto thee. May God lift up His countenance unto thee, and grant thee peace."

The Day of Atonement had come to an end. It was a very quiet, subdued and spent little flock that dispersed to their homes. Fanny walked out with scarcely a thought of Bella. She felt, vaguely, that she and this school friend were formed of different stuff. She knew that the bond between them had been the grubby, physical one of childhood, and that they never would come together in the finer relation of the spirit, though she could not have put this new knowledge into words.

Molly Brandeis put a hand on her daughter's shoulder.

"Tired, Fanchen?"

"A little."

"Bet you're hungry!" from Theodore.

"I was, but I'm not now."

"M-m-m—wait! Noodle soup. And chicken!"

She had intended to tell of the trial in the Weinbergs' pantry. But now something within her—something fine, born of this day—kept her from it. But Molly Brandeis, to whom two and two often made five, guessed something of what had happened. She had felt a great surge of pride, had Molly Brandeis, when her son had swayed the congregation with the magic of his music. She had kissed him good night with infinite tenderness and love. But she came into her daughter's tiny room after Fanny had gone to bed, and leaned over, and put a cool hand on the hot forehead.

"Do you feel all right, my darling?"

"Umhmph," replied Fanny drowsily.

"Fanchen, doesn't it make you feel happy and clean to know that you were able to do the thing you started out to do?"

"Umhmph."

"Only," Molly Brandeis was thinking aloud now, quite forgetting that she was talking to a very little girl, "only, life seems to take such special delight in offering temptation to those who are able to withstand it. I don't know why that's true, but it is. I hope—oh, my little girl, my baby—I hope—"

But Fanny never knew whether her mother finished that sentence or not. She remembered waiting for the end of it, to learn what it was her mother hoped. And she had felt a sudden, scalding drop on her hand where her mother bent over her. And the next thing she knew it was morning, with mellow September sunshine.

HOLY LAND

by LUDWIG LEWISOHN

I

THE blond man across the table from me, the man with a cheery, knowing squint, gossiped in a mixture of languages about Egyptian politics. Very gently the *Venetia* rolled on her way to Alexandria. The blue Mediterranean sea-line, visible through the port-hole at my left, rose and dipped by but an inch or two. I listened carefully to the blond man. But haphazard, half-articulate sounds farther to my right stole upon me with a winning, teasing familiarity. The blond man became for a moment intent upon his food and I heard the woman's voice, clear now even above a swishing on the deck without:

"I don't think much of *this* chicken, do you, Lee?"

Two thick, bulgy men separated me from the speaker. I had to crane a little. She was frankly middle-aged, tall, thin, wistful—wistful yet positive. She sucked her teeth in a comfortable self-satisfied way at the memory of the real chicken to which she was accustomed at home. Her husband, large, comfortable, fleshy, turned to her a kindly, crinkled, shrewd face.

"We've had worse'n this."

"I'd like to know where!"

"Oh, at a lot o' these places."

His vivid, unimaginative grey eyes met mine. He saw that I understood and grinned a grin of male fellowship. He almost winked as he said to her but, obviously, for me to overhear:

"The drinks are a whole lot better."

She followed his glance and, also for my benefit, gurgled in her genuine though so belated girlishness:

"Why, Lee Merriwether, I'm surprised at you!"

A few minutes later I came upon them on deck. She was resting on her deck-chair, eager even in her reclining position; Merriwether was standing by the railing generously moistening the end of a handsome American cigar. He nodded; Mrs. Merriwether leaned forward.

"I *thought* you were an American!"

In a moment, under his drily humorous, tolerant glance she was telling me about them, about herself. She spurted. It wasn't the tourist season. Americans had evidently been few. Since she could speak only English and that, as she said, may be "not so good," she was famished for communication.

"We're from Albion, Wisconsin. Did you ever hear of it? It's quite a town. Oh, yes, we've been all over Europe. London and Paris and Venice. Did you see the churchyard where Gray wrote his elegy? Didn't you just love it? London was crowded. Oh, wasn't it *just*? But the Exposition was dandy!"

"And now," I said, "you're going East too."

She leaned forward; she tucked a wisp of straight, brownish hair back under her Leghorn traveling hat. The wistfulness in her face was more marked now than the positiveness, than the communicativeness.

"I always felt like I wanted to see the places where our Lord lived. We're not so terribly religious." There was a queer little apology in her voice. She meant, of course, that they weren't bigoted and rancorous. But I knew that from the way she had teased her husband about drinking. "I've always thought—" She stopped. She was articulate enough in her way. But any speech beyond the special formulas of her environment found her shy. I sat down on an unoccupied chair beside her. She looked away from me. "It's like this. We're Congregationalists. But my father— he's been dead for years and years—he was a Methodist minister. I want to tell you: he was a saint if ever there was one. You know that old hymn: 'There is a green hill far away'?" A faint, beautiful emotion came into her eyes. "The way father used to repeat that! When I was about sixteen father had a charge in a little bit of a town in Southern Wisconsin. We lived right next to the little white church. My, but that was a quiet place. Sunday you didn't hear a sound hardly. Just the bell of the church and maybe a rooster crowing. You know the people in that congregation didn't have much of an education. Of course we've sent our boy and girl—I've got to show you their pictures—up to Madison. But in those days it was different. Well, I want to tell you: My father just told his people about Jesus. You just felt's if you could see Nazareth and Galilee and all the places that our Saviour was in, you know. And somehow . . ." She straightened up and brightened up into her more conventional self. "I've always said that early impressions last longest. Don't you think so yourself? My, but it's a grand day!"

Merriwether had turned around. He stood facing us with his broad, crinkly indulgent smile.

"Tell you a secret about the wife. The ladies got up some sort of a club in Albion a couple o' years ago. She's quite a leader in it. Well, they read papers there about authors, say, or the trips they've been on. So the wife sort of figured out that if we took this trip, she'd certainly have an original subject!" He laughed a merry but subterranean kind of laugh—an inward chuckle. She was accustomed to his teasing. Her protest was a formula: "Why, Lee Merriwether, how can you say that!"

I got up and joined him at the railing. He rolled his cigar comfortably. His tone was intimate—man to man.

"We had a pretty good year up our way. I'm in the contracting business 'n connected with the First National of Albion. The farmers had money—all of 'em, seems like. Well, I'd just as soon've gone to Florida or to the Coast. But she"—he nodded towards his wife—"wanted to take this trip. It's been a kind of a dream she's had. Just like she told you. Well, I'm having a good time, all right. They got some mighty fine Scotch down in the smoking-room and they don't hardly charge you nothing for it." He winked at me. "Shall we have a little drink?"

Merriwether and I, strolling towards the door of the smoking-room, heard her voice with its belated girlishness: "I know what you two are up to, alright!" Merriwether chuckled. " 'Snot so hard to guess!"

II

A Cook's agent met them at Alexandria and I lost sight of them in the turbulent Arab crowd. Alighting from the train in Cairo that evening I thought I glimpsed for a moment a slightly-bewildered face that was Mrs. Merriwether's. But I wasn't sure. They were stopping at Shepheard's, of course, for a week or ten days; I was hurrying through to make my connection for Palestine at Kantara. The Merriwethers faded from my mind.

It was exactly twelve days later that I came upon them again. They strolled hesitantly into the dining-room of the Allenby Hotel in Jerusalem. There were only a half dozen people in the rather bare room: a long-faced, bronzed old Egyptian merchant and his youngish European wife, a couple of blond, chirpy Englishmen, a well-groomed American Zionist. Mrs. Merriwether saw me at once and fluttered happily, as though in sudden sight of refuge, in my direction.

"Well, did you ever!" she exclaimed.

Her husband, following closely, grasped my hand with unexpected cordiality. They scarcely waited for my invitation to sit at my table. They were so obviously relieved to find me. We exchanged the inevitable questions. They had arrived only the day before; they had a guide of whom Mrs. Merriwether "didn't think much." His English was so fast and so unintelligible. I asked them what their impression of the Holy City was. Merriwether said: "Oh, I guess it's all right." His wife looked at me a little wanly. "It's wonderful, wonderful." I looked at her closely. She seemed unaccountably more faded than before. "The light is terrible," she said. I advised smoked glasses. They already had them. There was something pathetic about her, something at once eager and frustrated. "Suppose we take a walk this afternoon," I suggested. With a quite uncharacteristic gesture she put her hand over mine. "Oh, that would be dandy!" That word "dandy" seemed, in that place, of an innocent weirdness; it seemed of a strange, remote childlikeness. My eye happened to fall on the face of the Egyptian merchant. It had suddenly a Pharaonic cruelty and agelessness.

We met, at the appointed hour, in front of the hotel. The Jaffa road was very much alive. We dodged a few carriages on our short walk towards the Jaffa gate of the old city. At the corner I stopped and quietly pointed towards the left where the citadel of Suleiman rises loftily, where the long sublime slopes of the Judaean hills begin. Mrs. Merriwether was wide-eyed. But she seemed fascinated, despite herself, by things in the foreground—the Arab café at the corner, a tall, ragged Bedouin on a tiny ass, a group of agile, importunate boot-blacks.

We entered at the Jaffa gate. Mrs. Merriwether and I walked on ahead. Merriwether followed. I guided her down the steps of the uneven, crooked little street; I kept her from being jostled. She seemed frightened. I told her that the Arabs meant nothing by bumping into her. They simply had no sense of orderliness. She glanced shyly into the greasy, open shops, nervously dodged the large wooden platter of a cake-vendor, stared at the magnificently severe faces of two old Galician Jews. I pointed out to her a window in an immemorial arch that spanned the alley. "Look, here you have a symbol of the ancient East. There is something fantastic and humble and arrogant, something mean and yet elevated about this arch, this window." She said nothing. From behind came Merriwether's first remark: "I guess they don't try to clean up much around here."

The Via Dolorosa was fairly empty and still. It was no feast day. It lay forlorn between the blind walls in its alternation of fierce light and sharp, black shadows. A few filthy Arab children, waiting for stray tourists, cried for an alms. Mrs. Merriwether stumbled over the smooth cobble-stones. "This is where our Lord . . ." She panted a bit. I nodded.

"Did you imagine it differently?" I asked. "Oh, I don't know." She tried to sound cheerful.

We knocked at the gate of the French convent built over the house of Pontius Pilate. In the cool, little church a French nun with an expressionless face explained in accurate but uneloquent English something of the associations of the spot. In the cool gloom, behind the altar, amid a flat smell of faded flowers, she showed us the ruined façade of the Roman governor's house. The nun disappeared the moment her toneless voice had done its duty and we were back in the fierce glow of the light. The Merriwethers stood beside me. He was grave and non-committal. Her eyes wandered. "I suppose it's the way you're brought up," she said thoughtfully. There was a genuine gentleness in her tone. "I know, I know we mustn't judge. My father always said so. But do you feel just at home in Catholic Churches?" It was clear, at least, that she didn't. Nor did she feel more comfortable when I took them to the Wall of Wailing where in front of the gigantic and terrible stones a little group of Jews intoned their violent yet austere prayers.

Back at the Allenby she thanked me profusely. "I'm going to rest a while now," she said. "My, but it's hard walking. Tomorrow the guide is going to take us to the Church of the Holy Sepulchre and on a donkey-ride around the walls."

"And then?" I asked.

"Oh, we'll see everything here. Then we're going to Bethlehem and Nazareth and Tiberias. Isn't that the way it is, Lee?"

He nodded. His crinkly smile came back and his male confidentialness to me.

"I guess we'll live through it."

III

My business took me to the North. I saw Haifa glittering through the night from the heights of Carmel and Safed upon its holy hill. Through the thronging hills I drove over the lofty roads to Tiberias. There I heard about the Merriwethers. Mrs. Merriwether's left eyelid had become slightly inflamed. She had seen so many Arabs horribly blind from trachoma that a sort of panic had seized both her and her husband and he had asked whether there was such a thing as a decent doctor in this damned hole. The Jewish hotel-keeper had, of course, taken the Merriwethers to the clinic of the Zionist Medical Service where an English-speaking oculist had reassured them. They had been enormously relieved and grateful. Mr. Merriwether had wrung the doctor's hand. A fee being refused, he had sworn that he would send a cheque to the Zionist headquarters. Mrs. Merriwether had remarked, almost with tears of joy, that some of her *best* friends in Albion were Jews—lovely people, fine citizens. They had then driven off at once.

Since this had happened but a day or two before I thought it possible that I might see them again. And I wanted to see them. I found it hard to formulate the character of my interest in them. A pathos clung to them in my vision of them. To her, at least. He was detached enough from their whole adventure. Indeed, it wasn't his at all. After the manner of American husbands he was trying to please her. He could afford it. So why shouldn't he? But she! A touch of wistful poetry in her heart had brought her here; an aroma of religious romance that had clung to her Wisconsin girlhood of the saint-like father and the still, small, white church amid those Northern fields. And now?

I could have gone back to Haifa but instead I drove to Nazareth. It was late when I reached the Hotel Germania. Yes, their names were in that extraordinary hotel register where people are inscribed from all the ends of the earth from New York and Lebanon, from Teheran and Vienna. So I would see them in the morning.

I went to my small, austere, cell-like room. I was tired and slept. But in a couple of hours I awoke. A wind had risen, a wild, disturbing wind. I threw on a dressing-gown and stood before my arched window. I saw a wall that looked like the oldest wall in all the world. In the wall was a little wooden door and over the door swung a dim, sooty lantern. Behind the wall stood cypresses and their tops swayed in the wind. The night was cool. Caravans were on foot. The sound was the sound of camel-bells. I went out of my small room into the hall which had great arched, paneless windows through which one could see the roofs of Nazareth and the farther hills. The wind swept through the hall; the sound of the bells came nearer. The caravan came in sight. The tall, grave camels were like shadows. About them and their drivers there was something remote and eternal. The bells clanged.

Suddenly I heard a gasp behind me. I turned and saw Mrs. Merriwether wrapped in a kimono. Her frightened eyes met mine. "Oh, it's you!" There was a sob in her voice. I tried to be matter-of-fact. "It's hard to sleep in this wind. Do you see the caravan?"

She nodded dumbly. Her hands were clasped in front of her holding her kimono together. She stood quite still. Her face was tense. Her eyes were full of a helpless sadness, a childlike confusion.

"What is it?" I asked gently.

She shuddered. "Everything!"

"Didn't you have a pleasant time?"

"Do you know Bethlehem?"

I nodded.

"And the Church of the Nativity? Why, you can't see the stable. It's all over images and things. They're Greek, aren't they? Oh, and the Garden of Gethsemane. They're Russian monks all over it. And everywhere they're Arabs and Jews. Oh, please don't be offended. I don't mean nice Jews like you and the doctor in Tiberias but awful outlandish people. I couldn't imagine our Lord or Peter on Tiberias, on the lake, you know. I can't imagine anything anywhere—anywhere. I'm asking Lee to leave as soon as we can. I want to get away; I want to get out of this terrible dago country."

She sobbed.

"But this is the Holy Land," I said.

She gazed beyond me, beyond the arch of the tall window. She murmured: " 'There is a green hill far away!' "

"Well?" I urged her.

There was a wail in her voice. "It's all so different, so, so foreign . . ."

"Jesus was a Jew," I said quietly, "and a son of this ancient land."

She nodded. But her lips were compressed and something of her blithe, competent American positiveness came back to her.

"Of course. But I just somehow don't seem to feel right here. I guess things have changed a lot since our Lord's time. I can think of Him better at home. D'you know what I'm going to do?"

"What?"

"When we get home I'm going to take a trip to Liberty, Wisconsin, that's the place I always remember from the time when I was a girl. And I'll go to the little church in which my father used to preach and have a good prayer and a good cry and try . . ." she hesitated and finished with a little break in her voice—"and try to find my Saviour again."

She smiled at me pathetically.

"Don't tell Lee how I've carried on. I don't want him to think I'm the least bit disappointed. The trip's been kind of slow for him."

IV

I came down to breakfast a few minutes before the Merriwethers. It was a primitive, little dining-room with one long table. At one end of it sat a small, intense Sephardic Jew in a red fez. So I sat down at the opposite end to form a refuge for the Merriwethers. They came in. Lee Merriwether wrung my hand. She looked very wan but smiled bravely.

"I've got a surprise for you," I said. She winced. But I smiled at her reassuringly. "I bet you haven't had any good oatmeal for breakfast in a long time."

"I'll say we haven't," Merriwether grunted. "Say, d'you remember that stuff they called 'porridge' on the *Venetia?*"

"Wait," I said. "The inn-keeper here is a German and he cooks the most delicious oatmeal. I've ordered it and cream too."

The breakfast was brought in.

"I tell you," said Lee Merriwether, "we know how to live in America. I don't care what anybody says. I'll be glad to get back to the good old U. S. A."

His wife laid a hand on his strong arm.

"So will I, Lee, so will I. . . ."

OUR FATHERS THAT BEGAT US

A Genealogical Inquiry

by MARVIN LOWENTHAL

I

And some there be, which have no memorial; who are perished as though they had never been; and are become as though they had never been born; and their children after them. But these were merciful men.—BEN SIRACH, 44: 9-10.

1851-1920. My father, Richard (Reuben) Lowenthal, born Buffalo, N. Y., wood-carver and cabinet-maker. Read much, thought little, talked well and often said he ought to have been a lawyer. Although free-thinker (as he called it) by birth, upbringing, and conviction, he paid for a seat in the Reform Temple which he never sat in, and closed his shop on the two major holidays which he never observed. Not the result of unconscious influence of a hundred generations of Jewish forefathers; he had a very stern wife.

My mother, a Feuchtwanger, was daughter of first Jewish girl born in Buffalo. Her grandfather came from Stuttgart and her grandmother was a Pforzheimer of Pforzheim. Their family reputed the largest dealers in horse-radish between the Neckar and Rhine.

1822-1896. My grandfather Gustav (Gershon) Löwenthal, born in Buchau-am-Federsee, Wurtemberg, in reign of William I, and brought up to be a horse-dealer. As a child he rode to the Ulm Fair on horseback, between his father's arms, clinging to the pommel. Family soon moved to Stuttgart, lived on the top floor of a beam-and-plaster house on Eichstrasse, and were famous for their *Lebkuchen*. An ordinance of King William looking toward the liberation of the Jews removed little Gustav from the saddle at the age of six and sent him, together with most other Jewish boys of Wurtemberg, into the public schools. There he unlearned his *mame-loschen* and became proud of speaking German, even if it was only Schwabisch. Linguistic snobbery led him to take sides, without knowing why, against his father and in favor of the frightening reforms of Dr. Maier of the Oberkirchenbehörde—hats off in *Schul* and two-hour sermons in German. This early practice of taking sides soon developed into a habit of polemic. As a youth, he read Hirsch against Geiger and sided with Geiger. Then Sachs, lecturing once in Stuttgart, thundered against Holdheim and Gustav stood with Holdheim. He lived *neu-modisch,* and sped rapidly through the new "Jewish German Church" of Holdheim into a world where there was no church at all. Became partisan of the ideas of Kant and Hegel, and even as an old man pronounced their names intimately and unctuously, walking beneath the elms of Franklin St., Buffalo, without realizing he had never read a word of them. But when still a youth he had read Boerne and Heine, their words moist from the press, and dreamed of himself too as a *Ritter von dem Heiligen Geist*. However, a plethora of brothers and a dearth of horse-trading forced him to America a year before he could have borne with him the martyr's badge of a Forty-Eighter.

In the new world, a wife (an Einstein, likewise from Buchau), five children, and Buchau business methods applied to the cider trade—cider turns to vinegar when subjected to philosophic contemplation—curbed any further intellectual passions. Nevertheless he hired the hall and attended to the programs when Robert Ingersoll lectured in Buffalo. He was likewise permanent secretary of the Temple. The community insisted on this because it considered him a "smart man," and he obeyed because he was obliging—and vain. He was proud of his German blood, and an old man sitting under the thin leaves of his grape-arbor, he would sing *Der Wacht am Rhein* to the stunned, admiring ears of his grandchildren.

1774-1840. Reuben Löwenthal, my great-grandfather, born in Ulm, was an expensive baby, as it cost his father a gulden a day for permission to remain in that city. Three weeks before his birth, his mother had accompanied his father to the leather fair at Ulm, and feeling that her time was upon her refused to leave—and then the cost of bringing a Jewish midwife from Biberach. Reuben grew up partly in Biberach and mostly on the roads of Upper Swabia, a peddler's son and eventually a horse-dealer. Traveled once as far south as the Bodensee. Knew little about the world of politics, except that some years the peasants cried *"Mach'mores"* and knocked off his hat while other years they didn't; but he always maintained that if Napoleon had not lost the Battle of Leipzig—thereby reducing to poverty a ring of Wurtemberg horse-dealers who had supplied the French cavalry—he would have been a rich man, and his son a *chochom* like his grandfather *selig*. Instead, his boy read the books of gentiles and apostates—Goethe and Heine—and Reuben foresaw the ruin of Judaism.

1738-1811. My great-great-grandfather, Eliezer Gershon Löwenthal, known as the Stuttgarter, born Stuttgart, Feb. 4, 1738, the day Joseph Süss Oppenheimer, unpopular privy councillor to the Duke, was hanged (suspended in an iron cage) and Jews were expelled from the city. His family was accustomed to wandering; moreover his father gained a certain profit out of the coincidence. In little ghettos along the German Danube and down the Rhine the child was given the suspicion of a Messianic halo. A Frankforter dealer in old pewter was sufficiently struck with the possibilities to raise and educate the child, who was taught Talmud and chess. Married into a family of Swabian horse-dealers and in his old age occupied himself with reconciling Napoleon and the Zohar.

1702-1758. His father, Löb Solomon ben Eliezer (*der feiner Schmul*), born near Küps in the Frankenwald, while his father was decorating the synagog of Horb. Grew up to be a road-singer and leader of a troupe of wandering musicians. In 1730 found himself in Löwenstein, where his troupe played for the servants of the Count von Löwenstein-Wertheim at the wedding of the eldest daughter. Attracted by Schmul's lusty voice, a kitchen maid poured a pitcher of wine down his neck and baptised him *"Löwenmaul."* Some years later when he lost his voice, he drifted into calling himself *"Löwenthal."* Married a poor relation of the Dace's, who received from Oppenheimer the right to print playing-cards, turned devout, and sold amulets against the Evil One. Became assiduous in synagog attendance, for his greatest pleasure lay in assuring himself that he could have outsung any *hazan* if he had only kept his voice.

1670-1735. Eliezer ben Solomon Lopez, father of Löb Solomon, born in Amsterdam, the son of a trader in minerals, earths, pigments, oils, bristles, and other painter's supplies. Learned to paint from one of his father's unsuccessful customers—a poor devil of an Italian—and became an agent for his father's business in Germany. Decline in Dutch commerce induced decline in Dutch painting, which induced decline in Lopez's business, which induced Eliezer to induce the trustees of an occasional synagog to grant to him the contract for painting mural decorations with his own hands and the scanty remnants of his father's stock. (See fragments in Bamberg Museum.) He was killed one night on the highway by a band of robbers who mistook him for Baiersdorf, the *Hofjude* of Bayreuth.

1641-1711. His father, Solomon Judah Lopez, born in Amsterdam, banker and merchant. Portrait—with cast in one eye, wearing gold brooch and looking intolerably proud of his Dutch blood—by an artist of the Rembrandt school who ran too severely in his debt for ochre and pigs-bristles. Stricken at an advanced age with acute indigestion, after a life of overeating, he made a feeble plea to have the physician summoned; but his wife said, "You may talk as you please; I'll do nothing of the kind. If God has a will to help he can do so without doctors. But if the judgment of the Most High is upon us, not all the doctors in the world can help." And he died.

1605-1673. Eliezer Judah Lopez, father of Solomon, also born in Amsterdam. Prosperous money-lender. When Sabbatai Zevi raised the Messianic call for a return to Zion, Eliezer—then past sixty and living inland at Utrecht—dispatched two chests of eatables, dried fruits, nuts, flour, beans, dried peas, and smoked tongues, to his son-in-law, Aboab de Herrera, in Rotterdam. "Keep these chests in readiness," he wrote, "so when the word of glory comes, I can sail with the swiftness of Dawn to the waiting arms of the Bride, to the Beloved of the Most High, to our Holy City of David." Three years passed without the word of glory. Then Eliezer sped another message by special courier to his son-in-law. "Take out the smoked tongues," he wrote, "before it is too late, and 200 guilders of food is ruined."

1570(?)-1648. Solomon Benari Lopez, birthplace uncertain—somewhere between Majorca and the Zuyder Zee. Camphor merchant. Known to have lived in Tarragona, Leghorn, Marseilles, London (where he entertained Maria Nunes, the three days' favorite of Queen Elizabeth), and eventually Amsterdam. Lived through the Inquisition, Armada, Elizabethan Age, Rise of the Dutch Republic, Thirty Years War, Rebellion of Cromwell, and reign of Akbar the Great, without intruding upon history.

1542-1591. His father, Henrico Leon African (José de Louppes), sea-captain in carrying-trade between Lisbon and Goa. He had a wife in Portugal, a Marano of Santarem; and another in India, a white Jewess of Malabar. Died in a shipwreck off the Andaman Islands.

1495-1563. His father, Alfonso de Leon (Abraham Joseph Lopez, or de Louppes), born in Portugal, was famous for having an uncle who upon the expulsion of the Jews from Spain fled to Toulouse. The uncle is famous for having a daughter, Antoinette. She is famous for having married Pierre Eyquern in 1525. Pierre Eyquern is famous for having a son bearing the title of Michel de Montaigne.

1456-1512. José Leone Lopez (Master Joseph the Jew), born in Cadiz and later settled in Portugal. Astronomer and map-maker. Translated into Portuguese the Almanach of Zacuto. Frequently consulted by King John II, who on one occasion showed him plans of an obscure navigator for reaching India by sailing westward across the Atlantic Ocean. My grandfather twelve times removed, with generations of merchanting be hind him and with his vast store of geographical knowledge before him, had no difficulty in proving to the King the absurdity of the scheme. Some years later he saw fit to leave Portugal.

1424-1492. His father, Abraham Benari (Lobos) of Leon, pickle-merchant and talmudist. Born and raised in Cadiz. Inherited wealth and coat of arms. Pickle business entirely in hands of factor. When the accounts were brought to him, he used to say, "I am a rabbi and a grandee. What have I to do with brine?" Drowned with a shipload of refugees during the Expulsion, while fleeing from Cadiz to Oporto. His brother remained in Spain and died in the arms of the Church, after three weeks of the strapado, the ladder, and other instruments of per-suasion.

1404-1461. Joseph Isaac Benari (or Abbas), rabbi and ostrich-feather dealer, born in Leon and died in Cadiz. His wife suspected of being a Moor. In any case, he was known to have obscure connections in the Sahara exceedingly productive of ostrich feathers.

1367-1425. Abraham Gershon Benari, merchant of Majorca. Financier of bi-annual caravan from Fez to Touat, Tamentit, and the remote Jew-ish city of Ghana in the upper reaches of the Niger. Importer of ostrich feathers, gold-dust, camel hide, and negro slaves. Equipped an army of

blacks to fight the Touregs of the Sahara who called themselves Philistines, looked upon themselves as the hereditary enemy of the Jews and
destroyed their trade. Over three thousand blacks fell in the African
sands during this warfare. Dying of the stone, Abraham left an Ethical
Will in rhymed prose, the admiration of posterity. "Be gentle," he wrote,
"and when you are blessed with the chance to do a kind deed, have no
regard for your worldly career."

1338-1402. His father, Joseph Abraham Benabbas, talmudist and map-
maker of Majorca. Studied medicine at Montpellier. Exchanged his maps
for shares in a Sahara trading company.

1309-1380. Gershon Judah Benabbas, born in Palermo. Against the
prevailing Jewish opinion of the day—"Na," said his father, "we Floren-
tines are not afraid of knowing something"—he was permitted to study
mathematics and medicine at the University. Practised in Majorca.

1278-1353. Guiseppe Gersoni Benabbas, born in Florence. Banker to
the woolen guild. Enjoyed the friendship of Immanuel of Rome who
borrowed money from him and addressed him an ode entitled "Star of
Italy." When the House of Aragon took over the government of Sicily,
Guiseppe moved to Palermo. "Spain," he said, "is the ancestral home and
friend of the Jews."

1237-1301. His father, Judah Gersoni ben Abbas, born in Florence.
Rag-picker and porter to a Florentine wool-merchant. Killed by an intoxicated and over-enthusiastic goat-herd during the fête and procession
celebrating the installation of Cimabue's *Madonna* in the church of Santa
Maria Novella.

1192-1262. His father, Gershon Alexander ben Abbas, candy-maker
in Constantinople. Set out on pilgrimage to Palestine in a Greek galley.
Captured by the Venetians and ransomed by a Jewish rag-dealer below
the Rialto. Married his savior's crippled daughter, represented his father-
in-law's business in Florence, wrote "Twenty-Two Commentaries on
Rambam's Idea of Prophecy," and begot eighteen sons.

1143-1201. Judah David Ibn Abbas, born in Fostat, Egypt. Stricken
with consumption and died as a charity patient under the care of the
wisest physician of his day, Rabbi Moses of Cordova, the son of Maimon.

1110-1178. His father, David Gerson Ibn Abbas, bead merchant, likewise born in Fostat. Early in life journeyed to Paris, but could not endure the crudeness of life among the "Franks." Returned to Fostat, but
in 1148 set out again for Europe. (Beads, he found, were popular among
the barbarians.) Ascended the Danube as far as Belgrade when he re-

ceived news that the crusading armies of Conrad and Louis were descending the same stream, on their way to Palestine. He hurried back to Fostat.

1090-1152. His father, Judah of Alexandria. Born and died in that city, rabbi and bead merchant.

1061-1118. David Ibn Aryah, born in Smyrna, and later rabbi and bead merchant in Alexandria. When a wandering scholar brought him a copy of Judah Halevi's poem on the conversion of the Khazars, he exclaimed on its beauty but shook his head, "Alas for Israel, it is only a poet's dream."

1033-? His father, Eliezer ben Jehudah (the Knock-Kneed), sandalmaker of Smyrna. In the hope of reaching Jerusalem, acted as shoemaker and interpreter—with the little Greek learned from his father—among the rag and bob-tail of the First Crusaders. May have perished in the glorious massacres which celebrated the Christian entry into the Holy City. One good shoemaker and one bad interpreter the less.

999-1058. His father, Judah ben Jochanan (Leo Justus), born in Constantinople and died in Smyrna. His wife was a liberated slave bought at a reduction because of her violent disposition.

979-1034. Eliezer ben Jehudah (Elis Justus the Perfumer), born in Constantinople and a prosperous dealer in paints, powders, and perfumes. His shop was renowned as center of wits, dandies, and profligates. When his brother proposed journeying to Spain with a group of Jewish immigrants from Bagdad, he laughed at him. "A land of savages—Spain is no place for a Greek."

939-1002. His father, Justus the Merchant, born in Constantinople, importer of spices and perfumes from Bagdad, India, and Cathay. Had a brother in Crimea, an uncle in Bagdad, and a cousin in Baroda. When his Christian acquaintances told him of their fear that the world would come to an end in the year 1000, he laughed, "But it isn't one thousand—the year one thousand was long ago—more than forty-five centuries ago. But what does a Christian know?"

912-968. Judah ben Ephraim, merchant of Ityl on the Volga and purveyor of slaves to the Kagan of Khazaria. After the defeat of the Khazar army, for which he had been an able recruiter due to his knowledge of the slave-markets, he fled to the Crimea and turned from slaves to spices.

885-947. His father, Ephraim of the South (Ephraim ben Jehudah), born in Ityl. Hebrew teacher and amulet-maker in the Jewish colony, whose manners he learned to despise from his father.

849-903. Judah of Pumbeditha, building contractor and slave merchant of that city. Unwilling to pay the high taxes a spendthrift Caliph had placed upon realty operations and hearing of a Jewish empire across the Great Snow Mountains, he set out for Khazaria. There he ate up his capital and sickened with longing for home. Looking out across the dreary treeless plains that surrounded the mud huts and patchwork tents of the Jewish imperial capital, dreaming of the gardens and glow of the Euphrates, he sighed to himself, "Jews can never be happy in Sarmatia." Married a fat daughter of a horse-breeder from the Don who, when he chanted to her "By the Waters of Babylon," used to burst into warm Kalmuckian tears.

818-884. Omar Ibn Haukal (Omri ben Jehudah), building contractor and talmudist in Bagdad and Pumbeditha.

785-858. His father, Ephraim the Heckler (Judah Brill, i.e. Ben Rabbi Judah Löw), born in Worms, Germany. Apprenticed to a physician who was later sent by Emperor Charlemagne as a gift to Caliph Haroun of Bagdad. Ephraim accompanied his master; the journey took two years; and before they arrived Haroun had died without the benefit of their skill. Married the granddaughter of a Gaon.

738-794. Judah Löw of Worms. A rabbi.

697-753. His father, Ephraim Judah (Leo the Scribe), born in Paris and later died in Cologne. Dealer in vellum and ink-cakes which he exported in quantity to England and Ireland. (The Venerable Bede may have written on Ephraim's parchment.)

678-735. His father, Judah ben Manasseh (Manlius the Trader), born in Narbo Martius or Narbonne, merchant adventurer. While still a young man he transported dyed woolens and linens, partly by raft and partly by ox-cart, from Marseilles to Paris. Then cider from Rotomagus (which did not turn to vinegar, for Judah had no talent for the Law), and wine from Dibia and the hills of the Côtè d'Or. Built himself a stout stone house near the Petit Pont in Paris; hung the walls with Roman curtains bought up cheap around Arles and Nîmes; and loaned money to the Mayors in the palace across the river. Charles Martel eventually borrowed from him his entire fortune in order to equip the army which broke the Arab advance at Poitiers. After the victory Charles naturally felt it his duty to found an abbey (St. Michel-aux-Bois near Tours) with the spoils instead of repaying Judah—who died of starvation and exposure on the road to Lyons, his body devoured by wolves.

635-691. His father, Manasseh ben Manasseh (Armentarius of Narbonne), born also in Narbo Martius, the heir of an international family of shippers and wine-growers. Mornings he rode through his vineyards, superintended the field work, and treated his slaves and overseers with Deuteronomic kindness. Middays he slept. Late afternoons found him in his courtyard examining an antique piece of Roman furniture or scrap of mosaic bought from a co-religionist in the back alleys of Arles, or in his garden fingering scrolls of Greek and Latin poets and vaguely resolving to begin, one day, to dictate books long dreamed upon—a literary comparison between Theocritus and Shir ha-Shirim; the philosophic kinship of Horace and Koheleth; a history of Jewish navigation; a collection of Judean Nights to supplement Aulus Gellius. Occasionally a small packet containing an olivewood casket, scented with Byzantine perfume, would arrive in a shipment from the uncles in Constantinople. The color of joy would rise to his cheeks, for in loving things of the spirit he was no mere lover of the dead. He was fervent in his devotion to contemporary effort, to the passion and beauty of his day. He would draw from the olivewood casket the scroll of rhymed prayers still damp with the tears of the Jewish poets. He drank their sorrow tenderly and anxiously, as he drank his own wine. "Joseph ben Joseph Hayathom is not yet King David," he was wont to say, "but the vine, thanks to the Most High, still lives."

A cousin, expelled by the first Omar from Jeddah in Arabia, eventually found an asylum with Manasseh. He was never happy in Narbonne. "Beasts and barbarians," he complained to his host, "you live in an age of darkness."

606-662. Manasseh of Narbonne, spent his life tranquilly writing copies of the Torah, which sold in Provence and Spain. Through a brother-in-law he speculated in vineyards and became suddenly wealthy.

570-641. His father, Manasseh ben David (Merwig of Averni), born in the Auvergne. At the age of twelve, together with other Jewish lads, was forcibly baptised by King Chilperic I, who in order to acquire merit held him under the font with his own royal hands. However, Manasseh was not troubled by the authorities in his subsequent practice of Judaism. "Let him and the other backsliders be burned for relapse or harried from the land!" demanded Bishop Avitus, counsellor to Chilperic in these matters. "Nay," answered the King, "I have won merit in Paradise by baptising them. They have thus served their king and the glory of God. If now they choose to damn their own souls, it is their concern. In fact it serves the Jews right." "My masters," said Avitus when he had returned to the episcopal palace, "are as indifferent as savages and cruel as Huns."

532-589. His father, David ben Solomon (Gozolas the Scribe), born in Arles and spent his life tranquilly copying the Torah. Moved to the Auvergne because of an epidemic of colic.

498-554. Solomon ben Judah (Servius Romanum), born in Ravenna, building contractor who made a specialty of furnishing cheap labor for the demolition of pagan temples and public basilicas, and subsequently selling the material at high prices to Ostrogothic nobles and ambitious bishops for the erection of their palaces and churches. Through his influence in Arian circles, received a bid to carry out large reconstruction works (as the demolishment was called) in Arles. Rebuilt the synagog at Genoa despite the counsel and advice of Cassiodorus, the minister of Theodoric the Great. "You are seeking," he wrote Solomon, "what you should flee."

469-520. His father, Judah ben Judah (Justus Romanum), born in Rome. Married the daughter of a building contractor and moved his entire family to Ravenna. "A good son—he knows all the right people," said his father, when he saw Judah paying hush money to a young German captain of the guard.

441-508. Judah ben Eliezer ha-Shochet (Justus Lucernus), lamp-merchant and *shochet,* born in the Transtiberina, Rome, and lived most of his life in the damp stone chamber where he was born. In this stuffy, windowless, ground-floor cell, close to the Pons Aurelius, he displayed his stock of lamps, brought his bride—the daughter of a petty commission agent whom the Herulian masters of Rome would have called a *Luftmensch* had they spoken German instead of a corrupt Gothic—and raised nine children. To keep it from rusting, he concealed his ritual butcher knife in the straw heap which served as the family bed and the whole of the family furniture.

He never forgot the date 476, or rather its Hebrew equivalent (4237); for in that year the rival *shochet* of Rome died of sunstroke, and Judah attained sufficient affluence to buy a bench, a mirror to comb his beard by, and a bronze kiddush-cup.

He allowed himself to be moved to Ravenna with regret. "I am a

Roman," he complained bitterly, as the ox-cart jogged its slow way north-
ward.

420-481. Eliezer the Shochet, born in Rome and died there.

381-460. Samuel ben Judah, born in Rome and died there. Sold fish
in the market near the Pons Aurelius. As an old man, never ceased to
tell how the night before Alaric forced the gates of Rome, he found a
silver sesterce in the belly of a trout. "This," he said, "is the end of the
world. And the scepter will return to Judah." The next day his entire
stock of fish was destroyed, and it was only by the grace of the sesterce
that he bought himself safety in a cellar near the Palatine.

345-398. Judah ben Abraham (Aullus Pontium), money-lender, born
in Rome, died there, and was the last Jew to be buried in the catacombs
along the Appian Way. His entire family was impoverished in paying
for the burial. But none held their heads higher than his sons when they
spat at the Arch of Titus in the Forum.

325-361. Abraham ben Jochanan, marriage-broker, born in Hippo
(Africa). Lived near the Porta Capena, Rome, and died of heart-failure
upon hearing the rumor that the Emperor Julian proposed rebuilding the
Temple at Jerusalem.

290-358. His father, Jochanan ben Judah, born in Hippo, a skilled
worker in leather. When the news reached him that the cult of Jesus
the pretended Messiah had become adopted as the official religion of the
Empire, he wiped his hands on his apron, clasped his right knee, swung
back in his stool, and turned a perplexed face toward his informant.
"What of it?" he asked. "Will it lower the price of leather?"

257-316. Judah ben Abraham, born in Carthago, fruit-dealer.

199-272. Abraham ben Zadok, born in Carthago, dealer in spices and
dried foodstuffs. When a son was born to him in his old age, he blessed
God and said that the yoke was being lifted from Judah.

161-232. Zadok ben Hillel (Justus the Cripple), born in Alexandria
and deformed from birth. His father had been a redeemed slave, and
now as he too threatened to become a permanent charge of the Alexandrian relief committee, they secured him passage to Carthago. The Carth-
aginian committee in turn gave him money and set him on the road to
Hippo. The Hippo Jews gave him funds to take ship to Rome. Instead
he trudged back to Carthago, borrowing more money on the strength of
the fare he had saved, procured a stock of garlic and onions, and set
up a stall in the market place. There he lived, praised God he could

obey His commandments in peace, and die of heart-failure with the *Shema* on his lips.

124-168. Hillel bar Hiyyah, born in Beth-Shemesh, where the hills begin to climb toward Jerusalem. When Bar-Cochba failed and Bethar fell Hillel was a boy of eleven. His mother wailed and tore her hair; his father, a forbearing man, clasped the boy hard against him and seemed to tremble. In a few days the Roman soldiery were swarming down the hills. Then came a night of terror, screaming, and death. Hillel was dragged to Jaffa and despatched with a shipload of other likely captives to the slave market of Alexandria.

As the boat slowly made its way through a rough sea, the boy Hillel crouched by the rail, sick, frightened, and numb at heart. In an effort to forget himself he listened as attentively as he could to the talk of the older prisoners pressed close about him.

"The day of wrath has come," said one man who had been to the schools of Jabneh, "but it is our own fault. We should never have rebelled against the Romans. God was with them. It was His will that Rome should rule us. We have defied God and now he has led us into darkness. Let us teach our children, if God spare us and grant us children, always to obey His will."

"But how can we know His will?" asked another, whose wounds were still bound. "We—I mean we who fought—we were filled with the assurance that not the day of wrath but the day of glad tidings had come and that God was redeeming Zion."

"Did not God promise Ezekiel," interrupted a third, " 'They shall dwell in the land I have given Jacob, they and their children and their children's children forever?' Was not the Captivity over? Were we not redeemed?"

"I do not know," said the first man, his voice sinking low, "I do not know whether God is faithful to Israel. But I do know that if Israel is faithful to God, Israel will live; if not Israel will die."

"And why not die?" answered the second man, with the wounds. "We were not promised merely life—but peace and redemption. 'Moreover I will make a covenant of peace with them—it shall be an everlasting covenant.' Twice, yes, thrice we have been promised 'everlasting' things. Once it was Abraham our father; then it was Moses; again it was Ezekiel. Always 'forever.' What does the verse say? 'Forever is but as a moment in the eye of the Lord.' I think it is time to die."

Whereat a fourth intervened. "Suffer me to speak on God's behalf.

It is neither His Will that we should submit to the Romans nor that we should be redeemed nor that we should die. We are being sent to the four corners of the world to preach His Name, to witness His Unity, and to proclaim to all peoples justice and peace. We shall not halt until we have set judgment in the earth and the isles wait for our law. Our sons shall be a light to the Gentiles and men shall call our children the Ministers of God."

"You are talking in vain," said a fifth man, pushing into the circle and smiling darkly. "Who knoweth the interpretation of a thing? All things come alike to all, there is one event to the righteous and the wicked, and there is an evil among all things under the sun. But this I know: for him who lives there is hope; a living dog is better than a dead lion."

Little Hillel listened but understood nothing of what he heard. He thought of his father and mother whose fate he did not know and whom he would never see again. The boat rolled heavily, the waves were black, and Hillel sank to the deck too weak to cry.

II

"This painful labor of abridging, it was not easy, but a matter of sweat and watching."—II Macc. 2: 26.

96-135 C.E. Hiyyah ben Zadok, my grandfather fifty-two generations removed,[1] was born in Ono, a village in the Ge-Haharashim, the Valley of the Smiths. The sight of the sea, visible from any hillock round-about, filled his boyhood with dreams of travel. Market days when he helped his father drive their three asses to Lydda—where the Roman garrison were insatiable customers for leeks—Hiyyah listened to soldier tales of far countries, Britannia, Dacia, Parthia, and learned the usual Palestinian smattering of foreign tongues. When the family moved to their

[1] NOTE—In the previous section of this genealogical inquiry I refrained from publishing my investigations into our family records beyond 135 C.E., when my ancestor Hillel ben Hiyyah was obliged to leave Palestine. This was not for lack of further information, but the accounts going behind this date involved a number of questionable points. Meanwhile I have visited the ancestral home and gone over the old estate, with the result that I feel sufficiently clear about the records to continue their publication, making due allowance, of course, for the fact that I can pretend to no greater knowledge of my forebears than of my contemporaries or of myself—which is little enough. I should like to express my appreciation for the wealth of details given me, during my investigations in Palestine, by my cousins and other relatives, on both the elder and younger side of the family—the children, that is, of my uncles Esau and Ishmael.

patrimonial farm in Beth-Shemesh (see below), Hiyyah's father in ful-
filment of a vow left the lad at the schools in Jamnia. The young Hiyyah,
his mind on running away to sea, hated the sages as much as they despised, in turn, the peasantry. But he was not long in discovering a side
of current rabbinical life which absorbed him; his training completed, he
worked as secretary to a minor chief in the revolutionary movement then
being fostered throughout the East. Luckily he was still a harmless secretary when, inspired by the Jews, Cyprus, Egypt, Armenia, and Parthia
arose to shake off the yoke of Rome and were crushed by Hadrian.

He retired to mending walls in his father's vineyards; and when
his chief was crucified, he married the dowerless daughter out of sheer
patriotism.

A dozen years later, when Hadrian on his philosophic tour of the
world visited Palestine, Hiyyah stood with the throngs at Lydda, and
cursed the Emperor for giving his momentary permission to rebuild the
Temple. "It will only mean," Hiyyah explained to his neighbors, "a new
hostage for the perpetuation of our slavery."

Not long afterwards, an agent of Akiba urged him again to take up
revolutionary work, this time under divine protection. "Rabbi Akiba,"
the agent assured him, "and who knows better? has proclaimed Bar-
Cochbah the Messiah. Christ has come at last." But Hiyyah remembered
he had a father, a wife, and three children to support, and the vineyards
still needed repairs. He answered the agent in the popular phrase of the
day: "Before the Messiah comes, grass will sprout from Akiba's jawbone."

Hiyyah was killed on the hillside above his vineyards three days
after Bethar fell.

68-130. His father, Zadok ben Simon, born in Beth-Shemesh, grew
up in Ono. Eventually succeeded to his father's tenancy and married the
daughter of a tool-smith in Lydda. Taxes and ground rent were overwhelming, and his life was filled with dreams and wrath—dreams of
how pleasant the world would be if he recovered his father's vineyards in
Beth-Shemesh, and wrath against the Jews for having revolted, against
the Romans for having in consequence sold the vineyards over his father's
head to an absentee landlord in Antioch, against the landlord for remaining absent and allowing the terraces to crumble away, against the
Syrian tenants for their negligence, and against the few surviving Jewish
neighbors in the hills above Beth-Shemesh who sat about waiting for
the day when the Syrians would starve themselves out by incompetence
and drunkenness and the land could be bought up for a song. Zadok's

wrath was almost hereditary, for his father had bequeathed it to him and had spent his old age in fostering it in his children. Jerusalem had fallen, and with it the paternal vineyards in Beth-Shemesh.

Moreover Zadok's wrath against the Jews was deepest, for of all the provokers of his family misfortune, he knew them best. Nights, at the gate of Ono, the villagers took pleasure in hearing him rail at the vanquished and vanished Zealots, and deride the rabbis gathered at the nearby Jamnia. "What is the use of the Law," he was wont to query, "when there is no justice?"

But he died a devout and pious Jew, one of those hitherto nameless forefathers whose constancy and fine understanding of eternal values helped lay the foundations of the empire of precept and observance which has preserved the Jewish people to this day. For the rabbis at Jamnia promulgated an interpretation of the Mishnah, which forbade a Jew to buy up land that had been confiscated by the Romans from a previous Jewish landlord. So long as the Syrians held fast to their incompetency and drunkenness the vineyards of Beth-Shemesh were saved. Zadok vowed his only son to the schools in Jamnia.

33-99. His father, Simon ben Beri (commonly known as the "Fish Gate Joseph"), born in the new quarter of Jerusalem, near the Fish Gate, the day of the earthquake when the Temple veil was shaken from one of its hangers. While he was still a lad, the family became ruined financially through an uncle's speculation and extravagant living in Alexandria. A sensitive nature (taking after his uncle who, it was commonly said, spent a fortune on sculpture, actresses, and philosophic prostitutes of both sexes), Simon eventually became one of the "official dreamers" of the Temple. Although he was not of priestly lineage, his family had for generations maintained relations with the sacerdotal and learned classes (see below), and store was set on his dreams and interpretations. In his youth wealthy women were his chief clients; later, public officials and foreigners frequented his stall in the outer cloisters of the Temple; and the secret rivers of news, which are forever circling the globe and are never nearer the surface than in the Orient, fertilized his visions.

The night after the soldiers of Florus plundered the Upper Market, Simon dreamed an eagle came and tore away with its beak and claws the iron spikes that lined the cornice of the Temple to protect the pavement below from the pollution of birds.

When Eleazar, the son of the High Priest and a fervent patriot, persuaded the Temple officials to refuse all gifts and sacrifices on the part of foreigners, and the Romans and Greeks scenting trouble no longer frequented the stalls of the dreamers, Simon gathered together his possessions and retired to his brother's vineyards in Beth-Shemesh. Soon after, the brother died childless and Simon did his duty by the widow.

But a few years later, when the news came that Jerusalem had fallen and the Temple was burned, Simon climbed to the roof of his house, seated himself in the half-dried dung, tore open his robe, and heaped a handful of ashes on his head. His village honored him by appointing him chief of the delegation to welcome Joseph ben Matthias (himself a notable dreamer and erstwhile hero of Jotopata) who was passing through Beth-Shemesh on his way to the estates given him by the Romans. The villagers hoped that Joseph (or as the Romans called him, Josephus) might persuade his Roman friends not to confiscate their lands.

"Jerusalem has fallen," said Joseph ben Matthias.

"We know it," replied Simon.

"I told them so," added Joseph ben Matthias.

"So did I," said Simon.

There was a pause. "Is—is there nothing to be done?" continued Simon.

"I," answered Joseph ben Matthias, "I shall write a book about it."

29 B.C.-41 C.E. Beri ben Haggiah, the father of Simon, born in Jerusalem, a wholesale dealer in the balm of Jericho. Honest, charitable, hard-working merchant; and a Pharisee. He considered himself a learned man, for he knew all the rules for making incense and for preparing oil for the Sabbath lamps; and, like his father before him, every year he sent a jar of the wine of Cyprus (when it was procurable) to the renowned Hillel.

Although his affairs brought him into frequent intercourse with Greeks and Syrians, and once he had visited Alexandria to establish his brother in a branch of the business there, he scorned the culture of the heathen. "Why learn Greek," he said, "when I can hire all the Greek clerks I need? As for philosophy and drama, anyone can procure as much as he is willing to buy. Beautiful words are cheaper than the iron nose-rings of Damascus. They wait at a man's door like my brother's prostitutes. But Torah is like a bride; it can be won only by wooing it with heart and soul."

When Judas of Gamala preached the glad tidings that taxation was no better than slavery, Beri the balsam merchant rejoiced. "At last a prophet in Israel," he exclaimed, and predicted that the principle of free trade would wreck the power of Rome and establish the kingdom of heaven.

One day a new catchword ran scornfully through the bazaars: "Give Caesar what belongs to Caesar." Beri was not the least inventive of the merchants in cataloging the infamies which by moral right belonged to the Emperor, Tiberias.

The saddest day of his life—all Jerusalem howled and there was rioting at the gates—was when the news swept the bazaars that the governor of Judea, Pontius Pilate, intended to spend Temple money on bringing running water into Jerusalem. "Before they finish with their abominations," he cried to the merchants of the spice-*souk*, "they will be introducing Roman baths!"

He died confident that his children would live to see the Beri balm flourish as once had flourished the purple of Tyre, and Simon his youngest son a sage like Hillel.

61-6 B.C. His father, Haggiah ben Simon Beri, a spice and balm merchant. When Herod consecrated the new Temple, Haggiah received the contract for supplying the balm, onycha, galbanum, frankincense, myrrh, cassia, spikenard, saffran, aromatic bark, cinnamon, salt of Sodom, the herb Maaleh Ashan, and the odoriferous herb Cippath, for the manufacture of the ritual incense. He likewise undertook to supply the wine of Cyprus when it was procurable. He soon became the owner of large balsam groves in the plain of Jericho. It is said Hillel once greeted him in the Temple Court. The year he died the balsams of Jericho yielded the largest output of balm known in the annals of the trade, and Judea was formally annexed to the Roman Empire.

104-7. Simon ben Shashai Harim, born in Jerusalem, a petty dealer in amulets, incense, and other religious small-wares. The only thing recorded of his life was his tremendous capacity for gathering information which did not concern him. He knew of Samaritans who sacrificed their children and buried their bodies under their door sills for good luck. Not a Sadducee passed the doorway of his shop but he knew where he had last eaten swine and whether his children practiced wrestling. Not a Pharisee entered the bazaars—were he a visitor from Sepphoris in Galilee or Beth Tappuah beyond Hebron—but he knew of his marital infidelities. He knew what the priests did with the tithes. Only with respect to the Essenes he witnessed hesitation—they were so few, ignoble and remote in their wilderness monasteries—but, undoubtedly, since they lived with-

out women, their habits could best be characterized in Greek. He snickered as he dwelt on the proximity of En-gedi to the vanished cities of
the Dead Sea.

When a most just God permitted Pompey to capture Jerusalem despite the fact that the Jewish defenders refused to fight on the Sabbath,
and allowed the priests to be slain while sacrificing in the Temple though
not one of them abandoned the altar, no one was better prepared or
more willing than Simon ben Shashai to publish the names of the sinners who brought on these calamities, and the time, the place, and the
nature of their sins.

In his old age—and he flourished like a bay tree to an exceedingly
old age—the bazaars considered it worth a holiday to hear him discourse
on Herod.

160-94. Shashai ben Simon Harim, born in Modin, the year Judas
Maccabeus died. A lad of seventeen he put on the "glorious and warlike
apparel" of the young men of his time and town, and joined the army
of Jonathan ben Absalom in its march on Joppa, and there got his taste
of victory, spoils, and the sea. Within a week he was back into the low
hills by Hadid, an hour from home, helping Simon Maccabeus outface
the Syrian army. Under Simon he helped worry the Syrians up hill and
down dale—once, by Adora, with a snowstorm at his back. He fought
at the siege and capture of Gaza, and again, at Modin, against the army
of Antiochus when the Syrians were driven from the land—forever. He
stood with the guard of honor when the monument to the Maccabeans,
father, mother, and four sons, was dedicated at Modin and flashed its
granite to the ships at sea. By a diligent surveillance of the bazaars he
helped starve out the Syrian garrison of the fortress in Jerusalem. There
his youth and prowess won him the daughter of a wealthy donkey-
trader.

But his youth and prowess remained unabated, and his wife's jealousy compelled him to seek an honorable way of abandoning her, a way
that would leave the dowry intact. All Jerusalem spoke of Simon Maccabeus' purpose to send Numenius son of Antiochus (Shemei ben
Ahimaaz) on an embassy to Rome; Shashai secured the post of bodyguard to Numenius.

The journey took more than a year. Shashai gaped at Rome, although
he considered its fortifications and military location inferior to Jerusalem.
He visited Sparta and slept through a Greek tragedy. Numenius returned
to Jerusalem bearing a treaty of alliance with Rome which everyone
welcomed as an assurance of endless peace and prosperity; and his body-

guard, Shashai, came home with four new ways of throwing dice and a taste for cold baths.

His wife behaved more jealously than ever, and Shashai helped storm Shechem and was the first to set fire to the abominable temple of Jehovah-Jupiter-Hellenius on Mount Gerizim. His share of the spoils was six yards of silk and two women. He fought next in the campaign against the Edomites of Hebron and rejoiced in the forced conversion of these idolaters. In the prime of life he was off to Alexandria, captain of the guard of honor to the sages who journeyed to Egypt to undertake the translation of the Torah into Greek. He offered a sacrifice in the Temple at Onion, near Bubastes, and despite his experience in life he learned many new pleasures in Egypt, for he found the Egyptians a subtle and wise people. In fact he remained in Egypt until he received news of his wife's death.

Her dowry and his pension purchased him a small amulet and incense shop in the bazaars of Jerusalem. And in his old age Shashai ranked not the least entertaining of those "ancient men" who "sat all in the streets, communing together of good things."

185-121. Simon ben Asaph Harim, his father, born and died in Modin. A wealthy man, for his property included a watch-tower and a well. A brave man, for he lost an arm fighting under Judas Maccabeus. A learned man, and for two years member of the local Beth Din. To the traditional prohibition of cedar-bast, uncombed flax, floss-silk, and willow fiber in the lighting of the Sabbath lamp, Simon added water weeds.

229-150. Asaph ben Shashai Harim, born at Beth-Horon the Upper, and died in Modin, heir to his brother-in-law's sheepfold and flocks. As a well-to-do sheep owner he visited Jerusalem regularly, rarely missing a festival. He had social ambition, frequented the homes of the wealthy and the learned, and held in great contempt the lower classes. Walking through the bazaars one day with the cultivated and rich scholar, Jesus ben Sirach, he called attention to the smiths, potters, and seal-cutters, stupefied by their hard labor. "These are not men," he said, "but brutes and they have no portion in the Law." "True," answered his companion, "they shall not be sought for in public counsel nor sit high in the congregation, and they shall not be found where parables are spoken. But they will maintain the state of the world."

With the same zeal that he sought converse with the learned men, he held himself aloof from the Hellenists, wicked men who had made a covenant with the heathen, who went about wearing hats, who played "the game of Discus" in the gymnasium on the Akra, who wore artificial contrivances to hide their covenant with the true God when they strove at the Olympic games in Tyre, who gave money to keep in repair the stadium of Hercules, and who vaunted the Grecians above the fathers of Israel. He turned an indignant ear to their argument that since the Jews, generations ago, had departed from heathen customs, much sorrow had befallen them.

Eventually he abandoned his visits to Jerusalem, and the occasion was this: at a banquet given by a wealthy son of a priestly family he encountered a Greek from Athens who was being honored as a traveler of much wisdom and experience. Through an interpreter Asaph complained of the corruption Greek ideas and customs were introducing into Jerusalem. "You are right," said the Athenian, and Asaph bowed in gratification. "When a barbarous people," continued the Athenian, "comes in contact with a civilized people, they are not mentally or spiritually capable of assimilating the higher civilization; instead they ape only the lowest traits of civilized life, which is all they are able to understand. I have seen the same process among the Scythians."

Reposing on his estate in his old age, Asaph believed that the destruction and abominations Antiochus Epiphanes wrought in the Temple were a just punishment on Jerusalem and on himself for allowing the Greek traveler to return to Athens alive.

260-198. Shashai Harim, born in Beeroth and died in Beth-Horon the Upper. Owner of a few acres and two bullocks. His eldest son, Asaph, became an ass-driver and traveled as far as Jerusalem, and held him in scorn. "How can you get wisdom?" he would demand, after describing the luxuries of the bazaars of Jerusalem, "if your hand is always to the plough and your talk is of bullocks?" "Can you milk wisdom from your she-ass?" Shashai would reply, "How do *you* propose to get wisdom?" "How?" answered Asaph, "I shall marry a hunchback with a big dowry." He did, and his father praised him in the gate for his diligence.

306-233. Jakim ben Shashak, his father, born and died in Beeroth, north of Jerusalem. His occupation unknown, other than that he was always among the men standing about the market of the village. Inasmuch as the road to Damascus led through Beeroth he could always pick up his daily crust by watering the camels, passing along information on the activities of the robber bands in Samaria, and lighting fires under recalcitrant donkeys. To clothe himself was still less a problem, for his long robe eked out with bits of twine and camel-blanketing lasted him a lifetime. Once a year, no one knows how, he found means to sacrifice a paschal lamb and his problems of *kashruth* were greatly simplified by the fact that this was the only meat he ever tasted. In his prime, he and his wife and two children could devour the whole lamb at one sitting.

His intellectual forces were entirely occupied by a dispute which raged in Beeroth throughout the span of his life. The villagers were divided between descendants of David, of Aaron, of Asaph, of Levi, and of the Torah-watchers of the old days of Nehemiah. Jakim himself claimed to be a *chassid*. Between these various factions and their wives, rivalry was perennial and complicated every detail of village administration and etiquette.

Although Beeroth was (as it still is) only a haphazard stone pile lost in the hills, Jakim would have been the last man to call his life dull.

333-270. Shashak ben Asaiah, born and died in Beeroth. A stupid lad, he became a camel driver and saw considerable of the world between Jerusalem and Galilee. All Beeroth stood about to hear his description of the cistern Simon the Just had built in Jerusalem to receive the distant waters of the Pools of Solomon. All Beeroth agreed with him when he said there were three despicable nations—the Samaritans, the Philistines, and the Shechemites, and the Shechemites were no nation.

One of his sons migrated to the newly founded city of Alexandria and was reported rich through the rise in rents; another accompanied a caravan to Galilee and married there a Jewess who spoke with a terrible accent. The third remained in Beeroth, the pride of Shashak's old age.

370-302. Asaiah ben Jorah, born and died in Beeroth. Also a camel driver. He found himself once far from home, by Migdal-Gad on the road to Gaza, when his caravan was overtaken and run down by a vast army. Together with his fellow-drivers he fled to the sand dunes. Peering cautiously over a ribbed crest of sand, he saw the commander of the army, a youth, carried in by a litter. "You know his name?" a driver who had recently come from Tyre asked Asaiah. "No," whispered Asaiah. "Alexander," said the driver. Asaiah looked again and asked, "Who is Alexander?"

417-352. Jorah ben Beruel lived and died in Beeroth, well-born, pious, and poor. He blew the ram's horn which summoned the villagers from work on the eve of the Sabbath; on the second and fifth day of the week he helped read to the community the Law before which everyone was equal, and he complained piously of the new-fangled writing; he opened the first school for children in Beeroth. Although he honored the Law with his innermost fiber and although desperately poor, he so loved life that he would desert the school or his scrolls if he saw a wedding procession move down the village street, and join himself with the merry-makers.

451-412. Beruel ben Adiah ben Joed, born in Gibeah near the wilderness of Bethaven, where the winters are severe. Owned a herd of sheep and goats, and manufactured wine-skins and cheese. His life was consecrated to a hereditary hatred of the Samaritans, and when they dared to build a temple to Jehovah in the hope of rivaling the recently finished Temple at Jerusalem, Beruel's devotion mounted to poetic frenzy and he composed a song which began, after the usual flourish, "The Lord doth build up Jerusalem." The song dwelt on how the Lord casts the wicked to the ground and how Israel alone was His favorite; it praised the Lord for sending snow like wool and ice like morsels; and with a side-glance at the Samaritans it asked, who can stand before His cold? This song found favor in Jerusalem, and has substantially come down to us in Psalm 147.

497-421. Adiah ben Joed ben Baruch, born in Gibeah where his father and grandfather had been settled a few years after their return from the Exile. Tended his patrimonial goats and the manufacture of wine-skins. The outstanding event of his life was his divorce from his wife. She was the daughter of the former owner of his pastures; her father had been a Sidonian, although he claimed relationship with the children of Dan. Adiah had six children, and his wife was expert in sewing wine-skins. Nevertheless and against his will and affections Adiah became convinced by the eloquence and learning of the leaders in Jerusalem that Judea must be cleansed of foreigners. How could God consent to send rain on his pastures if he continued to live with his wife?

The issue was so grave, the event was debated so long, and the world in those days was so vast—he had sought to go to Sidon to examine his father-in-law's genealogy but the Samaritans barred his way—it is natural that Adiah knew of little else and cared less. Syria, the Empire, the King of Kings, the world were nothing to him—he never heard of Marathon, or of his contemporaries, Æschylus, Socrates, and Confucius. He never heard of Prince Gautama, who died not a score of years before he was born. But Adiah too was making world history, for, in the end, he divorced his wife.

532-481. Joed ben Baruch ben Hanan, born in Acraba, on the river Chabor, which is a northern branch of the Euphrates. While still an infant his father took him to Babylon and then to Susa. He remembered nothing except the tedium of these journeys. As a boy his head rang with the long days and nights of calculation and debate as to whether the family should return to Zion. "Is it far?" he asked, and when he was told that it was farther than Acraba, farther even than Arxata whither his uncle had wandered and prospered, he cried and said he did not want to go to Zion.

But youth changed his ideas. He was fourteen when the family began the exhaustive journey, and his mind was set on being a prince in Judah.

When the caravan crossed the Jordan by the ford of the Daughters of Jacob and prepared to descend the Derech Ha-Yam, the Way of the Sea, Joed wept with his family; but while they wept with timorous joy, for they knew not what was before them, he wept with exultation. And when from the hills on the north Joed first saw Jerusalem with its broken towers, he leapt from his ass and danced along the road, chanting a war-cry his grandfather taught him: "The sword of the Lord and of Gideon!"

But for long months he did nothing more princely than twist ropes and polish hewn stones, and his father made prolonged journeys to Gibea and elsewhere searching out the family records, in order that they should suffer no shame. Meanwhile they lived under a skin-tent beyond the Brook Kidron, and the second winter they would have starved had not the uncle in Arxata sent them money.

The day the foundations of the Temple were dedicated, Joed's grandfather who stood trembling at his side fell dead, and Joed's eyes shone with a perfect hope. He sang with the sons of Asaph, as the trumpets blew and the cymbals clashed: "The Lord is good, for His mercy endureth forever toward Israel."

III

"Let us now praise famous men."—BEN SIRACH, 44:1.

573-508 B.C.[2] Baruch ben Hanan Bakbuk ("Bakbuk" meaning, as Baruch said, an "extensive family"), my grandfather sixty-seven generations removed, born and raised in the back-room of his father's shop in Babylon, led a discontented life.

[2] NOTE—This is the final section of a genealogical inquiry which began with notes on my father and grandfather, and which is now carried back to the beginning of our line. The age and duration of my family tree may seem considerable,

His earliest instructions, his mother's cookery, the general run of his associates rendered him a Jew. But unlike his father, who continually insisted he could not sing the songs of Zion, although no one asked for them, Baruch extracted small satisfaction out of the sorrows of Exile.

As a youth he learned Chaldaic from the piles of second hand cylinders or "bricks" which ran along one wall of the shop, with the help of a kindly scribe who used to visit the shop regularly and turn over the cylinders in the hope of finding ancient Sumerian inscriptions for a wealthy patron's collection.

When his knowledge increased, Baruch became himself a collector of rare inscriptions and old impressions of hymns, legends, and decrees, which he sold at good profit to the newer generation of Babylonians whose fathers had grown rich through the conquest of Nineveh.

Every year he made a journey north to Nineveh in search of signets and small carvings which Babylonian dandies affected for their cane-heads; and south to Accad and Erech for Sumerian items. His sales were renowned. Babylon never forgot the three talents of gold paid by the Chief Eunuch for the earliest known Sumerian text of the eighty-seventh clause of Hammurabi's Digest.

But despite his financial well-being and his access, in a moderate degree, to Babylonian society, he suffered inwardly from his Jewishness. He hated his father on many grounds: the old man remained a foreigner; lived solely in the chimerical hope of a return to Jerusalem—a hope fostered by fanatics imitating the worst excesses of Jeremiah and Ezekiel, and spent the interim inveighing against Babylonian idolatry, immorality, and wealth. Baruch cherished no illusions of Jewish superiority. He had been permitted to mount to the summit of the terraced temple of Bel and knew the shrine was as empty as the Holy of Holies had been at

but this impression is illusory. Abram ben Terah, my grandfather one hundred and one times removed, is a parvenu in the family tree of mankind. In fact, compared with the founders of his own native city, Ur, themselves but modern in the human scene, he is so recent as to be almost contemporary.

The fact that the first men known to historical record are relatively our contemporaries creates certain apparent anachronisms in the reconstitution of these biographical notes. Many of their actions seem strange to us, yet nothing can lead us to suppose that their fundamental nature greatly differed from our own. Voltaire is taken to account for treating the ancients as men of the eighteenth century; but many of the ancients were. Consider your own grandfather whom, doubtless, you knew personally. He was much like you will be when you are his age. So, doubtless, his grandfather appeared, in turn, to him. You have merely to multiply this operation a few dozen times and you will arrive, too, at Abram ben Terah; and find in him only another grandfather.

Jerusalem. Although in a superficial, bibliographical sort of way, he was acquainted with much of Chaldaic literature, laws, and above all, science. Perhaps he was too much under the influence of Babylonian morals to judge of them fairly; anyway he considered their marriage system [3] much more humane than the Jewish dowry system; and being a man of his time and place he could not greatly differentiate between religious prostitution and circumcision; both rites seemed to him an admirable sacrifice to divinity. As for Babylonian wealth, he enjoyed as much of it as he could.

"After all, father," he would say, "this is our homeland."

"What do you mean?" the old man would scream.

"Our people came from Ur of the Chaldees; you are never satisfied, now that you are back you want to leave again."

But there was another Baruch at war with Baruch the arch-connoisseur of Rare Bricks. For Baruch loved his father out of blind affection as much as he hated him out of reason. Some of his wealthy Jewish associates, who had been brought to Babylon as poor boys, had sent for their aged fathers back in Jerusalem and installed them luxuriously in their new homes. This filial devotion appeared to Baruch the more worthy of emulation since it accorded with his hidden affection for the old man. Sitting before the wine shops and coversing with his Jewish friends (who were some of his best buyers), Baruch used to swear— since he could not very well bring his father to Babylon—he would take him back to Jerusalem if ever the Exile came to an end. The occasion seemed remote enough.

Through the son of a Babylonian tax-farmer, an excellent customer for old poetry, he met a young Jewish prophet who in the exercise of his profession appeared to possess a great influence over the Babylonians. This young Jew spoke eloquently of things that looked at closely had a tendency to vanish—universal peace and justice; but he touched strange chords in Baruch's soul. Baruch boasted that his heart was as hard as a baked-clay tailor's bill, but he knew—he knew not what he knew. And he helped the young man get his thoughts written out on enduring parchment. He kept a copy by his couch, and reading the bold words greatly wrought upon him. One day he tore the parchment to pieces and ordered his clerk to buy him a good treatise on mathematics.

Baruch would have undoubtedly gone to his grave in this sweet-sour unhappiness and success, if Cyrus had not captured Babylon and brought the Exile officially to an end.

[3] *Herodotus,* I. chap. 196.

The old man was for returning to Jerusalem at once. Baruch pleaded that it was wiser to see how things turned out. The old man thought Baruch meant affairs in Jerusalem, but Baruch was thinking of the Rare Brick trade. It turned out badly. The Babylonians were financially ruined and the Persians had no taste for antiquities. Baruch tried the slave business in Acraba, where his son was born; and later the signet and carved ivory business in Susa. But the Persians did not take to the use of canes. So nothing remained but to return to Jerusalem.

603-516. Hanan ben Obed Bakbuk, the father of Baruch, born in Jerusalem, a lad when Nebuchadnezzar laid siege to the city. Not old enough to fight like his father, he contented himself with slipping into the palace courtyard and taunting the old prophet of ill-omen who, in his chains, proclaimed and welcomed the fall of Jerusalem.

One night his father embraced him; and bade him farewell and never to cease hating the prophets and their sycophants, a rabble of chicken-livered slaves, without means or occupation, sold to the enemy, meek in spirit, worthless *anavim,* who hated the wealthy out of envy, the strong out of impotence, the priests out of vainglorious self-righteousness, who betrayed their people, their city, and their God. Then his father disappeared; and the next day revealed that the king and the army of defenders had slipped through a breach in the walls and taken flight toward the Arabah.

Because of his youth Hanan wore no chains in the long march across the Syrian desert to Babylonia; and he earned a pittance on the way, begging sheep-fat from the cooks and selling it to the wealthier captives to rub on their swollen wrists and ankles. His mother died on the march, and he was permitted to leave the caravan in the upper reaches of the river Chabor.

He drifted to Tel-Aviv, practically a Jewish city settled by the earlier captives, and became the servant of a Jewish slave dealer. Married a dowerless Jewess, a servant like himself.

The Jewish population of Tel-Aviv diverted themselves chiefly by singing psalms in the streets at night and listening to the discourses of a prophet named Ezekiel.

Despite the prejudices implanted by his father, Hanan found great satisfaction in the words of the prophet. He rejoiced to hear that Egypt, Sidon, Tyre, Seir and Magog were to be destroyed, even though he had no notion where or what these nations were, and consequently his satisfaction was never to be troubled by learning that these disasters failed to occur. He was puzzled to hear Nebuchadnezzar called a servant of Jehovah, but his perplexity was forgotten in the assurance that if he lived to be an old man he would see Babylon wiped out and the Jews and Israelites returned to Jerusalem, united into one kingdom, and planted forever in their own land.

He was very poor and it consoled him to learn that Jehovah had destroyed Jerusalem because the Jews had grown rich and that his poverty was a renewal of Jehovah's favor. With his scanty savings he moved down to Babylon and engaged in the second hand trade, buying and selling worn-out clothes, trinkets, cylinders, jugs, and pots. A foreigner, ignorant of the language and awed by the magnificence and power of the great city, his habits were furtive and his gestures humble. He remembered, however, the words of a song he used to sing at night in the streets of Tel-Aviv: "The meek shall inherit the earth."

Once only he rebelled against the words of a *nabi*. In his later years, through his son Baruch, he heard the discourses of a young prophet who proclaimed the right of the Babylonians and eunuchs to share in the Return. "The first," protested Hanan, "is against Divine Justice and the second is against the Law—this unknown prophet is a false prophet." [4]

639-576. Obed ben Joed Babkuk, born in Jerusalem. Engaged, with two partners, in the importation of Egyptian novelties bought from the merchants of Gaza, brooches and necklaces in colored stones, scarabs, ivory bedsteads, fly-swatters; for following the victory of Pharaoh Necho, Egyptian *articles de luxe* were greatly prized by the court, men of wealth, and priests of Jerusalem. He married the daughter of his elder partner.

Obed and his wife were extremely pious, and worshiped with a devout heart Jehovah God of Israel and Astarte Queen of Heaven. As a patriot he offered sacrifices to the God that watched over Israel his people, and as Protector of Israel put no other gods before Him. As a pious suppliant and worshiper of those forces of life which know no country, no patriotism, no city, which are beyond gods and men and are worshiped in all lands alike, Obed and, in the nature of the case, more especially his wife poured drink offerings to the Queen of Heaven and made cakes in Her image.

Despite the troublous times Obed was blessed with children and wealth.

---

[4] In the previous section it is related that Hanan returned to Jerusalem with his son and fell dead at his grandson's feet, the day of the dedication of the new Temple.

Because the priests and court were his customers, and also because of his natural piety and stout patriotism, Obed despised and hated the prophets of ill-omen. When such as these demanded the abolishment of drink offerings to the Queen of Heaven, Obed would appeal to the example of King Josiah, who had done this very thing, and behold his unhappy fate! His wrath against the prophets only increased when his wife succumbed to their persuasion and ceased pouring drink offerings and making cakes.

Obed joined the defense corps of the city, and the night Jerusalem fell, as the corps fled toward the Arabah, Obed, as he afterwards said, was guided by a vision that was like moonlight, and he turned aside at Adummim. Alone he took flight over a camel-track to the Kidron, then up the desert hills to Etam and Hebron. There he waited until word came of the destruction of Jerusalem and its inhabitants. So he fled to the city of Noph in Egypt.

He managed to work himself into the jewelry trade again, and remarried. As part of the marriage contract he enjoined on his wife exemplary piety toward Astarte.

"When we poured out drink offerings to the Queen of Heaven," he used to say to the community of Jewish refugees that led a meager and miserable existence at Noph, "we and our fathers, our kings and our princes, in the cities of Judah and the streets of Jerusalem, we had plenty of food and were well and saw no evil. But since we or our wives have left off doing this, we have wanted all things and been consumed by the sword and the famine."

675-609. His father, Joed ben Hashun Bakbuk, Jerusalem merchant of nose-rings (*nezamim*), bracelets and other adornments for women. Specialized in earrings, and his chief concern was to buy them from the Beni Kedar in the greatest variety at the lowest prices. Fulfilled his other functions in life with equanimity: begot many children, dutifully worshiped the Evening Star from the flat roof of his pleasant suburban house, circumcised his male offspring, attended the morning sacrifices in the Temple, paying his toll at the gate and praying fervently to the gods Milcam and Jehovah. A loyal subject of the king, he believed, in common with the entire jewelry *souk,* that Manasseh's long life and prosperous reign witnessed divine favor toward Judah.

The reforms of Josiah bewildered and vexed him. He was compelled to continue his old practices in secrecy, which he feared damaged their efficacy. He missed the old shrines at the gate of the Temple. But his vexation, if not his bewilderment, vanished when he saw Jerusalem filled at three seasons of the year with pilgrims from throughout Judea, and during the remainder of the time well frequented by country people who were no longer permitted to sacrifice at home. He was fortified in his satisfaction by the words of a traveling merchant from Tyre: "You people should have done this long ago. We permit only one temple to Melkarth the one god of Tyre, and our affairs prosper marvelously."

However, he allowed himself to wonder, in company as usual with the remainder of the jewelers' *souk,* if Josiah's defeat and untimely, violent death were not due to the removal of the Horses of the Sun from the Temple court.

726-649. His father, Hashun ben Shaphan Bakbuk, servant and later chief steward of a *soken,* or counsellor, of King Hezekiah, spent his life in the court at Jerusalem. It was a brilliant court, abounding in writers, historians, and prophets; but Hashun's concerns lay elsewhere, mostly in the purchase of fresh mutton and good linen, and in disciplining the maid servants. Nevertheless family tradition credits him with composing a proverb: "The blueness of the wound cleanseth away evil; so do stripes the inward parts of the belly."

757-?. Shaphan Bakbuk, born in Anathoth, began life as a water-carrier in the streets of Jerusalem, hence the origin of his name, Bakbuk, "leather bottle." Married the daughter of a camel-hostler of the big khan outside the Angle Gate. Children came too rapidly for his income; and after the birth of the tenth one, Hashun, he abandoned his family (to his father-in-law) and sought his fortune in Samaria.

He arrived just in time to leave before the siege of the Assyrians set in. Captured near Dothan by a band of Sidonians, he was despatched a slave to Sidon. He purchased his liberty by consenting to join a ship-load of colonists westward bound.

The ship moved from port to port along the northern shore of the Mediterranean, and the voyagers traded or pirated as the occasion determined. The Sidonians and Shaphan had no trouble outwitting or overpowering the barbarians of the Aegean and Ionian isles.

The only disagreeable episode of the voyage turned on an attempted landing at Syracuse, where the Sidonians were amazed to discover this ancient Phoenician city in the hands of barbarians from Corinth.

Reaching their destination, New Town or Carthage (which was then over four hundred years old), the colonists were granted land near the suburbs. Shaphan soon enriched himself by trading with the Berber coast tribes, married the daughter of a wealthy Punic merchant, begot three children, journeyed to Egypt on business, and there succumbed to a sudden longing to revisit Jerusalem. He traveled as a sutler in the wake of Sennacherib's army and entered Jerusalem by the same wave of circumstances which drove him from Samaria. Date of death unknown, and whether it was his Jewish or Punic wife who buried him.

His descendants, not without reason, changed the meaning of his name, Bakbuk, from "leather bottle" to "extensive family."

790-743. His father, Hashun ben Shaphan, born and died in Anathoth, a herdman.

818-751. Shaphan ben Elah, born in Bethel, a herdman. Many fat sheep and goats were laid between the altar-horns of the high-place and sacrificed to the golden calves of Jehovah, and Shaphan plied a thriving trade; but between tithes, taxes, first-fruits, and "free-will" offerings exacted by the priests and the king over Israel, and between the smallness of the ephah and the greatness of the shekel, Shaphan suffered from want of bread and "cleanness of teeth."

When a herdman from Tekoa came preaching in Bethel against the oppression of the poor, against the tithes and taxes and cheating scales, Shaphan listened with gaping mouth. And when the priest of Bethel ordered the man of Tekoa to return to Judah and there eat bread, Shaphan could not understand the preacher's refusal. He said to his family, "There is bread to eat in Judah; it must be a land without tithes and taxes; let us go." So he settled in Anathoth, near Jerusalem, and died as poor as he was born.

854-799. His father, Elah ben Zabad ben Ezer, a smith of Samaria. He was a young man when the King of Judah challenged the King of Israel, "Come, let us look one another in the face." Elah departed joyfully with the army of his king, and being a brawny man outlooked a great number of Jews at Beth-Shemesh. His valor was rewarded with a piece of land near Bethel, where he installed his second son, Shaphan.

889-828. Zabad ben Ezer, his father, a smith in Samaria. Married a Moabite captive named Hava, whom he purchased for a small sum after the defeat of Mesha, king of Moab. Of his three wives Hava was the favorite because of her modesty and quiet obedience. She obeyed her Jewish lord out of religious devotion, for she was convinced that her captivity with a divine punishment upon her people for their unfaithfulness to Chemosh, a jealous god, outraged at the corruption of Moabite manners: the Moabites, she was well aware, had sacrificed to strange gods, Astarte, Dagon, Milcam, Jehovah and Hadad; and many Moabite maidens—who could forgive the notorious Ruth?—had willingly intermarried with foreigners. She served her master, Zabad, the more patiently, in the implicit hope that after seventy years Moab would be gloriously restored to the favor of Chemosh.

928-854. Ezer ben Adonibaal, father of Zabad, born in Shechem, by trade a smith; but his exuberant nature chafed at hard monotonous labor, and early in life he associated himself with a band of young prophets. Won renown by his mastery of Solomonic lore and the cures he effected with it. Shechem echoed with his praise when he evicted a demon from Nehushta, daughter of King Ahab's second steward. The manner of it was this: he led Nehushta out of the city to Jacob's Well and attached to her nose a ring in which was inserted a virulent herb root. Near the girl's feet he placed a jug of fresh well water. When the demon residing in Nehushta smelled the root, it struggled madly, threw the girl to the ground, and finally abandoned her. Whereupon Ezer pronounced a spell in the name of Solomon, according to the formula the great master had established, and so forbade the demon from re-entering the body of its victim. Then, as a token of obedience, the demon was commanded by Ezer to upset the jug of fresh water, which it accordingly did.

For his prodigies and sanctity Ezer was granted a small holding, near the *souk* of the Damascus merchants, in the newly founded city of Samaria. It is said he aided in the discomfiture and massacre of the false prophets of the Tyrian Baal.

967-901. Adonibaal (probably not his original given name), born in Jericho, the son of a brass-founder. As a lad learned his father's craft, but had no liking for it. Ran away with a passing company of Tyrian ship-builders and Jewish apprentices bound for Ezion-geber, the port of the Arabah. When the ships were built Adonibaal enlisted as a sailor. The voyage lasted nearly three years and its miseries—for the Jewish apprentices and Adonibaal were not expert sailors—seemed eternal. The fleet visited Ophir, Tarshish, and other places equally unknown to Adonibaal. Some of the crew returned moderately rich, with gold, silver, and ivory. Adonibaal brought back four sickly she-apes, and when they died, in Jerusalem, without offspring, his dreams of fortune vanished; and he returned to his father's trade. Married the daughter of a comparatively well-to-do priest of Jehovah and settled in Shechem.

993-930. His father, Elon ben Geber ben Dodo, led an equally fruit-less youth. Born in Bethlehem he joined at an early age the army of

King David; a good soldier but lacking in wits, and although he enlisted in two promising conspiracies, although his tale of enemy foreskins was honorable in number, Elon obtained no advancement. He offered sacrifices to Jehovah, consulted soothsayers, told his dreams to powerful witches, poured libations upon the altar on the hilltop behind his native village, gave a quarter's wages to a priest of Baal, another quarter to a Levite, and six shekels to a community of prophets, lay all one night without the threshold of the sanctuary at Bethel, and seduced his captain's chief wife—to no avail.

His youth was passed when Solomon undertook the building of the Temple; and in resigned bitterness Elon accepted work (procured through the influence of the family) as a puddler in the brass-foundries established by the Tyrians at Jericho.

In his old age he saddled an ass and mounted to Jerusalem to admire the work of his hands. He criticized professionally the brass pillars, the lavers, and the molten sea with its lions, oxen, wreaths, and cherubim. "We would have done better," he insisted to a crowd before a wine shop near the Temple, "if the foreigners had been kept away from the job."

1040-930. Geber ben Dodo, born in Bethlehem, a sheep owner. His brother Elhanan became a valiant, successful soldier, and his name has been preserved among the thirty-seven "mighty men" of his day. His brother Eleazar became a thresher, partner of a Jebusite named Araunah whose property lay before the old Jebusite city; and they sold their threshing-floor for a good sum to King David. His brother Heleb became a scribe, a census officer, and the father of many children. Geber, however, remained in Bethlehem all his life, superintended his herdmen, begat one son, and died of the pestilence brought on by the taking of the census.

1080-1018. His father, Dodo ben Shamma ben Ishma, born in Etam near Bethlehem, and inherited considerable wealth. As he advanced in life his "border became extended," and together with Obed ben Boaz of Bethlehem and Ethnan ben Helah of Tekoa he was recognized as an elder and power in Judah. He owned vineyards near Etam, his flocks grazed the hillsides above Bethlehem, and his laborers cultivated wheat and barley in numerous bottom-lands. Every year he despatched asses down the Vale of Elah laden with the plowshares, goads, pitchforks, and axes of the entire district, to have them sharpened by the expert smiths of the Philistines; and his profits from this operation were considerable.

He was the only man in the country round about who furnished an ass for each of his sons and who possessed his own Levite to offer the sacrifices essential to good crops and rich vintages. His *terebim,* the little household gods which brought the "luck of the year," were the admiration of Ephrata; and his Levite often sacrificed for his neighbors and consulted for them the sacred lots on the time to sow or reap, the choice of a bride, or the whereabouts of a strayed ass—thereby earning for Dodo more than his ten shekels annual wage.

When Dodo made his yearly *haj* or pilgrimage to Shiloh he was signally welcomed by the priests, for in his generosity he was wont to overlook their haste in pronging out for themselves the choicest meat of the sacrifice.

An old man, he was tireless of recalling that he had been a guest of Samuel at the feast given on the hill of Ramathaim, the day an unknown youth, searching for three asses, was given a seat of honor and the whole thigh of a sheep. The climax of the anecdote was always the same: "And next morning Saul was anointed king. Behold, the ways of God are past finding out; for, think now, if Saul had asked my Levite the whereabouts of his asses—and there was every reason he should, for who fails to consult my Levite?—the Levite would have told him, and he never would have come to Ramathaim nor been anointed king."

"So much the better," the villagers would grumble. And they would debate the ways of God until nightfall.

1102-1041. Shamma ben Ishma, small proprietor in Etam. His greatest concern in life was the marriage of his eldest daughter. He could not afford a dowry of a magnitude to offset her plainness, and behind her waited five unmarried sisters. After numerous unsuccessful negotiations with his neighbors, he took his eldest daughter to Shiloh for the feast of Jehovah and instructed her to dance with the daughters of Shiloh in the vineyards. To Shamma's delight, a young Benjamite, intoxicated with dance and wine, abducted the girl—and her five sisters rejoiced equally.

1141-1083. Ishma ben Salman, born in Etam, proprietor of eighty sheep and six acres of vineyards. Lost three sons in the defense of his property against Philistine marauders. In obedience to a scrupulous consultation of an ephod manipulated by the Levite of the village, he despatched a fourth son with the Danites settling in the far north out of Philistinian reach. The fifth son he watched over jealously; and finally secured protection for his family and goods by helping to deliver to the Philistines an unrestrained trouble-maker from Zorah, named Samson.

1185-1129. Salman ben Nahshon inherited thirty sheep and four acres of vineyards near Etam. The vineyards bore little fruit, the sheep did not multiply, and their wool was light. In vain he sacrificed to Jehovah. His neighbors suffered from the same difficulties; and after many consultations they despatched Salman to a neighboring Canaanite village to learn how the Canaanites managed to secure luxuriant vintages and heavy wool.

The Canaanites explained that the Baal of Etam was doubtless angry because the newcomers, the men of Judah, did not sacrifice their first fruits upon his high place. "But we sacrifice upon the high place to our god Jehovah," protested Salman. "Who is your god Jehovah?" asked the Canaanites. "He is the Lord who brought us out of the bondage of Egypt," said Salman. "Where is his home?" asked the Canaanites. "On the mount of Horeb," answered Salman and told them the adventures of the Wilderness.

"Ah," said the Canaanites, "Jehovah is a mountain god, a god of storms and lightning, a god to bring people out of bondage; but he is not a god to grow grapes and thicken the wool of sheep. The Baal of Etam is the god for that. Moreover he is Lord of Etam and you are in Etam; whereas Jehovah is in Horeb which no doubt is very far away. If you will give us of the increase of your wine and wool we will come and show you how to sacrifice properly to the Baal of your land."

So the Canaanites came often to Etam and advised the men of Judah in all the mysteries of the land. The vintages increased, the sheep multiplied, and their wool grew thick. And Salman was held to be a "Judge" in Etam.

1214-1160. His father, Nahshon ben Amminadab, born in Etam, almost with a sword in his hand. Inherited a house which slowly fell to ruin and flocks and vineyards which dwindled yearly. However Nahshon needed little, his wives and children less, and he enjoyed life strutting before the village wall, sharpening his sword and rehearsing the war-like exploits of his ancestors. Occasionally he slipped off with a band of comrades, down the Vale of Elah, and raided the villages of a people called Philistines. He returned laden with iron pots, gold bracelets, and strange objects he could not use. Or he went lion hunting. Died comparatively young from consuming mutton once a week, wild honey daily, and wine at every meal—a diet too rich for his constitution.

1262-1195. His father, Amminadab ben Ram, born in a black camel-hide tent by Kadesh Barnea, in the wilderness south of the Dead Sea. As a child he was a favorite of the camp for his gentle ways. As a youth he practiced daily with spear and javelin in the open space around the standard of Judah. He learned to fight without passion—that is, to be cruel—and to live practically without food. Both of these accomplishments were frequently exercised in the early years of his manhood. He fought and fasted, as the case required, from the desert north to the Arnon; and once traversing its many gullies and streams—gullies hundreds of feet deep and shifting under foot—he won his first taste of booty. A day's fighting under the sun of Heshbon, that cost him no more than a bruised shoulder, brought him six anklets of brass, three young girls but freshly tattooed, a half sheep, and a camel's hide. Amminadab gloried in the pride of conquest and he boasted there was no god gave victory as his.

His eyes shone as he followed the great Leader to the rim of a promontory overlooking the Dead Sea and the Jordan; he gazed in astonishment at the sandy abyss, and in wonder and hope at the distant mountain wall, purple and gold in the rising sun, the wall of the Promised Land. Somewhere behind that wall, there was waiting for him ass's milk, anklets, sheep, honey, hides, and women.

Climbing the gulches of the Arnon was nothing to the grueling ascent of that mountain wall. Amminadab had been made captain of a company lusty as himself, and he boasted to be the first to reach the lip of the plateau. But undoubtedly many were first, the men who took Ai and those who crossed the pass to Gibeon and by Ajalon fought two days in one.

In the end Amminadab received, by lot, a house in Etam and acreage nearby. Three of the conquered villagers were detailed to work for him; he had mutton once a month and wine at his pleasure. But the care of it all, the bickering and hostility of the servants (whom he could not kill, for who then would work?), the cramped unventilated house, the inactive village life became a great burden.

Evenings he stood on the threshing-ground behind the village and looked back across the abyss to the wall of Moab and the desert world, now purple and gold in the sinking sun. A spirit of longing and fear would cross his soul; he was in the Promised Land and he felt big with prophecy. But what could he prophesy?

1289-1231. Ram ben Hezron, born in Pithom, Egypt, in the valley of the Tumilat. He was still an infant when the emigration of his family and tribe took place; and he grew up inured to the hardships of desert life and died of plague in Kadesh Barnea.

1321-1280. His father, Hezron ben Hamul, born likewise in Pithom. Joined the mass emigration of his people in search of new lands and free living conditions. However he was quite unfit for the venture; for the strength of his youth had been sapped by the hard corvées laid upon his tribe. He lacked the endurance to march day after day on scant rations; his worn body craved the stimulus of leeks and onions and its customary nourishment of flesh and fish. When the wanderings became protracted month after month, he was prepared to believe that the leaders had lost their way. He complained for water. He complained at the monotony of that unsubstantial evanescent desert plant which was his sole daily food and which he and his companions in mockery used to call, "What-Is-It?"[5] And for his complaints and miseries he was told by his leaders, he felt in even greater mockery, that he was stiffnecked.

One day a furious windstorm drove a vast flock of quail to ground. Hezron secured five of the birds; and in a pitiful effort to make the meat last, he fed himself on them, bit by bit, for over a fortnight and died from poisoning engendered by their putridity.

1362-1322. Hamul ben Hezron, born in a squalid Israelite village near Pithom. In obedience to the corvée laid upon his tribe, he worked on the construction of vast granaries in Pithom, erected by the Egyptians to forestall the possibility of years of famine. Killed by the fall of a scaffolding.

1409-1350. His father, Hezron ben Zerah, a small tradesman in the Israelite quarter of Pithom. His wife eked out their income by telling fortunes in sand among the Egyptians who frequented the market place.

1448-1392. Zerah ben Shelah, a camel-breeder of the Beni Judah, born in an encampment of the tribe in the plain of Mamre by Kiriath-Arba. For years the tribe grazed their flocks and camel-herds between Kiriath-Arba and Bethsheba, and sold their increase to the Canaanite merchants in the coast cities and to the caravans constantly going to and from Egypt. Then a period of bad crops set in, grazing grew poor, no one had the means to buy camels; and the tribe, following the caravans, emigrated south to the land of Goshen (now the valley of the Tumilat) in Egypt.

1487-1421. His father, Shelah ben Er, likewise a camel-breeder, born

[5] *Manna?*—in the Hebrew

in an encampment in the valley below Shechem. As the father of many children Shelah possessed a voice in tribal affairs. Partly on his advice the tribe enriched themselves by the sack of Shechem.

1522-1473. Er ben Perez, a tribesman of the Beni Judah, expert in the treatment of sick camels. When his ancestral tribe, the Beni Israel, became too numerous for their grazing fields in the Hauran, Er, because of his skill, was invited to join the clan of Judah recently organized for the search of new pastures.

1568-1499. Perez ben Zerah, grazer of the Beni Israel, born in the plains of Padan-Aram. His life, like that of his son and his father, was bounded by his sheep and goats and camels. While he was rolling the stone from the mouth of a well, it fell and crushed his foot, and he died of gangrene poisoning.

1609-1542. Zerah ben Er, a tribesman of the Beni Israel, renowned for his skill in bargaining with the caravan merchants. His fame in this direction was transmitted by his descendants, as well as that of other shrewd bargainers of the tribe, especially in their dealings with Edom, because on the whole his tribesmen were simple-minded and innocent in trading.

1641-1575. Er ben Perez, twentieth son of his father, by origin a Terahite, but later associated with the newly formed, dependent clan of Beni Israel.

1689-1603. Perez, head of a large family in the tribe of the Beni Terah, and, as he claimed, the great-great grandson of Abram ben Terah.

He possessed two hundred sheep, three hundred and fifty goats, sixty camels, five concubines, and three wives. His children, six of whom died young, numbered forty-nine; and in time their wealth nearly doubled his own.

Perez cherished many stories of his illustrious ancestor, whom he represented as beloved by Elohim and men. "Abram," said Perez, "one day approached his father, who was a camel-merchant in Ur of Chaldea, and announced that he intended to breed camels in the pastures of Syria, found a family, and create a heritage for his children. 'Our race is worn out,' replied Terah, 'and I am sure you will fail. Ur is so old; we are all so old; the generations of men are near their end.' But Elohim appeared to Abram, called him 'Abraham,' and promised he should be the father of many children."

When in his old age Perez was told of the birth of his ninetieth grandson, he gathered his sons around him, drew his *cafiyah* about his face, and said, "The word of Elohim has already been fulfilled; it is time for me to die . . . But the heritage that Abram sought, to give to our children—is it these camels, these sheep, these goats? My sons, seek you the heritage of our father, Abram ben Terah."

F OUR CORNERS OF THE EARTH

Since the earliest days of his historical career the Jew has made the world his home, and, as Zangwill shrewdly noted, his story depicts "the most remarkable survival of the fittest known to humanity." The Fathers of the Jewish people were themselves wanderers and their descendents kept the remembrance of it alive, not only in the national literature, but also in the declaration, "A nomad Syrian was my father." The migrations of the Jews throughout the ages is one of the most impressive facts of history. They are an index of the rise and fall of empires, of the growth and decay of economic structures, of the existence and absence of social equality. The wandering Jew is neither historical myth nor theological fiction. He is a measuring rod of society.

The perennial dispersion of the Jewish people had enormous consequences, for the Jew came to new lands as merchant, colonist, refugee, expatriate and adventurer. More than two hundred years ago, Addison neatly phrased a truth in *The Spectator*. The Jews, he pointed out, "are like the pegs and nails in a great building, which though they are little valued in themselves, are absolutely necessary to keep the whole frame together." And when he commented that through them "mankind are knit together in a general correspondence" he hit upon a fact that inevitably follows: A people whose home is the world would naturally create universal ideas and visions. As the first internationality, the Jews evolved the earliest conception of the unity of mankind and of the world.

Today, even more so than in the past, the Jews are a world people. Their total population—about sixteen millions—is greater than it has ever been, and their residence is more widespread throughout the habitable world. Centralized authority, which existed until the tenth century, and religious and social unity, which prevailed until the day before yesterday, are no longer present. A rapid glance at the picture of Jews in the sociological studies of Fishberg and Ruppin proves incontrovertibly that the Jewish "type" is as much a fiction as the Jewish "race."

The selections in this section present, in brief compass, the panorama of contemporary Jews and Jewries. Where can one find greater diversity in a living historic group? Medieval saintliness and credulity side by side with modern sophistication and cynicism; indescribable ghetto misery stalks behind brittle gold-coast luxury; winged utopians akin in spirit to impassioned realists. And the globe is their arena,—smug Samson in England, disillusioned Mr. Kahn in France, hopeful Bodana in the Soviet Union, a reflective wanderer in Palestine, adamant Saul in South Africa, pathetic Uncle Petacovsky in the Argentine. . . .

Here, too, one may observe the effects of modern life upon Jews and their inherited culture. Industrialism, nationalism and socialism have transformed the Jew as they have other peoples. The varied transformations are, by implication, present in the collective portrait that the following group of stories offer.

THE HAUNTED CINEMA

by LOUIS GOLDING

THE incident I am about to relate concerning Kravest and the cinema there, and the Strange Thing that befell that cinema, I should not myself believe had it taken place outside the limits of the province of Bessarabia; had it taken place, in fact, anywhere but in Kravest itself. I should probably not have shaken off my drowsiness to listen to Reb Laibel at all, had not the sainted syllables of Kravest fallen from his lips.

It was the dusk of the Sabbath, when the greybeards gather in the side-room of the synagogue and tell stories of Eastern Europe, punctuating their memories with subtle quotation or complex analogy. And as Red Laibel wound like a stream from meadow to meadow of his story, you would have thought that the country he had left three or four months ago was somehow immortally enwalled from our modern age. Until, with a pronunciation I dare not transcribe, he spoke of a cinema—spoke of it, moreover, with no less heat than his Hebrew compatriots must have spoken of Torquemada. And then it was that I heard the name of Kravest, Kravest and its sanctities, and I shook myself and listened.

For my father used frequently to speak of Kravest. It was to him a sort of Hesperides, and its golden apples were the Scrolls of the Law. The earlocks of the old men in Kravest hung down to their jawbones. The wigs of the married women were prompt and lustrous. Little boys could repeat by heart the whole Pentateuch. Babes had insisted upon fasting throughout the Day of Atonement. It was stated—and my father, for one, would not contravert the report—that one year, when the festivities of Simchas Torah were completed and Rabbi Avrom, with his flock of revellers, trooped from the synagogue of the "Godly Brethren," he had ordered the moon to perform a circle four times round a certain star, once for each wall of Paradise—and the moon had obeyed him. So the whole company swore, and who dared question it? And such was the holiness of Kravest that even the Gentiles of that town had been touched with the surf of her holy tides. It was not unknown that certain of them had been seen, on the Feast of the Tabernacles, to shake the palm and reverse the citron as the old Jews passed with them on their way to the "Godly Brethren."

Such, then, was Kravest. Had a cinema come this way? O dolorous event! And this was how it came to pass, as I learned it from the lips of Reb Laibel. Reb Avrom—peace be upon him!—had gone to his rest, and though his successor at the "Godly Brethren," Reb Zcharyah, had as much erudition—if that were humanly possible—as he, he had not the same strength of character, the same faculty for prophetic invective against any least transgression of the Law. This it was which had given their chance to the three principal merchants of the town, Reb Yankel, Reb Shtrom, and Reb Ruven. There was no doubt that they had long been working subterraneously to get the synagogue into their own hands, but they had never dared to emerge into the awful light of Reb Avrom's eyes. One flicker of that inspired eyelid and you saw them scuttle into their burrows with a shaking of timid abdomen and a flash of white tail. But the combination of the weak amiability of Reb Zcharyah with a certain deal in roubles which was little to their credit and much to their profit gave them their opportunity. A bribed and hectored majority elected them to the three positions of office and Reb Shtrom became the *parnass,* Reb Yankel and Reb Ruven the *gabboim,* of the synagogue.

Before very long rumors were abroad in Kravest that the new officers were convinced that the "Godly Brethren" was far too big and expensive a building for its purpose. It was stated that the upkeep of the establishment was robbing the children and widows. It was too near the centre of the town not to suffer a Gentile corruption. It could not be doubted that the barn-like building near the river, on the outskirts of the town, would be more satisfactory as a synagogue from every point of view.

There is no time to enter into the historic battle that raged in Kravest. With a sinking of the heart I narrate only that the "Godly Brethren" removed to the riverside, and the old building itself was sold to an anonymous syndicate who converted it (if I am interpreting Reb Laibel's curious accent aright) into the "Grand Cinéma de Paris." The "Godly Brethren" became a shadow of itself; for, whilst Reb Zcharyah, with pale and haunted eyes, entrenched himself deeper and deeper into the fortresses of his intricate and unworldly scholarship, its three officers paid less and less attention to its physical organisation. Some of the most valued and venerable old men had not the energy to drag themselves there three times a day. Some of the young men set out for the "Godly

Brethren," but were entrapped by the cinema *en route*. Ichabod! The glory was departed! And the material state of Reb Shtrom, Reb Yankel, and Reb Ruven, for no explicit reason, became more and more prosperous. They were not seen to be particularly industrious on the money-changing market. Reb Yankel gave up his flour-mill entirely. All three spent their mornings together drinking *schnaps* and playing cards. Yet their fortunes seemed to expand as under a personal and private sun.

And then God intervened. So said Reb Laibel, drawing his fingers through the thickets of his long yellow beard. And so the others repeated as the miracle was unfolded in the thickening dusk. It must be understood that no special provision of films was made for the cinema at Kravest. Chaplin and Gable were the heroes of Kravest as they are the heroes of Los Angeles. A month or six weeks passed in which the transports of the degenerating Jewry of Kravest knew no intermission. Gallop and gallop went the horses over the prairies! Crackle and crash went the crockery in the ineffably comic restaurants! And then a calamitous film was displayed. The scene was a very expensive hotel in New York. The viands were of the most wealthy and the most profane order. But when none other than Reb Ruven was seen to be helping himself to a liberal share of milk-pudding after several courses of meats—damnable and most damnable juxtaposition!—conceive the state of mind of the audience at Kravest! There was no room for doubt. The familiar twisted nose of Reb Ruven, the scar below the upper lip, came nearer and nearer to the camera. A howl of execration was heard. But not so formidable as the howl which rent the roof of the cinema two weeks later, when Reb Yankel, in the costume of an English labourer, his corduroy trousers tied with string below the knees and stuffed into a monstrous pair of boots, was seen to be feeding a large sow in her sty and fondling one after another of her litter of sucklings. Walking-sticks hurtled through the air, seats groaned and split. In vain did Reb Yankel plead an alibi. In vain he urged that he never had set foot an inch beyond Kravest, as all the world knew. It was the hand of God, said Kravest, the hand of God!

The climax came a week later. The film displayed a scene which may well have been Hampstead Heath. Three pairs of figures, male and female, appeared on the horizon. Closer and closer they came—Reb Shtrom and Reb Yankel and Reb Ruven—and closer the Gentile hussies on their arms. (The crowd was roaring like a sea.) Then the three couples sat under the shade of a chestnut; then their lips . . .

But there was a sudden shrill cry, a hissing and whirring, and at the moment that the cinematograph was flung to the ground, with a great rip the screen was torn from the beams. For the Above One, said Reb Laibel, who shall understand His ways?

And the "Godly Brethren" returned to their temple, after a solemn purification, and piety came back to Kravest, and as for Reb Shtrom, Reb Ruven, and Reb Yankel, may the Black Wind, said Reb Laibel, uproot their hair in tufts!

SAFE HARBOUR

by G. B. STERN

SAMSON for the fourth time proposed to Deb. She accepted him.

After the first interview, it was easy. She had only to be passive; or to smooth down any little creases in her texture that she perceived could still cause him uneasiness. That first interview was her greatest performance. She blended timid womanly solicitude with that type of earnest frankness in big and little things, which was to be interpreted—by him—as the outcome of an inner consciousness of once having failed greatly in moral steadfastness and the resolve never again to be betrayed into so doing. She thought his intelligence could be trusted to perceive that much sublety, unaided. He did perceive it. And approved. He approved also of her confusion at his jocular reference to the forget-me-not stream. "Don't tell me you went down there alone to pick forget-me-nots?" "Oh, but I did. I wouldn't—" she stopped. And hastily asked him how he liked his tea. "Wouldn't go with any other man." . . . Samson smiled under his moustache. So that special glide of silver beneath the plank bridge, had associations for her, too. Good! he liked sentiment in girls. He was a sentimental chap himself, but in his case it was sheathed in sternness. He was a soldier—and she was a sinner. . . . Never let him forget that.

She never let him forget it. Not once in the prescribed hour. Intuition pointed out that it was labour lost to try and make him forget. Therefore he must be brought to forgive.

"So Delilah has been shorn instead of Samson? That's poetic justice, isn't it?" Then, chaffing no more: "What made you cut your hair, Deb? I don't like it. It's like those artist-model girls you see about. I hoped you'd go on arranging it the way Beattie did it for you, once. It suited you."

"But it took so long," Deb explained. And further, in an outburst of confidence: "It was stupid of me—I'm sorry now. But—it was just a mood—one evening, when I had to dash off to the canteen—and it *would* keep on flopping down after I'd pinned it up . . . and it seemed to me there was so much to do in the world just now, besides one's hair—so much to do and so little time to do it in—And . . . oh, I lost my temper with and just sheared it off. Does it look hideous?"

He studied her in silence. And his face turned red and his eyes slowly kindled. . . .

"Not that it matters. Vanity is rather futile since the war, isn't it? But one can't help minding being a fright. . . ."

"You're not a fright, little girl," said Samson Phillips.

And then Nell slipped back inconspicuously into the room, and said it was time to go.

Otto Redbury had rubbed his hands with pleasure when Samson, via Beatrice, had made known his wish for Nell's attendance at the hospital between three and four on Wednesday afternoon.

"So! it gomes to something, then!" and he inspected Nell before her departure, and gave her five shillings for a taxi, that she might arrive unheated and unruffled. The taxi had stopped at La llorraine's, to pick up Deb, but this Otto did not know. Deb was very glad to arrive at the hospital unheated and unruffled. And Nell was very glad to spend the stray half-hour walking beside Timothy, whom Deb had notified to be accidentally outside the gates at that hour of the day. This Otto did not know either. Not that he could have gained much by prying on their dialogue, for the pair were still in that stage of dreamy ecstasy which prefers not to speak, in addition to their handicap of excessive shyness.

"Soon, zere vill be a vedding at the Synagogue," Otto prophesied to Trudchen. But Trudchen, who had lost one of her boys, had no happiness for the moment in either of her girls.

Otto was right in form but not in detail. A wedding did indeed take place on October the 12th, and Nell was bridesmaid; and the bride was given away by her father; and Otto for the look of things had to be coaxed out of the bathroom by his united family, and coaxed into a frock-coat, and coaxed into attendance as a guest. Otto's soul was very bilious, and he objected to paying for a present, and made several quite snappy and spiteful remarks concerning the folly of men who married a girl whose certificate of chastity bore a black mark and the scrawled name of Mr. Cliffe Kennedy. . . .

"Ach, Otto!"

Samson was aware of the enormity of such a choice. Aware, too, that he would have great difficulty with his family, who were still huffy with Deb for having dared to refuse Samson on three previous occasions. So he did an unprecedented thing—he proposed first, and consulted his family afterwards. Perhaps "proposed" is not the term which exactly sets forth his proceedings. He announced to Deb that he was willing to make her his wife—nay, that he considered it his duty to draw her from the gutter back to the pavement. Deb—who in spite of some deep inner scoldings that she was again behaving disgracefully towards Samson, and this time worse even than before—Deb stood before him with eyes downcast and folded hands, meek and wan—and wildly exhilarated by her success. She had, to quote La llorraine: "Made a muff from her chances" so often and so disastrously that a great deal of previous anxiety was inevitable. Anxiety was now allayed. She stood before her master, meek and wan, and exceedingly desirable: Israelite maiden in the slave-market. . . . Samson kissed her very carefully to show that his respect had suffered no diminishment. (He was so continually showing her this in all sorts of unobtrusive ways that Deb only now realized to what extent her lie of last year had earned his undying censure.) Samson kissed her carefully—and said, "My family will be pleased about this, Deb."

For which she rather liked him.

The family, of course, reminded him in an appalled chorus that Deb was—somewhat disreputable. Had she not run away from home, to live with that opera-woman? Samson replied inflexibly that they, by their contempt and reproach, might be responsible for driving a poor little girl to worse things.

"What worse things are there?" his grandmother demanded, for the rest of them.

Samson merely shrugged; and opposition perceived that the eldest son of the house of Phillips had chosen, and would not be swerved from his choice. His glucose fidelity was impressive. Samson was the Phillips' fetish, and Samson's wish the Phillips' law. Moreover, there remained still the Phillips' illusion that Deb had always loved Samson, had loved him all through his three proposals last Autumn, and must—poor child—have suffered terribly, refusing him. Certainly she deserved to suffer. But by this chance of making Samson happy, she might expiate her foolishness, and expiate it still more in giving Samson a fine healthy son. . . . So the many counsels in the dining-room of Mrs. Phillips resolved at last on a program of bounteous welcome, forgive and forget.

Deb, foreseeing complications, made more than one faltering attempt to explain privately to her fiancé exactly how the quaint mistake about her premature initiation had occurred. . . . But it was an impossible task. At each successive essay, Samson interrupted at the very start and in his well-known style: "I don't want to hear a word about it, Deb. It's all over and it's all forgotten. Let's turn over a fresh leaf and agree never to mention it again. I love you, and you know it, and nothing makes any difference, and I simply don't want to hear another word about it."

So she gave in. She was the flame, he was the extinguisher that stands beside the candle. However ardent her whim to burn, he could always put her out.

Ferdie Marcus was enraptured at the betrothal. It was what he had always desired for his little daughter—everyone was prefixing Deb with "little" just now—a good protector; a Jew; a husband in a solid position, both financially and—nowadays this was important—in point of nationality. He would never be quite healed of the unlooked-for wound dealt him by this same little daughter, last year; and he was rather puzzled as to how that affair had been glossed over where Samson was concerned. Did Samson know? But he hid both the scar and the perplexity; and without any formal reconciliation, it was understood that she had slipped into re-occupation of her old place in the home—home in the abstract and not literal sense; for she did not return to live at Montagu Hall. Neither Grandfather nor Aunt Stella were sufficiently cordial at the prospect; and Samson did not care either about the boarding-house. For the present he made special arrangement that she should stay with the Redburys—Beattie and Hardy. She should be married from his mother's house, and as he was to be discharged from hospital in a month's time, the wedding could quite well be arranged for October. In fact ("I'm a sentimental chap!") he asked Deb, with a twinkle of meaning in his eye, whether October the 12th would suit her? Just in time to prevent her features from slipping into utter blankness, she remembered that this might be the anniversary of the silvery-stream business, and replied with a pretty smile, that she thought October the 12th would be . . . nice.

"Will there be time to let your hair grow before then?" he teased her. "We can't have a bride with short hair. . . ."

The whole Phillips family had pounced, jabbering and shrieking and with white teeth all aflash in their olive faces, on the discovery that Delilah and not Samson had been shorn. Deb was prepared for this, and constant repetition of the joke did not afflict her in the measure of last year. The Phillips were themselves a joke, and her engagement, and Samson, and Otto Redbury sulking in the bathroom on the occasion of her formal visit on the arm of her fiancé; and the fact that she must ostentatiously refuse ever to meet Cliffe Kennedy again . . . all a joke! That was her mood, and it was not once interpierced. She saw very little of her old set during her engagement—very little of Gillian and Antonia and Zoe. All that had dropped away like a whirl of sparks in the forgotten night.

The sense of a hilarious joke followed her to the very porch of the Synagogue, pursued her through the ceremony, with its gabble of Hebrew and wonderful song. It prodded her midway in the fatherly old Rabbi's personal benediction, when he solemnly addressed Samson in these terms: "You are bearing away to a typically Jewish home a typically Jewish treasure. . . ." Deb felt irresistibly impelled to drop her eyelids and murmur deprecatingly: "Oh, no . . ." and Samson patted her arm reassuringly. . . .

And then the joke faded . . . for the old man spoke directly to her, and made her feel suddenly that at last she belonged; that this was her faith, and these her people; and that standing here under the white canopy, she was really fulfilling her destiny at last—the destiny for which Deb Marcus had been primarily shaped and intended. After all, she had not been able to achieve free adventure—and compromise was a poor substitute. It was kind of Jehovah to have guided her from debatable ground to safety.

And she would cease from baffling and bamboozling Samson, who was high-principled and faithful. What had she made out of her loose-jointed set of values, to enable her to scoff at his? Deb was now full to the brim of her being with contrition and clear sweetness and gratitude. . . . A few yards away Ferdie was beaming happily—Dear old dad— and she had been such a beast, blaming him for all her own freakish behaviour. And there was Richard, scowling a little self-consciously in his endeavour to appear absolutely at ease—all Samson's brothers were already married and ineligible for the office of best man, which devolved therefore upon Richard . . . brows hunched over eyes that were wonderfully at peace. Six weeks ago, he had looked like a man of thirty; now he looked what he was—a sturdy well-blocked-out pugnacious youngster of seventeen. It was all right—Deb had spoken to Samson about him, and Samson had spoken to his cousin Sir Ephraim Phillips, who had promised when the time of internment drew actually near, to interest himself, not only to the extent of (certainly) getting Richard off, but furthermore to get him (perhaps) into the fighting line somewhere. So Richard's state was that of a parched creature who had sighted water to slake his thirst. . . .

All the same, it was no joke being responsible for the ring and the fees—and the carriages and—and half-a-dozen other things. It rendered a properly nonchalant bearing impossible. And he had made a bad beginning by the reverent removal of a sleek silk hat from a sleek bullet head, directly on entrance . . . five bearded gentlemen draped in black had made a rush at him and besought him to replace his hat upon his head.

His eyes met his sister's in a swift comprehending glance. "Sure it's all right, Deb—for you, I mean?" "Quite, quite sure, old boy!" the unspoken question and answer between them.

The glass was set in the neighbourhood of Samson's foot, and he ground it vindictively into powder. His mother at the reception afterwards, called all her friends and relatives to bear witness with what spirit he had performed this part of the ritual. It was fortunate that she did not overhear David Redbury's remark to the effect that Samson had not only used all the energy which his great prototype had expended on the pillars of the temple, to crush one small wine-glass; but had then further deviated from Biblical history by inviting the Philistines home with him to champagne and iced cake. . . .

"Oh, hush, David!" from Nell.

"Well—look at us!" Israel was indeed enormously represented. The rooms glimmered and glittered with the clan Phillips. Already they owned Deb ("little Deb"); swarmed about her in heavy, jocular proprietorship; bore her triumphantly away to be robed for the honeymoon journey.

Mr. and Mrs. Samson Phillips left at 4.30, *en route* for Torquay.

.   .   .   .

"Why did you ever tell me that falsehood?"

"I—I don't know, Samson. What falsehood?"

"You do know, Deb."

"I don't know why I told it, Samson."

"You've always been a good girl." It was a statement, not a query. A statement weighted with perplexity.

And; "Yes . . ." she assented, "I've always been a good girl."

He was not so joyfully illuminated as might have been expected. Indeed, he was conscious of being defrauded of an essential occupation. He had married Deb, forgiving her. He had meant to go on forgiving her. He would never stop forgiving her. Now, in place of these anticipations, was a vacuum. . . .

THE APPARITION

by ARNOLD ZWEIG

TELL me a story!—that's easy to say. These mountains bring back almost too vivid memories of blessed, happy days when I was as carefree as a colt and of those others when I was preparing myself for the task (or was it preparing itself for me?) that, for the time being, I hold in abeyance yet dare not interrupt. But as my eyes trouble me and I cannot, just now, enjoy the flights of fancy of others in the delightful pursuit of reading, I must, for better or worse, pass my leisure time in telling stories.

It happened during the coldest part of winter in the eastern Carpathians. This is a country of mountains that rise abruptly from the plains, and of heavy-coated browsing sheep; little hamlets, villages, and farms dot the plain, divided from each other by tongues of woodland slipping down the mountainside, and by fields wrested, ages ago, from the stark Slovak soil. This region lies far away—fully four hundred years! Miracles, saints, and demons still remain familiar phenomena there while fear, superstitious fear, is felt—and perhaps rightly so—only towards government officials, newspapers, machinery, the telephone, and the radio.

The inhabitants are without exception religious. The Jews believe in the Jewish lore, the Slovaks in the Christian, literally and reverently, and they carry on the customs their fathers have handed down to them in writing and by word of mouth. They are also very poor in that region, the Slovakian peasants a little less so, the Jews a little more, and these two are dependent upon each other, inevitably and by turns, as in the good fable of the lion and the mouse.

In this state of poverty and intense cold, Rifke Leah left her cottage early one winter's evening and went into the woods where the snow lay deep and undisturbed. Rifke Leah carried a short spade and, arriving at a familiar spot near the edge of the wood which seemed shielded from prying eyes, she busily began to shovel away the snow and to break up the ice beneath to cleanse herself. She shivered as she cowered and washed herself in the crystal-clear, crystal-cold water which came down from the mountains under a crust of ice and which, suddenly freed of its coverlet, steamed as it came in contact with the warmer air—but she shivered chiefly because she feared someone might pass by and surprise her.

It was early evening, the moon was still low and yellow, but bright wintry stars were shining through the bare branches. . . . Then, as she had divined, she suddenly heard—a short distance away—the voices of some peasants taking a short-cut through the woods from the village tavern to their homes. Merciful God—men! They have been drinking, they are singing—good-natured men but ready for pranks when in liquor. She represses her cry of alarm, throws her skirt over her head so that no one recognizes her, and dashes, or rather glides, silently homeward through the snow under the light of the pale golden moon—a mysterious figure, swathed in white. Rifke Leah succeeds in eluding them; trembling, with beating heart, she makes a detour around the tavern and reaches her cottage a few minutes later.

Meanwhile the three peasants stood mutely beside the dark water, which had miraculously thawed in the midst of the snow and which was still steaming. What had they witnessed? A lovely, white form had floated away amid the trees; it must have been the Holy Mother of God come to assure the village of a better harvest. In their greatest need came heavenly kindness—take off your hats: a miracle has happened here in the midst of the snowy desolation of the forest. Indeed, the vapours were still rising like incense before their eyes! They corroborate each other—they have seen the Holy Mother of God, white and lovely, float away amid the trees.

The next morning and especially on the following Sunday they eagerly told of the miracle whose scene they had hastily marked by sticking branches into the snow around the pool of water. They had not neglected to cross themselves, kneel down, and thank the Mother of God for her visit.

The women and many people in distress made their way to the spot, which was frozen over again and covered with snow. One of the faithful hung a picture of the miraculous visitor and her Divine Child on the nearest tree, paper flowers from the church came next, then a little shed was built to protect the picture from the rain. Devout peasants and townsfolk, in ever-increasing numbers, made pilgrimages thither. The priests, hearing of it and being simple folk like the others, saw no reason to doubt a miracle that had already brought joy, solace, and cure from small ailments to so many of the faithful.

Spring came early that year; warm sunlight flooded the fields which peasants—cheered by the promise of the Queen of Heaven—were confidently tilling with their teams. The Jews had also, in due course, heard of the forest shrine. Oddly enough, Rifke Leah and her husband were the first to know its exact site. "Benjamin always was wide awake," the Jews said, and followed his lead. When the warm weather set in, he and his wife sold bread, wafers, biscuits, lemonade, and candles to the pilgrims.

The following autumn, after an abundant harvest, the foundations of a chapel commemorating the blessed visit of the Mother of God were laid. Before the winter began, the Bishop of Kosice came for the dedication. Not without heavy misgivings had he listened to the remarks of the local clergy, remarks which at first seemed harmless enough but which gradually came to reflect an urgent desire of the people. Many paths led to salvation and none should be carelessly disregarded, nor was this the time to ignore spiritual needs because of mental snobbishness. A miracle must have occurred; people believed it and it was working.

He visualized the brown, weatherbeaten faces of the peasants, their eyes opened wide in wonder; if he questioned and cross-questioned them as to what they had actually seen, they would insist it had been the Mother of God floating away through the wintry forest—nothing else. They had found the warm, dewy pool sending vapours into the night— nothing else. Let sceptics jeer, make insinuations, offer explanations of all sorts—he, the bishop, would be unworthy of shepherding these souls, if, through fear of fostering a delusion, he refused to bestow upon the scene of the apparition the dignity of official as well as spiritual consecration. He came; he stood before them simply and gravely, chanting praises in Latin and asking God's blessing upon the land and the simple faith of these country people.

For Kosice, far off in the east of Europe, is also some hundreds of yards behind the times. It isn't so long ago that bloody battles were fought there with gipsies who had made savoury meals of human flesh. The Jews of that region, when they are among themselves, say to each other that it is only fair that their trade, especially that with pilgrims, has so greatly improved.

Benjamin, Rifke Leah's husband, occasionally drinks a glass too much. That is why he happened to be so communicative to an eminent scholar and politician who came there a year later from the capital city of Prague to tell the Jews how and why they should vote. It was he— he clung to the ancient traditions of his land and people with tender mockery—who sometimes told this story, not to sneer at the incident but to characterize these distant people and places, where even today the Middle Ages are alive in human hearts. He possessed a sympathetic understanding of the sincerity and simple piety as well as of the humour and gentle roguishness of this tale. That is why I have retold it—at leisure, beneath green trees, surrounded by green mountains, facing the blue heavens, which we strange creatures so frequently fashion into figments of our own childish desires so that our dreams, fears, and hopes may be as much a part of them as the fleecy clouds and may pass as they do.

THE CASE OF AGATHON GEYER

by JAKOB WASSERMANN

THE boys were talking and shouting in the laboratory. As the teacher entered, they fell silent and rose to their feet. The benches were arranged in the form of an amphitheater, and cupboards containing minerals were affixed to the walls. On the long table lay retorts, burners, test-tubes, crucibles, perforated zinc, bottles and capsules. Shortly after the lesson had begun, the headmaster came in; he handed Boyesen an exercise-book, and said gravely: "You are Agathon Geyer's form master. Read this, and come to my room in an hour's time." He nodded indulgently and went out.

Boyesen went to his private room, which smelt strongly of chlorine. On the cover of the exercise-book were the words: "Agathon Geyer: German Essays." Boyesen turned over the pages of the last essay, which had been set by the headmaster. The subject was: What school should mean to the pupil. At first he read indifferently. The writing was bad, indistinct and feverish; the letters seemed to fall over each other, to stumble insensibly along, then one seemed to stand up rigidly, calling a halt to its fellows, but nothing could stem the general panic. Boyesen read with growing surprise, shook his head, flushed, turned pale, and, when he reached the end, he put his hand to his head, nodded miserably and began to read it through again. This time he read more thoughtfully, with growing amazement at the clear and almost poetic form the boy's ardent soul had created.

"School," so ran the essay, "should open the doors of life to us. It should help us to grow up courageous and yet aware of the dangers that beset us. It should mold us into capable and high-minded men. It should train us to love our teachers, and they in their turn should teach us to love life, our future calling, our fellow-men, the great figures of the past, noble ideas, the joys of friendship and communion with Nature. Our teachers should be superior to us. They should meet us with affection, and so make us happy. But is this the case? Does school prepare us for our work in the world? When we leave school, do we know what we ought to become, instead of merely what we are? School makes us a receptacle for information that is and remains dead. Our minds do not develop harmoniously. Nature and life are a dead letter to us, and we shall never comprehend their message. You are to blame for this, and I charge you with it. Why do the teachers never think of the minds of their pupils, but only of what they have learned? Why are we always regarded as geese to be fattened, and abused when we cannot go on feeding? Why do we fear or despise our teachers instead of loving them? You are the boys' enemies and that is why you spy out their weaknesses; you sit there at your desks, and are more like books than living men. The lessons you teach have grown lifeless, because you are bored with them. Why are you so arrogant, looking down upon us from your heights, making us feel so small? Too arrogant even to explain to us the most serious thing in life! Why do you not reveal to us the mystery of birth? Why is that never done at school in spite of so many opportunities? How much purer the boys' minds would be! Now they make it all beastly, giggling and winking and blushing when they read a poem, even searching the Bible for such passages. Now they are always full of dirty secrets. Is not this terrible? This is why they have no respect for people or things, why the whole world becomes something foul and indecent for them. They do things it almost makes one mad to think of, yet the teachers never notice them. Why do not the teachers prevent this? Why? Why do you sit at your desks, cut off from us as though by a high wall? Your pupils can never become happy men, and you are to blame for this, with your cold, icy hearts. On going out into life, we have first to forget you, to forget your school and your hardheartedness. Perhaps when we have done that we may become firm and strong, but happy?—Never! I had to write this and now my mind is relieved. An irresistible voice within me demanded it."

Boyesen's lips were quivering; his hands and his body were trembling. A feeling had been released within him of which he was ashamed; he was jealous of the noble and innocent courage which thus proclaimed the truth. He was so deeply moved that there seemed to be a veil between his eyes and the room where he was sitting. The ten o'clock bell rang outside and he went to dismiss his class. Then he walked through the corridor, came to a tall window and looked down into the playground, which was enclosed on all sides by walls and houses. He studied the crowd of boys, who were rushing about with wild shouts, but there was no sign of a sense of freedom, of youth and freshness. Yes, he could see it with his own eyes; these were the shouts of prisoners whose chains had been loosed. It was the convulsive joy of the conscript on a Sunday, when he forgets his home, his nostalgia and his barracks. These were not the young men who could serve the future, these boys with dark shadows round their eyes, with haggard cheeks, with cynical, brutal, joyless shrieks of laughter, with dull glances and ungainly movements. This type of human being could not last; he saw it himself.

As he walked on, he caught sight of Agathon, who was standing alone, leaning against a pillar. When Agathon saw him, he turned slowly away and went into his classroom. Boyesen followed him—the room was empty—and shut the door. Agathon turned deathly pale and closed his eyes, as though he were in pain. Boyesen took him by the hand, laid his right hand on Agathon's shoulder and looked at him fixedly. Then he stroked Agathon's hair, soothingly, caressingly, and never before or since did Agathon experience a sense of happiness so unearthly, so boundless, so joyous. The struggle of life that lay before him seemed easy to cope with, and the whole school, the very benches, seemed laden with happiness. He understood what Boyesen meant; he knew the significance of that caressing hand.

A quarter of an hour later he was called to the headmaster.

The teachers were gathered in a large five-cornered room. All wore a solemn expression and bore themselves like men fully conscious of their office and their responsibilities. They stared at Agathon with expressions of surprise, derision, reproach or hauteur. The cantor from the local synagogue, who gave religious instruction to the Jewish boys, wore an expression so grim and horrified that no one could look at him without feeling himself a criminal.

The headmaster turned slowly on his revolving chair and the cold glare of his deep-set eyes bored its way into Agathon's brain. "How did you come to write this—shall we say impertinent?—essay, this pamphlet —if I may use the word?"

The cantor attempted to interrupt, but the headmaster waved him aside with a dignified gesture, and went on in a louder voice: "I ask how you came to forget in such a monstrous fashion the respect you owe to your teachers? I believe, gentlemen, that we have here a case of extreme depravity. This boy is already slipping down the steep path of vice. He is a regrettable example of the moral level to which the youth of our town has sunk, and in such a case we must proceed with the utmost severity of which we are capable; the punishment must be exemplary."

The headmaster had risen, the whole room was quivering with the sound of his ringing voice; it seemed to Agathon that his tones must pass through the walls and be heard in every house in the town.

Again the cantor tried to speak, and again the headmaster silenced him with a wave of his hand. "I confess," he went on, "that a case of such depravity has never come within my experience. Let us hope, for the honor of this school, that it never will again. Geyer, when did you write this odious composition?"

"Yesterday, sir."

"Speak up!"

Agathon was silent.

"Speak up!"

"Yesterday. I did speak up, sir."

"And why did you do it?" thundered the headmaster, almost bursting with rage.

"I did it to help make the boys happier and better."

"That is an infamous lie!" roared the headmaster, furiously.

"It is true," returned Agathon, quietly.

"You vile creature!" grated the headmaster, giving the word a crushing intonation.

The cantor could restrain himself no longer. He stepped forward, crossed his arms on his chest, threw back his head and said in a sharp but unctuous voice, while his body swayed from side to side: "Who are you? Have you forgotten the Name of God? Have you forgotten your pious father's honor? Are you not a burden to yourself? Are you a

Jew, or are you not? I reject you; I ban you from the community of the righteous; I break my staff upon you."

"No, I am a Jew no longer," said Agathon, with a strange smile, still retaining the tranquillity which had hitherto distinguished him. The teachers looked up, dismayed, and shook their heads. Boyesen's head was bowed. He had sat down and his white hands lay motionless on his knees.

"Here you have a final proof of his dangerous wickedness, gentlemen," said the headmaster, contemptuously. "An obstinate, godless, irreligious character. You can go, Geyer."

Agathon went. Outside, a great weakness suddenly overcame him and he sank down on the stairs. He heard a low but firm voice from the room behind him. It was Boyesen. This voice went on speaking for some time, then suddenly the headmaster began to bellow in a wilder tone than Agathon had ever heard him use. Immediately afterwards the door opened and Boyesen came out alone. He saw Agathon and signed to him to follow.

When they reached the chemistry master's private room, Boyesen shut the door. "I understand your impulse," he said, in a strained voice. "I can respect it, though on this occasion it was utterly useless. But how did you come to do it? It calls for determination to trample your own future underfoot."

Agathon sat trembling on the edge of a chair. He looked into the coal fire, where strange shapes rose out of the scarlet flames. Then almost without willing it, he began to speak, and he was a little afraid of his own words: "I don't quite know. I thought of it a long time ago. It seemed to me that many people could easily get hold of what they need to make them happy. I've never loved the Jewish religion. I've often felt as though I had a word to say to all Jews which might set them free. But that was just a dream until the affair took place with Sürich Sperling."

"And what affair was that?"

"Sürich Sperling was the name of the landlord of St. Sebastian's Inn in our village. My father was so afraid of him that he trembled if he merely heard his name. He had got hold of a bill my father had given, and he tormented him with it. Once when we were rowing across the floods towards Altenberg, he came along in another boat and rammed our boat on purpose, and I was thrown into the water. Then I thought it would not be a sin to kill him. The same evening I saw him ill-treating a little old man, and I went up to him and spat in his face. He dragged me into his room, took a rope, bound me to a black cross on the wall and beat me. I have never told this to anyone else, but I know you will keep silence about it."

Agathon buried his face in his hands, and Erich Boyesen listened with starting eyes as the boy went on, still keeping his hands before his face: "Then I said to him: 'Sürich Sperling, this will be the death of you.' He laughed. 'Speak, you swine,' he said. 'Didn't you crucify our Lord?'

"Then it seemed to me that the door opened and Lämelchen Erdmann came in—the old man Sürich Sperling had been ill-treating—and I thought he sat down and nodded and smiled, and I recognized his face and yet somehow it was changed. 'Oh, Sürich Sperling,' he said, 'this is a matter of great importance, for from now on the Jews are free. Gentleness will never triumph. Only power will triumph. We shall hate our enemies, hate them, hate them! The Wandering Jew is redeemed, Sürich Sperling, and you will become the Wandering Christian. For the world grows new; it will slough its skin like a snake, and you will be the Wandering Christian, condemned to expiate the innocent blood that the Christians have shed.' Suddenly the vision melted away, and Sürich Sperling untied the rope. He was pale as death and trembled as he bade me go, and his eyes, as they looked at me, were full of fear and horror."

Boyesen glanced through the window into the street where people were walking past, singly or in twos, with raised umbrellas, for it was raining. Everything seemed to him unreal, as though life were no more than a fleeting vision, the dream of a dream in the mind, and the dreamer was near to waking, and longed or feared to wake. He went over, took Agathon's head between his hands and compelled him to rise. Then he looked into his eyes and perceived them to be the strangest eyes he had ever seen: black and deep, full of restrained fire that yet shone with effortless brightness, full of the gift of vision. When they looked at him it was as though their glance was recalled from a great distance, and hesitated long before it regained its steadfastness and clarity. Then Agathon got up (he was somewhat taller than Boyesen) and a terrible pallor had spread across his face. He pointed in front of him, sank on his knees and remained thus for several seconds.

"What is it? What is it?" asked Boyesen, in alarm.

Agathon shook his head, and his face was contorted as though he were about to weep.

"And what happened then?" asked Boyesen in a whisper. He was moved against his will and reason by the strangeness of this young man.

"I cannot tell you now," replied Agathon. "Sürich Sperling died that same night."

"That same night?"

"Yes. I lay and lay and willed death into his heart."

Incredulous and amazed, Boyesen stared into the boy's contorted face. He shut his eyes; his head was whirling. Agathon left the room with a quiet word of farewell, and Boyesen walked up and down in a state of deep agitation.

THE POOR JEWS

by ANDRÉ MAUROIS

"**Y**ou must find a bed for her," Mr. Kahn said to Dr. Rosenthal. The doctor lifted his arms and shrugged his shoulders. He wore horn-rimmed spectacles, which he took off and polished when he was worried.

"I *demand* that a bed be found for her," repeated Mr. Kahn with the authority of the timid. . . . "She has been recommended to me by several friends; she is very poor and there will be a child coming in a few days."

"It is against the rules of the hospital," the doctor said in a tone of annoyance. . . . "She is not Jewish."

He took off his spectacles and wiped them.

"Who founded this hospital?" asked Mr. Kahn. "I paid for everything: the building, the material, the staff. . . . I can change the rules if I wish. . . . She is not Jewish, but she is in need . . . that is enough."

"There are many in need," the doctor said, bitterly, "but as they are not princesses, the rules are not changed in their favour. . . . I know this one. . . . I have sad reason to know her. . . . She is the daughter of General Atnikov, who was the Governor of the Province during the Kishinev pogrom. Her father allowed hundreds of Jews to be butchered, did not send one single gendarme to defend them."

"That is one more reason to be kind to his daughter," said Mr. Kahn angrily. "We shall show her that Jews are not heartless."

Dr. Rosenthal ceased his protests as soon as he had Princess Baratinsky in his ward. She was pretty, sweet and grateful. The revolution and her exile had made her timid. She had had to fly from Russia on horseback, behind one of her uncles. Her father had been killed. In Paris she had lived a few months by selling her jewellery, then she had married Baratinsky who was just as poor as she was, and she had obtained a situation as a saleswoman in a little shop, at starvation wages. She had become pregnant at the very worst moment. Without Kahn, to whom she had been recommended by friends, God knows what would have become of her.

"Doctor," she said. "You will let me scream, won't you? When I am hurt, I like to scream."

Rosenthal smiled. She had disarmed him. Besides, everyone in the hospital loved the little princess. Her nurse, Mlle. Esther, knitted nighties for the baby. In the evening, Prince Baratinsky, who was a taxi-driver, came to see her and sat beside her bed. She leaned towards him and, speaking low, told him a thousand tender foolish nothings that made him laugh. Sometimes she said thoughtfully: "You cannot imagine, Pierre, how good they are to me. You know, when I think of the past I am filled with remorse. . . . How unjust we were, we Russians, towards the Jews. . . . My poor father . . ."

When her husband had left and she could not sleep, she spread some cards on the covers, and told her fortune.

"Well? Are the cards favourable?" asked Mlle. Esther gaily, finding her dreaming over the cards.

But the little princess shook her head. She believed in cards.

The hospital was scrupulously clean; the white walls curved to meet the ceilings, making the microbe nests vulnerable. Dr. Rosenthal, a crank for disinfectants, knew his work. Accidents were rare in his hospital, almost unknown.

"We have the best statistics in all Paris," said Mr. Kahn, rubbing his hands together. The confinement of the little princess was difficult, but without danger. She screamed a lot and demanded chloroform, which Rosenthal refused to give, belonging to the school that believes in the useful influence of pain. The child was a fair and rosy boy, too strong for such a frail mother.

Mlle. Esther was stupefied when, three days after the confinement, the patient's temperature rose. In the morning the thermometer showed 101, in the evening 103. The patient was hot and complained of pains everywhere.

"Doctor," Mlle. Esther said, when they had moved away from the bed, "Doctor, I don't like it. . . . It is a bad business. . . . As soon as Mr. Kahn brought her here, I was troubled."

Rosenthal took off his spectacles, took out his handkerchief and polished them.

"A bad business?" he said. "How? What could it be? . . . She cannot have become infected. Where could she have got the germs?"

He was never to know where the little princess had got the germs of puerperal infection, but, without question she had got them, for her temperature rose, ceaselessly. At first she made little of it. She talked of a mild fever. Then the obvious uneasiness of those around her affected her. She called for her husband.

It was difficult to find the prince who, in order to earn more money, was now working at night. At last he came and sat down by the bed. He was tall, with a shaven head, with the curious ease of an officer of the Guards. He had not had time to take off his taxi-driver's cape and cap which gave him a military appearance.

"What is wrong?" he asked Rosenthal impatiently. "What sort of treatment have you given her? . . . Something must be done. . . . Is there no serum?"

"There is a serum," Rosenthal said, anxiously and irritated. "I have made injections. . . . They mostly succeed. . . . But here . . . nothing. . . . Perhaps . . ."

The little princess was now in such a high fever that she no longer recognised anybody. She crumpled the sheets in her hands and said:

"The Jack of Clubs. . . . The Jack of Clubs. . . ."

Once only she looked at her husband and said, tenderly:

"Pierre, the poor Jews. . . ."

Towards evening Mr. Kahn arrived, accompanied by Mlle. Samson, the directress, respectful and uneasy.

"It has been explained to me," he said severely to Rosenthal. ". . . It is a disgrace . . . in my hospital. . . . For which I gave you authority to draw funds on me without limit. . . . It is a disgrace. . . ."

Rosenthal polished his spectacles and did not reply.

"We must bring down the greatest obstetrician," said Mr. Kahn. "The greatest. I want to save this little one. . . . We shall save her, Prince," he said to her husband.

The doctor telephoned to one of his old teachers and the great man came, bringing a friend with him. They, of course, approved of everything that Rosenthal had done, led Kahn away from the husband, and told him that there was no hope.

About midnight, when they were all standing round the bed of the little princess, she fell into a violent fit of delirium. Raised on the pillows, her pretty face red with fever, her hair dishevelled, she screamed. Suddenly she stopped, seized her husband's hand, leaned towards him and whispered:

"D'you see, Pierre? . . . All those Jews! . . . They must be burnt. . . ."

He tried to quiet her and looked at the others as if asking them for forgiveness, but she went on, earnestly, passionately:

"Go, call my father! Tell him everything. . . . My father is Governor of the Province. . . . Tell him to throw all these Jews to the peasants. . . . Have them hung up on the wayside trees. . . . That one, Pierre, the one with the spectacles . . . kill him . . . kill all the Jews!"

Her voice rose, sharp, anguished. Stunned, Kahn, Rosenthal and Mlle. Esther stood round the bed of the dying girl, looking at each other with eyes filled with tears.

THE OUTING

by JEAN-RICHARD BLOCH

A RIVER does not sweep down the water of its spring floods between the flanks of its valley with a more savage joy than that of the Simlers when, during the week that followed, they gave rein to their feelings.

Seventeen thousand francs are not a fortune. There was nothing perhaps, at first sight, to justify the patriarch in his wild cry.

But these seventeen thousand francs represented the net profit, after interest had been paid on the debt, and a certain sum placed to reserve. Nor did they even represent a full working year.

In any case it meant a livelihood, with some provision for the future.

And so the Simlers opened their bosoms to the flowing tide of hope. Hippolyte recovered, by nightfall, his youthful laugh, and made the windows rattle. Myrtil provided the children with the great surprise of hearing him sing an old Alsatian song, and Blum beat all his former records for ingenuity by arriving with two long-necked bottles of Kitterlé. As for Mina, she had made all her preparations for flight in the event of a disastrous balance-sheet. She found it natural and pleasant to prolong her stay.

They dined so late, on the evening of the stock-taking, that Justin and Laure were drooping with their noses in their plates, when the foremen began to arrive, in batches, wearing their Sunday clothes and a stiff, formal expression. The first glance reassured them, so far as they themselves were concerned. Each of them acted then according to his nature.

Zeller was there, rubicund, martial, cold and satisfied, Kapp waggling his long red nose with a joyous and sagacious air, Pouppelé like a good and faithful dog, his round head covered with tumbling locks of hair, Gottlieb in mourning, but his chin gleaming with the action of white wine, Fritz Braun, with his dyer's hands and his loyal flaxen moustaches, and the old book-keeper Hermann, bursting with the desire to go outside and triumph noisily among his peers.

It was decided that Tuesday should be a half-holiday, but on full pay. This announcement succeeded in awakening the children, who tossed for a long time between their clinging sheets in the scorching atmosphere of the little room in which they slept.

After Sunday, there was Monday, on which they awoke late and already baked by the sun. After Monday, there was Tuesday, which did not arrive without witnesses, but was watched for, from a skyline window, from the first break of dawn, by four eyes aflame with desire.

And the midday siren, which dispersed the workers fan-wise from the gate, did not lack an echo.

The fact was that gaiety had now a fine revenge to take. A whole year hung behind it like a debt which was to be wiped out in an instant. And what a year! Since the battle of Wissembourg, the sun had never yet shone upon a day free from anguish. An air was circulating at last which was beginning not to be the property of others; lips could now part in laughter and lungs expand.

And so it was with an exciting shock that, as soon as he had drunk his coffee, Joseph's heel rang on the pavement, while he hastened towards a mysterious goal. And each step that he took released a little eruption of white dust which seemed to assert a sort of further control of the external world.

The deference that had been paid to the Simlers, during the last two days, did not extend beyond a certain zone. In ranging as far afield as M. Antigny, who rented carriages, young Simler was entering unexplored territory.

But just as there are coloured glasses which allow only a certain number of rays of light to pass through them, so Joseph's spectacles seemed to be made of some subtle substance against which the most malicious intentions were shattered.

These spectacles had observed quite plainly, from a distance, in the streets, how M. Pierrotin gave a jump, and the sudden curiosity that seized that worthy secretary when he recognized young Simler. Nor did the rage with which M. Huillery turned away his head, at the corner of the Rue de la Bretonnerie, escape them either.

They remained impenetrable however to the horse-owner's attempts at insolence.

"Will he take us as far as the forest of l'Epine?" asked Joseph, as he gazed with a pitying air at the knock-kneed animal which a groom was harnessing to the break.

"It is Monsieur himself that intends to drive?" replied the ex-sergeant of the Impératrice dragoons.

"It is," Joseph assured him, with a glance at the man's yellow leggings.

"In that case . . ."

A slight hiss of his whip gave their full meaning to these three monosyllables.

"He is very thin."

"I feed my horses, but there are thin *mares* just as there are fat men."

"He has no vice?"

M. Antigny had exhausted his small stock of patience.

"That depends. If you drive *her* badly, *she* will land you in the ditch like any of them."

The groom, anxious for a tip, interposed, from between the legs of the resigned animal, where he was strapping the girth: "No need to be afraid with this beast! But with a driver from the stable, who'd have her well in hand, you'd get far better satisfaction."

Joseph turned abruptly towards the dilapidated break, while the groom went on, with a sly chuckle: "She'll trot right enough on the road home."

"This carriage is very old. Haven't you got anything more . . . decent?"

This unfamiliar realm of business made him ill at ease. M. Antigny had stepped back a few paces to master in an ostensible fashion the contempt in which he held this strange type of customer. He pinched his nose as he answered:

"I can put a mail-coach at your disposal."

"I mean another break," replied Joseph with a mild firmness. "This one . . ."

"Pardon me! Are we speaking of a break? This carriage is called a wagonette."

"Indeed? But I ordered a break."

"Is Monsieur taking his family out?"

"Y-es. What has that got to do with it?"

"Your family won't get inside my break. But that doesn't matter: Eugène, unharness."

Joseph saw red. He cracked one of the knuckles of his right hand in the hollow of his left.

"I did not tell you to unharness, but to show me a carriage less dirty than the one you have there."

M. Antigny found accents of a sovereign phlegm in which to order: "Jules, bring out the tilt-cart."

The bare arms of the groom swelled with muscular effort round a pole and four wheels. A tilt-cart, big enough to convey a choir-treat, thundered over the cobbles of the yard and halted, foundering in a gutter of liquid manure.

Then Joseph remembered that there were certain ugly rumors anent the business methods of M. Antigny, who was said to be sacrificing to the Queens of Spades and Hearts far more than the prosperity of his establishment allowed. And when he recalled the circumstances that brought him, Joseph Simler, into this stable-yard, there arose in him a joyous, irresistible force, comparable to the laughing ripple of an evening breeze on the surface of a lake. He looked round the yard blithely, and said: "I shall take the wagon."

Then he made them take the carriage out into the street, mounted the box and took up the reins with less awkwardness than the stableman expected to see.

As for the ex-sergeant-major, as soon as he had received the sum which he demanded in advance, he had let it be seen from his attitude that the cream of the farce was at an end in his eyes. He had withdrawn with dignity into his private office furnished with pipes, English engravings, a chair with a broken seat, an old iron stove, a porcelain racehorse on the chimneypiece, two evil-smelling fox-terriers, curled up on ragged mats, and a considerable quantity of old bridles, rusty spurs, broken curbs and whips.

"And they'll all be behaving like that worm," Joseph said to himself, as he urged the old screw in the direction of the factory. He added with disgust: "A town of rascals!" but did not succeed in suppressing the feeling of happiness which was making his head swim.

The break creaked and rattled and made an infernal din. It was sufficient to bring the children to the windows, not sufficient to damp their enthusiasm.

Decidedly Uncle Joseph had not his match in the matter of inventions. It was impossible to imagine a coachman more proud of his occupation. Laure climbed up from behind on to the box and kissed him on the cheek.

"You are all wet!" she cried, tapping him on the shoulder with the tips of her fingers. A cloud of dust rose from it and made her sneeze. They both of them burst out laughing, Justin stood in readiness at the mare's head, as though he were holding the charger of the Quartre Fils Aymon.

"You know, Cousin Benjamin has just come," Laure went on. At that moment, a sly, smiling face, red as a pantile, appeared framed in one of the windows. The family gathered round this fresh witness of their success. Joseph felt a painful contraction at the pit of his stomach. He greeted his cousin nevertheless with a gay wave of his whip. The other responded with a smile which seemed a grimace and wrinkled up his face like a venetian blind.

"Hallo, coachman, come down and let us give you a kiss."

"Hallo, passenger, come up and let me give you a kiss."

"I have come in the nick of time, it seems."

"You always come in the nick of time," replied Joseph, sardonically. Benjamin encircled with a more pronounced smile the gleaming potato which served him for a nose, and made a comical gesture of menace at the driver: "You, Chosef . . ."

He exaggerated his Alsatian accent. The family stood blissfully looking on at this exchange of banter. As for the real feeling that lurked beneath these provocations, it went beyond the sphere of their competence.

"All aboard!" cried Joseph.

"All aboard!" Laure screamed, casting a flashing glance at Benjamin over her uncle's shoulder on which she was leaning.

The women had meanwhile piled up a mountain of shawls, rugs and cushions.

"You'll have us all in the ditch. This old screw can never draw all that load!" Joseph protested.

"Don't forget the thermometer," Justin went one better.

"And the hot-bottle for our feet!" cried Laure in her shrillest tones. It was a day of Saturnalia. The slaves were mocking their masters. But a day that knew no morrow . . .

A few workmen, who had come back, having nothing else to do, after their midday meal, had stopped on the other side of the avenue. They looked on, good-humouredly, at this spectacle.

The appearance of a hamper of food calmed the automedon. He had his work cut out to trim the vehicle, when the passengers, armed with umbrellas and sunshades, scrambled into the break.

Mina Stern sat behind Joseph, with Myrtil facing her. Guillaume took his place on his cousin's left, having Hermine opposite him. Afroum was next the door on Hermine's side, Elisa on Guillaume's. She had asked for this place with a deliciously childish air "so as to get a better view of the country." Benjamin took his place on the box, by the side of Joseph, and set Laure on his knee, while Tintin found, between the two men, a scrap of scorching wood on which to seat his slender anatomy.

Hippolyte and Sarah would have nothing to do with this excursion. They had presided over the start, from the window, in company with Jacob Stern. Little Uncle Blum had been unable to find, in the state of his own affairs, any valid excuse for losing half a working day. He had nevertheless promised to join them in the forest, at five o'clock.

The break quivered on its back springs, grinding up the black dust from the roadway, and the party were left in doubt, for a full minute, as to whether the reins would hold. The children shouted: "Courage, ahi, hue, pull!" until Uncle Myrtil was moved to order:

"*Stiegen, Kinder,* silence!"

Sitting erect in the stiff casing of his frock-coat and beneath the aegis of his silk hat, his hands folded over the silver knob of his pear-wood cane, he personified the statue of industrial respectability.

Finally the four wheels began to turn and the whole party vanished in a moment from the sight of the old people. Until the first corner was reached, Mina, Hermine and Elisa had waved their handkerchiefs, and Guillaume the back of his hand, but without ceasing, in his case, to watch Uncle Myrtil's expression and to conform to it. Abraham kept a sharp look-out upon everything, with a smiling, crafty attention.

The slope up to the station brought the carriage to a crawling pace. Benjamin turned his mocking face to Joseph.

"Well, weaver, may we congratulate you?"

"You may," replied Joseph laconically, without taking his eyes off the mare's crupper.

"Do you know that, for the first year, it's quite decent?"

Joseph knew it. He knew indeed that the sentiment which had possessed them all, on the evening before last, had nothing "decent" about it. He could not help tossing his head, and said, with a trace of sadness in his voice: "You are always the same, Benjamin."

The other shook his own round, red head: "In what respect, my good Joseph? I maintain that, given the conditions, the environment, the possibilities, you have not got out of it badly."

"And you, are you satisfied?" said Joseph, to turn the conversation.

"Always the same jogtrot. Given the conditions, the environment, the possibilities, one has done one's little best."

Joseph thought: "He is getting out of it. At his leisure," and was silent, feeling vexed.

The children followed the conversation, turning to look at each speaker in turn. This silent jury weighed upon their uncle.

Behind them, the break was ahum with speech. People turned to gaze at them. They were not accustomed to seeing the Alsatians outside their own quarters, still less to seeing them holiday-making. A boy chanted:

"Voila les Guidal
Qui s'en vont au bal."

Shopkeepers hurried out to their doorsteps. Joseph, as the driver, had to endure laughter and criticism. Elisa's plump figure earned her several compliments.

And M. des Challeries, whom they met unexpectedly in the neighbourhood of the railway station, turned away his head, quickened his pace, and whistled to his collie which was going to sniff at these dubious persons.

Meanwhile Benjamin was taking in everything with his red, monkey-like eye. He shrugged his shoulders.

"A mere matter of working days. The result follows as 'in my snuff-box' follows 'good snuff.'"

"I don't understand you."

"This country is not worth a tinker's dam. Everything here goes by foresight and consequences. It is not life, I don't know what it is, geometry maybe. You raise the capital, you put it into building and stock, you cling on to it, like a hanged man on his rope, you never raise your nose for three-hundred-and-five, six or seven days (not forgetting Sundays and public holidays), and then you triumphantly gather the little profit foretold by Nostradamus and le Vieux Major. Hey, presto! Nothing in my pockets, gentlemen, nothing up my sleeve. Do you call that life? You were gazing at the coxcomb who stopped his nose as we passed, with his English penny cigar and his hair parted down the back? I don't know who he is, but I'm willing to bet that, in ten years, you will have ruined him. It's mathematics; besides you can see it written on his face. Seventeen thousand this year, it's a little nest egg. Next year fifty thousand, in ten years your turnover will be five millions, and you will have two hundred thousand to divide among yourselves. You can lie down and sleep, you, or your father, or your uncle, who seems to be repeating his catechism behind my back, it will make no difference. Because this is an old country, and what has once been begun continues of its own accord until the life of the world is extinct. That is why I am so bored here, why I knew that the war would be won by the Germans who are a young people, and why the Germans will be beaten by the Americans who are younger still."

He burst out laughing, and turned his potato-like nose in the direction of Joseph, whom his remarks were suffocating.

"Keep to the right, Giglamps, or these aristocrats who are coming along at full trot will heave you into the ditch with the entire firm of Simler. And don't upset yourself. What I have said is what everybody knows to be true."

Joseph gave a docile tug to his horse. But when you have been living in the conviction that nothing can come up to what you have just brought off, you cannot look on unmoved at the destruction of your ideal.

Then, as they had reached the top of the hill, he whipped the animal into a trot, and was not sorry that the rest of the conversation was drowned by the rattling of the carriage.

"All very fine principles. In the meantime you work like a horse, and your stock-taking was superb."

"Patience! That poor devil Lambert has handed in his checks. That, look you, is the only aspect of the question that deserved mention. Lambert was an honest man, a man who did his duty, and as brave as a lion; you don't see that sort any more. Enough said! I was within ten feet of him, sniping, and I could do nothing for him. There's nothing I can do for him now. And so, silence!"

Tintin stared with awe at the cousin who had been in battle within ten feet of that poor Lambert.

Joseph was not by nature inclined to bitterness. But there was, in this topic, more than he was able to endure. He began again, thrusting his spectacles on to his forehead, to which they remained glued, and raising his voice to drown the rattle of the wheels:

"You were heroes, Lambert and yourself. Others were left trapped like beasts, in the wake of the invasion, and had to devour their hearts for eight months."

"There is no such thing as heroes. There are men who march straight ahead and halt when there is nothing more to be done. I have heard some story of a shirt flung over the head of a Badische attorney. That is not so bad. I only had to follow, halt, fire and run, squealing like a pig, from a fixed bayonet. Lambert had his dose, I am still here. Four paces more to the left, and people would be saying: 'that poor Benjamin,' instead of saying: 'that poor Lambert,' and Lambert would have no need to play Benjamin, as Benjamin has to play Lambert."

"Don't swagger, Benjamin," replied Joseph, thoroughly angered. "Lambert was everything that could be said in his praise. But if he had remained in this world, there would be two of you to do what you are doing single-handed."

"A cigar?" said Benjamin, offering his cigar-case with a simultaneous gesture to Joseph and Tintin. "Do you know, my little mannikin," he went on, addressing Tintin this time, but without looking at him, "what it is that makes life worth the trouble of living? I am going to tell you, I, Stern, Benjamin, of Turckheim, Haut-Rhin, who knows what he is saying and speaks only when he is sober: it is, first of all, to construct the machine, and then to break it. Don't pull your beast like that," he added ironically in the direction of Joseph, who at once grew nervous. "We, the Sterns, set up a machine. That's all right for me. It's a life that suits me. But when the machine is going, and they have no more need of me, I hitch up my pants, and off I go."

"Where to?" said Joseph, as though he were giving the other a kick.

"Where? To Valparaiso, Melbourne, Boston, the Cape, Honduras, wherever results do not follow foresight, as a man follows his nose, where it is possible to work from morning to night without having to earn a fortune."

"That is play, not work," growled Joseph from the depths of his chest.

"It is the true form of work, Joseph. You don't love the machine, you only love what the machine produces. You don't love work, you only love the fruits of your work. You will be rich, very rich, until the day . . ."

"Until the day?"

"When Tintin parts his hair behind and starts buying English dogs . . ."

M. Antigny's mare never knew what was responsible for the lash of the whip that stung her flanks. The want of understanding that divided her already from her driver was from that moment intensified. In her obtuse equine mind, this outing began to take a definite shape.

"It's idiotic, what you're saying," growled Joseph.

"To Toul!" cried Benjamin, in response to a question which the break had left suspended in the air, for a moment, and which the little man's alert mind had picked up. "Must I repeat it a hundred times? The Levy's of Ingwiller at Nancy, the Sterns of Turckheim in Paris, the Frankels of Bischwiller at Elbeuf, the Aarons of Colmar at Epernay, the Simlers of Buschendorf at Vendeuvre, the Weils at Sedan, and a Dreyfus, a Spire, a Jacob, a Blum, a Hertz, a Kahn wherever the archangel has scattered them—is that what you were asking? The chosen people are regular slaves for work. I assure you that, as far as knowing the geography of the Promised Land goes, our revered ancestors ought to have known it by heart before they even reached it. It's positively stupendous, this redispersal of the tribes! We had gathered together in a regular little *kile* in the last generations, between Basel and Treves. We were quietly becoming citizens, burgesses, proprietors, mayors—all the honours. And then, bang! The Everlasting becomes angry and sends us packing to five thousand devils. To think that we are all going to *begin* by becoming as rich again as Croesus and as stupid as pigs! A true stroke of fate, that. There is a *moschelisch* about it."

Thereupon a silence fell over the break, because you can keep all Israel quiet, from the East End of London to the Dead Sea, with a well-told tale. And Benjamin had a reputation as a great teller of parables.

"Listen then to my *moschelisch,* O ye of little faith. Once upon a time the devil appeared on earth and was arrested, for some disgraceful business. Then he found three men, a Protestant, a Catholic and a *Yid,* to get him out of his trouble. And when he was set free, he gathered them round him and said to them: 'Before I leave you, I wish to give you each a proof of my gratitude. You will see that I am not such a bad devil, after all. Choose, therefore, each of you, what it is that you want most in the world, and your wish will be at once granted.'

"Then he began: 'You, the Protestant, what would you like most?' And the Protestant answered: 'I wish to have power upon earth.' 'Good,' said the devil, 'that is easily done. Power you shall have. And you, the Catholic?' 'I?' said the Catholic, "I, it is riches that I desire.' 'Bah! Bah!' said the devil; 'you shall have all the money you want. And you, the Jew?' 'I?' said the Jew, bowing, 'I ask one little thing only.' 'What is that?' 'Well, give me the Catholic's address.' "

Whereupon they all laughed, looking at one another with eyes of happiness, as it has been in their blood to do, in such circumstances, from the days of Abraham, and before.

Joseph, meanwhile, continued to feel a red, monkeyish eye fixed upon him, and to feel some discomfort. But they had reached the woods. There followed two hours of respite for Joseph, the mare and the cousin.

The party alighted, and shook off the dust which covered them from head to foot. Myrtil Simler paraded solemnly in his frock-coat with Afroum, while Elisa flaunted her coquetry in Joseph's honour, before the indignant but powerless eyes of Mina Stern. As for the children, they were greatly astonished to discover that a man who had fought in the war and spoke indifferently about going to the ends of the earth, could be an inexhaustible inventor of games.

Even Joseph himself, relieved by this diversion, entered into it whole-heartedly, ended by taking off his coat and collar and jumping the ditches with a surprising agility, in view of his weight. As for Guillaume, after various attempts, he consoled himself for his incompetence in such matters with the perfectly easy conversation of the people of age and experience.

At the stroke of five, the two Blums put in their appearance, in the guise of a humble party that had arrived on foot, arm in arm, very tired and dusty. The provisions were unpacked, and this scene furnished more than one passer-by, that evening, with an opportunity for impertinent descriptions.

Then, when the time had come, they all stowed themselves in the break, and Joseph took the reins. But the mare had had time to think. She displayed an evident ill-will. Roused by the convergence of all eyes upon himself, Joseph began pulling in every direction, which proved disastrous. Benjamin whispered advice, to which Laure and Tintin gave a blaring publicity. The women felt that the moment had come for them to scream. Myrtil stood up in the break, Guillaume cried: "Look out!" After a more stinging lash from the whip, the mare, who was backing determinedly, deposited the break in the ditch, one wheel after the other. Uncle Myrtil tumbled over the side, with his frock-coat and silk hat.

The Blums hastened to the spot. The passengers were rescued, as best they might. After everyone had decided that the beast would listen to no argument, Benjamin expressed the opinion that she must be unharnessed. Tintin, greatly to his father's anxiety, was detailed to hold the quiet animal by the head, a few paces away. Uncle Blum lifted the shafts, Benjamin, Afroum and Joseph put their shoulders to the wheels, without any result.

Heroic measures were required. Joseph for the second time took off his coat, waistcoat and collar, and everyone but himself admired the strength of the biceps which he revealed when he rolled up his shirt-sleeves.

Only the back wheels of the break were in the ditch. Joseph stepped down into it, became rather flushed, folded his spectacles, handed them to his sister-in-law, and stooped down to grip the step. The sweat streamed from his temples.

At that moment, Afroum shouted: "Let this carriage pass!"

Joseph, without straightening his back, raised his honest, shortsighted eyes.

Along the road, over which the sun was setting in a cloud of dust, a dogcart was approaching at full speed, driven, with taut reins, by an old man with white whiskers and a broad-brimmed hat. A girl, in a plain dress, was seated on his left, without a sunshade. Three dogs thrust their gaping jaws between the wicker bars of their basket.

It was not even necessary for the unusually high boxseat to make these people clearly visible. Joseph had guessed who they were, and flushed a deep crimson.

The old man showed an instinctive surprise, but was unable to pull up his horse until he had passed them by some thirty yards.

Joseph had detected this action. He bowed his bull-like neck, gripped the step of the break in both hands, and with a mighty thrust, lifting the heavy carriage, steadying its oscillation, placed it in position on the road. Elisa had uttered a shrill cry.

Guillaume ran along the road, after the strangers, without thinking of what he was saying: "There's no need . . . Go on . . . It's all right now!"

The old man made a gesture of polite regret, picked up the reins, and the dogcart bore away, in a cloud of dust, the barking dogs, the

grand manner of their master, and the indulgent, uneasy smile of the
girl in the brown silk dress.

"I always knew that he was as strong as a Turk," said Abraham
Stern, "but this time he has surpassed himself."

They all gazed with awe at Joseph. M. Antigny's Vendevoriate mare
had done enough for one day. She slavered abundantly on the hands of
the disgusted Justin. She allowed herself to be harnessed, and finally
carried back to the worn pavements of Vendeuvre a cartload of weary,
thirsty, anything but comfortable folk.

In the meantime, little Uncle Blum, having taken in the hollow of
his own arm the plump arm of little Aunt Babette, was making his way
home, on foot, to his house on the plain of Saint-Simplicien. But he
raised his head and remarked, as he went, to this wife, who did not
contradict him: "Babette, at Buschendorf, our Chosef used not to hire
a horse and carriage, and blush when goy girls stared at him."

As for Joseph, if he remained silent on the box, this afternoon had
furnished him with at least three excuses for silence. The best excuse was
not that which Tintin supposed.

MENDEL HERTZ

by MEIR ARON GOLDSCHMIDT

A CHANCE meeting on the street brought him back vividly to my
mind as he was at the time I was twelve or fifteen years old.
He was then a little over thirty, a shoemaker by trade, and
lived with his mother, who used to go round peddling secondhand
ladies' clothing. They lived in low rooms on the ground floor of a
house in Mikkelbrygger Street, and of course everything they had was
very simple. But on the Sabbath Eve and the Sabbath, when their living
room—his workshop—was tidied up, his tools put away in a box and
hidden in the alcove, and the old table, which on week-days crouched
up against the wall with one leaf folded down, was opened out in all
its roundness and placed in the center of the room and covered with
the white Sabbath cloth, upon which in the evening stood two shining
plated candlesticks and during the day an old Chinese potpourri jar—
then the room was filled with hushed solemnity peculiar to the habitation of the traditional Jew: there is an all-pervading silence, an atmos-

phere of expectancy; man goeth to his eternal home, and even in the
temporal home there is an apparent absence of poverty, or rather a survival from times before riches were discovered.

When you came in for the first time during a week-day and saw
Mendel sitting at his work, there was something impressive about him
because of the big head surrounded by light brown curly hair and the
longish face with the clear eyes. He seemed much too important for the
low, square little table strewn with scraps of leather, wax, and thread.
On closer examination his greatness was as a frame that was not quite
filled. Indeed, his face presented a measure of uncertainty, something
childish and undeveloped, an expression of extreme kindness and gentleness. It was not to his advantage to stand up; for without being dwarfish,
he was too small for his head; moreover, he did not walk well, because
one of his legs was a little shorter than the other. This slight defect was
perhaps due to his having been put at shoemaking as a child, thus limiting his future activities to his head—and, of course, his arms. To my
knowledge, he never questioned the whys and wherefores of this himself; nor did he complain, but was always childishly content with life
and with himself. I believe, although he never actually said so, that he
considered himself the world's, or at least Denmark's, leading shoemaker. To be sure, one has to have some such feeling to go on living
from day to day. It is possible, too, that by restricting his self-examina-
tion to his head—and that, after all, is what one sees in the mirror—
he had come to regard himself as a handsome man. And, to conclude,
it may be said that he was far from thinking himself stupid. Yet who
does? In any case, he was very humble, because all his life long he
had been one of the poor and insignificant, with the right to only a very
small corner.

His quiet, even contentment did not prevent his being extremely
melancholy, mainly over matters which really did not concern himself.
Over Moses, for example. Mendel, it may be said in passing, had thought
much about religion and as a result had become a freethinker. He found
it quite absurd that there should have been two of every living thing,
of cattle and of fowl, brought into the ark. As he deftly drew the waxed
thread through the holes made by the awl, or hammered out a sole, he
would adduce strict proof that there could not possibly have been food
for them in the ship.

"After all," he said, "one is not a child. How can Moses expect it of
one's intelligence!"

"There are many other things," he continued, shaking his head sagely, "but as long as mother lives, and may it please God that she live till I die, I shall say nothing to cause her sorrow. But if I were to speak out!"

His tone changed abruptly when he talked of Moses' death. "God," he said, "took him up into Mount Nebo; and because he had done wrong, He said to him: 'Here shalt thou sit and see the Promised Land with thine eyes! But thou shalt not enter!' So Moses sat there and stared and died of longing!" At this Mendel's pale face became still paler, as if he himself were going to die. "But, of course," he added to comfort himself and me, "we all owe the Lord one death, as my poor dear father used to say."

When his thoughts dwelt upon Napoleon at St. Helena, he felt a grief almost as deep as at the thought of Moses on Nebo. This particularly manifested itself when he sang General Bertrand's farewell song, a favorite of his. He used to sit quietly in a corner with his elbows on his knees and his head between his hands and gave the impression of weeping. And, he did weep—inwardly, being deeply moved. He had a slight lisp as he sang:

> "Napoleon, what though thy star did wane,
> This world a greater hero never knew,
> I stood with thee in gilded regal fane,
> And till my death I served my Emperor true."

So deeply sorrowful was his expression that it seemed to me, who learned the song from him, wonderfully grand and beautiful that Bertrand had stood in gilded regal fane. And it seemed entirely right to me, when with pale face and sad voice, as though he himself were dying of loyalty, he sang: "till my death" instead of "till his death."

Mendel sympathized also with other great human destinies, especially the less fortunate ones. He very seldom went to the theater. When he did, it was always to a tragedy, preferably *Axel and Valborg*. I had not seen the play, and had probably read it as a part of my school work, without profound understanding. Mendel cared nothing for that; he had not undertaken my literary education; he was wrapped up in himself and was seeking an outlet for his feelings. I had barely gotten inside the door when he declaimed, bent over his work:

> " 'O Love, thou art indeed
> No passion innocent and good; thou dost arouse
> Suspicion, hate, and fear in the heart of man!'

But then Valborg comes in. Before she was a bud, now she has blossomed!

'How lovely, lovely, lovely thou art grown!'

And then comes the tragedy; they cannot marry each other because of the priest, and then she says (here Mendel drew himself up to his full height and declaimed in a voice as much like a woman's as possible):

'Let me, I pray, once more for the last time
Gaze into Axel's beautiful brave eyes!
—— —— Now go! I shall never forget thee!'

Oh!"

It was comic beyond a doubt. Yet, as I remember it, something within me was touched and I got an inkling of what noble human grief could mean.

At the time I supposed all that sort of thing to be just on the surface in Mendel, or else I did not think about it at all. I assumed he was a quiet, contented shoemaker who used grief as a diversion. I should add, that occasionally I heard him indulge in lighter, happier verse. But this is taking me rather far back.

Mendel had a maternal aunt, and she had a step-daughter who was just like her own daughter and just like a real cousin to Mendel. She was fourteen. Her name was Salome; but she was called in Danish Frederikke. Mendel insisted, however, on Salome, and he never called her anything else. She was an arch little body; but she was said to be very dependable. "You could send her round the world," her mother said. She went to the Karoline School, a free institution, and had been well taught. Mendel did not altogether approve of this learning; in that respect he was old-fashioned and orthodox, suspicious of teaching girls anything beyond the art of housekeeping. He particularly disapproved of her writings. But her sewing he admired with all his heart. When he held in his hands a sampler that she had sewn, he would sit and gloat over it with a sort of artistic devotion, and on occasion it would inspire him to song:

"Clip, clap, clap!
Sing-a-sing-a-sing!
Piff, paff, paff!
Pretty little thing!"

Whether he had learned the song in his trade or had made it up himself, I shall not attempt to say; but he sang it in a peculiarly soft and blissfully caressing way, in an intonation that lingered in my ears. Once I saw Salome try to dance to it. She promptly cut short her dance, as though it were unseemly. Yet what a picture she and the singer made during those few instants!

> "Clip, clap, clap!
> Pretty little thing!"

Salome grew up imperceptibly and became eighteen.

About this time I met Mendel in the street. It was a surprising encounter, for it was broad daylight, on a week day, when Mendel otherwise never left his work.

He did not bid me good day or ask how do you do, or anything of the sort. Stopping and fixing upon me his most woe-begone look, he said: "A great deal can happen while you're sewing a pair of shoes."

Fumbling for some sort of answer, I said: "Yes, especially if you're a long time about it."

He stared out into space, began to whistle, "Napoleon, what though thy star did wane," and left me without saying goodbye.

Something must have happened. And, indeed, something had.

His birthday fell on the first day of Purim, the feast of Haman, when people make merry, give parties, pay visits in masks, but may also work if they so choose.

One evening shortly before the feast, Salome was paying a visit to Mikkelbrygger Street and they were talking of what people were planning in the way of amusement and of Mendel's forthcoming birthday.

With a faint smile Mendel said: "I'm not going any place, and I know more or less what my presents will be. From Mother I'll get a Butterkuchen and either two nightshirts or a silk handkerchief. From you a piece of needlework."

"You don't want anything else?"

"No, I don't want anything else."

"What would you *really* like?"

Falteringly he came out with it: "I've so often spoken against your writing, and I know I've been very unjust. . . . You have learned something. . . . Well, let me have a little letter . . . I have never received a letter. Let me see then, for once, what it's like to get a letter on my birthday."

She clapped her hands and cried: "Then you can get what you've asked for and still be surprised!"

"Be surprised?"

"Yes, for of course you don't know what the letter will say!"

"That's true too! I don't!"

The holiday arrived, and the postman brought a letter which Mendel opened with joy and excitement. It said:

"May you receive a kiss this year from the one you most desire!"

At these words the fire which had long been smouldering burst out into bright flames. He wanted to hurry over to her at once, fly on the wings of love. But he had to get a pair of shoes ready for a customer who paid well and promptly, and if he were to dress up and propose now, the whole day might be lost. Besides, she was probably not at home but at the sewing room. All things considered, it would be best to wait the couple of days before the Sabbath.

The time passed for him in happy dreams of Salome, of opening a shop and keeping a journeyman and an apprentice.

On the Sabbath he walked in at the door just as Salome and her mother were standing in the center of the room engaged in earnest and animated conversation. She, Salome, had received a kiss from the one she liked best, namely, Isaac Davidsen, who worked for a dry goods merchant but was now going to set up for himself and start a shop for everything that had to do with sewing.

"Now I woo you as Jacob did his Rachel!" said Mendel with outstretched arms.

Salome blushed scarlet and drew back. Her mother looked him up and down in amazement and exclaimed: *"Frisch und gesund und meschugge"* [Sound of limb, but off his head]! "Mendel, are you a marrying man? . . . And isn't she engaged to Isaac Davidsen? What were we just talking about? . . . What's that paper? You know I can't read."

Mendel read out dully: "May you receive a kiss this year from the one you most desire."

"Oh," said the mother appeased. "That's another matter. You've come *verstellt* [Disguised]. You are playing role to congratulate her. She'll get that kiss all right from Isaac Davidsen. . . . Won't you have a slice of meat and a pickled cucumber?"

Without answering a word Mendel went home.

"Mother," he said, "you'll see me going out of my mind now, and before the year is up they'll carry me out to the *guten Ort* [cemetery]."

"What sort of thing is that to say to your mother? . . . I am the one to go first! . . . Don't be a fool, Mendel!"

And it came to pass almost as he had said. Before very long he settled matters with life, and it was even as his father and he had said: We all owe the Lord one death.

THE ZADDIK

by ILYA EHRENBOURG

WITH difficulty I have at last succeeded in finding a real Zaddik. He is, perhaps, one of the last. His name is Reb Yosele from Skvernovic. He lives in Warsaw, in the neighborhood of the Jewish paupers. A tiny unheated room. I am reminded: "Do not forget to cover your head." This is his only request. The Zaddik is a tall, good-looking Jew of about fifty-five years of age, with a long traditional beard and the kind, yet sad eyes of a village dreamer. He is dressed poorly, and everything around him is poor and shabby. The chairs are broken and the tapestry torn. This Zaddik resembles a great poet who is read only by ten or twenty people. His followers are poor workers from the Nalevki.

The Zaddik offers me a cigarette and lights one himself. By the awkward movement of his fingers, and his strenuous puffing, it is obvious that he is not a habitual smoker. Perhaps he only lit the cigarette so as to soften the tension of our strange meeting. However, he soon feels at ease and answers my questions. I ask him about the essence of Hasidism. He answers readily without stopping to think a moment; sometimes smiling ironically, sometimes inspired, like a real poet.

"The Misnagdim consider the 'Law' above all. But soldiers are trained differently in different countries. The English soldiers are taught differently from the Polish. However, soldiers of all the world are trained to obey the commands of 'one-two'; the good one forgets everything he has been taught."

The Zaddik caresses his long beard and looks at me questioningly. It seems that he is not certain whether I understood. He adds: "All life is war. . . .

"You ask what is 'Heaven' and 'Hell'? After death a man with strong will power lives his life all over again. The joy from the love and kindness he dispensed through his life is 'Heaven.' And 'Hell'? 'Hell' is shame. . . .

"In order for a man to rise he must first fall. One cannot rise without having fallen. This is the law of life and the law of God. . . .

"Poverty is the path to God. In the book Zohar it is said that God has many attires, but he is always dressed in the prayers of the poor."

My last question: "What is more important, the relation between man to God or between man to man?"

The Zaddik smiles.

"At first it seems that his relation to God is the more important. For God is everything, and man—dust. But when you think about it, especially if you have lived and experienced, you will realize that man's relation to man is the most significant. If a man insults God, he has insulted God alone. But when a man insults a man, he has wronged both, God and man."

Reb Yosele has a score of followers. They always come to him for advice: "What's to be done, the daughter is sick?" or "Soloveichik will not return the ten zlotys he borrowed." His wisdom remains within the four walls, hidden under a faded cap, bent over an old book.

The Zaddik reminds one of an old master who remembers a secret of an ancient craft, but does not know where to apply it. Reb Yosele still remembers the words of the Besht, but his words nobody understands any more. He cures hearts not with his inherited wisdom but with his title of "Zaddik," and with a kind and generous smile.

The rich Jews go to the better-known Zaddikim. There, they too may expect some honor or benefits; the right to sit with the Zaddik, at one table, or with his influential assistants in some commercial scheme. These Hasidim wear silk talletim (prayer-shawls), their beards are neatly trimmed, and on Saturdays, they wear silk caps with borders of yellow fur. They call themselves Hasidim, but if you ask them about the teachings of Besht, they will not be able to answer. For them more important than the joy and ecstasy is—who will sit today next to the Zaddik, Aaron Shmulevich or Hayyim Rosenberg?

There are still other places where Hasidism is yet alive, not its philosophy but spirit—amid the poor of the synagogue of the so-called "Brazlav Hasidim." They have no Zaddik at all. Their Zaddik died long ago— a century and a half ago. His name was "Reb Nachman from Brazlav." He was a great philosopher and poet. His sayings, legends and poetry were recently published in a German translation. This first emergence of historical Hasidism from the borders of the Ghetto was full of belated glory, to the classical astonishment of the descendants. "Whence such daring thought? Whence such poetry? From Brazlav? . . . Nobody ever knew about it. . . ."

Yes, only his Hasidim knew it. For them Reb Nachman was a great Zaddik. And when he died, they did not take another one in his place. They have chosen for their adviser the memory of this Zaddik-poet. Among the Brazlav Hasidim there are neither rich nor hypocrites. These have nothing to do here, their place is at the table of the living Zaddik. And here? Here are only the paupers of the Nalevki: peddlers, tailors, cobblers.

I enter the synagogue. It is a small room in a worker's house, dimly lit by a tiny electric lamp. It is crowded to capacity, and with difficulty I manage to elbow my way inside. At first it seems as though it were a trade union meeting. But no, here is a different century, a different chronology. Perhaps it is altogether beyond the concepts of our time. Bearded men in dirty caps who toil the whole week selling rags and herrings, pounding out a monotonous dreary existence. But now is Sabbath Eve. They came here to rejoice. And they are happy, not because it has been prescribed to be happy. No, in them is still alive the belief which is already dead outside of this tiny room. They are meeting the "Sabbath-Queen." They clasp their hands and sing. At first, they say words of prayer. But neither the tongue nor the mind can keep up with the gayness of the soul. Soon, the words are heard no more, only a gay, wide, soul-captivating melody. The feet will not stand in one place any longer, and they begin to jump. And they dance in this tiny and dimly-lit room. Happiness! Life! I observe the faces and wonder. Who changed them? Who erased from their minds the memory of insults, hunger and "Zlotys"? One can speak here even about Catholicism, Freud or "Mass Hypnotism." But is it worth while? These things can be read by everyone in solid books. Would it not be better now to accept the smile of the Brazlav Hasidim as an extraordinary happiness? Even though it is foreign, inaccessible, but human till the end. The joy of losing oneself in a greater joy, the joy of honesty and forgetfulness, the joy of simple and childish souls. Rejoice! ! ! . . .

FROM BODANA'S DIARY

by I. KIPNIS

THOSE who had met me in this big town, particularly my patients, know what a busy man I am. Still, sufficient time is left for me, after office hours and after my visits to the sick at home, to call on a girl I know, a communist pioneer. Whenever I find her home I am glad to spend an hour or two with her.

My visits to this girl are no secret at my home. Bodana (that's her name) is of my native town. Moreover, she is my sister, to boot. In the town which we left behind lives a dear and lovable woman who longs for us unremittingly. That woman is our mother.

Back home I was the oldest of my brothers and Bodana the youngest of my sisters. Here she visits me rarely. She says she is busy. I therefore put pride aside and visit her, for which I am well rewarded. For there I often find a letter on the table from our mother, and also a tastily baked wheat cake which she sends us from home. In addition Bodana's friends, both male and female, are there when I call. She places a hand on the open book before her, or on her diary which she keeps, and narrates incidents which remind us of home.

I would put the best book aside in order to listen to her stories. It is not so easy to retell them. But recently while rummaging through her papers, I came upon some notes in her own handwriting. And I am passing on their content to you, word for word:

I. HOW THE BIG CITY FRIGHTENED ME FROM AFAR

. . . Many things are probably sorry that I have left home. But, on the other hand, I miss them as much, if not more. . . . I shall never forget the scene of my leave-taking, and that of my sitting on the wagon. We were eight miles from the town. I sat on the wagon with eyes closed. The few passengers around me were talking quietly among themselves. I heard nothing of their talk. I mused as though I were in a sleep. Only the evening before everything had been just as any other day. Now I had a peculiar feeling. The driver was prodding his nags. The wagon was shaking me up. The dust irritated my face. Under the seat, hard by my feet, was my bundle. Still I didn't know where I was heading for and that made me sad.

It seems to me that I am a good pioneer. Nevertheless, I thought, what am I going to do in a big city where no one knows me? They might even run after me as though I were some queer-looking creature. . . . I know that my brother and sister-in-law live there. I shall go to school and study, which will be a good thing. But last night when our calf came home from the pasture (and I am beginning to miss our calf), it looked so tiny that I believed I could have lifted it on my back and carried it wherever I pleased. Of reddish skin, with blue fresh horns, and with somewhat dark streaks in the face, particularly around the mouth and eyes. Our calf understands everything.

It was then that I did not feel like leaving home. I was beginning to take notice of things which I had ordinarily ignored. The box upon which I used to sit while milking the cows had a square hole in it. The chimney in the kitchen, where I would strain the milk, was black with smoke and soot. Helping out my mother was apparently little in my mind. . . . Why didn't I rise in the middle of the night and polish the stove, bring in pails of water from the well and tidy up the kitchen until it looked like a palace? . . . Weeping isn't the thing for a pioneer to do. But what can I do when I journey forth far away? I don't know anybody in the big city nor about what to talk with people.

I took farewell from my circle but they promised to come again in the evening. The children of our aunt and neighbours were all envious of me because I was to ride on the train and live in a big city. A week ago I was envious of myself for it. Now, however, the children appeared to me so foolish that it made me bawl. And in the depth of my thoughts lurked an idea that the whole story was a lie. I was riding nowhere. I should remain a good pioneer at home and study. And in good health. One always is in a small town. And help out my mother in the house.

However, my things were all packed. The calf probably understood that all my things were packed, for she often turned her head and looked at me with the eyes of a saddened human being.

My things were all ready and my little brother went out to reserve a place for me with one of the horse and wagon drivers.

The pioneers of my circle visited me again that evening. They sensed at once that I felt disheartened. What was the use of laughing when in the morning the wagon would come and take me away and I wouldn't know whether I shall ever return! . . .

When the wagon came to a stop before a well in some village in order to water the horses, I opened my eyes.

—Were you dozing?—inquired the driver.

I answered him with a "hm." Just the same I couldn't keep my eyes open. I felt groggy but tried to recall one thing to my mind: that my mother spoke little to me the day before I left. She did not want me to leave home. I also recalled (in the morning the driver was hurrying me so that I had no time to think, but it was clear to me now) that at night, while asleep, I suddenly felt someone standing beside me and stroking my head for a long, long time. When I opened my eyes no one was there. But as soon as I closed them again I felt someone bending over and kissing me. As I stirred someone hastened away. When I lay inert someone was again beside me. Finally when I sat up fully awake I saw my mother retreat to her room with a light trembling in her hand. . . .

The wagon stumbled over a rock and jerked me out of my reverie. . . . The driver turned to me merrily:

—Are you asleep, Bodana? Sleep, sleep! I can already hear the train shrieking in the distance.

And the wheels spun into a lively clatter upon the Iskorosta road.

II. IN THE WOODS

Once I was coming from the Tsotchen district. . . . Tsotchen is a village, three miles from us, where I was delegated to organize the peasant children. Mother refused to tolerate it and father wouldn't hear of "my imparting the Torah to Gentiles."

—They don't want to become communists—said he—and if they did, God would send them a teacher from elsewhere!

The youngsters of Tsotchen clung to me as though for dear life.

—Remember!—my people would warn me—a bandit will catch you some day and wrench your head off. Bandits have no use for such as you! . . .

It was twilight when I walked home from the village. The peasant lads asked me to bring them more paper on my next visit.

—And matches—added Kalistrat.

—I shall,—I promised and felt elated that nineteen boys had listened to my talk.

I was already beyond the village gate and out on the fields. As the dusk was settling, the idea of taking a dip in the pond near Hrischke's flour-mill occurred to me. At home the cow would be attended to, and I was looked upon askance by the family anyway (they often accused me of shirking housework). . . . I felt that a different path was laid out for me. . . .

I walked and walked. The trees, the hills, appeared familiar and yet strange . . . I quickened my pace. It grew dark. Suddenly, unexpectedly, I found myself in an unfamiliar forest. Tsotchen, I knew, was fringed with woodland leading to the rear of the town through scattered hamlets. I quickly turned back towards Tsotchen. But not a glimmer of the village was anywhere to be seen. Then, how could there be if I was already an hour and a half from the village? Nevertheless I retraced my steps. I walked and walked—and came to a point where roads crossed. I didn't remember having seen roads cross. And they appeared alike. And that had to happen to me at night! The roads that stretched before me had rugged surfaces. They extended in silence as though conspiring against me.

That was, after all, a small matter. For how far was I really from home? A two-hour walk at most. I could see the bowl of steaming hot potatoes on the table. And I could sniff the grease in the ante-room. I could feel the warmth of the chickens huddling in the coop. . . .

I stood before the crossroads and the darkness made me dizzy. I was beginning to see the things with which my mother would scare me:

Decrepit hags?

No.

And brigands—Yes!

They are tough fellows and my mother is right about the terror they instil. Ah? What is that? Really? No. It's not true! I turn about and take the road leading away from Tsotchen. Maybe I'll see there a guiding gleam of the light, or smoke from a chimney. . . . I stray again into the forest. I have nothing on my person—am barefoot and in only a red dress.

—Forest, forest,—I muse—where are your bears? Where are your tigers and leopards? Let me see them at once! And where are your roving cut-throats? Nothing here. Just forest. Only my steps have a strange sound, as though I walked on broken wires.

Well, whatever will happen, will happen. If only it weren't so quiet. There is no trodden path under my feet. The grass is astir with hopping, circling insects. Somewhere an owl is hooting, like the crying of a child. The devil take it! I had better find an elevated dry spot where I can rest till dawn. It is dry under a pine tree, not under an oak tree. I take shelter under a pine tree. Let the owl hoot! Let the moon taunt me—as if to imply:

—Aha, pioneer woman! At home you are brave hiding behind your mother's apron.

—Well, so what? How does it concern you?

The long summer day tired me out, so let the forest be my home, not the whole forest, but the place where I am resting. And, as at home, so here I would not mind something to eat: a hot potato, a slice of bread—anything. We pioneers would do well to pitch tents here for at least a month during the summer. . . . A summer month in the woods would be good for us. But now I want so terribly much to talk to someone. If there were only a dumb animal beside me,—a dog, a cat, or a cow. I am aching to call out to someone. Let it be an old woman, a murderer! ! !—

With these thoughts in mind I fell asleep. . . .

I was dreaming that I was cold.

I dreamt I was at home sleeping on a hard couch. The room is like any other room. Maps decorate the walls. Then my cover dropped to the floor. I opened my eyes but felt too lazy to pick it up. Mother, after all, is right when she says to me: "For the sake of her friends she would run the world around, but for herself she wouldn't lift as much as a glass of water." . . . Mother, I believe, is right. For what could be simpler than to reach down and pick up the quilt? . . . I forced my eyes open. I searched and scratched in the grass and wondered how I came to be out here, in the open, instead of at home. . . . Trees, the moon, and an owl somewhere . . . I know that it is perched on a tree even if it stopped hooting. . . .

My younger brother sleeps with our cousin Moische on the hayloft in the barn. He will make believe that I had not yet returned from the lectures.

Good, let him think so. I turn on the other side and draw my feet up under my dress. The boys of Tsotchen probably know the way out here better than I do. . . . Recently I lectured them on why one mustn't kill birds in their nests, mustn't pick unripe cherries, and destroy branches of fruit trees. . . .

Old peasants edged closer in order better to catch the substance of my talk, and they seemed to like it.

—That's the very thing—they agreed—they should know.

—This is so fine a lesson—echoed the peasant women—that nothing better is needed. . . .

A horseback rider passed not far from me among the trees and whistled. Chilled to the bone I lay still and thought of nothing. Afterwards I reproved myself: What if someone did pass by on horseback and whistle?

Meanwhile the moon grew dim. Again I opened my eyes and imagined myself in an orchard guarding the fruit. I want so much to sleep but I am in charge of the fruit trees and afraid of thieves. I am a janitress, my husband a janitor. A wedding is in progress at my home which is on the outskirts of the town. . . . I run off with my braids flying, trying to escape someone. . . . The music pursues me. . . . My home is brilliantly lighted and glimmers in the night. . . . The wedding guests dance drunkenly. And someone is trying very badly to embarrass me in their presence, to drag me back by my hair and in my weekday clothes. . . .

Galia Ovsayevna, my oldest school teacher, is attempting to protect me. She says something about a child, someone's child. Anyway, she says, we know everything. The child is a pioneer, four years, six years, twelve years old, and already a communist.

Galia's words fill my heart with tears. A warm smoke spirals upward from the chimneys. And as I walk and walk and walk a lake spreads out into view. The lake is wide but not deep. In it flocks of gold fish swim about playfully. They are within reach of my hand. In some places the water runs as thin as cigarette paper. It laps against the shore and is iridescent in the sunlight. I'd like to thrust a hand into the water and catch some of the fish, but I don't. Perhaps I am dreaming. As I wake up, a warm sun ray darts at me through the foliage. I close my eyes and hear the gurgle of a warm water stream. Finally, when I open my eyes once more I find myself in the woods. I feel so hungry that my heart goes out. Yet I am in no great hurry to get up. For I still want to sleep, if only for another wink. . . .

At last I rouse myself to my feet with great effort. The breeze braces me up and I feel refreshed all over my body. It is not a field breeze, but one of the woods, secretive, penetrating. And I am already on my way.

I don't care where I am going, so long as it is daytime and I am going.

III. THE MEETING WITH KIRILKA

At this point begins the story of Kirilka. A dog barks forlornly in the distance. I see fenced-off fields, grazing cows, and a barn. When I come closer to the barn I hear someone groaning inside. I look in to see if it is any one of my pioneers. The dog shuffles towards me. I don't know what the dog wants. Maybe he is one of those quiet, sullen creatures who may, at any moment, seize me by my bare feet. So I call inside the barn and out comes, crawling on hands and knees, Kirilka, the younger son of Ivan, our neighbor. He recognizes me at once and begins to whimper:

—Akh, Bodanka, dear girl, save me! . . .

He speaks like an old man but his eyes light strangely at the sight of me.

He is an orphan, without a mother, and his father hired him out to a peasant farmer!

This is his second summer working for the same employer. Well, it's nothing. He is alone in the forest and his job is to mind the cattle. The employer sends him food two or three times a week. Now he complains of a severe pain in the stomach. Yesterday when the boss passed by he found him sick.

—What's the matter?—he inquired.

Instead of answering, he grasped himself by the abdomen and burst into tears.

And what did the boss say to that?

—Ignore it, Kirilka,—he said,—it's nothing. You must have over-eaten a bit. Drink less warm milk and eat more small dried pears.

And he rode off.

I listen to him carefully and conclude that he is suffering from dysentery. His eyes are glittering. His face looks tired. He shivers and squeals for help.

What can I do?—I think to myself—carry him on my back I couldn't. For him to walk is equally impossible. He can hardly stand on his feet, and has no mother to the bargain.

The employer's counsel is not at all unwise.

—Ignore it, it's nothing. You have simply overeaten yourself.

—Do you know what?—I say to Kirilka—I am going over to your house and will bring your father with me.—

—Sure?

—Sure.

—You won't forget, Bodanka?

—No—I promise—I give you my word as a pioneer!

And he cries, poor thing, bathing his face in tears.

Home is about seven miles from here. He tells me exactly how to go. The dog, ostensibly, feels that Kirilka is in need of human contact. He runs after me for a few paces, then turns back. I hasten my steps.

The distance shouldn't take more than two hours to cover. But I want to save Kirilka, to spare him more than ever before.

Three years ago, while they carried his mother out of the chapel to the grave and he followed her coffin in white sandals, I did not feel too sorry for him. Afterwards he hated me for a different reason. When the seven-year school reopened in our district and the blackboards and books were missing, I told the teacher that Philip and Kirilka had stolen them. . . . So they went there with policemen and recovered about two hundred books. . . .

But now I am ready to forgive him everything, only let him be well again.

Wagons come rattling by. Many of them are familiar to me. Most of them are without uprights, heading to the forest for timber. I walk faster. Meet flocks of cattle at the beginning of the forest. It is still early. It is the first time in my life that I meet with so many cattle (our cow is not among them for it grazes near our home). . . .

And . . . as I enter the house they are still in bed. I tell them I'll be back shortly. They think I spent the night at a friend's house. Without taking as much as a piece of bread I rush out of the house and straight to Ivan.

I find Ivan puttering around in the yard near the shed.

—Harness your horses—I command him—and let's go and fetch Kirilka. He is very sick.

Ivan begins to scratch his head. . . .

He thought, he says, of taking manure out to the field. . . .

—To the devil:—All right! . . . We'll go. But I'll have some stew first before I hitch the horses to the wagon. . . . Want to come along, Bodana?

—Certainly!—I answer.

In less than an hour I am on Ivan's wagon and we are making fast for the woods through the outlying hamlets to where the owner of the barn lives. He isn't in, but nearby, and is soon called.

And you should have seen how two peasants talk between themselves. It's really curious. As though they take nothing to heart.—

As we approach the barn Kirilka is so overjoyed that he raises himself on his knees, supports himself with his hands on the floor, and gives us one long look.

—Ah—he says—our horses have arrived! . . . and a strange luster creeps into his eyes and he drops to the floor. The dog circles around him, sniffs him in a peculiar way. And when we place Kirilka on the wagon, his head hangs down. The dog rests on his hind legs, with snout upraised, and begins to whine mournfully because Kirilka is no longer living.

The two peasants did not exchange a word. Ivan pulls a cloak over Kirilka and rides off without saying good-by.—

Abandoned the flock, abandoned the owner, abandoned the forest, abandoned the dog.—

On the way home Ivan does not say a word to me nor I to him.

The team of "our horses" runs along and snorts in the sunlight. I sense that Ivan is angry at the interference with his work. He might have brought out two wagon-loads of garbage on the fields when suddenly—the interruption. . . . Now he will have to drive the horses to the grazing ground, to go in search of boards for a makeshift coffin, run for a priest, and call a few people together—too much work! . . .

I reflect that if Kirilka's mother had been alive she would not just have wept, but screamed and beat her head on the ground. For a mother is not a father. And if she had bawled right then and there on the wagon the pity for Kirilka might have been lessened.

My brother asked me:

—Where did you spend last night? At Eva's home?

I answered him:

—Have patience and I will tell you.

At first my mother was angry with me. But as I cleaned my hands, rolled up my sleeves, and dived straight into the vat of dough to knead the bread, she softened considerably. Then I told them the story of "our horses have arrived." . . .

Mother raked up the fire in the stove, listened attentively, and tears welled up in her eyes.

—What foolish children!—she exclaimed—what tasks they take upon themselves! !—she couldn't finish, smiled, and turned away with brimming eyes.

—It is really tragic—she said—and the way you told the story can grip the heart of anyone. . . .

MY PIGEON-HOUSE

by ISAAC BABEL

IN my childhood I intensely desired to possess a pigeon-house. A more passionate desire I have never had in my life. I was nine years old when my father promised to give me money for the purchase of planks and three pairs of pigeons. This happened in 1904. I was studying for the examinations for the preparatory class of the Nikolaevsky High School. My parents lived in the town of Nikolaev, in the province of Kherson. There is no longer any such province; our town is now included in the Odessa district.

I was only nine years old, and the prospect of the examinations filled me with fear. Now, after two decades, it is scarcely possible for me to give you an inkling of how horribly afraid I was. In both subjects—that is, in Russian and in arithmetic—I simply could not afford to get less than a mark of five. The number of Jews admitted to our high school was very limited, five per cent in all. Out of forty boys taking examinations for the preparatory class only two Jewish boys had a chance of being accepted. The instructors subjected the Jewish boys to questions cunningly put; none of the others was examined in such an equivocal manner as we. Hence, in promising to buy me the pigeons, father demanded that I obtain at least two fives-plus. He tormented me to exhaustion, and I fell into an endless strange daydream, a child's lingering dream fraught with despair, and I went to the examination still wrapt in this dream. Yet I passed better than anyone else.

I had a bent for knowledge. The examiners, even though they used all their cunning, could not rob me of my understanding and of my avid memory. Yes, I had a bent for knowledge and received two fives. As later it turned out, it availed me nothing. Khariton Efrussi, a grain merchant who exported wheat to Marseilles, gave a bribe on behalf of his son, a matter of five hundred roubles or so, whereupon they made my mark five minus instead of five plus and accepted the little Efrussi in my place. My father was in despair at this. From the time I was six years old he had left no stone unturned to teach me. The unfortunate occurrence of the five minus almost drove him out of his wits, and he was quite prepared to beat up Efrussi or to instigate a couple of longshoremen to do it for him. Mother dissuaded him from this evil design.

Instead, I began to prepare for another examination for entrance during the coming year into the first class. Behind my back my parents engaged one of the teachers to coach me, so that I might pass both the preparatory and the first class courses at one go, and to quell the growing apprehensions of the family I learned three entire books by heart. These books were Smirnovsky's grammar, Evtushevsky's arithmetic and Putzikovitch's textbook of elementary Russian history. These textbooks are no longer in use. In any event I learned their contents, line by line, by heart, and in the examination in the Russian language during the following year the teacher, Karavaev, awarded me the unattainable five-plus. Our little town went on whispering for a long time about my fabulous success, and my father was so pitifully proud of it, that I was driven for the first time to give thought to his fretted, unstable existence and of how helplessly he submitted to all changes, either rejoicing or meekly accepting his lot.

The teacher Karavaev cut a larger figure in my eyes than father. He was a ruddy, indignant fellow, a former Moscow student, scarcely thirty years of age. His manly cheeks were always flushed, like those of the peasant children who were not yet occupied with heavy labors, and upon one of them there projected an ugly wart, with a tiny tuft of ash-grey hairs, like a cat's feelers. For examining colleague Karavaev had Piatnitzky, assistant superintendent of the school, an influential personage whose reputation extended throughout the province. The assistant superintendent questioned me about Peter the Great, and I was suddenly gripped by a mood of utter forgetfulness, as though I were standing on the brink of doom, on the edge of a parched abyss, emanating rapture and ultimate despair.

I knew all about Peter the Great by heart from Putzikovitch's book and the poems of Pushkin. I suddenly sobbed out these verses, and even as I did so, motley human faces showed themselves before my eyes and all mixed themselves up like cards from a new pack. They went on shuffling before my eyes, and during these instants, now trembling, now bolt upright, now swaying, I went on shouting the Pushkin lines with a fierce ardor. I kept up this shouting for some time. No one interrupted my mad shrieking, choking, mumbling. Through blood-red blindness, through frenzied freedom which suddenly possessed me, I saw only the aged face of Piatnitzky with its silvery beard intent upon me. He did not interrupt me, and merely turned to Karavaev, exulting in me and in Pushkin, with the words:

"What a people," the old man whispered, "these Jews of yours! The devil's surely in them . . ."

And when I lapsed into silence, he said:

"Good. Now you may go, my little friend . . ."

I went out of the class-room into the corridor and there, leaning against a whitewashed wall, I began to return to consciousness from the agued strain of but lately experienced dreams. Russian boys were playing around me. The school bell hung at no great distance above the stairway. The tiny watchman was dozing in a rickety chair. I gazed at the watchman and awoke out of my trance. The children were coming up closer to me from all sides. They apparently intended to push me or merely make sport of me. At this moment there suddenly appeared the figure of Piatnitzky. He was about to walk past me, but pulled himself short, causing the back of his coat to move as in a slow heavy wave. I read perturbation in this broad, corpulent, aristocratic back, and I started toward the old man.

"Children," he said, addressing himself to the high school boys, "don't touch this boy," and he laid a fat, kindly hand on my shoulder.

"My little friend," Piatnitzky, the assistant superintendent, turned toward me, "tell your father that you've been accepted for the first class."

A resplendent star flashed on his breast, and decorations tinkled round the lapels of his coat; the large, dark-uniformed body began to move away on its erect legs. It seemed cramped between the gloomy walls, it receded between them as a barge recedes along a deep canal; it finally disappeared through the doorway of the superintendent's study. The tiny attendant brought him his tea with a solemn clatter, while I ran home to the shop.

A peasant-patron was sitting in the shop and in a perplexed way was scratching his head. On seeing me, father abandoned the peasant and, without hesitation, believed my story. He shouted to the assistant to close the shop and rushed to Cathedral street to buy me a cap with the school crest. Poor mother could scarcely tear me away from the demented man. She was pale, and experienced great qualms. She caressed me, and at the same time pushed me away with disgust. She said that the names of all successful candidates to the high school were always announced in the newspapers, and that God would punish us, and the neighbors would have a good laugh at us, if we prematurely bought my school uniform. Mother was pale, she sought to fathom fate in my eyes, and gazed at me with bitter pity, as upon a cripple, because she alone knew how unfortunate our family was.

All the males of our blood were trustful of other human beings and quick to act without deliberation; little wonder that happiness did not come to us. My grandfather was at one time the rabbi of Bielotzerkov. He was driven out as a blasphemer. And after a great to-do he managed, rather skimpingly, to exist another forty years, studying alien tongues and finally losing his wits in his eightieth year. Uncle Lyov, my father's brother, studied in the Volozhin yeshibah; in 1902 he ran away from military and carried off the daughter of a commissary serving in the military district of Kiev. Uncle Lyov took this woman with him to Los Angeles, California; there he abandoned her and died in a house of ill-fame among Negroes and Malays. After his death the American police sent us his effects from Los Angeles—a bulky trunk encircled with rusty iron bands. The trunk contained dumb-bells, locks of women's hair, grandfather's praying-shawl, gilt-handled whips and some special tea in caskets encrusted with paste pearls. Of our whole family there remained only the daft Uncle Simon, my father and I.

My father was incredibly trustful of other human beings. He offended them with his friendship, which exhaled the rapturous mood of first love. They did not forgive him this, and deceived him. Hence, my father believed that his life was being directed by a malignant fate, some inscrutable power which pursued him and dogged his every foot-step. Of our whole family I alone was left to mother. Like most Jews, I was small of stature, sickly, and suffered headaches from over-study. Rachel, my mother, saw all this. She had never been blinded by the beggarly pride of her husband and his incomprehensible faith that our ancient race would some day become mightier and greater than any other people on earth. She had no expectation of success for us, she did not want me to buy a new uniform, and only allowed me to have a large picture taken at the photographer's.

On September 20, 1905, our high school displayed the list of new entrants into the first class. It included my name. All our kinsmen visited the school to gaze at this piece of paper; even Shoyl, my great-uncle. I loved this bragging old fellow, because he sold fish in the market-place. His huge hands were always moist, covered with fish-scales; they stank of cold, beautiful worlds. Shoyl had been set apart from ordinary men by this, as well as by the cock-and-bull yarns he used to tell about the Polish insurrection of 1861. Long ago Shoyl had been an inn-keeper in Skvir; he had seen the soldiers of Nicholas I discharge their rifles at Count Godlevsky and other Polish insurgents. It is quite likely, he had seen nothing of this. Today I know that Shoyl was above all an old ignoramus and a naive liar. All the same, he told some mighty good yarns, and to this day I haven't forgotten them. Anyhow, even stupid Shoyl, as I was saying, came to the high-school to look at the announcement containing my name. And in the evening, fearing no one, reckless of the fact that no one in this world loved him, he danced and stamped at our beggarly ball.

My father, indeed, had arranged a ball to celebrate, and he invited all his comrades—grain merchants, real estate agents and salesmen who trafficked in agricultural machinery in our district. These salesman could sell their goods to anybody. The peasants and landowners feared them. It was simply impossible to get rid of them without buying something. Of all Jews they were the most worldly-wise and the most gay. At the evening father gave they sang Hassidic songs, which consisted wholly of three words but which were drawn out endlessly in a series of absurd intonations. Only he can know the touching charm of these intonations who has greeted Passover among the Hassidim or he who has visited their noisy synagogues in Volynia. Old Lieberman also came to our party; he had taught me the Torah and the ancient tongue. We used to call him Monsieur Lieberman. He consumed more Bessarabian wine than was good for him; the traditional silken tassels crept out from under his waistcoat, and he pronounced a toast in my honor in ancient Hebrew. The old fellow also congratulated my parents in this toast and affirmed that in the examination I had conquered all my enemies, I had triumphed over Russian boys with fat cheeks and the sons of our coarse rich men. Thus in the ancient days had David, King of the Jews, vanquished Goliath; thus would our imperishable nation, with the might of its intellect, conquer the foes surrounding us and desiring our blood. Monsieur Lieberman wept upon saying this and, as he wept, he drank more wine and shouted: "Viva!" Our guests formed a circle around him and began to dance an ancient quadrille, as at a small town Jewish wedding. Everyone was gay at our ball. Even mother consumed enough to become intoxicated, though she had no liking for vodka and never understood how anyone could possibly like it; for this reason she regarded all Russians as daft and she could not understand how women could endure Russian husbands.

Our really happy days, however, came later. They came for mother when she had become used to the happiness of preparing sandwiches for me before leaving for high school and when she went to the shops to buy my school outfit—a pencil-case, money-box, school knapsack, new books with cardboard bindings and copybooks with shiny covers. No one in the world is so conscious of the newness of things as children. Children tremble at their smell as a dog on the trail of a hare, and they experience a madness which when we grow up we call rapture. And this clean childish feeling of ownership of things that smell of the gentle dampness and coolness of new things was communicated to mother. For a whole month we were getting used to the pencil-case and to the unforgettable dusk of morning when I drank tea on the edge of the large lamp-lighted table or gathered up my things in my knapsack; for a whole month we were getting used to our happy new life, and only after the first term did I suddenly remember about the pigeons.

I had everything ready for them—a rouble and fifteen kopecks for their purchase, and a pigeon-house made out of a wooden case by Uncle Shoyl. The pigeon-house was painted brown. It had nests for twelve pairs of pigeons, carved designs on the roof and a special grating which I myself had devised, the better to lure strange birds. Everything was in readiness. On Sunday, October 20, I was starting for the market-place, when sudden misfortune barred my way.

The events which I am here relating, i.e., my entrance into the first class of high school, occurred in the Autumn of the year 1905. Tsar Nicholas at this time gave a constitution to the Russian people; orators in ragged coats climbed up on the projections at the foot of the columns of the town Duma building and made speeches to the people. There was firing in the streets at night, and my mother would not allow me to go to the market-place. Beginning early in the morning of October 20 the boys in the neighborhood were flying kites right opposite the police station, and our water carrier, chucking his work, walked about in the street, with pomaded hair and red face. Then we saw the sons of the baker Kalistov drag a leathern horse out into the street and perform gymnastics in the middle of the pavement. No one hindered them; indeed, policeman Semernikov goaded them on to jump higher. He sported a belt of woven silk, while his boots were polished to a gleaming brightness they had never known before. The policeman, who had left off his uniform, had quite frightened mother. It was on his account that she would not let me out, but I stole into the street through the backyards and at last reached the market-place, which was situated far beyond the railway station.

In the market-place, in his accustomed spot, sat Ivan Nikodimitch, the pigeon fancier. Besides pigeons, he sold rabbits and peacocks. A peacock, his resplendent tail spread out, was sitting on his perch and poising his beautiful calm head now this way now that. One of his feet was bound with a twisted cord, the other end of which was attached to Ivan Nikodimitch's cane chair. I promptly bought of the old man a pair of cherry-tinted pigeons with sumptuous tails and a pair of crested ones and thrust them into a bag which I carried in my bosom. I had forty kopecks left, but the old man would not part for this sum with a pair of pigeons of this particular breed, of whose short, granular, friendly beaks I was especially fond. Forty kopecks was their right price, but the fancier thought he might get more. He turned away from me his yellow face, ravaged by the unsocial passions of the bird hunter. After much bargaining, seeing that there were no other buyers, Ivan Nikodimitch called me back. Everything happened as I had wanted it, but everything turned out ill.

At twelve o'clock or a little later a man came striding across the square in felt boots. He walked lightly on his swollen legs, while his eyes blazed in his lean face.

"Ivan Nikodimitch," he said, as he paused for a moment before the fancier, "put your things away. Over in the city the Jerusalem gentry are being granted the constitution. In the fish-market they've given the old fellow Babel a treat. He's done for—for good!"

He said it so lightly and passed on between the cages, like a barefoot plowman, walking along a hedge.

"What's the good of it?" murmured Ivan Nikodimitch after him. "What's the good of it?" he shouted louder and began to collect his rabbits and peacocks, thrusting the desired pair of pigeons into my hands for the forty kopecks. I hid them in my bosom with the others and began to observe the people scattering from the market-place. With the peacock perched on his shoulder, Ivan Nikodimitch was the last to leave. He sat there as the sun sits in the damp Autumn sky, he sat there as July sits on the rosy river bank, the white-hot July in the long cool grass. I stared in the wake of the old man, walking away with his charming cages, wrapped in colored rags. No one was left in the market-place, and the firing sounded near at hand. Then, cutting across the square, I ran toward the railway station, and fled into a deserted lane, stamped down with yellow earth. At the end of the lane, in a wheeled arm-chair, sat the legless Makarenko, who navigated his chair through the town streets and sold cigarettes from a tray. The urchins in our street used to buy cigarettes from him, the children loved him, and I flung myself toward him through the lane.

"Makarenko," I said, gasping for breath, as I patted the shoulder of the legless one, "have you seen my Uncle Shoyl?"

The cripple did not answer. His red face, compounded of fat, of brutishness, of iron, gleamed. In terrible perturbation he fidgeted in his wheel-chair, while his wife Katiusha, her wadded back turned to us, was sorting things scattered about on the ground.

"Have you finished counting?" asked the legless one and turned with his whole body away from the woman, as if he knew in advance how unbearable her answer would be.

"Neckties—fourteen pieces," she said, without turning round, "bed-sheets—six. Now I'm counting the caps . . ."

"Caps!" shouted Makarenko, panting, a sobbing note in his voice. "It's clear, Katiusha, God has picked me out to suffer punishment for all. . . . There are folks carrying whole rolls of linen. . . . They know what they're about . . . but we must be satisfied with caps. . . ."

And, actually, a woman with her handsome face all aflame came running just then down the lane. She had an armful of fezzes, and a roll of cloth. In a desperate yet exultant voice she was calling for her lost children; a silken dress and blue blouse trailed after her flying form, and she did not hear Makarenko rolling behind her in his chair. The legless one could not catch up with her, the wheels of his chair clattered, he worked the levers with a kind of frenzy and still could not catch up with her.

"Little lady," he shouted deafeningly, "for God's sake, little lady, where did you get that cloth?"

But the woman with the flying dress was soon gone. From round the corner where she disappeared there hove in sight a peasant's cart. A peasant lad was standing up in it.

"Where have all the people run to?" he asked, raising the red reins above the nags, restless in their harness.

"They've all run off to Cathedral street," answered Makarenko imploringly. "They're all there. Now run along and grab all you can. Then come back. I'll buy everything!"

The peasant lad, on hearing about Cathedral street, lost no time. . . . He bent forward and whipped up his piebald nags. They tore from the spot with startling suddenness and broke into a gallop. The yellow lane was once more yellow and deserted, it was only then that the legless one turned upon me his now dimmed eyes.

"Sure enough, God's picked me out," he murmured lifelessly. "Why? Ain't I human . . ."

And Makarenko reached out towards me a blotched, swollen, unsightly hand.

"What have you in that bag?" he asked and snatched the bag which had been warming my heart.

With his heavy hand the cripple tore open the bag and drew out into the light one of the cherry-tinted pigeons. The bird lay in the palm of his hand, its tiny claws upward.

"Pigeons," said Makarenko and, with a creaking of wheels, he rolled nearer me. "Pigeons," he repeated, like an irrevocable echo, and struck me across the face.

He struck me full force, with clenched fist. The pigeon was crushed against my temple. Katiusha's cotton-wadded bottom spun around before my eyes, and I fell to the ground in my new great-coat.

"It's necessary to destroy their seed," said Katiusha then, and bent over the caps. "I loath their seed and their stinking men . . ."

She said something else about our seed, then I heard nothing more. I was lying on the ground, and the entrails of the crushed bird were running down my temple. They ran down my cheeks, oozing, bespattering and blinding me. The pigeon's tender entrails crept along my forehead, and I closed my one yet unblinded eye, in order not to see the world which spread out before me. This world was small and horrible. A stone was before my eyes, a stone beaten into a shape which was like the face of an old woman with a huge jaw; there was also a bit of rope lying at no great distance, and a tiny heap of feathers with still a breath of life in them. My world was small and horrible. I closed my eyes so as not to see it, and pressed against the earth lying under me in soothing muteness. This stamped-down earth in no way resembled our life, with its fretting over examinations and the like. Somewhere far away misery rode over it upon a spirited steed, but the sound of its hoof-beats was growing fainter, vanishing into the distance, and the silence, the bitter silence, which sometimes overwhelms children in affliction, suddenly swept away the barrier between my trembling body and the motionless earth. My earth smelt of its damp depth, of the grave, of flowers. I hearkened to its aroma, and I began to weep without any sort of fear.

I was walking in a strange street, piled with high boxes; I was walking, decorated with blood-stained feathers, alone in the midst of pavements, swept clean as on Sunday; and I wept so bitterly, so unrestrainedly and so happily, as never before or since in my whole life. The whitened wires hummed overhead, a tiny watchdog ran on ahead, and in a side lane a young peasant in a waistcoat was smashing in a window in the house of Kariton Efrussi. He was doing it with a wooden hammer, swinging his whole body, and, sighing, looked around him with a good-natured smile of intoxication, a smile of sweat and of spiritual strength. The entire street was filled with sounds of crunching, crackling, with the song of scattering wood. The peasant was hammering away merely that he might bend, sweat and shout unusual words in some unknown, un-Russian tongue. He shouted and he sang, and stared out of his blue eyes, until a religious procession suddenly appeared from the direction of the Duma. Old men with painted beards were bearing in their hands the portrait of the sleek-combed Tsar; banners with graveyard saints swayed above the procession, and frenzied old women unrestrainedly ran on ahead. On sighting the procession, the peasant in the waistcoat pressed the hammer to his breast and ran after the banners, and I, waiting until the procession had passed by, fled home. It was empty, our house. Its white doors stood wide open, the grass near the pigeon-house was trampled down. Kuzma alone had not left his place in the courtyard. Kuzma, the yard-keeper, was sitting in the out-shed near Shoyl's corpse and laying out the body.

"The wind's carrying you along, like a bad chip," said the old man on seeing me. "You've gone off for an age. . . . You can see what the people have done to our uncle. . . ."

"They've settled our uncle, and no one else," said Kuzma. "He cursed the whole lot of them, sent them all to hell in proper style, the fine fellow he was. . . . You might fetch a couple of five-kopeck pieces for his eyes."

I was but ten years old at the time, and I did not know why dead people needed five-kopeck pieces.

"Kuzma," I murmured, "save us . . ."

I walked up to the yard-keeper and embraced his crooked back with one shoulder higher than the other, and I surveyed my uncle from behind this beloved back. Shoyl lay in a pile of sawdust, with his chest crushed in, with his beard thrust upward, his rough shoes drawn over his naked feet. His legs, drawn apart, were dirty, a pale grey, dead. Kuzma worked over them, then he tied up the jaw, and stood there thinking as to what he ought to do next. He acted as if he had acquired a new possession, and he ceased from his preoccupation only after he had combed the dead man's beard.

"He cursed the lot of them to hell," he said, smiling, as he surveyed the corpse with affection. "If the Tartars had gone for him, he'd have sent them scampering. But then the Russians came too, with their hefty wives; they are a tough lot! I know the breed. . . ."

The yard-keeper threw some more sawdust round the body, flung off his carpenter's apron, and took me by the hand.

"Now I'll take you to your father," he murmured, pressing my hand hard in his. "Your father has been looking for you since morning, he almost died. . . ."

And together with Kuzma I went to the house of the tax inspector, with whom my parents had taken refuge from the pogrom.

THE ACCOUNT

by HAYYIM HAZAZ

ALL the praises and laudatory epithets with which Jewry so dexterously adorns philanthropists were monopolised in that large town outside the Pale of Settlement, by four or five rich men. They seemed to have become strange, outlandish creatures, if one might be permitted to say so; no more or less than chimaeric adjectives. Like that species of vegetable which consists of nothing more than skins one within another and neither food nor satisfaction of any other kind as its centre, since its skins are their own reason for being. But Baruch Yalover was an everyday fellow, whom folk did not credit with thousands and million in coin; there was no particular praise accruing to him, no special adjective, nor was he renowned; he was just a plain straightforward common noun, like potato or black bread or loaf.

He did not belong to the class of the well-to-do, and what was seen and heard on all sides must be stated; so everyday was he as to be the acme of everydayness. Just the sort of man to dismiss with a snap of the fingers. Rabbi Doctor Spitz, the one who was neither a rabbi nor a doctor but who was a rabbi because he was a doctor and a doctor in order to be a rabbi, used to say of him that he was an ignoramus by the grace of God. Nevertheless he had adopted the exalted merit of doing more charity and opening his hand wide to scatter more money than could be expected, like one of the great philanthropists. Well, his fame did not spread abroad, neither in his town nor in the world at large. He was not doing charity for the sake of that. Those who knew him knew him: communal workers, wardens, treasurers, patrons and all who were in charge of charitable institutions. He was known best of all by Rabbi Doctor Spitz, who called on him at any hour and under any circumstances when funds were required for the poor and needy in Israel, no matter for what reason.

He never permitted himself to join the philanthropists and well-to-do when they assembled in meetings. Where would he fit with his shabby, creased clothes, his meagre height, full belly and bent back, which made him look like something pleated over and over, with his gross everyday face red as a fine piece of meat fresh from the butcher's, his nose fleshy and ruddy as the comb of an old cock, and lined with fine blue veins like a kind of spleen. The others were all such fine wealthy folk! Important and respected individuals of good stock, of fine appearance and plentiful knowledge and the gift of gab and the manners of the great. They were artists, artists! They were not like all other folk nor even like themselves; they did not look like Jews nor did they speak like Jews; they did not have the same movements nor the same twists nor the same habits. You could almost say that everything about them was borrowed from other folk, such as counts and dukes. And you could almost say that they were always playing a theatre-piece, nobody could say whether for themselves or for other people, maybe as a joke, maybe in earnest; they spoke as though they whispered from on high, and made themselves far bigger than was in the power of any ordinary man who goes his own way.

They went according to their standards and he according to his. They were important and well-known, and he was a simple fellow; they seemed to wear masks, and behaved like spoilt lightheaded boys, while he was like an experienced and firmly-established old man. They did what they did out of pride and competition and so that folk should have something to speak about, while he did it for the real reason and the necessity of his deed.

Requirement, necessity and the work which had to be accomplished —these were the outstanding principles by which he had guided himself since he came to know his own mind. According to them he did business, according to them he built his house and according to them he expended his money in charity. His house was a basic requirement, and his money was like his house and the love of Israel like his money and the Awe of the Name was as the love of Israel; and all were intertwined and united within him in a single uninterrupted strand.

But in this bitter generation of ours in which peace has been taken from the faithful houses of Israel, a man's house is not a house and his security is not security, he has no actual strength and power, and all principles have been effaced save the principle of suffering alone. First his daughter tore his world to shreds about him by marrying a gentile, a public prosecutor in one of the towns along the Volga. And it was not long thereafter that his son went on the long journey for he rebelled against the Government and was sent to Siberia. For him there was nothing left but charity and the fear of Heaven. As before he feared God and served him without excessive fervour and without excessive dread; he neither increased nor diminished, but served God at heart in his usual quiet way, which kept the scales evenly balanced between the two sides as always; but charity he began to do even more than before, and though all the poor folk of Israel had become his sons, all their needs and troubles were left him to satisfy and put right, and he had to support them with his labour as if they were so many infants.

When the Bolsheviks came and deprived him of rights and took away everything he had, they did not find in his house, as they had found in the homes of the philanthropists and the well-to-do, either salons or boudoirs, either bedrooms or tearooms with frescoes and paintings by renowned artists; either Karelian birch or furniture of black oak or white oak; either Abramtziva majolicas or porcelain of Sèvres and Copenhagen; no collection of tom-toms or idols brought from South Africa, nor yet fine pictures of Monet, Cézanne, Degas, Gaugin and all the other ultra-moderns. They found no more than a flat of four rooms with stout plain utensils, his wife lying sick with all the suffering she had passed through, and twenty thousand roubles to his credit in the bank. His wife did not remain sick long but departed from this world which is so much worse than all the Curses written in the Fifth Book of the Torah, and from this life which is more bitter than death. When he was robbed and despoiled and flung from his house and his wife died on his hands, everything vanished and he was left a lonely, forsaken old man, possessing neither goods nor needs of the body. Submissively, silently, without knowing what had befallen him, he bowed his head before every wave that passed over it and accepted the judgment; it was decreed from Heaven and no human being had any power or dominion over it. For only if it were all decreed from Heaven was there any sense in the sufferings; and only then could he have the strength to suffer patiently, and only then were all recriminations prevented; he had no place to enquire, and all accusations and remonstrances were vain. It had been decreed from Heaven that he must be imprisoned and imprisoned over and over again, and that he should be pursued and driven from pillar to post and oppressed, and all the rest of those sufferings and afflictions. It had been decreed from the Heavens even when he went to entreat his daughter to repent and found her killed by the authorities, both she and her husband the former public prosecutor. And the hardest decree to bear of all was when they arrested his son who had returned from exile, and imprisoned him for being a social revolutionary.

After they arrested his son he used to wander about as though bemused and dazed, his mind in a whirl, his heart rent and weeping within him and his eyes weeping on their own, silently and secretly. It seemed as though he had reached the end of the road. Old age leapt upon him. His face grew lined, dark as pitch; his belly, which had already disburdened itself, drew inwards, and he seemed to lose height. The whole of him seemed like a mushroom that had shrivelled with age. Day by day his strength diminished and his spirit recoiled, since what was it all for? The world was a gloomy Gehenna; some men were led out to be killed and others came to their end by starvation; the malevolence of humankind was hardest of all to bear; justice and mercy, freedom and equality and all the promised good were not to be found; and why should the streets and the houses remain standing in rows with this sun and these skies? . . . He felt like a child, and everything about him seemed childlike; his height, his appearance, his tiny toddling steps and the thoughts he was thinking; and all the world round him was mysterious and unclear. He felt just like a little baby. Sometimes his heart would be soothed by fine hopes which had no foundation in reality, and weird fantasies, almost an entire mythology, went round in his mind and fashioned of all kinds of hopeful tidings; wonderful things were done to him and his son and they were miraculously delivered. Thus he once happened to cross a bridge. He stood staring at the water, his thoughts running on as though he and his son were transformed into fishes that swam side by side through the water till they reached a second river, and from that second river to a third, and from the third river the sea, and from the sea they came out on the coast of some other country and were delivered. . . . But it was not always with fantasies that his mind was occupied. Sometimes he conjectured on actualities, and every fresh thought then seemed more likely and more probable; such and such reasons under such and such circumstances would finally lead the Cheka to free him and his son from suspicion, and thenceforward they would be considered full citizens, and they would devote themselves to making a living and would live quietly; and so on and so forth.

Weary and hopeless he would wander through the streets and markets looking for enough to give him his daily food, any sort of living.

Fearful and quivering, startled and quick as a broken hare pursued by relentless dogs, his bowels were taut and clutched with hunger, and his spirit would all but leave him before all authority or the shadow of authority or the shadow of that shadow. The whole atmosphere seemed to be suffused with a spirit of tumult and dread, as a forest is steeped in the scent of greenery. The windows of houses opening on the street were dangerous, the pavements, the terrifying posters, the crowds of the street, the public thoroughfares when they swarmed with men; and even more when they had emptied and stood weirdly broad and vaguely frightening. . . .

There was fear round about. Fear and dread. All life was fear and dread. A freezing dread, as though all had frozen into immobility and history no longer occurred, and the world were an empty void and there was nothing—"His Blessed Name alone knows what it all is and why." . . . And nonetheless all would end well. Or was it possible that things would never be well any more? Was it possible that the world would not return to its former conditions, to a beauty greater than it had formerly possessed? Impossible, it would have to go back! The heart demanded its own; everything would be all right in the world. It was of no account that for the moment everything was evil and bitter. And it did not matter that he derived no benefit whatsoever from all his devoted running hither and thither, to the associates and associates of associates of the authorities, to plead mercy for his son. Salvation must come at last! No one can take oath that improvements will never be brought about. For if indeed truth will grow out of the earth, then out of the world which is deeper now than the earth, it will certainly grow. And when truth will grow from the earth justice will be seen from Heaven and the Lord will also give that which is good. . . .

When he came out of the prison gate he walked strangely, as though walking were a craft he had never been trained in. The ground rocked under his feet, his head whirled and all sorts of rainbows revolved in confusion before his eyes. The city heaved about him as through a gilded veil; its restless streets, its mixed motley crowds, the glaring posters which menaced the passers-by at every streetcorner, the height of the dusty, weedy-looking neglected trees—what were all these here for? . . . It was a hot summer's day when there is no escape from the heat and it is impossible to breathe. He did not know whither he should go and what he should do. Just as though he had been transferred from one prison to another which was even more severe.

A few days after he came out of prison he visited Rabbi Doctor Spitz, finding him in one of the two rooms of his former dwelling, to which the authorities had limited him. The room was small and dirty, crowded with all kinds of different things tumbled together, blankets and cushions and pillows tossed about, plates, cups, piles of books standing crazily on the floor in a corner, pairs of shoes, his top hat in all its shine and glory, and a good deal more of the like. The room contained elements which made it equally resemble the shop of a dealer in old junk, the temporary lodging of a man whose house has been burnt, and the abode of an emigrant to whom something has happened on his way to America.

It was with an important request that Baruch Yalover came to Rabbi Doctor Spitz; to ask him to make an account of the charity he had done in his lifetime; since his own head felt heavy and his mind was confused and he could not think. To begin with Doctor Spitz treated the thing like a sort of joke. When he saw it was not a joke he tried to divert his attention to other matters in one way or another. Since he did not succeed, he began to argue, to mock and to make him look silly. Finally he saw he would not get rid of him, since the old man insisted on his account as though he were a monomaniac; so he gave in despite himself and against his will.

"You've done your full share of charity, I know. More than your full share!" he said with annoyance, his face angry. "How much money you've laid out through my hands alone! Treasures!"

He rose, brought some paper, armed himself with a pencil, sat down at his disordered table and took down by dictation the details of Baruch Yalover's account.

"For the Society for Providing Cheap Meals for the Needy," he dictated in a weak and shaky voice, "membership dues for twenty-seven years, in all, eighty roubles."

"Eighty-one roubles," noted Doctor Spitz in annoyance on the paper, and sat back to hear more.

"Shoes for a hundred and fifty lads of the orphanage at six and a half roubles a pair, every year, amounting to nine hundred and seventy-five roubles a year; and then for six year—it amounts—it amounts—it seems to me it amounts to five thousand eight hundred and fifty roubles. I think that's right. Please go over it and see. . . ."

"And fifty roubles," concluded Doctor Spitz, holding the pencil loosely in his hand.

"Clothes and linen for the orphanage, nine hundred and nine roubles ninety-eight kopeks a year. How much in six years?"

"Five thousand four hundred and fifty-nine roubles and eighty-eight kopeks," reckoned Doctor Spitz and noted it down.

"Right. Now note down: One thousand and six kosher meals for prisons; if I do not err I remember paying in all one thousand nine hundred and seventy-three roubles."

"I've noted it," nodded Rabbi Doctor Spitz in boredom and impatience.

"Now seven thousand five hundred eggs for the hospital to commemorate my silver wedding, amounting in all to one hundred and sixteen roubles and sixty-one kopeks."

"And sixty-one kopeks. Noted! Go on. . . ."

"Wood for fuel in the hospital, thirty-one wagonloads, amounting in all to three hundred and seventy-five roubles and twenty-two kopeks."

"Twenty-two kopeks. Go on. . . ."

"To Jewish soldiers for Sabbaths and festivals seventeen thousand one hundred and four kosher meals, amounting in all to three thousand three hundred and eighty roubles and forty-five kopeks."

"You have a memory!" laughed Doctor Spitz ironically.

"Now one hundred heads of cattle for the kitchen, and I don't remember any longer how much I paid. . . ."

"How shall we enter it?" Rabbi Doctor Spitz stared at him with a mixture of laughter, astonishment and simple perplexity how to enter it.

Baruch Yalover closed his eyes, thought it over a moment, while his face grew soft and as dark as a crack in a tub.

"Note them down as they are: a hundred of cattle!" he said.

"A hundred head of cattle!" responded Rabbi Doctor Spitz with a laugh, "and may the Holy and Blest One reckon them as though they were a hundred offerings."

"Passover flour for the hospital sixteen pood and twenty pounds, which are sixteen roubles and sixty-seven and a half kopeks a year, and I donated it for four years, how much is it?"

"Here you are. Audited and found correct. Sixty-seven kopeks and a half, ha! ha! ha!"

"Yes. And another four thousand roubles I gave anonymously for the site of the handicrafts school. . . ."

"So that was you?" Rabbi Doctor Spitz turned his sharp, surprised eyes on him.

"Note it, note it. . . . Small disbursements for writing books, pens, ink, etcetera, for the orphanage on the day of the confirmation of my son, long life to him . . ." his voice trembled and broke, but he controlled himself at once and continued whispering, "three hundred and thirty-seven roubles and ninety-eight kopeks."

"I've noted it," responded Rabbi Doctor Spitz in a low voice. "I've noted it, Boris Yakovlevitz."

"Now an account for the war refugees," Baruch Yalover returned to his theme. "Write: one thousand five hundred and eighty-six sacks of flour which are in all . . ."

He continued dictating an account of all the disbursements he had made, each disbursement on its own, a long list which seemed to have no end or limit. . . . Rabbi Doctor Spitz grew weary with the toil, sweat already covered him, and still the other sat there and went on enumerating.

When he finished Rabbi Doctor Spitz's face grew bright, he stood up, straightened his back and stretched himself.

"Bless be He who has freed me!" he said jokingly and began to total up the account and see how much it all amounted to.

While he prepared the account Baruch Yalover fell asleep, for his weariness and hunger had sapped his strength. But he had not been sleeping long before Rabbi Doctor Spitz awoke him.

"Boris Yakovlevitz! Boris Yakovlevitz!" he shook him by the shoulder.

He wearily opened his eyes and looked at the rabbi as though he did not know what the other was doing there.

He spent a moment collecting his thoughts, wrinkled up his deeply furrowed brow and said:

"Rabbi, what will happen when we come over yonder? Immediately, the first moment we come over there yonder? . . ."

Doctor Spitz was startled and surprised at his words. Although he knew that the other's words referred to the World to Come, he pretended not to understand.

"Yonder where?" he asked in astonishment. "Were you dreaming or what?"

"Just asking, just asking. . . ."

"Here's the account. One hundred and nineteen thousand roubles and forty-three kopeks in gold coin, gold!" he said with a smile. "You did plenty of charity. Would that there had been many like you in Israel! How much were you worth, Boris Yakovlevitz?"

"All I had was forty thousand roubles. Neither more nor less, but exactly forty thousand roubles."

"Forty thousand? Only forty thousand!" exclaimed Doctor Spitz in a low astonished voice as though he had been suddenly reduced from his glory.

Boris Yalover took the paper and studied it, while it shook in his hot hand.

"A good balance," said he after a moment. "A fine balance. . . . Only I myself am worth nothing, whatever there is of me doesn't get entered into the world's accounts among the lists of the creatures of the Holy and Blest. . . ."

"A great sum!" said Rabbi Doctor Spitz, waiting for him to go. "The Holy and Blest One owes you a great deal, a great deal, Boris Yakovlevitz. Keep your mouth covered and say nothing—you mustn't tell how much He owes you. . . ."

Baruch Yalover, who felt that the other wanted to be rid of him, wished to rise and go, but his legs paid no attention; weariness was creeping over him and he could not move.

"Just a few minutes," he excused himself. "I'm tired."

"By all means, Boris Yakovlevitz! The pleasure's mine," answered Rabbi Doctor Spitz politely with secret annoyance, and returned to his desk.

Baruch Yalover sat weary and weak, his face sunken and sickish, his head resting on his palm and his eyes staring afar, as though he might be thinking or listening to an answer to the problem that had been gnawing at his brain: what would happen *there,* the very first moment he would arrive *there,* just at that very first moment?

Rabbi Doctor Spitz sat in annoyance thinking: here he comes troubling you three hours on end, and you have to go sitting with him, Devil knows why! An ignoramus like him. . . .

"You did plenty of charity while you had the opportunity!" he turned to him. "Blessed be the hands that donate so!"

Baruch Yalover turned his head toward him, dropping his eyes at once in uninterested weariness. Slowly he stretched out his hand, took a Bible that was lying on the table, and began glancing at it. In a few moments he raised his eyes from the Bible, put his hand in his pocket and took out two bundles of Soviet paper money.

"Rabbi . . ." he began slowly and calmly, his face growing still paler, "I am leaving four hundred thousand roubles with you. . . . And I ask you to do me the last true kindness and bring me to a Jewish grave. . . . And my son—long life to him . . . if the hour does not come . . ."

His voice broke and he stopped.

"Already he's . . ." he dropped his head, his voice quivering and sinking, "he's been eight days already neither eating nor drinking, on hunger strike . . . the eighth day. . . ."

He rose, put the paper money on the desk, patted the bundles two or three times and urged his limbs to move. Rabbi Doctor Spitz hastily began to try and comfort him with the encouragement suitable for such a moment and such a subject. But the words did not enter his ears. He bent over the Bible for a while. Presently he turned aside, looked across the room, placed his finger on the open text and said:

"How strange this people is! They saw clearly . . . eye to eye they saw . . . and all the same, 'And he did that which was evil,' and 'they did that which was evil' . . ."

There was silence in the room, that difficult silence which sounds excessive and high-pitched, like an essence of the whole of life, all things and all paths.

"Goodbye, Rabbi." He took the hand of Rabbi Doctor Spitz in his own and retained it a long while. "Goodbye. . . ."

Vainly did Doctor Spitz hasten from one side of him to the other, trying to comfort him and raise hopes in the aid of His Blessed Name. Slowly he shifted himself, walking heavily and with difficulty as though his feet were being sucked down by the floor. And Rabbi Doctor Spitz stood stock-still looking after him, his mouth twitching, his eyes big, his face wonder-struck, with nothing whatever to say.

THE GRAVES OF THE MACCABEES

by DAVID SHIMINOWITZ

I SIT down to rest on a large stone, smooth and white, growing out of a hill which stands stalwart, peering, like a sentinel to the valley below. Looking down, I see boulders and stones, black and white, arrayed as by some hand; delicate blood-red flowers swaying on their tall stems among the burnished stones; beauty arising from a desolation seared by the sun. Where the valley ends there stands an aged carob tree, many-branched and hedged in with rocks. A stag leaps from stone to stone, springs like a flash round the tree and hides again in the shadow. The sun beats down upon me as I walk on the side of the wall of stones which guards the valley.

It was sunrise when I set out for Modin, birthplace of the Maccabees.

I jump from one stone to another along the narrow path. What are the tiny forms I see, moving in the valley? I strain my eyes and discern a group of ploughmen following their ploughs. On the other side of the valley a young shepherd wrapped in lambskin leans on his staff and examines me with curiosity. Lambskin on a hot day like this! He has apparently not yet forgotten the cold of the night; or perhaps it is still cool in the shadow of the hill. My limbs crave for the coolness; but the day is short and I wonder whether I can reach Modin before sunset.

I go forward, uncertain of the way. The path? Scores of paths stretch before me. But from the distance I see a polished mirror flashing and my heart rejoices. It is the sea, and now I know that I am near Modin. It is the highest point from which one may see the sea, many hours distant. I climb higher and see the scattered huts hewn out of the rocks. There is still an hour and a half before the sun sinks.

I reach the village.

How wild the country is! Caves and crags, pits and wells partly covered with stone slabs. The little Maccabees must have played hide-and-seek here. Jonathan, Simon, Johanan: "Find me!" And the hills echo: "Find me!" Jonathan, Simon, Johanan leap like stags from stone to stone, scatter over cave and pit; they look for Judah. Judah, "Where are you?" And the hills echo: "Where are you?" Suddenly he appears, climbing out of his hiding place, laughing. The rays of the setting sun tinge the stones. A shepherd bearing a new-born lamb in his arms is going homeward for his flock. The youngest of the Maccabees leaps up, snatches the flute from the shepherd, runs in front of the flock, frolics and makes merry. His mother stands at the door of the tent, shading her eyes. When she learns the cause of the noise she scolds the mischievous children and smiles. Blue shadows creep down from the hills.

But the graves? Near them stand the ruins of a building, hewn out of the rock. The door has been destroyed; there remain only the pillars, thickgrown with weeds. Behind the wall facing the entrance stands an ancient olive tree with a broad and hollow trunk. I sit in the doorway and recapture from the surrounding stillness snatches of song of the past. It was here perhaps that the mother lion sat and sucked her whelps. Judah lay in her lap and could not sleep. He heard the roar of the sea, the cries of the eagles, the echoes of the hills. The crests of the hills are shadowed; mist has covered the valleys; but the eyes of the child are wide open and fixed on the distance. His mother rocks him slowly. She sings softly:

> "Sleep, my eagle, sleep,
> All the world is quiet,
> Hushed is all the singing
> In the gardens round.
> Every ship's asleep
> On the mighty sea.
> Living things are still;
> The eagle on his rock,
> The wild goat, the lion."

But the child will not sleep. His ears are open to every sound. The mother sings on:

> "Sleep, oh, sleep, my son,
> The chilly night descends;
> When cold of night has gone,
> Warm morning will be here.
> The honey dew,
> The rubied sky,
> Living things will waken;
> The eagle on his rock,
> The wild goat, the lion,
> And with them you, my son."

Judah stirs, closes his eyes, opens them again. The mother lowers her voice to a whisper:

> "Everything is asleep,
> Songs are stilled.
> And you, my cub,
> Will grow to strength.
> Suck from my breast,
> Grow—hunt the prey,
> Grow—become a lion.
> Now sleep, my son, sleep."

Judah falls asleep, but she remains sitting, afraid to stir. I too fear to move, lest I wake him from his sleep. Suddenly I jump up as if stung; my imagination is playing tricks with me . . . had clothed me in woman's form so that for a moment I imagined myself a mother, mother to Judah asleep in his cradle here.

The last rays of the sun spread over the great stone which covers the cave of the graves, and are caught in the moss that grows in its cracks. It is evident that the heavy could not be rolled away from the mouth of the cave but was moved a little from its place. Here is a narrow oblique opening. I push into the cave; and I am swallowed by darkness.

The roof is covered with the handwriting of visitors. Joseph Rahamin from Acre, Aaron Moshe from Jerusalem, Haim Herman from Elizabethgrad. I erase the scribbling; no stranger shall intrude in this holy place! Weary and spent I stretch out on the floor.

From the moment that I entered the cave I felt a tightness round my breast, a pain of love. I came to visit my heroes in the name of my childhood which was lit up by their glory and glowed in their splendour. My heart is still filled with awe and overflows with love; but before those inanimate blocks of stone my childhood's blessing is stifled and my heart is no lighter than before.

The olive-tree outside becomes enveloped with flame—a huge, wonderful Chanukah light above the graves of the heroes. The Creator himself has lit it with the fire of His lightning. But now a wild storm bursts out, a cry of distress from a thousand mouths. Myriads of the brave are treading the hillside, coming to bury their leader. The olive-tree burns but is not consumed; sparks dance and flare in the darkness. I feel as if I were bewitched by the sparkling tower of flame. My ears detect a muffled murmur, far-off and unceasing—the dirge of the sea in honour of the brave.

The rain pours down, drums on the stones, falls dully into the dust. I gaze up. There is a large undefined blackness between sky and earth, whispering, pleading, despairing, yet humming with hope, like the hum of a brook in spring. Bands of fire pierce its depth, sink immediately and appear again as distant lights. Now they are lit, now dim again. Are they not Chanukah lights, flickering in the ends of the earth, from the parched deserts of Yemen to the cold snows of the North, in fog-bound Whitechapel and in the new Ghetto in New York, in an attic in Paris and in a tent in Polesia? For a moment the stones and the thorns that grow among them flare up into fantastic forms, flare up and recede as if fleeing from sudden terror. The darkness is intense. The olive-tree has perished, the lightning has ceased for a moment, and I hear broken sounds of lamentation and the tapping of staffs against the stones. Here they hover, these eternal wanderers, fleeing from Yemen and Russia, from the suffocating atmosphere of Whitechapel and New York; they flit like ghosts from rock to rock, feel their way in the blackness with their staffs —weak, dull tapping as of feebleness, decay, despair.

But why do I tremble, why is my body on fire? How the hills resound, like the ring of hammer on anvil! Here they come, tramping, marching on the heights, the multitudes of the brave bearing their leader to his grave. Is the earth crumbling? Are the graves opening? Hush! I hear a plaintive voice. Who is crying? Ah, I recognize the cry, it is Judah. . . . I am here, I am here!

LATIFA

by MOSES SMILANSKY

'IF you never saw Latifa's eyes—you don't know how beautiful eyes can be.'

So I used to say when I was still a lad and Latifa a young Arab girl, hardly more than a child.

And I still say so, for all the many years that have passed.

It was January, the rainy season.

I was in the fields with a group of Arabs, preparing the ground for planting my first vineyard. My heart was in a festive mood, which seemed to be shared by all my surroundings. It was a fine bright day. The air was clear and calm, warm and invigorating. The sun stood in the east, shedding a reddish early-morning radiance over all things; it was a pleasure to breathe, to fill the lungs to their utmost capacity. Everything around was green, and graceful and beautiful wild flowers nodded on the untilled hills.

Among the Arab women clearing stones and 'injil' I saw a fresh face. It was that of a young girl of about fourteen, upright and agile, in a blue dress. One end of a white kerchief covered her head, while the other end fell on to her shoulders.

'What is your name?' I asked her, wishing to note it down.

A small face, brunette and coy, turned to me, while two black eyes sparkled.

'Latifa.'

Her eyes were lovely—large, black, flaming. The pupils sparkled with happiness and joie de vivre.

'The daughter of Sheikh Surbaji,' added Atala, a young Arab who was at that moment shifting a big stone. His remark was flung into the air as though casually.

'Like to two stars on a fine summer night . . .' Atala began lilting in his rich, strong voice, glancing mischievously at me as he sang.

Henceforth my work acquired a fresh interest for me. When I felt heavy or dejected I would look at Latifa, and my depression and melancholy would vanish as at a magic touch.

Often I would feel the gaze of Latifa as she watched me. Often I would feel the flashing of her eyes, and sometimes her gaze was sad.

Once I was riding to the field on my small grey ass. At the well I met Latifa, a pitcher of water on her head. She was bringing water for the labourers.

'How are you, Latifa?'

'My father will not permit me to go on working. . . .'

The words came pouring from her lips, as though she were emptying her heart of something that had long been oppressing it. Her voice was sad, as though some misfortune had befallen her.

'Would you not rather stay at home than work?'

Latifa looked at me, her eyes becoming dim as though a shadow passed over them. For a few moments she remained silent.

'My father wants to give me to the Sheikh of Agar's son.'

'And you?'

'Sooner would I die. . . .'

She was silent once again. Then she asked:

'Hawaja, is it true that your folk take but one?'

'But one, Latifa.'

'And your folk do not beat their women?'

'Nay. How shall one beat the woman whom he loves and who loves him?'

'Among you the maidens take those they love?'

'Assuredly.'

'While us they sell like beasts of burden. . . .'

During those moments Latifa's eyes were even more beautiful, deeper and blacker.

'My father says,' she added a moment later, 'that he would give me to you, if you would become a Moslem. . . .'

'To me?'

I burst out laughing in spite of myself. Latifa gazed at me, her eyes full of anguish.

'Latifa,' I said, 'become a Jewess, and I will take you.'

'My father would slay me, and you too.'

Next day Sheikh Surbaji came to my vineyard.

He was an old man with a fine white beard, a tall tarbush on his head, riding on a spirited white mare that pranced and curveted beneath him.

He gave greeting to the labourers, who on their side all bowed to him with great humility and became silent. At me he threw an ill-tempered look, and he greeted me with a snarl in his voice. I responded with equal coolness. There was no love lost between the Colony and the Sheikh, who bore a fanatic hatred toward the Jews.

When the Sheikh saw his daughter his anger grew to fury.

'Did I not order you to cease going to the Jew?' he stormed.

'Shame upon you, Moslems, who sell your toil to the unbelievers!'

The stick in his hand fell several times on the head and shoulders of Latifa. Thoroughly angered, I made a motion toward him, but the sad, black, tear-filled eyes of Latifa looked at me as though entreating me to be still.

The Sheikh and his daughter departed. The labourers breathed more freely.

'Sheikh Surbaji is pitiless,' said one.

'He is furious because he can no longer get his labourers at half the wages, and make them toil from morning to night. The Jews compete,' said a second.

'And I know why he is in a rage today,' said Atala, a cunning smile hovering about his lips.

Latifa did not return to work.

One afternoon a few weeks later, when I left the house where I was accustomed to take my meals, I met her. She sat on the ground outside offering chickens for sale. When she saw me she rose. Her eyes were more beautiful, and more sad than ever.

'How are you, Latifa?'

'Thank you, hawaja.'

Her voice shook.

And Latifa often brought chickens for sale, and always at the noon hour. . . .

One day Atala said to me:

'Hawaja, Latifa has gone to Agar; the Sheikh's son has taken her— a small and ugly fellow. . . .'

To me his words were like a stab in the heart.

Afterwards I heard that the house of Latifa's husband had been destroyed by fire, that Latifa had fled to her father's house, and that they had taken her back to her husband against her will.

Some years passed. I was living in the house which I had built for myself. Other black eyes had made me forget the eyes of Latifa.

One morning I went out and found two old Arab women holding chickens.

'What do you want?'

One of the women rose from the ground and gazed at me.

'Hawaja Musa?'

'Latifa?'

Ay, this was Latifa; this old woman with her seamed and wrinkled face. She had grown old, but her eyes still retained traces of their former brightness.

'You have a beard—how changed—' she whispered, not moving her eyes from me.

'How are you? Why have you changed so?'

'All things come from Allah, hawaja!'

She was silent. Then:

'Hawaja Musa has taken a wife?'

'Yes, Latifa.'

'I would like to see her. . . .'

I called my wife out.

Latifa looked at her for a long time.

There were tears in her eyes. . . .

I have not seen Latifa since then.

THE DECISION

by SARAH GERTRUDE MILLIN

EXCEPT for a vacation five years ago, Saul and his father had not been together for eight years. And for months before Saul's arrival the old man had gone about in a state of beatific anticipation. They would be such friends, he thought; he would take such an interest in Saul. He knew there was more than the ordinary difference of the generations between them: there was also the difference of tradition and early environment. But, on the other hand, he was a man of fluid mind (so he told himself), he wasn't set. He could still run with the times.

He dreamed of the great talks they would have. He loved talking.

But Saul had not been back three days when Old Nathan saw that things were not going to be as he had imagined. After Saul had finished telling him about his work as a student and as a young doctor walking the hospitals—the mere facts—he suddenly had no more to say. Old Nathan knew who had been his son's friends in London, what were his opinions, his disappointments, his aspirations. Saul was greatly reserved towards his father.

The days passed, and Old Nathan settled down to a kind of minor happiness in his son's presence. Now and then—because there was, after all, a tie which painfully pulled him towards his begetter—Saul did say: "Come, father, let us have a game of chess." But when he played it was merely as a duty—to give the old man fun, not to give himself fun. His deep-set, introspective grey eyes above the prominent cheekbones looked through the window, or at something lying in his neighbourhood, or at far-back happenings, while his father stared, in immovable meditation and with grinding brain, at the board. Sometimes Saul watched with a sympathetic amusement his father's little tricks, which did not elude him, because he was the better player. And, since he did not really care about the result of the game, and since he saw how his father despaired when he lost and exulted when he won, he did not press him too hard, he allowed him an occasional victory. It was a virtuous gesture, but it was a gesture grounded in the same feeling which irritated him when his father asked him questions or challenged him in argument. Its base was the pitying contempt, the impatient dutifulness, the fundamental desire for separation which lies between the straining child and the yearning parent.

Something of all this Old Nathan soon understood, and there were times when he asked himself whether, deeply as he loved his son, he had not, undisturbed by Saul's reservations concerning him, known a larger peace and a profounder self-confidence in his loneliness. This, however, Saul never realised as his father realised his son's mood. He had, like all children, a naïve complacency about his parent's enchanted regard for him. . . .

When Saul came home now from his case his father told him that Arnold Duerden had been looking for him. "He wants you to join the Vigilance Association," he mentioned.

"I've been wondering when they'd come to me," said Saul.

"Will you join?" inquired Old Nathan.

Saul did not answer him at once. Then he asked him what the Vigilants were actually doing.

"Well," explained Old Nathan, drawing out the word into two singing notes and swaying his head, "well, you know what such a thing means. It means people are going about with a light to see if everything is in order—a little gunpowder, so to speak—they examine it very close with the light and they make an explosion."

Saul smiled. "I see. Now, of course, I know all about it."

"You think not?" queried his father. "Then you ask Duerden and let him explain. He will tell you the Kaffirs are on the hill and the Indians are in the town. And if he will not tell you the Jews are over everything he will have it in his mind."

"I must go and see those Kaffirs."

"They will not let you. It says on a notice outside their camp: 'No Admittance!'"

"What is Duerden afraid they will do?"

"Fall on the town, perhaps."

"What do you think yourself?"

It was not often Saul invited his father's opinion, and the old man was correspondingly flattered. He knew quite well that, however outsiders might like a man to be a character, his own family treasured him according to his rigidly conventional merits, according to the way in which he met the world's accepted standards. The quaint grandmother, the artistic father, the exotic sister—their mumblings, their temperaments, their vagaries—were merely to their own people an irritation inside the home and an embarrassment outside it. Saul would have quite liked his father's manners and mannerisms if he had been someone else's father. But, since he was his own father, he wished that his soul and body, both, were frock-coated and top-hatted.

Old Nathan, struggling like an orator against a doubtful audience, responded eagerly to his son's interest.

"These natives call themselves Levites and believe they are of priestly standing," he replied. "Is it then to be expected they will leave their tabernacle for the kerrie and the assegai?"

"Dervishes fight," Saul pointed out.

"Perhaps because they are not left alone."

"Then you don't agree with Duerden?"

"I disagree with Duerden by nature."

"That isn't reasonable."

"It isn't unreasonable, for Duerden is by nature nearly always wrong."

"The end of it is you don't think I ought to join the Vigilants."

"Did I forbid you to go to the war? Everywhere is Rome for the Jew, and he tried to do like the Romans. If there is no interfering with the Kaffirs and their tabernacle, if it is only to make secret signs, and stand and talk at the corners, and run about the streets in the cold nights and catch a little influenza—" he shrugged his shoulders—"why should I say something to you? I will keep quiet my mind, and you will do, anyhow, what you wish."

Saul looked at his father as if he rather liked him. "You aren't quite a fool, you know, father," he said. And Old Nathan felt that he had been greatly complimented.

"Speak to Duerden yourself, then," he suggested.

"Will he be at the office now?" asked Saul.

"I can see you don't know much about Arnold Duerden yet," said Old Nathan. "What has he to do with an office? If he is not at the club, he will be practising golf or playing with his child at home. He is a good father, I hear."

Saul stretched himself.

A good father, he mused. Why did that sound derisive?

The Duerdens lived in a five-roomed white bungalow, and there was a small garden in front of it. Although land was very cheap in Gibeon, no one had the large grounds which customarily surrounded the best houses in the bigger and more expensive towns. Perhaps, indeed, the very fact that the land was cheap rendered it unattractive—made it seem not worth coveting. If one could always get as much land as one wanted, it was obviously not necessary to strain oneself to possess it. The houses in the streets of Gibeon stood almost as close together as they might have done in a London suburb. And everywhere in and about the town lay stretches of unused acres. And if one stood on one's stoep the whole veld lay empty beneath one's eyes.

It may be, then, that the houses crowded together for company. There was the great, lonely world outside. One wanted, perhaps, to hear the little noises of next door.

Saul rang the bell beside a half-glass door, and a native in white drill suit and bare feet answered it. Saul asked him if Mr. Duerden was at home, and the native told him that he was not, but that if Saul wanted to see Mrs. Duerden he would fetch her. As Saul stood hesitating, a voice which he thought very attractive, a voice clear and extremely audible, called out: "Of course, you want to see me. Do go inside. I'll be with you in a moment. Get tea. Silence."

And Saul had hardly reached the living-room when she was there too, a woman with light-coloured eyes under very black brows, and black hair curling briefly about her round head.

She examined Saul quite frankly.

"I know you very well," she said. "Your father has been telling me about you for years. I have seen your photograph in uniform, and I've been looking forward to meeting you. I'm particularly glad it's you now, because I was expecting someone else. A woman."

They sat down. The room was large and rather untidy. There was a grand piano littered with sheets of music. A dog had left a few bones on the floor. Rain had soaked through one of the roughly whitewashed walls and made a map-like design on it. But there was a tall jar of Irish roses on a gueridon, and a mass of winter bramble leaves on a corner cupboard. The curtains were heavily and coarsely and brightly embroidered. The chairs they were sitting on were disreputable to look at, but very comfortable to sit on. Saul felt that the room was as it ought to be. He was happy.

"I'm not in the mood for a woman today," added Hermia Duerden.

"Are you sometimes?" asked Saul, startled at the ease with which they had fallen into intimacy.

"Yes. When I want to be understood. But now and then, you know, you have a need to spread your personality. And you can't do that if people know too much about you."

She looked seriously at Saul.

"And then, again, what I want in almost everyone is a certain helplessness. I don't like strong, reserved people. I feel frustrated when they don't want to lean on me, and snubbed when they don't want to confide in me."

"You will find me weak and loquacious," said Saul, but he did not smile as he spoke, and that pleased Hermia.

"Well, then, we shall get on," she said. "Now tell me about yourself while we wait for Arnold. Have you met Arnold yet? What do you want to see him about? Nothing professional, I suppose."

Saul smiled slightly as he shook his head.

"Then may I know what it is?"

"Certainly. It's this Vigilance affair."

"It would be. I needn't have asked. I suppose you're joining. Everyone is."

"Shall I?"

"Do you really want me to tell you?"

"You sound as if you'd rather I didn't."

"I'd rather nobody did," said Hermia, with even more than her usual energy. "I'm utterly against it. I've told Arnold a hundred times that you create a thing spiritually as soon as you oppose it. Your act of tilting against windmills makes the windmills. Those Vigilants will feel so foolish if they find they have nothing to do that they will, consciously or unconsciously, see to it that they don't find nothing to do. And, on the other hand, the Kaffirs on the Heights will begin to wonder what it is the Vigilants are so afraid of, and, in wondering what it is the Vigilants are so afraid of, will call it into existence. . . . Well, but do you think I can get Arnold to see it? I tell you, Dr. Nathan, our household isn't worth living in these days. Arnold and I are having continual disputes about the Vigilants. I wish he were a busy lawyer and hadn't time for such things. Why isn't he, do you think?"

She had never before put anyone such a question. She could not have explained why she did so now, why this encounter had excited her to this excessive frankness.

But Saul, for his part, reflected that he had known this woman not fifteen minutes, and here she was demanding not only a mutual unreserve, but asking him to account for her husband's professional failure. And, although he may have taken the first in jest, the second he could not. Accordingly, being a Jew, and having behind him generations of people who might not speak their minds, he felt embarrassed and distrustful.

"You forget, Mrs. Duerden, I'm a stranger in Gibeon," he said cautiously and excludingly.

She heard the withdrawn note in his voice, and swiftly looked into his eyes.

"Oh, yes, I do forget," she replied, and continued pleasantly: "Are you glad to be back? Do you find Gibeon at all different?"

Her tone had changed at once to a completely conventional level. It was the difference between a fresh and living spring and a standing pool. Saul had not expected her to respond so quickly to his uneasiness. But, since she had, that uneasiness took now a different form. It ceased to be a doubt of her and became a doubt of himself, and it grew speedily, as the moments passed, into a definite sense of loss. He felt as though he had had something precious thrust into his hand, and, distrusting its value because of its easy achievement, had let it drop. And, as he had not wanted what was offered, so he now wanted what was lost.

The tea came in, and Hermia went on chatting agreeably, and he talked and smiled too, but their association had moved to another sphere, and there it stayed until Saul, feeling unhappily that it was time for him to go, took his departure without having seen Duerden.

The consequence of all this was that Saul felt he must now please Mrs. Duerden by not joining the Vigilants.

Next morning at eleven o'clock, Duerden saw Saul sitting on the stoep of his father's house which adjoined the shop, and he walked up the four steps to it, and smiled at him in the way which still could make people think him very attractive.

Saul gave him coffee, and they talked about football and golf and musical comedies and politics, and they discovered some mutual friends, and Duerden forgot that Saul was a Jew, but Saul did not.

And he looked at Duerden, and, all at once, felt sorry for him. He could see something young and frightened in Duerden. Duerden was puzzled by the sinister whims of destiny as a child is puzzled by the thwartings of its elders. He had once believed himself as good as any man, and better than most—at moments even now the illusion came back to him, but he had not received the world's endorsement of his opinion, and the heart within him was shrinking because his main fear these days was that the world might be right and he wrong. That was why he was a bully. It was his defiance of the world, his attempt to fling back in its sceptical face the distrust of himself with which it had infected him, and so free his laden soul.

Saul pitied Duerden, too, because Duerden was so feeble a mental match for him. There he was, unfortunate man, earnestly offering his opinions on things which seemed to Saul quite unimportant, and he was unaware of the ironical negligence which inspired Saul's polite agreements.

Saul looked at Duerden and thought how strange it was that Duerden belonged to the conquering race, and he, Saul, to the conquered one.

For he possessed the mental arrogance of a people which placed too high a value on its cleverness; and he did not realise that, however poor a receptacle Duerden himself might be for it, it was precisely this simplicity which went ahead and won, and this complexity which turned back on itself and failed. A great man or a great nation needed to have a blind spot, had not to see too much, had to shut one eye to hit the mark.

They spoke, of course, finally, about the Vigilants. "You're joining us, aren't you?" asked Duerden.

"I couldn't be a very reliable member," said Saul.

"How do you mean 'reliable'?"

"Well, as a doctor, you know, I couldn't undertake to do any particular thing at any particular time."

"We have two other doctors. We could arrange for a substitute when necessary."

Saul realised that he was in the presence of a man who was child enough to ask "why?" until he was told the truth. Evasions were useless. He had a desire, too, to please himself and impress Mrs. Duerden by being courageous.

"I may as well be frank with you, Duerden," he said. "I don't want to join your Vigilants because I don't believe in them."

Duerden stared at him.

"Don't believe in them? Why not?"

Saul wondered how exactly Mrs. Duerden answered such questions from her husband. Would she speak in the same terms to Duerden as she did to him, Saul? Would she, in actual fact, as well as in animated explanation, tell him about "creating a thing spiritually" and "making windmills by the act of tilting against them"? He could not believe so. He understood, in the light of this thought, how far apart in all essentials the two of them must be. She could talk to him, fifteen minutes ago a stranger, but she could not talk to her husband. Well, he had seen that sort of thing before. Did contempt go with it? Yes, it must, he supposed, whatever its cover or disguise. . . .

He smiled as he looked at Duerden. What was the use of making subtle explanations to such a man?

"I don't think those Kaffirs mean any harm," he said negligently.

His indifference was an affront to Duerden's passionate interest in his cause.

"Oh, you don't," he said. "You've been here a week, and you know more than the rest of us?"

Saul thought about his own father and about Duerden's wife, but he mentioned neither.

"Well, it's my opinion," he said, amused within himself to remember how recently, and under what circumstances, he had formed that opinion, and how it was now, curiously, his unalterable possession. So casually, sown in imitation, did principles spring up whose roots grew to a power that could crack the very rocks which opposed them.

"And if," said Duerden, "in spite of your opinion, there should be trouble?"

"I don't deny there may be trouble."

"Then—"

"You may force it," said Saul, taking his place beside Hermia and his father.

Duerden stood up.

"Let me assure you, Nathan, that this talk of yours isn't going to stop us from going on with the Association. That being so, there's a question I want to ask you: If the blacks do come down on Gibeon, will you avail yourself of our protection?"

Saul's dark skin grew greenish, but there were strips of red under his eyes.

"Oh, I'll have my job then," he said lightly. "I'll attend to your honourable wounds."

"There are only two men who have refused to join," added Duerden, his face pale too. "Diethelm and yourself."

He wanted to say something about their respective nationalities, and Saul knew it, and stood waiting for him. But he refrained, and their eyes met in a combat of silence.

Then Duerden turned to go. "There are some Indians you haven't asked," Saul threw at his departing back. But his heart was heavy. Was this victory? He did not know whether he was the garlanded conqueror or the chained captive in the triumph. But what was the difference? The unseen third who always rode with these two, and whose name was Hate, was so much more powerful than either that, by comparison, victor and defeated showed equally insignificant.

BITTER MATÉ

by SAMUEL GLUSBERG

THE murder of his first-born in the Kishinev pogrom and the abnormal birth of his second child, caused by the excitement which the mother suffered then, were good enough reasons for Abraham Petacovsky's deciding to emigrate and to give up his position as *melamed* [Hebrew teacher].

At first he thought of going to the United States. But once in Hamburg he found himself obliged, for diplomatic reasons, as he afterwards jested, to change his plans. As a result, in November, 1905, he arrived at Buenos Aires with his wife and their two babies.

Abraham Petacovsky was a friendly little Jew, with an air of intelligence and sweetness. His small clear eyes made his face, lengthened by a black and irregular beard, seem deathly pale. Typically Jewish, his nose seemed to precipitate itself down toward his mouth with its thick, ironic lips. Although he was only about thirty, his appearance was that of an old man. It was due to this that his relatives in Buenos Aires called him Uncle Petacovsky, despite the protests of Jane Guitel, his wife. She was a faithful woman, as devoted as she was ugly, but with much pride. Although she had passed many trying years with Uncle Petacovsky, she would continually refer to the "good old times in our Russia." Not quite twenty-seven, she was already resigned to Fate, and rested all her hopes on the two children who had lived through the horrors of the pogrom. They were Elisa, seven, and Beile, one.

Uncle Petacovsky never regretted his choice of Argentine. Buenos Aires, the city about which he had heard varying reports on the boat, turned out to be much to his liking.

Waiting for him in the old Immigrants' Hotel were two of his wife's relatives, and some friends. With the help of these people, to whom he was already indebted for some of the passage money, he succeeded in finding a place in which to live. It was a room, sublet to a Creole family, and was in the old suburb of Los Carrales. In order to live there Uncle Petacovsky, as well as his wife, had to set aside certain religious scruples and make up their minds to live with *goyim*.

Jane Guitel, of course, offered a little resistance.

"My God," she cried, "how can I possibly cook my *gefilte* fish right next to the Christian woman's pork stew?"

But when she saw the wooden cooking pantry perched in the front of the room like a sentry-box near a jail, she finally yielded. The owners of the apartment made every effort to help the newcomers and showed great respect for the strange Jewish customs. The new arrivals soon felt at home.

Even as the Creoles were politely curious about the strange way the Russian woman salted her meat out-of-doors and about Uncle Petacovsky's habit of keeping the Sabbath, so did the immigrants reveal a similar curiosity about the ways of their Argentine neighbors. After a few days they understood each other by gestures. Jane Guitel was renamed Doña Guillermina. As for Uncle Petacovsky, he learned to take maté [Argentine herb used for making tea] without sugar and drink it with the sons of the landlady, two good, industrious Argentine boys. Although like a real gringo he thanked them after each cup of maté, he never stopped drinking until after the seventh cup, for he found that maté without sugar had the same medicinal virtues which his wife attributed to tea with lemon.

Next to bitter maté, the discovery which gave Uncle Petacovsky the greatest pleasure was the Creole sandals [alpargatas]. From the very first morning he went out to sell pictures he found them invaluable.

"Without them," he would say, "I never would have been able to go on with that accursed peddling," a business so characteristic of the wandering Jew, which his relatives had given him.

The use of alpargatas and bitter maté were the first signs of the adaptation of Uncle Petacovsky to Argentine life. Definite proof of this was shown two months later when he went to see the funeral of General Mitre. That imposing manifestation of popular sorrow moved him to tears. For many years he recalled the event as the highest expression of an anguished multitude at the death of a patriarch. As a pious Israelite, Uncle Petacovsky knew about great men and great mournings.

We have already said that the good man began his life as a resident of Buenos Aires by hawking pictures through the streets. But we do not know if the reader, because he may once have seen a man of Talmudic appearance sandwiched between two pairs of religious engravings, has realized we were referring to religious pictures. This, besides being quaint, is important and has its history.

Selling prints of saints was in 1906 a business but lately initiated by the Jews of Buenos Aires. Until then the Israelites who did not go to

work on the farming colonies of Entre Rios or Santa Fe devoted themselves to selling on the instalment plan: furniture, jewelry, furs, and so on,
—everything except pictures. Uncle Petacovsky was perhaps the very
first to sell engravings on the instalment plan. And he was in his way an
efficient salesman.

Possessed of an inborn ecclesiastic sense, Uncle Petacovsky knew just
how to boost his pictures. In his strange Judeo-Creole speech he found a
way to praise in a few words every one of his pictures. Some for the delicate blue of the Virgin's eyes, others for the downcast mien of an apostle.
Each was recommended for its most impressive characteristic. No one
could explain the virtues of Saint John the Evangelist better than Uncle
Petacovsky. Sometimes, forgetful, he would confuse a Saint Joseph with a
San Antonio. But never did he fail to point out some aspect of color, some
pathetic touch, which could move a Mariá to tears.

He often lamented his limited vocabulary. He was constantly forced
to resort to pantomime, to use his hands, his face, and his shoulders, all at
one and the same time. Yet he never failed to make a sale because someone had not understood him or because he wrote out receipts for a
Joseph or a Magdalena in Hebrew. He failed because of the lack of religion among the people.

Despite his work, he, who was so religious and said his daily prayers
and kept the Sabbath, could not understand why with so many churches
in Buenos Aires there were so few believers. With this in mind, he
searched through the whole city and found that it was in La Boca that
the greatest number of the faithful congregated. He tried to form his
clients from among them and, to tell the truth, his business improved.

After working for a year near Riachuelo, where he went out to sell
his pictures almost every day except Saturday and Sunday, Uncle Petacovsky acquired a steady clientele. He could devote his time to collecting
and delivering pictures which people ordered directly from him. It was
then that he settled his debts with his relatives and rented another room
in the same house on Caseros Street. He conceived the plan of a business
to be carried on with the sons of his landlady. This consisted of manufac-
turing the frames for the pictures which Uncle Petacovsky sold.

Thanks to Uncle Petacovsky's enterprising spirit, the plan proved a
success. The two Creole boys, who had only been workers in an electri-
cal wood-working shop, found themselves suddenly transformed into
petty industrialists. In the meantime Uncle Petacovsky stopped peddling
in order to take charge of the shop.

In his name, or rather, in the name of the Petacovsky-Bermúdez

Company, worked various Jewish peddlers. Many others bought pictures from the company, and went out to sell them throughout the Republic.

The Bermúdez brothers worked with Uncle Petacovsky for nearly three years. Since from the start they had liked the work, they labored happily without setting any definite hours for themselves. At six in the morning the three would be at the factory and they would breakfast on "amargos" and "galleta" [onions and biscuits]. Then, while the boys prepared the orders, Uncle Petacovsky, who learned how to scribble in Castilian, would make out the bills and note the number of engravings it was necessary to buy at the dealer's.

In addition to selling evangelical pictures, they added, through the initiative of Uncle Petacovsky, seascapes, landscapes, still-lifes, and a great number of scenes from the Shakespearean theatre, *Othello, Hamlet, Romeo and Juliet.* At eight o'clock when Doña Guillermina (or Jane Guitel) sent Elisa to school, Uncle Petacovsky went shopping in the art market. He did this almost every morning, yet the Bermúdez brothers never failed to make some parting wise-crack when he left.

"Tío Petaca," they would yell, "don't forget to bring me a nice little peasant girl." "Tío Petaca, I like a blonde one. What do you say, Tío Petaca?"

But he never got angry. With a blend of irony and condescension, he would answer, "All right, but don't forget the nine San Antonios for San Pedro." And he would depart laughing, while the boys would mock him, "Have a good time, Tío Petaca."

From the beginning, Jane Guitel did not like these jests. She heard them every morning, and every night she reproached her husband for permitting them. She begged him to put a stop to them at once, so as to avoid "so much intimacy."

"Business is one thing," his wife would protest, "friendship is another. I don't like you to place so much confidence in them. Have you, by any chance, smoked the same pipe together?"

In reality, what Jane Guitel was inferring when she asked her husband this question was not exactly whether he had smoked the same pipe, but quite another thing. But why go over that? What above all else bothered the woman was that the Bermúdez brothers kept calling her husband "Tío Petaca." Since Elisa had started going to school, Doña Guillermina had been finding out through her the meaning of every strange word. Although the girl was only in the third grade, she could speak Spanish correctly. She even went so far as to want to speak Spanish with her own mother.

Two more years passed. At last, at the beginning of 1910, Jane Guitel could realize her wish of moving away from Caseros Street. Once the decision was made, the firm of Petacovsky-Bermúdez split up without the partners breaking off their friendship. After three years' work, each retired with nearly 10,000 pesos. The Bermúdez brothers decided to build the old family house with their share and to establish a woodworking shop there. As for Uncle Petacovsky, he kept what remained of the old clientele of La Boca as his share of the business.

It is well-known that ninety-nine out of one hundred Jews who manage to get together some thousand pesos like to show off their riches and live like really wealthy people. Uncle Petacovsky, no exception to this rule, furnished his house lavishly and bought a piano for little Elisa. When an Argentine son was born to him, he held a big feast in classic style on the day of the circumcision. It was no more than right. Ever since the murder of his first-born in Russia, Uncle Petacovsky had been looking forward to such an event. Like Jane Guitel, he had always dreamed of a male child who at his death would say the *kaddish* of recall, the mourner's prayer . . . the *kaddish,* that noble prayer of the Jewish orphan, which Heinrich Heine himself remembered on his wool-draped deathbed:

> "No one will sing mass for me;
> No one will say *kaddish* for me,
> Nor celebrate with songs and prayers,
> My death anniversary."

But enough of poetry and poets. Now that he did have a *kaddish* (by extension the Jews thus call a male child), Uncle Petacovsky did not die. Quite otherwise. The celebration of the unknown Argentine soldier on the eve of the centenary of 1810 suggested a patriotic enterprise to him. And with the same faith and enthusiasm as of old, Uncle Petacovsky carried out his idea. It was really the same old business. But now, instead of saints' pictures, there would be pictures of heroes, and, in place of Shakespearean scenes, patriotic allegories.

The Bermúdez brothers, who were still his friends, told him the history of their country, but with the stress placed so on the side of the Federalists that Uncle Petacovsky suspected that their information was biased and one-sided. It wasn't that he was against anybody, but that proof of the glory of Rosas (Argentine dictator) was lacking.

Good peddler that he was, Uncle Petacovsky had learned his national history in the streets of Buenos Aires. Thus he judged as heroes of the first water all those whose names adorned the principal squares and streets. This curious way of learning history had already been used by the pedagogue, although he who had been a teacher in the true sense of the word back in Russia was not unaware of it.

But even though he did not know the scientific term for this approach—visioaudiomotor—the method gave him the best results. As for Sarmiento (verbi gratia domine)—who at that time had an alley of La Boca named after him, Uncle Petacovsky had formed a very low opinion of him. If he had not known that he was an author,—and what Jew ever failed to admire a man who writes books?—he would have left out of his collection a truly great figure.

This exception to his hitherto unchallengeable system saved him from the "pedagogic" method. When he did not come in contact with a patriot in a visible place, he resolved not to allow himself to be guided by the empirical method. He bought illustrated samples of all the patriots, those he knew as well as those he did not know, and thus solved his problem.

A few days before May 1st, the day chosen to start his new business, Uncle Petacovsky had nearly a million engravings of all kinds. The sale began promptly. Various peddlers took charge of the provinces and Uncle Petacovsky of the capital. For six months things went at full blast. But despite the great hustle and the centennial celebrations throughout the Republic, the enterprise proved a failure.

Toward the end of 1910 an inventory was made of the goods sold in the interior of the country, and of the merchandise left over. Six hundred thousand pictures remained. In his six months' venture he had lost his earnings of five years.

This first failure naturally disturbed the good nature of Uncle Petacovsky. As he lacked the nature of a businessman, he felt upset. And even though a few months later he thought of some business which would take advantage of Carnival time, his relatives, mocking him, refused to give him credit. Who trusts a man who has once failed?

Uncle Petacovsky suffered more from this lack of confidence than from the loss of his money. He moved to cheaper quarters, sold his piano, and put off registering his child in Normal School. But none of these things helped, as a new misfortune (how many more, O Lord?) made him forget the previous one. It was nothing less than the death of Beile, the younger of his two daughters.

This sad event made his relatives forget his failure in the centenary. On the one hand, his relatives, and, on the other, his friends, with that solidarity in mourning so characteristic of the Jew, competed in helping the unfortunate man. And thanks to them, once again he was able to become a peddler. Now he sold not only pictures, but also furnishings, clothes, jewelry and furs.

For five years Uncle Petacovsky worked to regain his clientele. His accursed business gave him grey hairs. Indeed, what with the competition of the big stores and the great rise in prices because of the war it all came to nothing. But until the middle of 1916 he could not leave it. Then only a happy circumstance took him out of it. The event can be summed up in the following way:

The younger of the Bermúdez brothers, Charles, recommended him to the manager of a cigarette factory, and this man bought from him, as propaganda for the Independence centenary, the patriotic pictures that he still had left.

Uncle Petacovsky got 1500 pesos for his pictures. With this money in his pocket he felt more cheerful. Promptly he gave up his clientele, as he now suffered from rheumatism. He set to work looking for a store he could open in the heart of the city. He did not care whether it was a cigar store or some other kind of tiny shop. What he wanted was a store with a door on the main street. Let the customers look for him. Not the other way round, as had hitherto been the case. He was sick and tired of peddling.

Again his relatives laughed at his plans. While some, alluding to his fondness for maté, advised him to buy a maté plantation, others advised him to open a maté factory. But Uncle Petacovsky, against the advice of the world in general and of Jane Guitel in particular, bought a tiny bookstore near the food market.

The new business completely changed the life of Uncle Petacovsky. He no longer made the rounds of the city. Dressing as he pleased, in a thick sail-cloth dust-cloak and a small, silk skull cap, he would spend the mornings reading and drinking maté near the counter, while waiting for customers. His daughter, Elisa, who by now had become like a friendly little Creole of eighteen years, would prepare the bitter drink and send it to him by her brother Daniel while she tidied up the house before Jane Guitel returned from the market.

After his lunch, Uncle Petacovsky would take his siesta. At four o'clock he would be at his post again, and Elisa would again prepare maté for him to last until night.

Now, if the daily sales had provided a little more than the money necessary for bread and yerba maté, it is probable that they would all have lived happily ever after. But since, after a year of vain dreams, it was clear that this was not happening, the quarrels at home started again.

"If you didn't want to reform the world, but did what so many Jews in Buenos Aires are doing, we'd be all right," Jane Guitel would scold.

To which he would answer:

"It's simply that when I'm not fit for a thing, it's no use."

And if Jane Guitel pressed him to sell the store, he would retort with bitter sarcasm:

"I am sure that if I set out to manufacture shrouds, people would stop dying. It's the same thing."

Such arguments were almost daily repeated in the same tone. Since the death of her little girl, Jane Guitel had been sick, and frequent nervous attacks weakened her. Aware of this, Uncle Petacovsky would try to calm her by telling her of some event of the day. And if Doña Guillermina, as he would jokingly call her on these occasions, resisted, he invoked the aphorisms of Sholem Aleichem, his favorite author:

"Laughter is healthful; doctors advise people to laugh." Or "When the pot is empty, fill it with laughter."

The truth was, despite his Sholem Aleichem, Uncle Petacovsky had become infected with the melancholy of his wife. He was no longer the jovial "Tío Petaca" of his picture-frame factory. None of the enthusiasm and good humor of that period remained with him. If he still laughed, it was only to hide his tears. For as he himself said:

"When business is bad, one can be a humorist, but never a prophet." And he certainly did not try to be a humorist.

When school reopened he tried, with some success, to buy and sell old books. But when vacation came, because he was already known as a second-hand dealer, no one entered except to sell used books. In the meantime, the long days, all alike, passed by tediously. The man, always with his bitter maté; the woman with her incessant harping on the good old times and constant protest against the present.

"My God," she would complain to her husband, "see what you've made of yourself in America, a second-hand dealer." And she would cry.

In vain did Uncle Petacovsky try to defend the intellectual aspect of his work and promise great results for the following season.

"You'll see," he would say to her, "as soon as classes begin, all these great wise men and poets hidden in my books will leave the store. Why, it's even possible that by then I'll find a buyer for the whole business and I'll keep only the medicinal books so that later on Daniel may study to be a doctor."

The woman never stopped nagging. By no means the dreamer that he was, she was looking forward to the future of her daughter. In her bitter moments, insults were always on her tongue.

"Second-hand man! My God, who will want to marry the daughter of a second-hand dealer!" Jane Guitel found out who wanted to marry her daughter much before she expected. Gossip had it that Elisa was being courted by Carlos Bermúdez. She would not believe it. Then someone who had seen them together confirmed the malicious rumors. Her suspicion was aroused. At last, prevailed upon by her father, the girl confessed her intimacy with his ex-partner. There was the deuce to pay. Jane Guitel shrieked to high heaven. Her daughter to marry a goy! Was it possible that the ungrateful wretch had forgotten that her great-grandfather (may he rest in peace) was the chief rabbi of Kishinev, and that all her relatives were pure and holy Jews? Where was the girl's modesty?

In her despair she blamed her husband's business for the thousandth time.

"So that's what comes of your great tea-drinking friends! (Would that God had poisoned them!) Here's the result of your dealings with them! (If only a streak of lightning would blast them!) It's all your fault."

And, overcome by her excitement, she began to cry as if it were the Day of Atonement.

Uncle Petacovsky, who despite his maté had not stopped being a good Jew, tried to calm her, assuring her that with God's grace the marriage would never take place.

He was against the marriage for other reasons. He respected the ancient code of the nationalist Jews: "We cannot cease being Jews while others do not cease being Christians." And, in truth, since he believed that neither he nor Bermúdez could be said to have free will, he did everything in his power to inculcate Elisa with his philosophy.

"Look," he said to her one night, while the girl was making maté, "if I forbid you to marry Carlos, it is not a whim. You know how much I respect him. But you are different; you were born in different countries; you have been brought up in different ways. You have prayed to different Gods and you have different histories. Above all, he is still a Christian and you are still a Jew."

At another time he said:

"It is impossible. You won't get along. In your first arguments, and first arguments are inevitable, I can swear you will yell at him, 'You goyishe kopf' (Gentile head) and by way of insult he will call you a 'lousy Jew.' And he might even make fun of how your father says *noive* (neuve)."

The honest logic of Uncle Petacovsky was as futile as the frequent fainting spells of Jane Guitel. A few months later, the girl, deeply in love, eloped with her sweetheart to Rosario.

Elisa's elopement gave her mother a nervous breakdown. She cried for two weeks, hardly taking a bit of food. Nothing could pacify her. At last, under doctor's orders, she was sent to "San Roque," where she died shortly afterward, aggravating the scandal made in the community by the escapade.

The death of Jane Guitel brought the girl home. With her came Bermúdez. The couple acted as if they had been the direct cause of her death and they wept bitter tears over the grave of the poor woman.

Bermúdez himself, who before had been so inflexible, now renounced Elisa and consented to her remaining behind to take care of the little boy. But Uncle Petacovsky was honorable enough to forgive them and to sanction the marriage on condition that they live together happily and forever in Rosaria.

After making them realize at what a price they had married, Uncle Petacovsky, against everybody's judgment, determined to go on with his second-hand book store with his son Daniel.

"I alone," he said, "will see to it that Daniel becomes a man. Don't worry. We won't die of hunger." And there was no way to make him change his mind.

Neglected for so many months, his was now a run-down shop with little merchandise except for such Spanish books and pamphlets as are to be found in all second-hand book stores. Now that Jane Guitel could no longer reproach him, and Elisa was married and far away, Uncle Petacovsky gave himself over whole-heartedly to his books, determined in this way to provide for his son. Now he lived wholly for his son's sake. He rose early every morning and, after preparing the maté, he woke Daniel. After breakfast they went to the synagogue, where the son said *kaddish* in memory of his mother. At eight o'clock both would be outside the school and while Daniel went to his class Uncle Petacovsky went to open the shop, which he now kept open until nightfall.

In this way they lived through six long months.

When vacation came, the miserable little store failed to produce enough for the small necessities of the house; so Uncle Petacovsky brought together several Jewish boys to teach them Hebrew. Thus, returning to his first profession, he faced his difficult situation. And he was prepared for any other sacrifices in the hope of seeing Daniel a grown-up man some day.

Unfortunately, Uncle Petacovsky was not going to realize even this dream. We shall soon see why.

The first few days of 1919 went by. A great strike of metal mine workers had broken out in Buenos Aires and the most incredible report of a communist uprising was spread from one end of the city to the other. On the afternoon of January 10th, Uncle Petacovsky was seated as usual near his books, sipping maté. He had sent the boys home a little earlier because it was the Sabbath eve and because there was a certain restlessness in the neighborhood. Corrientes Street, usually crowded, now looked strange on account of the halt in traffic and the presence of policemen bearing rifles.

About five-thirty o'clock a group of well-dressed young men started shouting outside the shop—hurrahs for the republic. Attracted by the shouts, Uncle Petacovsky who kept on sipping his maté, looked out the window, fearful, because only just a moment ago Daniel had left to say *kaddish*.

One of the mob, seeing Uncle Petacovsky's frightened face, called the attention of the others to the shop, and the youths came in and stopped before the counter.

"Marxist books!" the nearest one shouted. "Marxist books!"

"There's the Russian over there!" put in another.

"What a hypocrite, trying to fool us with his maté!"

And a third:

"We'll teach him to carry books with goat-like men on the covers!" And stepping forward, he aimed his revolver at the beard of Tolstoy, whose picture was on the cover of a red volume. His comrades, spurred on by his example, imitated him. In an instant, amidst laughter, all the books of bearded authors in the show case tumbled down. And, to tell the truth, the sport of the youths would have been great fun, had not one shot gone wrong and cost Uncle Petacovsky his life.

Now the good old man must be in Heaven together with the saints, heroes, and artists who, through his industry, inspired so many people. And if it be true that divine justice is less slow and more sure than human justice, it must certainly have granted him that which he craved most as he entered Heaven, just as the chosen ones have always been favored. Then surely, even as Perez' Bontche Shweig, who in identical circumstances had asked the angels for bread and butter,—so Uncle Petacovsky was entitled to ask for maté amargo forever.

OUR FATHERS THAT BEGAT US

Although the theater in which the drama of the contemporary Jew is being staged is immense, the historical framework upon which it is built is even more vast. Its foundations have been laid and scaffoldings erected by historians—from Graetz to Dubnow—but the final structure awaits stout minds and loving pens. What of the interior? What of the social organism whence our generation has sprung? What of the inner spirit and power of Israel, which produced so incredible an army of saints, scholars, poets, visionaries?

To glimpse the inner world of the generations that begat us, one must turn to literature. And here one is amply rewarded, for Jewish literature, if not as varied as other European literature, is deeply rooted in life. The roots are deep and firm; their soil is fertile; their substance, compounded of the waters of suffering and the sun of faith, is sturdy. It may be, observes a sympathetic interpreter, that Israel is "warped by evil growths of cunning and covetousness developed in the struggle with superior forces; distorted not infrequently by the perverse action of a religion that lent itself too easily to formalism; here and there, too, materialized and vulgarized by the sudden sun of prosperity; but strong by force of standing alone, tenacious, energetic, soberly adventurous, brilliantly intellectual, spiritual and idealistic in certain directions, domestic, civic, patriotic, infinitely adaptable, a marvelous reservoir of intellect and emotion and will and sanity, sufficient to renovate a decadent civilization."

However emancipated and modernized, the modern Jew hears the echo of his forefathers' lament. The ghetto has left an imprint which can be more clearly visualized in the pages that follow. Each tale depicts the impact of a different aspect of his heritage upon the individual Jew. Considered as a whole, these stories of atmosphere and character reflect the Jewish character in the making.

The trail leads us back to the Marranos in the sixteenth century. They were the forerunners of the modern Jew in that they were the first Jewish group to enter fully into European civilization. Their epoch-making story has been told fascinatingly in Roth's *The History of the Marranos* (1932). The experiences of David Reubeni and Uriel Acosta foreshadow many paradoxes and problems in modern times.

The story of the centuries which intervened between Reubeni's and our own is told in a library of fiction, chronicles, memoirs, notably in the Hebrew and Yiddish languages. Some part of it has been utilized in other sections of this book, and the curious reader is directed to *The Jewish Caravan* (1935) for additional material.

THREE GIFTS

by ISAAC LOEB PEREZ

I. THE SCALES OF JUSTICE

SOMEWHERE, many and many a year ago, a Jew breathed his last.
No one, of course, may live for ever. The man was dead; the
attentions due the dead were paid, and a grave among the folk
of his own faith lodged him.

The grave closed over him, the orphaned son recited his *kaddish*
and the soul flew upward—to Judgment.

On arriving there it found the scale of Justice already swinging in
the court chamber. Here the good deeds and the evil were to be weighed.

And forthwith the dead man's Advocate enters, the Good Spirit of
his former life. A pure, snow-white sack is in his hand and he stands
near the right scale of the Balance.

And behold the dead man's Accuser enters—the Evil Spirit of his
former life. An unclean sack is in his hands and he stands near the
left scale of the Balance. The sack of pure white contains the good deeds.
The sack that is begrimed and black—the evil, sinful deeds. And the vin-
dicator of the soul pours out the contents of the white sack on the right
scale. The good deeds are of the odor of incense and glow with the
radiancy of the stars. The Accuser pours out the contents of the unclean
sack on the left scale of the Balance. The evil deeds—Heaven protect us
—are as black as coal, and reek of the very stench of tar and pitch.

And the poor soul stares at it all—and gasps. It never dreamt to behold such a distinction between the "Good" and the "Evil." "There" it
had often recognized neither of them and had mistaken the one for the
other.

The scales rise gradually. Now the one, now the other moves up
and down . . . and the indicator oscillates now a hair's breadth to the
left, now a trifle towards the right. But a hair's breadth variation and
that gradually . . . an ordinary mortal this soul must have been; neither
rebellious to the Holy Spirit nor yet dwelling much within it . . . ca-

pable of trivial virtues and trivial vices only. The scales held but little particles, tiny dots of things, at times hardly visible to the eye.

And yet, what a clamor of joy and of gladness from the empyrean when the Balance indicator turns but a trifle towards the right and what racking cries of agony mark every turn to the left. And slowly, ever so slowly, the angels empty the sacks. With a zest they show up the tiny particles, just as decent burghers will add one farthing to another in self-exhibition to a seeing world.

However, the deepest well will run dry—and the sacks, too, are soon empty.

"Is that all?" inquires the court-usher. He, too, is an angel among his like. Both the Good and the Evil Spirits turn their sacks inside out. Absolutely nothing more. The court-usher steps forward to the Balance. He examines the indicator to see whether it is inclined towards the right or the left; and he stares at it good and long; for he beholds something that none ever saw since first the Heavens and the Earth knew creation. . . .

"Why such hesitance?" demands the Chief Justice. And the usher mutters:

"But one moment! The index is exactly in the center. The Evil deeds and the Good are exactly of the same weight."

"Is that absolutely so?" queries a voice from about the table.

The usher looks yet again: "Yea, even to a hair's breadth."

The Heavenly Tribunal holds its consultation and the decision as to the sentence is thus pronounced: "Since the Evil deeds do not weigh more than the Good—the soul, of course, is free from Hell. But, on the other hand, since the Good deeds do not prevail over the Evil—neither can Paradise receive her.[1] Therefore she is to be neither here, nor there, but a wanderer between the realms of Heaven and Earth, until the Lord have mercy upon her and in His goodness call her unto Him."

And the usher of the court leads the soul away.

She sobs, and bemoans her fate.

"Why art thou weeping?" he asks her. " 'Tis true thou wilt not know the joy and the gladness of Eden, but neither will the agonies and pangs of Hell be thine."

But the soul, unconsoled, replies:

"The worst agony is preferable to nothing at all. Nothing is most dreadful. . . ."

And the heavenly usher pities her and offers her some advice.

[1] Soul is feminine in Yiddish.

"Fly downward, little soul, and hover about the living world of men. Gaze not unto heaven. For what canst thou see on the other side, but the little stars. Radiant little people—they certainly are, but alas, very cold. They know no pity. They'll never speak to the Lord about you. Only the pious souls of Paradise will go to such trouble for a poor, exiled soul . . . but they . . . hearken unto me . . . they do love gifts, fair and beautiful gifts."

The usher talks bitterly. "Such are the ways of Paradise, nowadays. Fly downward, then, to the living world and watch life there and its course. And if thou only catchest a glimpse of something that is surpassingly fair or good, seize thou it, and fly up to Heaven. Present it as a gift to the pious there. Knock at the little window and in my name speak to the angel-guard. And when thou wilt have brought three gifts —why, then, you may be sure that the gates of Heaven will be unbarred . . . they will manage to have it so for thee. . . . At the Throne of Honor, the well-born are not loved . . . but the well-grown. . . ."

And, in this wise, and with compassion, he thrusts her out of Paradise.

II. THE FIRST GIFT

The poor little soul flies downward to the world of the living in search of gifts for the pious people of Heaven. It hovers about, everywhere; about the villages and the towns, about every habitation of man, amid the burning rays of hottest summer; amid the drops and water spears of rainy autumn; amid the silver web, fantastical, in the last days of summer; amid the snowflakes that fall from above. . . . It gazes about and about till it well-nigh spends its sight.

Wherever and whenever it spies a Jew it runs hastily up to him and looks at him intently—perhaps he is on his way to Prayer—to bless the name of the Lord. Wherever a light breaks through the chink of a shutter—she is there, to peep inside, to see whether the Lord's fragrant flowerets, the secret deeds of good, blossom in that silent house. Alas! . . . most of the time it must dart away from the window in agony and dismay. . . .

And thus season follows season, and year follows year. Oft, the soul becomes moody and sullen. Cities turn into graveyards, the graveyards into fields of pasture; forests are felled. The pebbles of the brook become sand; rivers have changed their courses; myriads of stars have fallen and myriads of souls have flown upward; but the gracious Lord has never thought of her; neither has she found aught that was beautiful or good.

And she thinks within herself: "How poor the whole world is. Its people—how mediocre; their souls—how dark and obscure. . . . How can aught good be found here? Alas! I must rove about—an exile, forever."

But suddenly a red flame bursts before her. Out of the dark and gloomy night a red flame leaps forth. She stares about her. . . . 'Tis from an upper window of a house that the flame has shot forth. Robbers are attacking a wealthy man. Masks are on their faces. One holds a burning torch in his hands; another holds a blazing knife at the man's breast and repeats his threat again and again:

"Jew, make but the slightest motion and you are dead. The knife will most assuredly pass through your back, then." The others are all busy, opening chests and drawers. The man looks serenely about him, although the knife is at his breast. The brows above his lucid eyes do not quiver. Not a hair of that gray beard that reaches to the waist moves. All of it seems to be something that is not his concern. "The Lord hath given, the Lord taketh away," he muses, and his pale lips mutter: "Blessed be the name of the Lord."

"One is not born thus and one may not carry it all to his grave." He views them calmly when they are about to clear the last drawer of the last bureau and watches, in absolute silence, the pillage of the gold and the silver, the jewelry and other precious things!

Perhaps he is renouncing it all!

But all at once—as the robbers are about to lay hold upon the last hidden treasure—a little sack, hidden in the most secret nook of all—he forgets himself,—trembles all over, his eyes are bloodshot, and he stretches his right hand forward, to the weapon. He would, as it seems, cry out!

"Touch it not!"

But the cry is unuttered. A red, vaporous stream of blood shoots forth, the knife has done its work. . . . It is the heart's blood that sprinkles the little sack. He falls to the ground. The robbers tear the little sack open in a hurry. That will be the best—the most precious gain of all!

But what a grievous error! The blood had been shed in vain—neither silver, nor gold, nor jewels were there. Naught of any value in this world. It is a little measure of sand from the Holy Land, to be strewn on his face at burial. That, the wealthy man had wished to save from the hands of strangers. That had shed his blood . . . and the soul seizes a blood-soiled particle of the sand and knocks at the little window of Heaven. Her first gift found ready acceptance.

III. THE SECOND GIFT

"Remember now," said the angel as he barred the window. "Remember—two more offerings."

"The Lord will aid me"—thinks the soul, grown hopeful; and joyously flies down again. However, her gladness lasts but a little while. Again, years follow years and she can find nothing that is surpassingly beautiful. And her melancholy returns to her. "The world has, it seems, forsaken the way of the Lord, and like a spring ever runs out and out. The more the water that flows into the soil, the more sucked in—the more the soil becomes foul and unclean. Fewer are the gifts for heaven then. Men become ever petty and more petty. Their good needs grow tiny; their evil deeds blacker and blacker dust—their deeds are hardly visible to the eye! . . ."

And thus speaking to herself she seems to think that should the Lord command all the evil deeds and the good of the world to be weighed in the Balance, that the needle would hardly move, yea, not even tremble. The earth can hardly rise or fall now, she is but a wanderer from the empyrean above to the black abyss of Sheol below. A splendid cause for an eternal disputation between the spirits of good and of evil; just such a one as the eternal dispute between darkness and light, heat and cold, life and death. . . .

The earth rocks to and fro. She can neither ascend nor descend. Thus we ever have weddings and divorces, parties and funerals, love and hate—ever, forever.

Suddenly the blare of trumpets and of horns resounds. The soul looks down—and beholds an ancient German town. All sorts of roofs, narrow and bent, surround the courthouse. A motley crowd fills the place. People peer out of the windows; others throng the roofs, and some sit astride the beams at the edge, where they are propped up by the wall.

A table covered with a green cloth stands at the head of the court-hall. The cloth has golden tassels and fringes. The men of the court are held with golden hooks. They wear sable caps and large feathers stick from the shining buttons to which they are sewed. At the head of the table, the President of the court is seated. An Eagle hovers overhead. . . .

A young Jewess, all bound, stands on one side. Ten slaves hold a white horse firmly near her. The President has risen and with his eyes towards the market-place, he reads the paper he has in his hand—her sentence.

"This Jewess," he says, "is guilty of a monstrous sin. Even the Lord, in his graciousness and great mercy, could not forgive her that. . . .

"On our last and most sacred holiday, she slunk out of her ghetto and walked through the clean streets of our town. . . .

"She has sullied the Holy procession. Her eyes have defiled the sacred images that we bore with hymnal song and music through the streets. . . .

"The hymns of our innocent children, or our young, clad in snow-white garments, her ears have sucked in—and the beating of the holy drum likewise . . . who knows whether the devil, the foul fiend, has not transformed himself into this image of the Jewess, of this cursed Rabbi's daughter? Who knows whether thus, he has not touched or polluted a holy treasure of ours?

"What was the fiend up to, in this fair disguise? We need not equivocate. Undoubtedly, she is fair; a devilish beauty is hers— Do but look at the wicked sparkle of her eyes, and the modest and humble pose of her silken eyelashes. . . .

"See you her alabaster face? It has indeed grown paler since her imprisonment, but duller not a whit! . . . Look at her fingers. How thin and long and how transparent they seem in the sunlight! . . .

"What could the fiend have wanted but to dissuade a soul from its Holy faith, and that he has done indeed."

"What a beautiful maiden!" exclaims one of our own Knighthood —a member of one of our best families. . . .

"It was more than patience could endure. The crowd noticed her and laid hands upon her— The fiend did not even stir for defense— How could she? They were all pure of sin. They had been absolved. He had no power over them.

"Let this then be the sentence of the devil—of the fiend disguised in this form of a Jewish maiden:

"Bind her hair, her fiendishly long hair, to the tail of this savage horse. . . .

"Let the horse fly over the streets and drag her like a 'corpse' across the very streets she has polluted in defiance of our sacred laws.

"May her blood besprinkle them and wash those that her feet have besmirched!"

Savage cries of joy fill the market-place and when the great din is over the convicted woman is asked her last wish.

She answers calmly: "I have one wish. Give me but a few pins."

"Her grief has made her mad!" think the men of the court.

"Not so," she answers serenely and frigidly: "This is my last wish; my last desire."

They gratify her in that.

"Now, bind her!" commands the President of the court.

The hands of the servants tremble as they bind her long dark braids to the tail of the horse, which is so wild that he can hardly be controlled. . . .

"Make room!" the command is heard. There is a wild rush forward. The crowd huddles close to the walls of the buildings. All raise their hands. All are ready to goad the horse along. Some have whips, some have cords, others wiretips. Their breath is stifled for the moment; their faces are aflame, their eyes sparkle and in all this hubbub no one notices how the convicted maiden bends down and pins her skirts at the seam and pushes the pins deep into her body, so that it may be wholly covered when she is dragged about in the streets. Only the exiled soul notices it all. . . .

"Free the horse," the command is heard again. The slaves have leaped away. The horse bounds forward. A deafening shout fills the air. Whips and cords and wires are whirled about and whistle loudly. The horse, wild with terror, rushes across the market place, across the streets, over the alley and far, far out of the town. . . .

The vagrant soul has drawn a blood-stained pin out of the victim's body and is on her way to Heaven with it!

And the angel at the little window soothes her, saying: "But *one* more gift!"

IV. THE THIRD GIFT

And downward again the souls wend her way. But one more gift! And as before, year follows year and melancholy has its grip upon her. The world has grown little indeed. Men are becoming ever more insignificant. Their deeds too are tiny and more so; the good and the evil alike. . . .

And a new thought occurs to her:

"What if the Lord, Blessed be His name, were to halt the world process this very moment and announce the final Judgment; would not then the Advocate appear on the right side of the Balance and pour out the contents of his white sack, its tiny particles and little grains of sand; would not the Accuser follow and empty his sack on the left scale—his little wee bits and fragments? What a long process that would be! What a multitude of little things!

"And when the emptying of the sack is completed, what then? Of course, the indicator would be pointing right to the center!

"Such insignificant things weigh nothing; no matter what their number. Indeed, what can be the weight of a tiny thread, of a straw or of an empty husk?

"What might the decision of the Lord be then?

"Would he turn the whole into a void again? Certainly not; for the Evil deeds do not weigh more than the Good.

"Perhaps he might grant salvation to all. But that, too, is unlikely, for the deeds of Good do not prevail over those of Evil.

"It is hard to see what would follow then.

"Might he not say: 'Pass ye along. Rove ye from the realms of Hell to Heaven amid Love and Hate, in tears of mercy or vaporous blood . . . from cradle unto grave, rove ye farther—even farther.'"

However, Destiny seems to have planned the deliverance of the Soul from her gloomy reflections. The din of beating drums arouses her. . . .

"Where am I now, and what the time?" She cannot recognize the place. She has no idea of the time.

She beholds the courtyard of a prison. The rays of the sun hover about the little windows and even penetrate the iron bars. . . . They glide along the wall and fall upon a heap of sundry weapons supported there. The soldier-guards have but a moment ago received their whips. . . .

Two long rows of soldiers and only a narrow passage between.

Who is it that must run the gauntlet here? Oh, it is but an insignificant Jew. A torn shirt is on his emaciated body and a skull-cap on his half-shaven head. There he is being led forth.

But what is his crime? What has he stolen? Has he robbed anyone,—murdered? . . . Perhaps it is but a false accusation. Is that not an ancient custom and were not many such before?

The soldiers smile as they ponder: What was the use of having all of us here? Would not half the number have sufficed!

He is thrust into the passage. He steps forward. He walks directly on. The lashes fall upon him. But he curses no one, neither does he falter or fall. . . .

A fit of rage overwhelms the soldiers. He walks on and on!

The whips whistle in the air, fiendishly. They grip and coil around the body as serpents do. The blood of the emaciated frame gushes forth and does not cease!

Whoop—whack! Whoop—whack! Suddenly a whip falling high

throws the skull-cap down to the ground. The doomed man notices it
after a few paces. . . . He stirs and reflects. He turns round again and
walks onward, serenely calm though covered with streaming blood. The
skull-cap is on his head. He walks on till he falls. . . .

And when he falls thus, the Soul runs swiftly up to him, and seizes
the cap that has cost so many innocent lashes, and with it she flies upward to the little window of Heaven.

And the third gift also finds acceptance! The pious Souls try their
best and spare no trouble; the doors of Eden are now open! And the
voice of the "Oracle" is heard:

"These are truly beautiful gifts, of surpassing fairness. . . . They may
be of no practical use. They may not even serve for show. . . . But they
are marvellous."

MALKAH

by I. J. SINGER

DURING all the festive Seven Days of the Seven Benedictions, the
aunt and uncle of Malkah lived in an agony of fear. Malkah
was gunpowder! Malkah could explode at any moment! Malkah
could get up in the middle of everything, leave Nyesheve and disappear
without a trace.

From the day on which the stammering uncle came back from Nyesheve and announced that the great Rabbi wanted Malkah to be his
bride, he and his wife had not known peace. Side by side with the incredible joy of the event—they, the obscure, the fallen, the penniless
house of a long-dead Rabbi, were about to be lifted into an alliance with
the world-famous head of the dynasty of Nyesheve!—together with that
joy, almost intolerable in itself, there was the unremitting fear of their
niece, Malkah Spitfire. Their lives were in her reckless hands. One characteristic gesture of hers, and they would be back in the dust from which
the Rabbi of Nyesheve had raised them. And there was not one moment
in which their happiness was not overshadowed by distrust and anxiety.

When the stammering uncle came home, and imparted the news to
his wife she looked at him pityingly, contemptuously, and answered in
one word:

"Idiot!"

Aunt Aidele wore the trousers in that house. She considered herself the brains of the family. The proposal made by the Rabbi of Nyesheve, and brought home enthusiastically by her husband, was ridiculous.

"*The* match for our Malkah Spitfire," she said, mockingly. "And if you want to have your beard torn out by the roots, just tell her about it, that's all."

But in the first momentum of his joy, the stammerer rushed straightway to Malkah. Without preparation, and only fearing that his wife would interrupt and silence him, he broke the news.

"*M-m-mazel-tov,* good luck! Congratulations!" he babbled at his niece. "You're g-going to be the wife of the Rabb-bi of Nyesheve!"

Aunt Aidele rushed after him in time to hear these words, and she became quite white with fear. But Malkah Spitfire only laughed. She laughed naturally at first, as at a good joke, but gradually her laughter worked itself up into an uncontrollable spasm. She could not stop. And when the laughter exhausted itself for a moment, she did not ask what kind of man this famous Rabbi of Nyesheve was, what he looked like, how old he was; she only panted until the fit of laughter returned and doubled her up.

"Oh, Mama!" she cried, and continued to laugh.

They stared at her.

"Are you mad?" her uncle stammered. "Don't you want the Rabbi of Nyesheve?"

Malkah mastered herself for a moment. "Of course I want him! Only you've forgotten the cake and brandy to celebrate with. . . ."

The stammerer looked at his wife. This was the first victory he had ever scored over her, probably the first he had ever score over anyone. In his exultation he forgot his fear. He became aware suddenly of qualities of manliness. He approached his wife, tucked his thumb between two bent fingers, and thrust it derisively under her nose.

"Well!" he crowed, "Aristotle! Who's the wise one now?"

Taken aback, Aunt Aidele turned up her eyes to heaven and murmured: "God grant it!" Then she turned them back on her husband and said, warningly: "But be sure you get your bear before you skin him!"

And so the match was arranged.

When the news became public, every relative of Malkah, close and distant, took on a new dignity. But everywhere, mingled with that dignity, was uncertainty. They could only explain Malkah's acquiescence to the fantastic match with the aged Rabbi as one of her characteristic, mad tricks. Malkah was capable of anything—just like her mother. By the time she was sixteen years old Malkah had run away three times; and three times she had been brought back, and the matter had been hushed up.

"Wicked blood!" they said of her in the family. "She has it from her mother. She took it in with her mother's milk."

Malkah's mother, a daughter of a Rabbinic house, and daughter-in-law of a Rabbi, had also run away—but successfully. She had been, in all, fifteen years older than her daughter. They had married her off at the age of fourteen, and within a year she had given birth to Malkah. Eleven years after the mother's marriage, when Malkah was already ten years old, and marriage proposals were already coming in, the great tragedy took place. The twenty-five-year-old wife of the Rabbi of Przemysl left her husband and her daughter to run away to Budapest with a cavalry officer of the local garrison.

The family cursed her and wiped her name from their records. Her husband, a sickly scion of a Rabbinic house, died of loneliness and humiliation. But no one outside the family knew the truth. It was given out that the Rabbi's wife was a very sick woman, and that she was living abroad in a sanitarium under the constant care of doctors.

Malkah the orphan was taken over by her aunt Aidele. Aunt Aidele had had no children by her husband, the stammerer; and as she was widely known for her irreproachable religious life, the family decided that she should have the upbringing and education of the orphan. Malkah was to be made, by her aunt and uncle, into an example of Jewishness and God-fearing piety.

The stammerer set to work at once. The ten-year-old girl received, every day, long instructions in the duties of a daughter of Israel. For hours at a stretch her uncle explained the laws to her, and read her fearsome passages from morality books, in particular the descriptions of hell and its fires. The stammerer was a scholar and an authority on the infernal regions; he knew all the paths, fiery river and lakes, all the instruments of torture, the grids, the blazing pitch and sulphur baths, the white-hot prongs of the devils, and all the beds with their upright spikes. His wife, not as learned as he, had her own way of instilling reverence and dutifulness into the little girl. Lazy by temperament, too poor to have the many servants she would have liked to have, she taught the girl obedience by making her fetch and carry, by turning her into a mixture of scullery maid and personal attendant.

But the little girl already had a character of her own. She stood up against her aunt and uncle, and gave as good as she got. She would listen once to any story her uncle told her about hell and its compartments. The second time she rebelled.

"I've heard that!" she said sharply, and turned her back on him.

After the first instant of submission, she ignored her aunt's orders. She had to be called a dozen times before she answered. And when her aunt, emulating her husband, began to recount stories of the saintly lives of Rabbis and their chaste spouses, Malkah exploded.

"I don't want to hear that! I want to hear about my mother in Budapest!" she cried, right in the middle of a tale about the Master of the Name and his battles with a spirit from the nether regions.

Aunt Aidele tightened her lips and answered frigidly: "Don't ever dare to mention her name. You have no mother. I am your mother."

"No, you're not!" Malkah shouted, stamping her foot. "My mother is my mother. You're only my aunt!"

The family began to be afraid of the little spitfire.

"Her mother!" they murmured, horrified. "The dead image of her mother, may her name be blotted out!"

Like her mother, Malkah grew swiftly into a tall, slender woman. She had blazing, dark eyes, but with all their darkness they were not Jewish. They had the wildness of the gypsies in them. Her hair was thick and black, with a blackness that glimmered blue. It lay on her head straight and smooth, without a suggestion of a curl. Equally black and thick and smooth were her eyebrows, which met above her thin, straight nose. Only toward the tip her nose broadened slightly, curving into the wide, sensitive nostrils.

As her aunt combed the little girl's hair, and braided it, she sighed.

"Nothing Jewish about *you;* the same smooth black hair, the same straight Gentile shoulders as—as *she* had."

"*She*" was the mother, who was never mentioned by name. *She* had had a sharp tongue, and had spared no one; Malkah was the same. Malkah was wild and obstinate and rebellious. There were times—days at a stretch—when Malkah behaved like some young untamed animal. She laughed at the top of her voice, without rhyme or reason, ran from room to room, shouted, leaped on and off chairs. And there were times when, equally without rhyme or reason, she sat silent, obdurate and motionless.

"There's something evil in that child," the aunt said frequently to her husband. "A devil, a spirit out of hell!"

That something evil showed itself whether Malkah was in high spirits or in low. Her playfulness was not like the playfulness of other children. It was furious, ungovernable. She would fill the house with children, upset the leather chairs, shove the furniture around, pull the drawers out of the desks and scatter her uncle's papers on the floor. Her favorite games were to build a train, seat the children on it, and set out on a journey to Budapest, to her mother, or to make marriages.

Next to this she liked most to play at marriage. She would pull out her aunt's dresses and furs and crinolines and hats, and deck herself out as a bride. She would unearth her aunt's jewelry—brooches, chains, necklaces, stickpins—and cover herself with them from head to foot.

Her aunt, coming in, would scream, "Malkah! You'll ruin me! Malkah! Am I not poor enough already?"

Malkah was unmoved. As soon as her aunt left the house, she was at it again. She infected the other children with her own spirit. She yelled, danced about the room, sang, turned the house into a bedlam. "Shout!" she commanded. "You're on the train! We're getting near Budapest!"

The "marriages" were as noisy as the "train-rides." On one occasion a neighbor came to Aunt Aidele, confused and horrified. Malkah had made herself a bride, and had chosen an eight-year-old boy to be her bridegroom. After having gone through a mock ceremony, Malkah had commanded two of the little girls to conduct bride and bridegroom to their room! The children, going home, told their mothers, and the "bridegroom's" mother came in, weeping.

"I can't understand that," she complained. "Where does that child get it from?"

For a long time Aunt Aidele tortured Malkah to find out who had told her about bride and bridegroom going to their room. But Malkah set her teeth and did not answer. In the night Aunt Aidele, unable to sleep, woke her husband.

"Listen, you," she said, tugging at his skull-cap. "That little demon will bring shame on us, as her mother did."

Malkah developed an intemperate love of little children, a love so wild that children ran away from her, and mothers were frightened. Whenever she could lay her hands on some tot, she would press it so fiercely to her bosom, kiss it so rapturously, that the little one began to scream.

"The demon!" mothers exclaimed, when they saw her in the distance. And they pulled their children into the house. Under their breath they muttered: "Salt in your eyes! Pepper in your nose!"

It came to such a pitch that whenever a child fell sick in the village, the mother would come to Aunt Aidele, and beg her for a thread from one of Malkah's shawls. A thread from the shawl of a possessed woman was a specific against the evil eye. Aunt Aidele wept with the shame of it.

At the age of thirteen Malkah ran away for the first time.

With nothing but the clothes she had on, without a coin in her purse, she boarded the train for Budapest, where she knew her mother lived. What her mother was doing there, she did not know; nor did she have an address. She only knew she was going to find her mother. She was stopped by the train police and turned back home. Aunt Aidele thought that, on being brought back, the child would weep, would be frightened and ask to be forgiven. But Malkah was hard as stone. She stared at her aunt out of eyes which already showed the first hunger of adolescence and said:

"Wait! I'm going to do it again! I'm going to find my mother!"

Then Aunt Aidele and her husband explained things to Malkah. Day after day they spoke against her mother, explained what an evil woman she was, how she had brought shame and humiliation on the family and how, because of her, Malkah's father had died before his time. That woman, they said, had a forehead of brass and a heart of stone. She had cared nothing for her husband, nothing for her child.

Malkah was unmoved. "I'm going to my mother," she repeated.

"If you go to your mother, they'll make you eat swine."

"I'm going to my mother."

"You'll have to live with non-Jews."

"I'm going to my mother."

"They'll make you wear a cross."

"I'm going to my mother."

Malkah was as good as her word. She ran away twice. But she did not find her mother. The woman had disappeared, had been swallowed up, and Malkah had to return to her aunt and uncle. And after her last attempt something came over the girl. Her silences became more obstinate. She no longer played with other children. She sat at the window by the hour, staring at the garrison officers as they passed down the street, staring mutely at them as they approached and as they receded into the distance.

It was at such a moment that her uncle burst in on her with the great news from Nyesheve. No wonder he and his wife were beside themselves with joy, for, apart from the good luck which it meant for them in the way of prestige—and something more substantial than prestige—it also meant that they would be relieved of their impossible niece. What hope had she? Poor, friendless, eccentric, evil-tempered, she might well stay on with them until her hair turned gray or until (God forbid!) she stooped to marry some laborer.

They could hardly believe it.

"If it was only over! If I only could see her standing under the canopy!" her aunt repeated. And she prayed to all her ancestry, to the Rabbis and pious wives in paradise, to stand by and see the match through.

They stood by, and Aunt Aidele saw her niece standing under the canopy side by side with her bridegroom, the Rabbi of Nyesheve. She went along to Nyesheve herself, and took part in the Seven Benedictions. And she was still incredulous. *Something* was going to happen. Malkah *always* had something in reserve.

"I don't understand it," she said nervously to her husband. "It's too good to be true. My heart tells me something is going to happen."

But nothing happened. During the months that passed between the announcement and her marriage, Malkah asked no questions about her bridegroom. She danced with joy over every present he sent her. He sent her a great many—diamond rings, earrings, brooches, bracelets and even diadems set with precious stones. All of these had been worn by one or another of the three wives he had buried. As each one of these had died, her respective daughters had claimed their mother's jewelry. But the Rabbi had accumulated a three-fold store, and even when the third wife died he still refused to divide the heritages. He locked the jewels away in the big iron safe which stood in his room, and he never let the key pass out of his possession. He was in no hurry. He had calculations of his own. Now he sent the jewelry piecemeal to Malkah, and Malkah danced with joy. She covered herself with precious stones from head to foot, and tried to see herself all at once in the single half-size mirror which stood in her aunt's room. She strutted from one end of the room to the other, and made great gestures, such as she imagined proper to a princess or a countess. Besides the jewels, the bridegroom sent large sums of money for her trousseau. At first he tried sending her some of the costly clothes which had been worn by his three wives, priceless satins, silks and furs. But Malkah would not have them. It took a long time to make Rabbi Melech understand that clothes may be made of the finest materials, and may be as good as new, but if they are no longer in the fashion, they cannot be worn.

"So?" he said in astonishment to the stammerer, who repeated from memory, phrase by phrase, what his wife had told him to say. "Not in the fashion? There's no understanding these strange creatures."

He therefore sent money, and plenty of it. All day long Malkah flitted from one shop to another, buying silk, velvet, satin, wool and linen. She brought the brightest and most striking colors, materials as stormy as her own moods. She bought at first glance, luxuriously, in fantastic quantities. And she refused to let her aunt bargain.

"Lunatic!" her aunt exploded. "What do you need all that stuff for? You're throwing money out."

"I want it!" was the sharp answer.

The tailors brought their sewing-machines into the house to make up her wedding clothes. The older men sat with crossed legs, crooning melodies; the younger men sang snatches of German songs that had been carried by devious routes into the village, and made eyes at the bride. The whirring of the machines, the singing, the constant dressing and undressing, the measuring and re-measuring, filled Malkah with happiness. She even caught her aunt around the waist and kissed her furiously on both cheeks.

"Lunatic!" her aunt panted. "Let go of me! You're leaving red marks on me."

The idea of the wedding, too, filled her with ecstasy. She did not think of her husband to be. She knew he was old; and therefore she demanded that the wedding be held in another town. Then she forgot Rabbi Melech completely. When the wedding came, she liked it. She had always liked the game, and here she was, playing it on a grand scale, with real clothes, real ceremonies, real banquets and wine and musicians. Even the preliminary clashes with her husband did not upset her. The first time, when he asked her to let them shave her head, he had given way easily. The second time—in the dark room there—he had been terribly angry, an angry, scolding old man. It did not matter. She was even pleased by the spectacle; she had almost laughed aloud.

She did not look into the future. The excitement of the moment, the crowds of Chassidim, the flattery, the noise, the good wishes, the importance bestowed on her—everything was good while it lasted.

She liked, too, the long ride from Kiteve to Nyesheve. It was jolly. The Jews of the villages on either side of the road came out to see the Rabbi of Nyesheve and his bride pass by in state. They asked for his blessing and they brought presents. They brought their children to be blessed, and they paid for it with bottles of wine and jars of honey. The wives of the village Jews begged to be allowed to kiss Malkah's hand.

"Like a queen!" they exclaimed. "The Spirit rests on her face."

Wherever the procession stopped for the evening, there was a public festival; lanterns were hung up; there was dancing, drinking and singing. Malkah was in a continuous fever of excitement. She jumped up and down, and clapped her hands. Her attendants, the pompous womenfolk of the Rabbinic court of Nyesheve, blushed for her.

Her reception in Nyesheve was all love on the surface, all hatred underneath. Daughters, daughters-in-law, grandsons—all sorts of relatives of the Rabbi who had not come to the wedding—met her with smiles and compliments which did not conceal their envy and hatred. One after another the daughters of former wives of the Rabbi approached her, looked at her ornaments and sighed.

"Oh, that was mother's, blessed be her memory. May you wear it many, many years."

Malkah was not at all displeased. She felt the envy and liked it. She realized at once that this place was filled with hatreds and intrigues and gossip, that the court was divided into hostile cliques which watched each other venomously. She had not been there one day before attempts were made, by flattery, by ill-natured reports concerning the attitude toward her, to win her into some of the cliques. She liked it all. Malkah Spitfire felt at home in this atmosphere; it appealed to her love of mischief and her hunger for domination. She was happy, and Aunt Aidele— if she had but known it—had as yet no grounds for anxiety.

A PASSOVER EVE

by HEINRICH HEINE

RABBI ABRAHAM sat in the large dining-room of his house surrounded by relations, disciples, and many other guests, to celebrate the great feast of Passover Eve. Everything in the room sparkled with an unusual brilliance. Over the table spread the gaily embroidered silk cloth, whose gold fringes touched the floor; the small plates with the symbolic food shone in a comfortable home-like way, as did the tall wine goblets, adorned with embossed images of sacred legends. The men sat in their black cloaks and black broad-brimmed hats, with white collars. The women, in wonderful glittering garments of Lombard stuffs, wore on their heads and necks ornaments of gold and pearls, while the silver Sabbath lamp poured forth its pleasant light on the smiling faces of parents and children, happy in their piety. On the purple velvet cushions of a chair, higher than the others, and reclining as the Law enjoins, sat Rabbi Abraham, and read and chanted the *Haggada,* while the mixed assembly joined with him, or answered at the appointed places. The rabbi, too, wore the prescribed black festival garment, his nobly-formed but somewhat severe features had a milder expression than usual, his lips smiled out of the dark brown beard as though they wished to tell pleasant things, while his eyes seemed to be filled with happy remembrances and anticipation. Beautiful Sara, who sat on a raised chair with a velvet cushion beside her husband, wore, as hostess, none of her ornaments; only white linen enveloped her slender form and gentle face. Her face was touchingly beautiful, even as all Jewish beauty is of a peculiarly moving kind; for the consciousness of the deep wretchedness, the bitter scorn, and the unhappy circumstances amid which her kindred and friends dwelt, give to their lovely features a depth of sorrow and an ever-watchful apprehension of love that invariably bewitches our hearts. So on this evening sat the lovely Sara, looking into the eyes of her husband, yet glancing now and then at the beautiful parchment edition of the *Haggada* which lay before her, bound in gold and velvet. It was an old heirloom, with aged wine stains on it, which had come down from the days of her grandfather. In it were many boldly and brightly-coloured pictures, which she had often, as a little girl, looked at so eagerly on Passover evenings, and which represented all kinds of Biblical stories;—how Abraham with a hammer smashed the idols of his father; how the angels came to visit him, how Moses slew the Egyptian, how Pharaoh sat in state on his throne, how the frogs gave him no peace even at table, how he—the Lord be praised!—was drowned while the children of Israel walked cautiously through the Red Sea; how they stood open-mouthed before Mount Sinai with their sheep, cows, and oxen; how pious King David played the harp; and, finally, how Jerusalem, with its towers and minarets, shone in the splendour of the setting sun.

The second wine-cup had been filled, the faces and voices of the guests grew merrier, and the rabbi, as he took a cake of unleavened bread and raised it, and with a happy greeting read the following words from the *Haggada:* "Behold! This is the food which our fathers ate in Egypt! Let everyone who is hungry come and eat! Let everyone who is sorrowful come and share the joys of our Passover! In this year we celebrate it here, but next year in the land of Israel. This year we celebrate it in servitude, but next year as free men!"

Then the hall door opened, and there entered two tall, pale men, wrapped in very broad cloaks. "Peace be with you," said one of them.

"We are fellow-Jews on a journey, and would like to keep Passover with you!" And the rabbi replied promptly and kindly: "Peace be with you. Sit down near me!" The two strangers sat down at the table, and the rabbi continued to read. While the company repeated the responses he often whispered an endearing word to his wife. Playing on the old saying that on this evening a father of a Jewish family regards himself as a king, he said to her, "Rejoice, O my Queen!" But she replied, smiling sadly, "The Prince is missing," meaning by that a son, who, as a passage in the *Haggada* requires, shall ask his father, with a fixed formula of words, the meaning of the festival. The rabbi said nothing, but only pointed with his finger to a picture on the opened pages of the *Haggada*. It was quaintly and touchingly drawn, showing how the three angels came to Abraham to announce that he would have a son by his wife Sara, who, meanwhile, urged by feminine curiosity, is listening slyly to it all behind the door of the tent. This little sign brought a crimson blush to the cheeks of the beautiful woman. She looked down, and then glanced lovingly at her husband, who was now chanting the wonderful story how Rabbi Joshua, Rabbi Eliezer, Rabbi Azaria, Rabbi Akiba, and Rabbi Tarphon sat reclining in Bne Brak, and conversed all night long of the Exodus from Egypt till their disciples came to tell them it was daylight, and that the morning prayer was being read in the synagogue.

As the beautiful Sara, with devotion in her eyes, listened to her husband, she saw his face suddenly assume an agonized expression, his cheeks and lips grow deadly pale, and his eyes gleam with a cold stare as though they had turned to ice. Almost at the same moment, however, he became as calm and cheerful as before, his cheeks and lips grew red again, his eyes sparkled with cheer, and it seemed as if a mad merry mood, strange to his nature, had seized him. Sara was frightened as she had never been in all her life and a cold shudder came over her, less because of the momentary signs of blank despair which she had seen in her husband's face than because of the subsequent joyousness which now changed to rollicking merriment. The rabbi cocked his skull cap comically from ear to ear, then pulled and twisted his beard clownishly, sang the *Haggada* texts like tavern ditties. In the enumeration of the Egyptian plagues, where it is customary to dip the forefinger in the full wine goblets to cast the drops of wine to the floor, he sprinkled the young girls near him with the red wine and there was great wailing over spoiled collars, and ringing laughter. Sara became more and more mystified at the convulsive but apparently forced merriment of her husband, and, seized with nameless fears, she stared at the buzzing swarm of gaily glittering guests who comfortably spread and rocked themselves back and forth nibbling the crisp Passover cakes, drinking wine, gossiping, or singing aloud, full of joy and merriment.

Then came the time for supper. Everyone rose to wash the hands. Sara brought in a large silver basin, richly adorned with embossed gold figures, and held it before each of the guests, while water was poured over his hands. While she held it before the rabbi, he gave her a significant look, and quietly slipped out of the door. Sara followed him. He seized her hand, and in the greatest haste hurried her through the dark lanes of Bacharach, out of the city gate to the highway which leads along the Rhine to Bingen.

It was one of those calm and starry nights in spring which inspire the soul with uncanny feelings. There was something of the churchyard in the flowers, the birds sang peevishly and as if vexing themselves, the moon cast spiteful yellow stripes of light over the dark stream as it flowed and murmured its music; the lofty masses of the Rhine cliffs looked dimly like quivering giants' heads. The watchman on the tower of Castle Strahleck blew a melancholy tune, and with it rang in jarring rivalry the funeral bell of Saint Werner's church. Sara carried the silver ewer in her right hand, while the rabbi grasped her left. She could feel his ice-cold fingers and the trembling of his arm, but still she accompanied him in silence, perhaps because she was accustomed to obey blindly and unquestioningly;—perhaps, too, because her lips were mute with fear and anxiety.

Below the Sonneck castle, opposite Lorch, about the place where the hamlet of Lower Rheinbach now stands, there rises a cliff which arches out over the Rhine bank. The rabbi ascended it with his wife, peered around on every side, and gazed at the stars. Trembling and shivering, as with the pain of death, Sara looked at his pale face, which seemed spectre-like in the moon-rays, and seemed to express by turns pain, terror, piety, and rage. But when the rabbi suddenly snatched from her hands the silver ewer and threw it far away into the Rhine, she could no longer endure the agony of uncertainty, and crying out *"Shaddai!* Be merciful!"* threw herself at his feet, and begged him to solve the dark enigma.

Unable at first to speak from excitement, the rabbi moved his lips without uttering a sound. At last he cried, "Do you see the Angel of Death? There below he hovers over Bacharach. But we have escaped his sword. Praised be God!" And in a voice still trembling with excitement he told her that while he was happily singing the *Haggada* he glanced by chance under the table, and saw at his feet the bloody corpse of a little child. "Then I noticed," continued the rabbi, "that our two guests were not of the community of Israel, but of the congregation of the godless, who had plotted to bring that corpse craftily into the house so as to accuse us of child-murder, and stir up the people to plunder and murder us. Had I given the merest sign that I saw through that fiendish plot, I should simply have hastened our destruction; only by craft did I preserve our lives. Praised be God! Do not fear, my lovely Sara. Our relations and friends will also be saved. It was only my blood for which they thirsted. I have escaped them, and they will be satisfied with my silver and gold. Come with me, Sara, to another land. We will leave our evil fortune behind us, and that it may not follow us I have thrown to it the silver ewer, the last of my possessions, as an offering. The God of our fathers will not forsake us!"

JOSEPH CARO

by J. OPATOSHU

His tall sister, with a black kerchief drawn over her darkly arched eyebrows, met him in the quiet rooms with the heavy double doors.

They did not greet each other but stood there as though hewn out of stone, in the hollow stillness. She felt stifled in the oppressiveness of the atmosphere, conscious that the walls of the room were closing in on her, and when it seemed that she could no longer breathe, she wrung her hands and paced forward with a slow, graceful stride. Her white stockings gleamed from under her black dress, like the curve of white birds' necks, and her mournful steps seeped into the thick carpet.

"When did it happen?" he asked without raising his eyes.

"A week ago today. Father, as usual, went out on the balcony to say the evening prayer. At that very moment the soldiers were investing the town, in hot pursuit of the enemy. No civilian dared to appear on the streets. But father stood on the balcony, with a red kerchief in his belt, chanting the prayers with fervid devotion. That's all there was to it. The soldiers came while he was in the midst of prayer and took him away. The whole Jewish community turned out and tried to intervene. Many offered themselves as hostages. In vain."

"And father?"

"Father remained silent. He only pleaded that they should not offer any hostages for him. He regretted that he did not have a son to keep intact his family's five-hundred-year-old rabbinical heritage, that it must end with him . . . We did not know, Joseph, whether or not you were alive. For six years you wandered abroad in evil ways. The war broke out and you were neither heard from nor seen."

"And father?"

"He died a martyr's death."

Brother and sister straightened up, became taller, and their dark eyes took on a glow. The sister cracked her fingers in silence, hid her eyes behind the fringe of the kerchief, and appealed to her brother :

"Joseph, go to the synagogue and say kaddish [a prayer for the dead]; then come home and sit through the seven days of mourning. Father deserved it."

He stared at his sister's white stockings and did not utter a word. Then the double door closed dully behind him.

He had reached the outskirts of the town and was crossing through fields where prickly corn-stalks added to the gloom. A windmill capped with moss stood brooding on a hill. Its cross-shaped vanes were decorated with fir trees to signify that the Polish legions had driven out the foe.

Joseph walked toward the cemetery. Tall, lanky, mobile in reflection, his tired face shone with gentleness. Wisdom and inarticulate sorrow brooded in his dark fathomless eyes. His shoulders were narrow, very narrow, and the movement of his limbs had a swing of assurance,—the calm of a feather caught up between gusts of wind! Century after century the Caros tormented their bodies, disciplined them to thrive on crumbs, and made them as wiry and flexible as arrows. The body, lithe and supple, laughed at both the wind and the storm as it was carried from land to land.

Joseph stood before the tombstones which were more than two centuries old and faded with age. His great-great-grandfather, the grandson of the renowned Rabbi Joseph Caro, had been brought over to Poland. He had little in common with the people, and acquired a knowledge of the vernacular from grandmother's Judeo-German collection of Bible tables. The Caros had been stern rabbis. The most distinguished of them, the author of the *Shulhan Arukh,* a monumental code of Jewish law, had cause to feel unashamed. His learned treatises were handed down from father to son. Upon the title page were printed the counsel of Rashi, the greatest of Jewish commentators:

". . . Eat little, drink little, restrain your wrath, be humble. As long as you enjoy health do not permit another human being to serve you, for the servant, too, was created in the image of God. There is no greater virtue than to die for the sake of God . . ."

The deep yearning to die for God had gripped one of his grandfathers who lived in Safed, one of the four holy cities of Palestine. He had lived in the hope that God would grant him his wish . . . He who had compiled the *Shulhan Arukh* could ill afford to ignore any one of the six hundred and thirteen commandments. One night an angel appeared in a dream and promised that his wish would be granted: Its fulfillment came four centuries later in Poland. . . .

There was a rustle in the old graveyard. A wind swept up the yellow leaves and hurled them across the headstones. An echo, as though from glass, lingered in the still, blue twilight. . . .

Far away a thought was born out of anguish and martyrdom. Joseph Caro only had to close his eyes to visualize his friend, the preacher, discoursing and chanting from within him, and those around him falling on their face in sublime fear, and trembling with the great joy of dying for God. . . . The thought, uprooted, forlorn, and homeless, was wandering over the world, like the Caro family who begat it and, after four hundred years, finally found fulfillment and rest in the graveyard of an isolated Polish town. . . .

It was growing darker. Something was stirring in the leaves.

The gravedigger, a bent old Jew, came shuffling by, leading a goat. Before he had passed the young man standing still at the rabbi's grave, he caught himself:

"Joseph? Joseph, the rabbi's?"

"The same, Reb Simcha."

"One doesn't take the hand of a mourner. The young run away from us and you, Joseph, you have returned. It's not so good! It's not so good!"

The goat with its bursting udder became restive, and was pulling at the old man.

"Wait, Joseph, I'll take the goat home!"

Joseph did not wait. Behind the graveyard the sun was setting in a pool of blood. A military orchestra was playing in the park, telling of the triumph over the enemy.

Joseph was standing on a hill, his narrow body tapering like a reed in the twilight blue. Below in the valley where the town spread, roofs hunched upon roofs. In each house they lived by the tenets of the *Shulhan Arukh* as they did a hundred, two, and three hundred years ago. If a

Jew died in the name of God, a day of fasting was decreed. . . . From the red bathhouse where the women performed their ablutions, a column of smoke was curling upward into the evening haze . . .

He descended from the hill and made his way to the train. The night was spreading its cloak of darkness, carrying with it the strains of the military orchestra.

The nebulous lawns startled, throbbed into song, which weaved itself, animate, plant-like, around the figure of Joseph, smothering the voice in his heart. And he, a lean man, divested of the burden of the flesh, was wandering over the earth on his way to meet his grandfather.

A LETTER FROM AMERICA

by LEON KOBRIN

THE first letter from Mirke's daughter Leah has arrived from America, and it is filled with good news. Mirke weeps for joy and begs her Mayshe-Ityse to read it for her, over and over again. . . . Mayshe-Itsye reads it and is so deeply moved that he keeps pulling at his nose and swallowing his tears. Old Avrom-Layzer, his ear well-cocked to catch the words, the end of his flowing white beard clutched in his fist, bends over toward his son-in-law; he is careful not to lose a word of the letter, and his countenance glows with an expression of wonderment. Leah's sisters read the letter, too, in agitated voices, and tears of joy glitter in their eyes. Even little Shlayme is seized with the happiness of the occasion; during the past year he has grown taller, paler, thinner, but he has remained the same mischievous creature as before. And for sheer joy he begins to beg: "Mama, give me a kopek!" And for sheer joy Mirke gives him a kopek at once, bestowing the same largess upon the other children, too. Then she seizes the letter and dashes off with a glowing face to the market-place, that the shopkeepers may read the wonderful news.

And somewhat later Mottel is standing before his store, reading the selfsame letter in a loud voice, with Mirke beside him, surrounded by all the storekeepers and the women who own the market stands; all listen to the letter with mouths agape and eyes distended in wonder. Mirke drinks in every word, smiles with enthusiasm, wipes her eyes and every other moment interrupts Mottel's reading. "Oh, thanks be to God! Do you hear? Well, what do you say to *that,* ha? . . ."

And the rest shake their heads, smack their lips and murmur their wonderment.

"My, my! Ay! Ay! . . ."

"Why not confess it?" reads Mottel. "Never in my life have I seen what I saw at the home of my brothers-in-law in New York. On the very sidewalk lay precious things such as I only wish you could have on your table for the holidays. It's only too bad that people step all over them with their feet. And there are golden mirrors here that reach to the ceiling. And there isn't a trace of a lamp in all New York. And at night you press the wall, and a lot of moons in glass cases light up, just like on the ship on which we came across. . . ."

"Well!" interrupts Mottel. "What do you think of that? Ha? . . ."

"Do you hear?" adds Mirke, and her whole countenance is one smile of exaltation.

"My, my! Ay, ay!" chorus the listeners.

Mottel resumes his reading:

"And the walls here are so red and velvety. I touched one of them, and it's so soft and even, and I thought to myself: 'I hope I have a cloak made of it!' "

"She knows what's good to have!" called one of the women shop-keepers.

"And as for eating," the letter went on, "they eat of the very best here. The don't lack even bird's milk! Roast hens in the middle of the week and so many other dainty dishes that I don't know how to name them. . . ."

"There's a Rothschild existence for you!" interjects Mottel once more, continuing to read:

"And the buildings in New York are so high that even when you turn back your neck you can barely see the roof. And over the roofs there fly machines filled with people, and the people aren't at all afraid, and my brothers-in-law tell me that none of the machines has ever fallen down. . . ."

"My, my! Heavens! Ay, ay!"

"—And they rented a home for us in which even a count might live. Six rooms in a fine building. And in three of the rooms, on the floor they've laid down a kind of oil-cloth with such nice squares, and in the hall on the floor they put a big piece of velvet with flowers painted on it. I don't let anybody into the house, because I don't want them to step on it. Then I've got chairs, a bureau and what not else, which they sent in. It simply dazzles your eyes to look at them. And mother-in-law is living with us. And there's water in our home. All you have to do is turn a faucet and water comes from the wall. And you don't need any lamps, either, for when you want light, you simply turn a sort of screw and you bring a match close to it and it gets light. And there's no oven here, either. When you wish to cook you turn another screw, and pretty soon the stove is hot and you put your pots on top of it and you make the finest dishes. And my brothers-in-law have taken Orre into their iron factory, where they make iron ceilings and stairs for the buildings, and they pay him, thank God, twenty dollars a week. In our money that's every bit of forty rubles."

"Listen, folks! Just listen to that!" cries one of the women. "I could pinch my cheeks. . . ."

"Read on, Reb Mottel!" urges Mirke with ardor, drying her eyes. Mottel continues:

"Yes, where was I? 'In our money that's every bit of forty rubles. And later, say my brothers-in-law, he'll get even more.' "

Mirke can no longer restrain her sobs.

"Well? Ha? Well?"

"—I hope to God that I'll be able to send for all of you, and bring you across. And my brothers-in-law tell me that in New York there are a good many Jewish policemen, too. . . ."

"That's so," cries Mottel. "I heard that long ago,—that Jews over there have equal rights!"

"Really?" asks one. "And they have Jewish policemen there, too?"

"What do you think?" shouts Mottel in reply, his voice ringing with confidence. "Even Jewish intelligence-officers. . . ."

"You don't say!"

"It would pay to pawn our wives and children and take a trip over there!" jests one of the men.

"And the men, too!" retorts one of the women. "But I'm afraid Berel-Itsye the money-lender wouldn't advance a groschen on them."

The rest of the women burst into laughter.

"Unless the Gentile butcher would give something for them as impure meat," suggests another woman.

"Shoo, ladies!" exclaims a shopkeeper, and waves his hands at them as if he were driving geese along.

The laughter waxes louder. Both the women and the men are now guffawing.

Mirke now stands with the letter in her hands, taking no part in the general merriment. She feels provoked that they should not now be talking of her daughter's good fortune. For a moment she remains thus, then she remarks:

"And I, fool that I was, tried to keep her from going! . . ."

Nobody notices her reflection. Out of envy, they all pretend not to have heard anything that she had said. So she approaches close to one of the women with whom she is wont to quarrel all the year long,— Elke, the daughter of Chaye-Dvoshe, a gaunt woman with a crooked nose, wearing a white bonnet under a red, flowery kerchief,—thinking to herself, "Let her burst with envy!" and she says:

"What do you say to that, Elke? Such a fool I was trying to hold her back. . . ."

"You never can tell," replies Elke maliciously. "Maybe your heart told you that she ought not to go? Maybe. . . . Who knows what misfortune may yet befall her there! . . ."

Mirke, flaming with rage, almost jumps upon her.

"Tfu! Tfu! Tfu!" She spits out thrice. "On your head! May it befall your own wicked person! You crooked serpent, you! Burst with envy! Explode with jealousy! Aha! Whose daughter has a husband that makes forty rubles a week? Aha? Burst! Burst! Burst!"

And she dashes into her shop. Elke replies with a volley of curses. The other women set up a clamor. The men hold their sides with laughter, while Mottel cries: "Livelier, Elke, livelier!"

"Hush! Here comes the lord with the brass buttons! . . ."

The sergeant issues forth from the apothecary's, stops and eyes the crowd around the shops.

And when the sergeant disappears, Mottel cries to one of his neighbors, in a voice breathless with wonder:

"And in America there are even Jewish policemen. There's no grief of Exile over there. Full rights. . . ."

For the next few weeks there was talk of this letter all over the town, and of the "full rights," and on a certain Saturday morning, when Mottel caught hold of little Shlayme in the synagogue and asked him: "Well, youngster, are you going to sail to America, too?" Shlayme replied, "You bet! I'll be a policeman there! . . ."

At about this time Sholom the Gentile entered the home of Shmeril the cobbler, whistled mysteriously and held out both his hands.

Shmeril happened to be holding a shoe in his lap, heel upwards, and his mouth was filled with wooden nails; he stared at Sholom in amazement, removed the nails from between his lips and asked quietly:

"What's the matter?"

"From Broche . . ." he managed to utter in a stifled voice, making a pitiable attempt to smile. "She is . . . phew! . . ."

Again he whistled and brandished his arms.

"Well, what about your Broche? Speak. . . ."

"Sailed for America yesterday."

"America? Your Broche? . . ."

"Yes, yes. Broche, my Broche. . . . She fell in love, in the city, with a rascal of a salesman and he turned her head with stories of America, and go try to talk her out of it! . . . I and my wife Gittel rushed to the city, begged of her, wept before her: 'What do you mean by this sudden craze for America? To foresake your father and mother, your brothers and sisters,—the whole world? What do you mean by it, the devil take your father? Haven't you any pity?' . . . But you might as well have spoken to the wall! She went away! And my Gittel came back from the city half dead; she could scarcely drag her feet along. She just left for the burial-ground, to pray at her mother's grave. . . . Oh, may she at least arrive there in safety . . . Did you ever hear such a tale, Shmeril? It's a terrible blow. Come, let's have a glass of brandy! . . ."

Shmeril arose, shook out his black apron with his black, grimy hands, and said:

"Drinking a glass of brandy is by no means the most foolish thing a fellow can do! But that you should be sorry to have her go, my friend,— now *that's* folly! I've been thinking this America over, and it seems to me that it's not a bad place to go to."

"Are you crazy, Shmeril? What are you talking about?"

"Just what you hear! I have heard about America for a long time, and that it's possible to work yourself up to something over there. And ever since Mirke's daughter Leah went there and sends such letters from her place, I can't get America out of my mind. I keep thinking all the time: Shmeril, what will all your striving here come to? You've got four sons and three daughters. The sons—one of them is going around altogether idle until he'll be taken away as a soldier; one is a tinsmith, earns twice nothing, not even enough to provide water for porridge; the third calls himself a dealer, and makes nary a groschen from his business; and the fourth, may the devil seize him!—I taught him the cobbler's trade, and he's as much a cobbler as I am a Rabbi. Every day he catches a blow with the bootleg from me. Is that any prospect for me? Maybe things would turn out altogether differently over there? They say that America is a great country, even vaster than Russia. . . . If it was all right for the Jew to travel deep into Russia, why not yonder? . . ."

"But deep Russia isn't under the earth. . . ."

"Much that should worry you. . . . Isn't it true that there is bread and something to chew there? And that you don't have to worry about your sons? And that Jews have full rights? And that you don't have to give girls a dowry when they marry? Then who cares whether it's in the earth or under the earth, as long as it's a merry life over there?"

"And how about my never seeing my Broche again, and her never being able to see me again, and not even my grave, when I die? Ha?" asked Sholom with deep gloom.

"Well, isn't it possible that you and your family will sail there sometime?"

"I? You're talking like a fool, indeed, Shmeril! I wouldn't go there even if I knew that I'd get rich yonder. Here in the village my father lived,—my grandfather and my great-great-grandfather, may they add to my years, and they lie in our graveyard here, and there I, too, shall lie, in a hundred and twenty years. . . ."

They entered a tavern and ordered a half-quart. After they had drained the contents, Sholom became gloomier than ever; he beat himself over the heart and sobbed:

"She was the apple of my eye, and now I'll never see her again. . . ."

Shmeril, on the other hand, became lighter-hearted than before, and suddenly bent over toward Sholom, and whispered a secret:

"I'm selling my place and getting ready to go to America with my two oldest sons and Chyenke. May we both so truly enjoy long life as I'm telling you the truth. . . ."

And his words were accompanied by a powerful blow across the shoulder with his black, grimy palm.

THEY'RE LEAVING . . .

by SIMEON YUSHKEVITCH

For the first time since the funeral of her daughter Manitshka, who had been killed in a pogrom, Khova appeared in the little grocery store. . . . How hard it was for her to be walking out of doors! For it was here that . . . Yes, it was here that it had happened . . . No, she must not think about it. It seemed to her that from all windows curious eyes were levelled at her and, restraining her tears and thinking that God had vainly punished her with such a terrible humiliation, she glided through the open gate. . . .

"There are less of us now," she begun, greeting the woman shopkeeper. "Well, such was God's will. And when God wills that . . . Well, here I've come to you again! Yes, yes, I know how much I owe you. . . . But . . . my fool will pay. Don't be afraid."

The shopkeeper Hella, a gaunt woman with wild eyes, drew her thin bloodless lips taut. . . . What then? Hadn't the hooligans pillaged her shop? Hadn't they gotten away with everything that had been here on the shelves? After all, had she a million roubles' worth of goods on her shelves?

"Don't waste your breath to tell me," said Khova timidly. "Why waste words? But you're new in our street, and you don't know . . . How does the broker live? By credit! And my fool hasn't paid rent for two months now, yet our landlord won't chuck us out into the street. He knows. If God wills it, the broker will suddenly earn a hundred roubles. . . . And so you see, my dear, everything has to do with credit, all life turns 'round credit."

"I understand," Hella replied after a silence, "but where am I to get things for everybody? What am I now with my little shop? There was a time my husband used to bring home each week four roubles, sometimes five. But you know as well as I that they've made a cripple of him . . . They've broken both his hands—his right and his left. . . . What's he to do now? Try sewing with his feet?"

"My dear, my dear . . ." Khova implored. "I'll pay you soon."

Both began to talk in whispers of the horrors of the massacre, and both, frightened by their own words, broke into sobs.

"We all ought to leave this place," Hella persisted. "No matter what they say to me, I know one thing: they'll wipe out all of us. Some time a

night will come, such a night, and from house to house the murderers
with axes in their hands will come, and they'll take all of us, as many of
us as there are here, and they'll kill us. And I say to my old man: 'Let's
leave! . . . Let's sell our little shop, and let them be accursed!' "

Two more women customers came in and, recognizing Khova, began
to talk to her about poor Manitchka. Then suddenly—it is hard to tell
how—they passed on to the subject of the fate of the Jews.

"They're all getting ready to leave," said the eldest in a harsh voice.
"Now do you think I intend to remain here long? I have a son . . . I
have a good son . . . A little while longer, and he'll take me to live with
him . . . *over there!* Thank God for that, thank God!"

"And I have a son-in-law," said the second woman. . . . *"Over there*
he has a fruit shop, and I'll help to sell fruit in his shop . . . Yes, that's
what I'm going to do—I'll save him a pretty penny . . ."

As one stupefied Khova started for home. Everywhere one and the
same thing . . . Fears and talk of flight. Indeed, why should they remain here? Wasn't one sacrifice—poor Manitchka—enough? She suddenly looked up at the sky, as if Manitchka's soul lured her there, and
with pent-up emotion and grief she thought:

"You are now well off, my dear, my poor dear—but what's yet to
become of us? . . ."

She found visitors at home: the broker Leyzer and Weitz. Cohan, her
fool Cohan, was walking up and down the room and flourishing his
arms.

"Come, come in!" he shouted in a distraught voice. "Listen to Leyzer
. . . Just hear what he says!"

Khova loved Leyzer for his sobriety as well as for his ability to talk
roundly and beautifully even about trifles. He was tall, portly and had
the appearance of a merchant. He had big hands, broad shoulders, a large
nose, and all this pleased her no little. He was not a bit like her Cohan,
who was small, like a chick, with a slender little voice . . .

"I listen to you as I listen to my own father," she said softly, as she
seated herself and put the potatoes and the flour on the table. "Why didn't
you bring Rose along with you?"

"Look-a-here . . ."—Cohan interrupted, and at the same time buttoned up his waistcoat—"Semka doesn't allow him to talk. You speak
to him, Khova. He's been going on like this for some time."

"Semka," sternly pronounced Khova, but suddenly, on second
thought, she took the youngster in her arms. "All right, put your head

against your mother's breast . . . Is this better? Now keep quiet, keep quiet . . . Listen to what Uncle says."

"If you're asking about my Rose," said Leyzer, when quiet was resumed, "then I must tell you that she couldn't come. Are you satisfied with that, Khova? No, I see you aren't. Then let me tell she isn't quite well."

"Go on with what you were saying," Cohan burst out, as with a single movement of his fingers he undid all the buttons of his waistcoat. "Why, you were beginning to say something about Russia."

"Yes, it's interesting," said Weitz in a deep bass voice; he sat in a corner, a dark, gloomy man.

"We'll come to Russia in good time," Leyzer quieted them and slouched down in his chair in such a way as to half recline in it. "I must finish about Rose first . . . Stones! What are stones? Are they too a kind of disease? But when they happen to be in the liver, they become a problem. It comes to this: the stones creep their way into the liver. Well! And we've crept into this world . . ."

He noticed that he interested them all, and gradually he grew more heated. He gave the impression that he was playing with words as a cat with a mouse.

"Listen then! Either my Rose eats delicate food, because delicate food contains no stones? Then that leaves nothing more to be said. What then? Well, then, Rose's heart has begun to thump loudly in her breast. Let it be so! And why not, I ask you? Doesn't your heart thump hard? Or, thank God, we have no pogroms? And if you'll be such fools as to ask me, aren't my Rose's feet healthy, then I'll answer you that you know better than I how my Rose feels. Her feet are all swollen . . . Why? That's what I can't understand. A human being must walk. Why then should the feet swell? Or must a human being lie—why give him feet? The question comes down to a couple of words: Yes, or no . . ."

"I don't see what there's to feel gay about?" said Khova gloomily.

"And if I tell you," answered Leyzer satirically, "that whether I'm gay or not gay, that such good will come pouring down upon us? . . . All stones will become cured, all hearts will cease to thump hard, and our petty Jewish sorrow will rot away . . ."

"That's well put," again responded Weitz, flourishing his fists high.

"I'll put it better than that," Leyzer brusquely interrupted him. "In this place our petty Jewish sorrow will never get cured, and that's why we ought to run away from here."

"Go on, go on, dear Leyzer," began Cohan, panting with agitation.

as with the quickness of lightning he buttoned and unbuttoned his waistcoat.

"Yes, do go on!" put in Khova. "One can learn something from you. You're not a bit like my fool here. When he talks, I get nervous . . . He doesn't speak clearly, not at all simply, but . . . in a way that frightens you."

"Let it be as you say," answered Cohan wearily. "But I do bring you money when I earn it, don't I? Am a good husband, eh? . . . I don't drink and I don't play cards. As for running away from here, like everyone else, with everyone else, can't I do that? Maybe, I could be the first to run away, if need be."

"You'd best keep quiet," cried Khova with evident suffering, shutting her ears with her hands. "Why should you be talking? Leyzer, it means we must all run away? Speak the truth. Everyone says, they're going to leave . . . It's what you think that I want to know!"

"Aha!" broke from Leyzer. "That tempts everyone: there and here! Who are we?"—Rapidly he began to bend his fingers, beginning with the tiniest.—"Oh, you poor, you helpless, you accursed, you hungry and . . . the earth! That's five things to bear in mind. But let's proceed . . . Millions of children, millions of illnesses, millions of worries, millions of pogroms and . . . Russia! That's another five things to bear in mind. But multiply five thousand times five and it won't be all? Aha! Above everything . . . there is Russia. What does Russia mean? Russia means a land in which they cut Jews' throats. Don't torment my poor head with the question: Why? What? Is it a civilized nation? A gentle nation? Tartars, Tartars and Tartars! . . . No, no—no, don't tell us fairy tales, that because they've begun to cut Jews' throats, it foretells good to come for everyone. They've cut Jews' throats before, they're cutting Jews' throats now, they'll go on cutting Jews' throats in the future—just as if Jews were sheep. Whose throats are they cutting? Those of the Jews? Maybe you think they're doing it only to poor little fellows? No! Every Jew's! Then comes the question, what should the Jews do? We know. And what should someone like you, Cohan, or like you, Weitz, or like me, Leyzer, say? Well, what? What?"

"I know," responded Weitz.

"You all know," said Leyzer angrily. "Well, I'll tell you what. Well, then—ought to say I—Leyzer, with sick wife and little children, show me how you're going to run away from Russia . . ."

"Excellent!" shouted Cohan.

"Well, just try and do as well as Leyzer!" cried Khova warmly.

"You're a fool! Sit down! Why do you run up and down the room? And let that waistcoat of yours alone. Why, you've already torn off all the buttons . . . And where do you intend going, Leyzer?"

"What do you mean, where?" There was astonishment in Leyzer's voice. "Are there two places to which one may run? Straight to America, of course! Perhaps not straight, but to America. Stop a moment, don't raise such a din . . . The question arises: What am I, Leyzer, here? Answer: A dog! Two dogs! And what else? A scabby Jew. Whom everyone might beat, rob, and anything else you like, as you all know. And there? Do you know? Well, tell me if you do."

"I know," replied Weitz.

"Keep quiet, Weitz," whispered Khova.

"There," cried Leyzer triumphantly, "I am—a Yankee! Not Leyzer, but Yankee Eliezer. That's what I am. Yankee Eliezer! I stroll in the street with my wife and little ones . . . There goes Yankee Eliezer in America with his wife and little ones and . . . he is afraid of nobody, of nobody! . . ."

"If I had the money," shouted Cohan, "my feet would shed the dust of Russia tomorrow!"

"No, no!" cried Khova, distraught, for she was frightened of Cohan's outburst. "Let me think about it. Don't you go meddling in this business. You frighten one. Now you flame up, then you go out. Once you suddenly took it into your head to become a tailor . . . Do you remember? Then suddenly you got the idea that you wanted to deal in horses . . ."

She began to relate of the achievements of Cohan, and he listened as one listens to a fairy tale about someone else, and devoured her with his eyes, and shook his head and laughed, like an infant, especially when she recalled how once he had decided to become a cabby . . . But in his head there were already floating alluring pictures of their departure from Russia.

"Just hold, there, just hold!" he shouted. "What's this being born in my head? What did Leyzer say? Yankee Eliezer? And how will I be called there? Yankee Cohan? I tell you, I'm going . . . For the name of Yankee I am ready to give my life. Tomorrow I am going to town. I shall find a purse full of money. I'll have to do a hundred things. Don't hinder me, Khova . . . Listen to me . . ."

His perturbation grew and he raised his voice. So intensely did he desire the good, the human, that the whole truth of their terrible life vanished from him as by magic, and they all, captivated by his voice, his gestures, the sparkle of his eyes, yielded to him . . . Yes, within a week, they would be all leaving, all leaving!

"Well, well," Leyzer goaded him on, "don't stop! Go on, go on . . ."

And Cohan went on creating his fairy tale, finding at his every call new astonishing words, and so passionate was the thirst for a quiet, tranquil life that even Khova yielded to him. . . . Within a week they would be leaving! . . .

THE KISS

by L. SHAPIRO

RAB' SHACHNEH's hands and feet trembled, and he felt an awful bitterness in the mouth. It seemed to him, sitting in the chair, that the wild uproar of the street, the howling and the whistling, the cracking and the ringing of the shattering window-panes, were taking place within him, within his own head.

The pogrom had broken out with such fearful suddenness that he found himself forced to fly home without stopping to lock his shop. But on reaching home, he discovered no one there. Sarah and the children had, seemingly, managed to hide themselves somewhere, leaving the house and their few belongings in God's care. He himself, however, did not think of hiding. IIe did not think of anything, in fact. He was conscious only of the wild noises of the street, and of the unbearable bitterness in his mouth.

The noises sounded now nearer, now more distant, like the roar of a neighboring conflagration. But suddenly, it surrounded the house on all sides at once. The window-panes cracked, rocks flew into the room; and the next instant, young peasants with flaming, drunken faces, carrying knives and clubs, came crawling through doors and windows.

It then occurred to Rab' Shachneh that he ought to do something about it. And he lifted himself laboriously from the chair, and began to crawl under a sofa, right before the eyes of the rioters. The peasants roared with laughter.

"Nah! *There* is a fool for you!" and one of them grabbed him by a leg. "Eh, you! Get up!"

This brought Rab' Shachneh to his senses, and he began to weep like a child.

"Boys," he pleaded, "I will let you have everything—the money, the jewelry—everything. Spare my life! Why should you kill me? I have a wife and children."

But nothing availed him. They took everything, and beat him besides, struck him in the face and chest, kicked him in the abdomen with mad fury. He cried, pleaded, and they kept up their beating.

"Vasily, Vasilinka, you know me! Your father worked for us. Haven't we always paid him well? Vasilinka, save me! Save . . ."

A violent blow on the chest cut short his pleading. Two young peasants sat on him and pressed their knees into his abdomen. Vasilinka, a small spare fellow with a crooked face and grey eyes, spoke up proudly:

"You paid him, did you! Father worked, so you paid. I would have just liked to see you refuse to pay him."

Nevertheless it pleased Vasilinka greatly that Rab' Shachneh should have appealed to him for mercy, and he thereupon turned to the others.

"Now, boys, enough! Let the carcass be. You can see that it's barely gasping."

Reluctantly, one by one, the peasants tore themselves away from their victim, and began to leave the house, smashing whatever articles had previously escaped their notice.

"Nu, Shachneh," Vasily turned to him, "you have me to thank for being still alive. The boys would have made short work of you, if it hadn't been for me."

He was on the point of leaving with the others, when something occurred to him that made him halt.

"There!" he said, extending his hand to Rab' Shachneh. "Kiss!"

Rab' Shachneh raised his bloodshot eyes and looked at him bewildered. He did not understand.

Vasily's face darkened.

"Didn't you hear me? Kiss, I tell you!"

Two of the peasants halted in the doorway, watching the scene. Rab' Shachneh looked at Vasily and was silent. Vasily's face turned green.

"Ah, Jew-face that you are!" He gnashed his teeth, and drove his open hand into Rab' Shachneh's face. "You hesitate! Oh, boys! Come back here!"

The two peasants came up closer.

"Ah, nu! Get to work, boys. Since he's such a fine gentleman, he's got to kiss my foot! If he won't . . ."

He sat down upon a chair. The two peasants grabbed hold of Rab' Shachneh, and flung him at Vasily's feet.

"Pull off that boot!" Vasily commanded, kicking Rab' Shachneh in the mouth.

Rab' Shachneh slowly pulled the boot off the peasant's foot.

They stood face to face—a red dirty foot smelling strongly of perspiration and a beaten-up face with a long, noble, dark beard. Strangely enough the beard wasn't harmed much. It was torn and plucked in but a few spots, but it retained the dignity of respectability. From above, Vasily's crooked face looked down, glaring with its grey eyes.

"Kiss, I tell you!"

And another kick in the face followed the command.

For a moment all was silent and motionless, then Rab' Shachneh bowed down his head, and Vasily emitted a sharp frightful cry. All of the five toes and part of his foot had disappeared into Rab' Shachneh's mouth. The two rows of teeth sank deep into the dirty, sweaty flesh.

What followed was wild and lurid, like an evil, revolting dream.

The peasants struck Rab' Shachneh with their booted feet. They kicked him with fury. They pulled out his beard in handfuls. They dug their nails into his eyes and tore them out. They searched out the most sensitive parts of his body and ripped out pieces. His body shivered, trembled, bent and twisted. And the two rows of teeth pressed on convulsively closer and closer, and something cracked inside the mouth, the teeth, the bones, or perhaps both. All this while, Vasilinka raved, shrieked, screeched like a stuck pig.

How long this lasted, the peasants did not know. It was only when they saw that Rab' Shachneh's body no longer moved that they stopped. A shudder shook them from head to foot when they looked into his face.

His torn out eyes hung loose near the bloody sockets. His face was no longer recognizable; while what was left of his beard hung in blood-congealed strands. The dead teeth, with a piece of the foot still between them, glared like those of a dead wolf.

Vasilinka still wriggled, no longer upon the chair, but upon the floor. His body was twisted like a snake, and from his throat came long-drawn-out, hoarse sounds. His grey eyes grew large, dim and glassy. It was evident that he had lost his mind.

"God help us," the terrified peasants screamed, as they fled from the house.

Out in the street, the pogrom, in all its beastly ferocity, was still raging, and amidst the many noises, no one heard the broken cries of the living man who was slowly expiring within the jaws of the dead man.

GLASS

by I. D. BERKOWITZ

D R. FEITELSON, a former Yeshiva student and now a small-town doctor, a bachelor, sat in his bedroom before the mirror, tying a knot in the new blue tie that he had just bought, and thinking of the anecdote about glass which the storekeeper had told him, while he was selling him the tie. A certain Jew was riding in a train without a ticket. He hid in a box, marked with big letters, *Glass, take care.* When the conductor entered the car, he spied the box and began kicking it. The Jew shouted from the box, "Take care!" The conductor asked, "Who's there?" The Jew answered, "It's we!" The conductor asked, "Who's we?" The Jew answered, "We—the glass!"

It was already evening, after his visiting hours, and in honor of the new blue tie and the new anecdote, the doctor was preparing to spend several hours at the Bronstein's, a house which lately attracted him more than the other homes of the town. At table, Madame Bronstein, a most hospitable woman, always honored him with the first glass of tea from the samovar, meanwhile raising her opaque, velvet eyes and giving him a glance so caressing, motherly and meaningful, that it actually made the doctor red with pleasure. And Mania, the oldest daughter of the Bronsteins, tall, beautiful Mania, dressed in black, retreated every evening to a corner of the sofa, and sat there solitary, secretive, immersed in herself. Often, her head was thrown back upon the soft cushion of the sofa, her lovely soft brow clouded, as if veiled in dim, maidenly dreams! Then, Dr. Feitelson would think with sweet terror of the happy hour when he would be privileged to approach the forbidden corner boldly, boldly sit down beside her on the sofa, and with bold arms embrace her soft young shoulders which no one yet had touched.

When the doctor finished the tie, he began to pose before the mirror, attempting to call a pleasant expression to his face. Unfortunately, his face was birdlike, his eyes small, pointed, also birdlike. But his moustache, his luxurious blond moustache, with the ends turned up, offered courage and pride.

Suddenly, he rose from his chair, feeling revived, energetically smoothed his little figure, firmly expanded his chest and felt that he had suddenly grown a head taller. Having paced up and down the room several times, his thoughts became lighter, and Hope shone to him with all her rays. He thought of Mania, picturing how she would soon be his wife. Courage! Courage! The main thing—not to lose his nerve. Bronstein's home was open and bright, the people pleasant and friendly, and there were means to succeed a-plenty. With Madame, he must hold a strictly literary conversation about Ibsen's *Doll's House,* the relation of the Talmud to women, and other topics of a similar vein. He must listen with interest to her stories about Moscow, which she had visited fifteen years ago. Mania, he must attract with his autobiography, which he had many times intended to tell her—how from a talmudical student, he had become a doctor. There would be an interesting episode to recount—his friendship with the general's son and the summer which he spent at the house, the manor of his friend's father, the general. With Mania's younger sister, Anuta, he would go ice-skating every Sunday. He would even become friendly with the smallest Bronstein, the fat red-cheeked youngster, and call him by the sweet name, which everyone used: *Sugarplum.*

There was only one person in this family in regard to whom the doctor was doubtful. That was the master, Bronstein himself, a handsome man, blackbearded, tall, as powerful as a tree, always fresh and lifeloving. When Dr. Feitelson happened to stand next to this colossal figure he would smile involuntarily, feeling servile, small and insignificant. But there is no sense in standing before Bronstein and keeping silent. Bronstein likes to hear merry stories, so that he can laugh. When he is told a particularly nice thing, he clutches his sides, runs into a corner and laughs there in a loud and booming bass: Ho-ho-ho!

The doctor now pictured with pleasure what laughter he would elicit from Bronstein with his anecdote. So that the joke should really turn out peppery, he would tell it in a Yiddish-Russian. . . . Wouldn't it be merry today!

Rubbing one hand against the other and feeling a fresh stream of energy within, the doctor stuck his head through the door and shouted gaily,

"Stepan, ready to dress!"

Five minutes later, Dr. Feitelson was standing at Bronstein's house, looking at the frozen illuminated windows, drying his thick moustache with a handkerchief and smiling into his fur coat,

"Glass!"

Having entered the house, for a moment he remained standing on the threshold of the dining room, a new book in his hand, a drama, blinking his little, point-like eyes at the light and wondering—. No one in. Over the table, the big lamp burned brightly, and the room was empty. Upon a chair and on the sofa, where Mania always sat, open satchels lay carelessly thrown, cardboard boxes revealing new ladies' silk waists, and several unfamiliar men's belongings. From another room came the sound of many voices, and every once in a while, above the noise would ring a silvery, tinkling laughter—Mania's laughter, which was heard very seldom. What had happened?

Soon everything was explained. The door of a side room opened, and Madame Bronstein appeared.

"I thought I heard someone enter— Oh, it's you, doctor! Come in, you won't be in the way . . . Oh, dear! You don't know yet what joy we're having today! Our nephew came from Moscow. . . . Here he is himself!"

The entire family crowded in from the other room. In their midst, was the guest, a young man dressed in a light grey English suit, with a fresh, laughing face, tall, handsome and strong, greatly resembling the older Bronstein. The Madame introduced the doctor to him.

"This is our doctor. One of our intelligentsia, a Talmudist . . ."

"And no more?" the doctor thought, deeply hurt, meanwhile shyly bowing to the guest. He shifted the book from one hand to the other and squinted his little point-like eyes. He glanced stealthily at Mania. Transformed, she stood next to the guest, trustful, confiding. Her eyes shone clear and open with the first rays of maidenly happiness. The doctor felt as if his former energy and courage vanished at one blow.

Everyone sat down at the table. Mania and the guest huddled in a corner of the sofa, chatting gaily, peeping into the cardboard boxes and laughing. Madame Bronstein was telling the doctor that she had not seen her nephew for fifteen years, ever since she had been in Moscow, but that she recognized him immediately, from the very first glance—he was the image of her husband in his youth. It doesn't matter that now her husband is on his last legs—at one time, he was the handsomest beau in town, and all the girls would peep at him from their windows. Just let him try and deny it!

Bronstein clutched his sides, ran into a corner and laughed there loud and booming, Ho-ho-ho!

All this time, Dr. Feitelson spoke little and listened even less to what was being said to him. He just smiled queerly and crookedly, and kept pulling at his moustache—the only bit of sustenance in his life. The samovar was served at the table. Madame Bronstein honored her nephew with the first glass of tea, meanwhile caressing him with her opaque, velvet eyes and giving him such a soft, fond, motherly glance, that Dr. Feitelson actually ran cold. The doctor now realized that fortune was slipping out of his hands, but he felt powerless to retain it. Stealthily, he looked at the guest in the elegant English suit and scrutinized his hands—large, powerful, white hands with long, handsome fingers. On the pinky of the guest's right hand he noticed a long, carefully-reared, polished nail, in which the bright light of the lamp was mirrored.

"Probably a charlatan, an empty-headed fool!" The doctor clutched at the long nail like a drowning man.

The guest recounted many interesting things about his city and about the journey that he had just completed. Like his uncle—he laughed loud and boomingly. When it became too hot at the table, uncle and nephew rose, both tall and powerful as trees. They stood in the middle of the room talking to each other, and every once in a while they would clutch their sides, run apart, one here, the other there, and burst out laughing, each in his corner, in a loud and booming bass, Ho-ho-ho! The doctor sat at the table constrained, oppressed, hearing how the laughter of the two made something weep within him, and mutely observing Mania's eyes shine with a peculiar beaming radiance. A lock of black hair that slid from her temples to her flushed cheek only deepened and ennobled her soft, untouched youth.

Suddenly the doctor remembered, and he was lifted from his seat—Glass!

How could it have escaped his mind? Why, he had come specially for its sake! Here, he would tell the two this anecdote about glass—let them see what people should really laugh at!

He rose from the table and quietly approached the uncle and the nephew who stood in the middle of the room, upholding each other in lively conversation. Having made several steps, the doctor remained standing, looking down at his feet, and it somehow irked him that his feet were so awkwardly small in comparison with the big strong ones of the two tall men.

"There's an anecdote, a fine Jewish anecdote about glass . . ." several times he prepared the phrase and wanted to enter the conversation of the two men. But the words froze on his tongue. He shifted around hesitating, ashamed, discouraged. Why glass all of a sudden? How did it fit here?

Once, he did have an opportunity to introduce the anecdote. At table, fruit was served upon a handsome vase, made of cut glass. Dr. Feitelson revived, stretched out his hand, took the vase by the stem and was all ready with the sentence.

"There's an anecdote . . ." but Madame Bronstein noticed his movement, gently took the vase out of his hand and asked him with a hospitable smile,

"What do you want, doctor, an apple or an orange?"

"No . . . I really don't want anything. . . . You see, there's an . . ."

"I'll tell you what—here's both for you, the apple and the orange—"

"No, God forbid . . . I was thinking of something else . . . an anecdote . . . a . . . a . . . talmudical anecdote. . . ." The doctor blabbered beside the point and felt that his face was suffused with fire. "You see," he turned to the men, "In childhood I studied the Talmud. I'm something of a talmudist, as Madame Bronstein expressed it . . . It seems, in the Talmud is written that . . . that he who wishes to be a bankrupt, should use cutglass dishes . . . He-he!"

Madame Bronstein smiled kindly,

"Doctor—God be with you! You already consider us bankrupts?"

The uncle and the nephew, who were now sitting at the table, both glanced at the doctor's embarrassed birdlike face, both slapped their knees, one bent to the left, one to the right and burst out laughing in bass, Ho-ho-ho!

Dr. Feitelson, abashed, cowed, his face red and anguished, went to the soft sofa, sat there all alone and with trembling fingers caressed his thick moustache. Now, all sorts of foolish thoughts climbed into his head. He thought of approaching the guest and suddenly offending him, of telling him that salesmen like himself, he had seen in his lifetime by the thousands, that only an unworthy salesman would spend all night long laughing at such idiotic things. Then the thought of a duel occurred to him—he was ready to fight a duel with him—he had nothing to lose! Then he thought that he was bitterly mistaken in Mania, that this Mania must really be naturally evil and cruel, for it was because of her that his life was darkened. . . .

"Doctor, a boy came for you. He says that his father is dying," Anuta, Bronstein's second daughter, interrupted his meditations. "He's in the kitchen, crying."

The doctor started from the sofa and for a moment stared at everyone silent and bewildered, then he at once began to take his leave.

"It's too bad that you are leaving so early! I thought that you would recite something for us!" Madame Bronstein expressed her sorrow, with a friendly mien.

"It's a matter of life and death, madame," the doctor answered coldly, with an official expression, and his point-like eyes looked piercingly at the entire family, at all who had accompanied him to the door.

The patient, whom the doctor had treated for pneumonia during the last few days, was now much worse. Around the bed were gathered several poor men and women, watching the doctor with dumb, questioning eyes. That day, there had been a faint hope for the invalid, but now the doctor shook his head: God knew, if he would pull through the night.

Near the table, in the dim light of a little lamp, stood the sick man's oldest daughter, a girl of eighteen, with a frightened face. The doctor looked furtively at her thick, blond, uncombed hair, her pale, pretty, anguished profile, and her soft, still childlike limbs, that shuddered mutely with terror. Involuntarily he compared her with the tall, strong Mania, who had remained there—in the warmth, in the brightness, in peaceful, quiet happiness.

"I believe you're a seamstress?" the doctor asked the girl, sympathetically.

The girl painfully nodded her head.

"And what if I should marry this girl! Marry this lonely orphan, below *my* station, to spite everybody, and let them see!" the doctor suddenly thought, while writing the prescription. But he knew himself that it was a mad thought, and that it was not the thing to quiet his heart.

The girl leaned on the table, looked with fright at the doctor's hands, which made mysterious, significant characters upon the paper, and glanced at her dying father as if eager to guess whether these characters still had the power to perform the last miracle and avert the terrible doom. . . .

The doctor began to dress. The girl accompanied him to the corridor, snatched his hand and burst into childlike tears.

"Mister doctor, dearest doctor . . . What will happen? What'll be now?"

The doctor became confused; he awkwardly stroked her soft, young shoulders, which confused him all the more, and began to stammer, soft-lipped.

"It's nothing . . . nothing. . . . After all, it's a human being. . . . What can be done here? Here, I'm a human being, too. . . . What do you suppose *my* life is? Worth nothing . . . just like . . . just like . . . like, glass, honestly!"

The doctor knew that he was uttering foolish words. He felt strangely empty, exhausted, as if he were sinking headlong into some depths. He leaned his faint head on the door, looked at the girl's grief-stricken, puzzled face, and continued.

"Honestly, like glass . . . I break . . . glass breaks. Here I have an anecdote about glass. The anecdote is quite to the point. . . . It was on a train. The conductor kicked the box, and the Jew shouted, 'Take care! You'll break it! It's we, glass. . . .' He-he! A stupid story . . . a storekeeper told it to me, today . . . evidently an empty-headed fellow, a salesman . . . ugh!"

Pop-eyed, the girl looked at the doctor's face, distorted by a crooked smile. Then she turned and went back, stifling her sobs.

When the doctor ran out of the poverty-stricken house, he was hit by a cold, frosty wind. He huddled deep into his coat, ran with quick steps in the middle of the snowy street and kept muttering:

"Ugh, ugh, ugh! What an empty life, empty, empty, empty. . . ." He turned the corner.

MILITARY SERVICE

by JUDAH STEINBERG

WELL, I was caught, and put into prison. I was not alone. Many young boys had been brought there. Some were crying bitterly; some looked at their companions wonderingly. We were told that the next day we should be taken away to some place, and that the rabbi wished to come to see us, but was not permitted to enter our prison.

"Yes, a good man was the rabbi, may he rest in peace; yet he was compelled to cheat for once. And when an honest man is compelled to cheat he may outdo the cleverest crook. Do you want to know what the rabbi did? He disguised himself as a peasant, went out, and walked the streets with the rolling gait of a drunkard. The night guards stopped him, and asked him what his business was. "I am a thief," said the rabbi. Then the guards arrested him, and put him into the prison with us.

In the darkness of that night the rabbi never ceased talking to us, swallowing his own tears all the while. He told us the story of Joseph the righteous. It had been decreed in Heaven, said the rabbi, that his brethren should sell Joseph into slavery. And it was the will of the Almighty that Joseph should come to Egypt, to show the Egyptians that there is only one God in Heaven, and that the Children of Israel are the chosen people.

Then the rabbi examined us: Did we know our *Modeh Ani* by heart? Did we know our *Shema?*

He told us that we should be taken very, very far away, that we should be away many, many years, and should become soldiers when grown up. Then he warned us never to eat of any food forbidden by the Jewish law, and never to forget the God of Israel and our own people, even if they tore our flesh with thorns. He told us also the story of the Ten Martyrs, who sacrificed their lives to sanctify the God of Israel. He told us of the mother and her seven children that were killed for having refused to bow before idols; and he told us many more such things. All those saints and martyrs, he said, are now in Paradise, enjoying the bliss of the Divine Presence. That night I really envied those saints; I longed with all my heart to be forced to bow to idols, to have to withstand all sorts of trials, so as to enjoy, after my death, the bliss of the Divine Presence in Paradise.

Many more stories the rabbi told us; many more words of warning, encouragement, and praise came from his lips, till I really believed I was the one whom God had picked out from among my equals, to be put through great trials and temptations. . . .

Morning came, and the guard entered the prison. Then the rabbi turned towards us, and said: "Lambs of the God of Israel, we have to part now: I am going to be lashed and imprisoned for having entered this place by a trick, and you will be taken into exile, to undergo your trials! I may hardly expect to be found worthy of surviving till you return. But there, in the world-of-truth, we shall surely meet. May it be the will of God that I may have no reason to be ashamed of you there, before Him and His angels, in Heaven!"

We parted, and the words of the rabbi sank deep into my heart.

Then they began dumping us into wagons. The obstreperous boys, who tried to run away, were many of them bound with ropes and thrown into the wagon. Of course, we all howled.

I did not hear my own voice, nor the voice of my neighbor. It was all one great howl. A crowd of men and women followed our wagon— the parents of the boys. Very likely they cried, too; but we could not hear their voices. The town, the fields, heaven and earth, seemed to cry with us.

I caught sight of my parents, and my heart was filled with something like anger and hatred. I felt that I had been sacrificed for my brother.

My mother, among many other mothers, approached the wagon, looked at me, and apparently read my thoughts: she fainted away, and fell to the ground. The accident held up the crowd, which busied itself with reviving my mother, while our wagon rolled away.

My heart was filled with a mixture of anger, pity, and terror. In that mood of mixed feelings I parted from my parents.

We cried and cried, got tired, and finally became still from sheer exhaustion. Presently a noise reached our ears, something like the yelling of children. We thought it was another wagonload of boys like ourselves. But soon we found out our mistake: it was but a wagonload of sheep that were being taken to slaughter. . . .

Of course, we ate nothing the whole of that day, though the mothers had not failed to provide us with food. Meanwhile the sun had set; it got dark, and the boys, who had been bound with ropes, were released by the guard: he knew they would not attempt to escape at that time. We fell asleep, but every now and then one of the boys would wake up, crying, quietly at first, then louder and louder. Then another would join him; one more, and yet one more, till we all were yelling in chorus, filling the night air with our bitter cries. Even the guard could not stand it; he scolded us, and belabored us with his whip. That crying of ours reminds me of what we read in Lamentations: "Weeping she hath wept in the night. . . ."

Morning came, and found us all awake: we were waiting for daylight. We believed it would bring us freedom, that angels would descend from Heaven, just as they had descended to our father Jacob, to smite our guard and set us free. At the same time, the rising sun brought us all a feeling of hunger. We began to sigh, each and every one of us separately. But the noise we made did not amount even to the barking of a few dogs or the cawing of a few crows. That is what hunger can do. And when the guard had distributed among us some of the food we had brought with us, we ate it with relish, and felt satisfied. At the same time we began to feel the discomfort we were causing one another, cooped up as we were in the wagon. I began to complain of my neighbor, who was sitting on my legs. He claimed that I was pressing against him with my shoulder. We all began to look up to the guard, as if expecting that he could or would prevent us from torturing one another.

Still I had some fun even on that day of weeping. I happened to turn around, and I noticed that Barker, my dog, was running after our wagon.

"Too bad, foolish Barker," said I, laughing at him in spite of my heartache. "Do you think I am going to a feast? It is into exile that I am going; and what do you run after me for?"—

Once in a while our guard would get angry at us, curse us bitterly, and strike us with his whip. "You cursed Jews," he would say, "do I owe you anything that I should suffer so much on your account, and undergo all the hardships of travel?"

Indeed, there was a good deal of truth in what he said. For, willingly or unwillingly, we did give him much trouble. Had we died, say the year before, or even at that very moment, he would not have been put to the necessity of leading a crowd of half-dumb boys. He would not have had to stand the hardships of travel, and would not have been compelled to listen to the wailings of children torn from the arms of their parents. Or do you think it is agreeable to feel that little children consider you a hard and cruel man? When I grew up and served in the army myself, and had people below me in age and position under my command, I came to understand the troubles of our guard; so that now, after having gone through many experiences, after I have passed, as they say, through fire and water, I may confess that I bear no malice towards all those at whose hands I suffered. There are many ex-cantonists who cannot forget the birch-rod, for instance. Well, so much is true: for every misstep, for every sign of disobedience a whipping was due. If one of us refused to kneel in prayer before the crucifix; if one of us refused to eat pork; if one of us was caught mumbling a Hebrew prayer or speaking Yiddish, he was sure to get a flogging. Twenty, thirty, forty, or even full fifty lashes were the punishment. But, then, is it conceivable that they could have treated us any other way? Why, hundreds of Jewish children that did not understand a word of Russian had been delivered into the hands of a Russian official that did not understand a word of Yiddish. He would say, Take off my boots, and the boy would wash his hands. He would say, Sit down, and the boy would stand up. Were we not like dumb cattle? It was only the rod that we understood well. And the rod taught us to understand our master's orders by the mere expression of his eyes.

Then many of the ex-cantonists still remember with horror the steam-bath they were compelled to take. "The chamber of hell," they called the bath. At first blush, it would really seem to have been an awful thing. They would pick out all the cantonists that had so much as a scratch on their bodies or the smallest sign of an eruption, paint the wounds with tar, and put the boys, stripped, on the highest shelf in the steam-bath. And below was a row of attendants armed with birch-rods. The kettle was boiling fiercely, the stones were red-hot, and the attendants emptied jars of boiling water ceaselessly upon the stones. The steam would rise, penetrate every pore of the skin, and—sting—sting!—enter into the very flesh. The pain was horrible; it pricked, and pricked, and there was no air to breathe. It was simply choking. If the boy happened to roll down, those below stood ready to meet him with the rods.

All this is true. At the same time, was it mere cruelty? It is very simple: we were a lot of Jewish lads snatched from the arms of our mothers. On the eve of every Sabbath our mothers would take us in hand, wash us, comb our hair, change our underwear, and dress us in our Sabbath clothes. All at once we were taken into exile. Days, weeks, nay, months, we passed in the dust of the roads, in perspiration and dirt, and sleeping on the ground. Our underwear had not been changed. No water had touched our bodies. So we became afflicted with all kinds of eruptions. That is why we had to pass through what we called "the chamber of hell." And this will give you an idea of the rest.

To make a long story short: there were many of us, and we were distributed in various places. Many of the boys had taken ill; many died on the road. The survivors were distributed among the peasants, to be brought up by them till they reached the age of entering the army. I was among the latter. Many months, maybe even years, I passed in knocking about from village to village, from town to town, till, at last, I came into the joint possession of a certain Peter Semionovich Khlopov and his wife Anna Petrovna. My master was neither old nor young; he was neither a plain peasant nor a nobleman. He was the clerk of the village. In those days that was considered a genteel occupation, honorable and well-paid. He had no sons, but he had one daughter, Marusya by name. She was then about fourteen years old, very good-looking, gay, and rather wild.

According to the regulations, all the Cantonists in the village had to report daily for military drill and exercise on the drill grounds before the house of the sergeant. He lived in the same village. At the request of my patron Khlopov I was excused from the daily drill, and had to report but once a week. You see, Peter expected to derive some benefit from me by employing me about the house and in the field.

Now it was surely through the merits of my ancestors that I happened to be placed in the household of Peter Khlopov. Peter himself spent but little of his time at home. Most of the time he was at the office, and his free moments he liked to spend at the tavern, which was owned by the only Jew in the village, "our Moshko" the Khlopovs used to call him. But whenever he happened to be at home, Peter was very kind to me, especially when he was just a little tipsy. Perhaps he dreamt of adopting me as his son: he had no sons of his own. And he tried to make me like military service. "When you grow up," he used to say, "you will become an officer, and wear a sword. Soldiers will stand at attention before you, and salute you. You will win distinction in battle, and be found worthy of being presented to the Czar." He also told me stories of Russian military life. By that time I had learned some Russian. They were really nice stories, as far as I could understand them; but they were made nicer yet by what I could not understand of them. For then I was free to add something to the stories myself, or change them according to my own fancy. If you are a lover of stories, take the advice of a plain old man like myself. Never pay any attention to stories in which everything has been prepared from the very start, and you can tell the end as soon as you begin to read them or listen to them. Such stories make one yawn and fall asleep. Stories of this kind my daughter reads to me once in a while, and I always fall asleep over them. Stories are good only when told the way Khlopov used to tell them to me.

But that is all irrelevant. In short, Khlopov was kind to me.

As to Anna, she was entirely different. She was close-mouthed, ill-tempered, and a great stay-at-home. She never visited her neighbors, and they, in turn, called on her very rarely. In the village she was spoken of as a snob and a hypocrite. Peter was afraid of her as of the plague, especially in his sober hours. All her power lay in her eyes. When that strong man—he who had the whole village in the palm of his hand—felt her eye fixed on him, his strength left him. It seemed as if some devil were ready to jump out of that eye and turn the house topsyturvy. You fellows are mere youngsters, you have seen nothing of the world yet; but take it from me, there are eyes that seem quite harmless when you first look into them. But just try to arouse their temper: you will see a hellish fire spring up in them. Have you ever looked into my Rebekah's eyes? Well, beware of eyes.

The look Anna gave me when I first entered her house promised me nothing good. She hated me heartily. She never called me by my own name. She called me "Zhid" all the time, in a tone of deep hatred and contempt.

Among the orders the Cantonists had to obey were the following:

to speak no Yiddish; to say no Jewish prayer; to recite daily a certain prayer before the image of the Virgin and before the crucifix, and not to abstain from non-kosher food.

With regard to all injunctions except the last, Anna was very strict with me. But she was not very particular as to the last injunction. Out of sheer stinginess she fed me on bread and vegetables, and that in the kitchen. Once she did offer me some meat, and I refused to touch it. Then she got very angry, flew into a temper, and decided to complain to the sergeant. But Peter did not let her be so cruel. "Let him grow up, he will know better," said Peter, waving his hand at me.

Then Anna made up her mind to force me to eat forbidden meat. But I was obstinate. And she decided once more to complain to the sergeant. Just at that time another Cantonist had been found guilty of some offense. He belonged to the same village; his name was Jacob. I did not know him at that time. His patron complained that Jacob persisted in reciting Hebrew prayers, and that he abstained from meat. Jacob was condemned to twenty lashes with rods. An order was issued that all Cantonists should assemble to witness the flogging of the offender.

In the course of time we got used to such sights; but the first time we were terribly shocked. Just imagine: a lad of about fifteen is stripped, put on the ground face downwards; one man sits on his head, and another on his feet. Two men are put on either side of him, each with a bundle of birch-rods in his hand. Ten times each of them has to strike him with the rods, to make up the twenty lashes. I looked at the face of the culprit: it was as white as chalk. His lips were moving. I thought he was reciting the prayer: "And He, the Merciful, will forgive sin, and will not destroy. . . ." Up went the rods, down they went; a piercing cry . . . blood . . . flaps of loose skin . . . cries . . . "one, two, three" . . . again cries . . . sudden silence . . . more cries . . . again silence . . . "four, five" . . . "stop!"

Because the culprit fainted, the sergeant in the goodness of his heart divided the punishment into two parts. Jacob was carried off to the hospital, and it was put down in the book that he was to get ten more lashes after his recovery.

I went home.

Had Anna given me a piece of pork to eat that evening, I do not know what I should have done.

That night I saw the old rabbi in my dream. He was standing before me, with bowed head and tears dropping from his eyes. . . .

A TALE OF BARNOW

by KARL EMIL FRANZOS

You know that a Jew is looked upon nowadays as a man like everyone else; and that if any noble or peasant dares to strike or oppress a Jew, the latter can at once bring his assailant before the Austrian district judge at the court-hall, and Herr von Negrusz punishes the offender for his injustice. But before the great year when the Emperor proclaimed that all men had equal rights, it was not so. In those old days, the Lord of the manor exercised justice within the bounds of his territory by means of his agent; but what was called justice by these men was generally great injustice. Ah, my friends, those were hard times! The land belonged to the Lord of the manor, and so did all the people who lived on it; and the very air and water were his also. It was not only in the villages that this was the case, but in the towns too, especially when they belonged to a noble, and when their inhabitants were Jews. The noble was lord of all, and ruled over his subjects through his mandatar [agent].

At least it was so with us in Barnow. Our master, Graf Bortynski, lived in Paris all the year round, and gave himself no trouble about his estates or their management. His agent was supreme in Barnow, and was to all intents and purposes our master. So we always used to pray that the mandatar might be a good man, who would allow us to live in peace and quietness. And at first God answered our prayers, for stout old Herr Stephen Grudza was as easy-tempered a man as we Jews could have desired. It's true that he used to drink from morning till night, but he was always good-natured in his cups, and would not for the world have made anyone miserable when he was merry. But one day, after making a particularly good dinner, he was seized with apoplexy and died. The whole district mourned for him, and so did we Jews of Barnow. For, in the first place, Herr Grudza had been kind to everyone; and in the second—who knew what his successor would be like!

Our fears were well grounded.

The new mandatar, Freidrich Wollmann, was a German. Now the Germans had hitherto treated us less harshly than the Poles. The new agent, however, was an exception to this rule. He was a tall thin man, with black hair and bright black eyes. His expression was stern and sad—always, always;—no one ever saw him smile. He was a good manager, and soon got the estate into order; he also insisted on the laws being obeyed; taught evil-doers that he was not a man to be trifled with; and I am quite sure that no one with whom he had any dealings defrauded him of a halfpenny. But he hated us Jews with a deadly hatred, and did us all as much harm as he could. He increased our taxes threefold—sent our sons away to be soldiers—disturbed our feasts—and wherever we had a lawsuit with a Christian, the Christian's word was always taken, while ours was disbelieved. He was very hard upon the peasants too—in fact, they said that no other agent at Barnow had ever been known to exact the tax due from the villein to his lord with so much severity, and yet in that matter he acted within the letter of the law; and so there was a sort of justice in his mode of procedure. But as soon as he had anything to do with a Jew, he forgot both reason and justice.

Why did he persecute us so vehemently? No one knew for certain, but we all guessed. It was said that he used to be called Troim Wollmann, and that he was a Christianized Jew from Posen; that he had forsworn his religion because of love for a Christian girl, and that the Jews of his native place had persecuted and calumniated him so terribly in consequence of his apostasy, that the girl's parents had broken off their daughter's engagement to him. I do not know who told us this, but no one could deny the probability of the story who ever had looked him in the face, or had watched his mode of treating us.

So our days were sad and full of foreboding for the future. Wollmann oppressed and squeezed us whether we owed him money or not, and none that displeased him had a chance of escape. Thus matters stood in the autumn before the great year.

It isn't the pleasantest thing in the world for a Jew to be an Austrian soldier, but if one of our race is sent into the Russian service his fate is worse than death. He is thenceforward lost to God, to his parents, and to himself. Is it, then, a matter for surprise that the Russian Jews should gladly spend their last penny to buy their children's freedom from military service, or that any youth, whose people are too poor to ransom him should fly over the border to escape his fate? Many such cases are known some of the fugitives are caught before they have crossed the frontiers of Russia, and it would have been better for them if they had never been born; but some make good their escape into Moldavia, or into our part of Austrian Poland. Well, it happened that about that time a Jewish conscript—born at Berdychev—escaped over the frontier near Hussiatyn, and was sent on to Barnow from thence. The community did what they could

for him, and a rich kindhearted man, Hayyim Grünstein, father-in-law of
Moses Freudenthal, took him into his service as groom.

The Russian Government of course wanted to get the fugitive back
into their hands, and our officials received orders to look for him.

Our mandatar got the same order as the others. He at once sent for
the elders of our congregation and questioned them on the subject. They
were inwardly much afraid, but outwardly they made no sign, and denied all knowledge of the stranger. It was on the eve of the Day of Atonement that this took place—and how could they have entered the presence
of God that evening if they had betrayed their brother in the faith? So
they remained firm in spite of the agent's threats and rage. When he
perceived that they either knew nothing or would confess nothing, he
let them go with these dark words of warning: "It will be the worse for
you if I find the youth in Barnow. You do not know me yet, but—I swear
that you shall know me then."

The elders went home, and I need hardly tell you that the hearts of
the whole community sank on hearing Wollmann's threat. The young
man they were protecting was a hardworking honest fellow, but if he
had been different, it wouldn't have mattered—he was a Jew, and none
of them would have forsaken him in his adversity. If he remained in
Barnow, the danger to him and to all of them was great, for the mandatar would find him out sooner or later—nothing could be kept from him
for long. But if they sent him away without a passport or naturalization
papers, he would of course be arrested very soon. After a long consultation, Hayyim Grünstein had a happy inspiration. One of his relations
was a tenant-farmer in Marmaros, in Hungary. The young man should
be sent to him on the night following the Day of Atonement, and should
be advised to make the whole journey by night for fear of discovery. In
this manner he could best escape from his enemies.

They all agreed that the idea was a good one, and with lightened
hearts partook of the feast which was to strengthen them for their fast
on the Day of Atonement. Dusk began to fall. The synagogue was
lighted up with numerous wax candles and the whole community
hastened there with a broken and contrite heart to confess their sins before God; for at that solemn fast we meet to pray to the Judge of all
men to be gracious to us, and of His mercy to forgive us our trespasses.
The women and the men were all dressed in white. Hayyim Grünstein
and his household were there to humble themselves before the Lord, and
amongst them was the poor fugitive, who was trembling in every limb
with fear lest he should fall into the hands of his enemies.

All were assembled and the service was about to begin. Little Mendele had placed the flat of his hand upon his throat in order to bring out the first notes of the Kol Nidre with fitting tremulousness, when he was interrupted by a disturbance at the door. The entrance of the synagogue was beset by the Graf's men-at-arms, and Herr Wollmann was seen walking up the aisle between the rows of seats. The intruder advanced until he stood beside the Ark of the Covenant and quite close to little Mendele, who drew back in terror, but the elders of the congregation came forward with quiet humility.

"I know that the young man is here," said Wollmann; "will you give him up now?"

The men were silent.

"Very well," continued the mandatar, "I see that kindness has no effect upon you. I will arrest him after service when you leave the synagogue. And I warn you that both he and you shall have cause to remember this evening. But now, don't let me disturb you; go on with your prayers. I have time to wait."

A silence as of death reigned in the synagogue. It was at length broken by a shrill cry from the women's gallery. The whole congregation was at first stupefied with fear. But after a time everyone began to regain his self-command, and to raise his eyes to God for help. Without a word each went back to his seat.

Little Mendele trembled in every limb; but all at once he drew himself up and began to sing the Kol Nidre, that ancient simple melody, which no one who has ever heard can forget. His voice at first sounded weak and quavering, but gradually it gained strength and volume, filled the edifice, thrilled the hearts of all the worshippers, and rose to the throne of God. Little Mendele never again sang as he did that evening. He seemed as though he were inspired. When he was singing in that marvelous way, he ceased to be the absurd little man he had always hitherto been, and became a priest pleading with God for his people. He reminded us of the former glories of our race, and then of the many many centuries of ignominy and persecution that had followed. In the sound of his voice we could hear the story of the way in which we had been driven from place to place—never suffered to rest long anywhere; of how we were the poorest of the poor, the most wretched amongst the miserable of the earth; and how the days of our persecution were not yet ended, but ever new oppressors rose against us and ground us down with an iron hand. The tale of our woes might be heard in his voice—of our unspeakable woes and our innumerable tears. But there was some thing else to be heard in it too. It told us in triumphant tones of our pride in our nation, and of our confidence and trust in God. Ah me! I can never describe the way little Mendele sang that evening; he made us weep for our desolation, and yet restored our courage and our trust. . . .

The women were sobbing aloud when he ceased; even the men were weeping; but little Mendele hid his face in his hands and fainted.

At the beginning of the service Wollmann had kept his eyes fixed on the Ark of the Covenant, but as it went on he had to turn away. He was very pale, and his knees shook so that, strong man as he was, he could hardly stand. His eyes shone as though through tears. With trembling steps and bowed head he slowly passed Mendele, and walked down the aisle to the entrance door. Then he gave the soldiers a sign to follow him.

Everyone guessed what had happened, but no one spoke of it.

He sent for Hayyim Grünstein on the day after the fast, and, giving him a blank passport, said, "It will perhaps be useful to you."

From that time on he treated us with greater toleration; but his power did not last long. The peasants, whom he had formerly oppressed, rose against him in the spring of the great year, and put him to death. . . .

ESCAPADE

by MAX BROD

As the years went on David became more closely attached to his mother; for although he was more and more impressed by his father's tranquil absorption in his devotions, he also found him more and more distant and inaccessible. His mother was different. Always worrying from morn till night with never a smile on her small deeply-lined face. Never satisfied that she had toiled enough. And David was like her.

He now often went with her into the Christians' town. Although the Jews were strictly forbidden to trade in Christian market-places—a prohibition that was constantly reinforced by municipal decrees—they somehow contrived to sidetrack the authorities and set up a few stalls in front of St. Gall, which stood in the mart of the Old Town. Once they had gained a foothold they proceeded to enlarge their base and even bought houses near by through men of straw, until eventually a new rag-market came into existence where they could dispose of their goods more advantageously than in the Jews' street. The enterprise was carried through partly by encroachments for which they had no authority and partly with the silent connivance of the townsfolk; but always at the risk of calling down on themselves rough treatment and expulsion from one moment to the next. Now David's mother occasionally took selected specimens from her scrap-heap to the market. Her skill lay in fitting an odd metal bottom to some bottomless vessel. For instance she would find an iron pot that had lost its base and fit it with some other piece of metal—such as an old helmet—thus making a new and serviceable article out of it. David went in terror for her safety. As he did not like to trust her to the deaf-and-dumb apprentice he fell into the habit of going with her himself to guard her pots and pans. His friends, who regarded this non-scholastic occupation as contemptible and unworthy of a serious student, made mock of him but he would not give it up. At the same time he did not fail to question himself severely as to whether it were not rather his sinful laziness and not his guilty love for his mother that provided the motive.

Certainly it was not curiosity which tempted him outside the gates He walked behind his mother with eyes fixed on the hem of her skirt for it was written that he should refrain from looking more than four ells in front of him.

To the onlooker, therefore, it was as if the woman had taken the shy youth under her wing rather than that he was there to protect her.

To invade the Christians' domain was no light undertaking. Within their own walls the Jews might wear ordinary clothes. The rich one dressed like the landed nobility in plumed hats, fur cloaks and expensive ruffs. David himself, as the son of a respected family wore a fashionable biretta and a silk jerkin—within the Ghetto. But when he set out with his mother he had to don the high peaked yellow cap, which wobbled on his head with ludicrous effect. Instead of his fine ruff he had the narrow regulation drill, and on his good cloth coat he displayed the small yellow Jews' tab. Thus adorned he was conspicuous from afar. The moment he passed the gate he was jostled by a crowd of boys. But his mother walked firmly ahead with a quick step and had her own method of dispersing the youngsters with a joke here and a gingerbread there Behind her stumped the deaf, feeble-minded apprentice with the basket his red-rimmed eyes glaring with sullen fury, and woe betide the gamin who came within reach of his fists in a quiet side street! David ra along beside him in a dazed manner, looking neither to right nor left in his agitation. But even so he had an impression of something white and spacious and splendid, while behind him something black—the dirty wooden houses of the Ghetto—sank crashing into the ground. He took no notice of anything, not daring to look up; for he was convinced that all the passers-by, covered all over with eyes like the angel of death, were looking at him. At last the strange trio reached its stall. Then followed the slow torture of standing there until night. David bore it bravely.

After he had been ten or twenty times to the St. Gall market his mother, who had a hacking cough, considered him sufficiently experienced to be sent alone on an errand to Pertschlitz the smith at the Old Town gate. From him she bought at stated intervals, for half a groschen, odds and ends of iron which were as priceless to her as they were useless to him.

The assistant stayed at home to run the business, with his mistress superintending from the bed which she had had put up in the adjoining room. David had therefore to march forth alone. Leaving the Ghetto by the gate leading into the Three Fountains Square he first came to a halt on the great stone pavement in front of the town hall, where he stood looking helplessly about him. The vast circular space seemed to revolve slowly round him like an expanse of water with houses bordering its shores. He realized that never before had he looked up or around him on his spot. And standing there in the cool March sunshine he hardly dared to breathe or move a finger. There stood the tall palaces in white stone with coats-of-arms, oriel windows and wonderful carving set between gleaming windows. He was forced to look at them now if he would find his way. The hem of his mother's skirt was no longer there, that hem to which his eyes had been glued these eighteen years.

A great crowd had gathered in front of the new clock on the town hall, to admire the gay painted mannikins passing in and out of the two little doors and the skeleton which rang the chimes. There was a Jew-puppet too, beating time with its money bag. David remembered seeing a description of this highly artistic creation in a news sheet not long before. To think that there should be things like that in Prague just over the threshold! No need to travel to distant lands, then, to see the marvels that he knew only from Hirschl's woodcuts! Why, up there in the decorations above the door-way were actually monkeys from over the seas, squirming among stone grapes and strange thick-leaved fruit-branches. The Jagellon King Vladislav he remembered hearing, was known as a great builder, like Lorenzo di Medici and other princes in

Italy. But when reading of such things, they had seemed to him all equally far away. And yet here was all this new splendour at his very door.

To make things worse, a master-joiner began to abuse him. He complained that the Jews were picking up and concealing Christian apprentices who had run away from their rightful masters; there would soon have to be a search made of their dirty holes to see where all the bungling work came from that was taking the bread out of honest men's mouths. David ran on. It would never do for Jews to get into the way of standing still to look at fine buildings. He had known this long while that there was no rest for Jews. On account of their sins there was not so much to-do about Christians when they did wicked things. But that was evidently quite in order; David had no objection to make. The nations were stronger. The sins of our fathers, he reflected, have weakened us and now we are a peculiarly delicate musical instrument in the hands of God, at whose light touch the least vibration of the strings becomes a whirling roar of judgment. One reason the more for gratitude to Him. For only in this way are we led to examine our hearts and become holy. David's break with one of his friends, Aaron Prossnitz, occurred solely on account of that young historian's insistence on the fact that Isabella of Spain had been punished for her expulsion of the Jews by the early death of her children and children-in-law. Absurd—when, on the very day of expulsion, Columbus had set sail from Palos and, with God's blessing, had discovered vast territories full of treasure for the wicked queen. Could there be clearer proof that the sins of the nation were judged by other standards than those of the Jews!

David loved the truth and insisted on getting it. But after all what did the sins of the nations matter? We have enough to do with our own, he thought. This was no time to meditate on his favourite topic, however. He had lost his way three times. He crept close round the cream-coloured walls of the palace, that stronghold of sin—a tower of Babel. Beside it, framed in scaffolding, stood the gigantic new gate. There it was, unfinished, because two architects were quarreling as to who should do the work. Wherever one looked there was strife and obstinacy, violence and hatred and fighting.—Here came the guard, with a ring of feet and a quiver of crested helmets, wild beasts and man-eaters that they were! David had learnt in the Talmud that weapons do not grace man but disgrace him; yet here were healthy, laughing, brown young faces— Oh, it was a wicked world—this other people's world, not his—but a very lovely one.

Filled with such thoughts David reached the town wall. This he followed, keeping within the Old Town until he came to the smithy called The Frog by the Puddle.

Fearfully he approached the master-smith who was holding down red-hot iron on the anvil while two apprentices beat it with sledge-hammers.

"Wait a bit, Jew."

The swarthy men were possibly not trying to push him when they swung their hammers, but there was so little room. After a quarter of an hour of it, David squeezed past the bellows and escaped from the intolerable din and glare through a little door leading into the yard. He could wait there just as well. The hammering was no more than a melodious tinkle now and his head grew cool and steady.

There was a scent of trees and soil. David had only seen trees in the cemetery. These were different, taller and more branching. Some quite low ones with thin stems had had all their branches cruelly cut away and the white wounds gleamed against the black wood. Was this one of the evil doings of the nations. Did they take pleasure in torment-ing trees as they tormented men and beasts?

"Do come and help me, Jew!" He was not alone then. It was a child, struggling with the door of a shed in a corner, who had called him—a Christian child by her dress. Not until she turned round did David notice that it was a girl, but having realized it he turned away, remembering the old commandment: "Do not prolong your conversation with your wife," which was interpreted by the strictest sect as applying to all women, and not only to the continuation but to the beginning of a talk. David had always observed it accordingly. But the tall slender girl was after him like a flash, holding his sleeves: "No, you're not to run away. Let the Jew work a bit too."

"But what do you want?" asked David in surprise.

"I can't open the door of the shed over there." She dragged him by the sleeve up to the wooden door, which had a derelict lock, so old and rusty that no power on earth could make the key turn in it—or so David felt convinced from a distance.

"Set about it!" cried the girl imperiously, stamping her foot.

"Why should I?" he replied indignantly. No one was going to speak to him like that.

"Because I ask you," she returned smilingly. "Please do. I can't manage it. Look how I have hurt myself already."

But at the sight of her hand he was horror-struck. Never had he seen such long nails, rosy shining nails as long as claws. Jews did not have such nails. They cut them off close; for nails were lifeless things, a part of the body which could not be used to serve the Lord, any more than the hair. Evil spirits dwelt in them. David was afraid of the girl, he saw nothing of her but these flashing nails.

But he had no time to consider, for they had arrived at the shed. He was quite ready to oblige her; "for the sake of peace," it was customary to be obliging even to Christians. But was he not acting in obedience to a certain confusion, without reasonable cause? He could not account for his own zeal in working at the lock. He had never attempted anything of the kind before, never as much as laid a finger on his mother's wares. Yet he instinctively felt that he must pose as if this were a trifle for him, as if he could pull open far more elaborate locks, the lock of a town gate, say, in a trice. And strange to say he nearly did open it in a trice, once he put his back into it.

He drew a deep breath. Without thanking him the girl went into the shed and pulled out a chest from which she took all sorts of tools.

David watched her dreamily. "What is that?" he asked, almost unconsciously.

"What that is?" The girl looked at him scornfully, as if she suspected him of impertinence. "I suppose you don't know a spade when you see it?"

"No," he answered sadly. Then, realizing too late that it had been a rhetorical question, he cast down his eyes in shame. Dark loose earth came up in spadefuls while withered shrubs and grasses flew out sideways. But many a flower was spared. Perhaps the spade was making room for the ground growth, clearing away the remains of autumn. It was all new to David. He would have liked to know the name of the yellow blooms—no one had taught him such things—but the girl was too unfriendly. But he could not resist asking one thing; the meaning of those wounding cuts in the trees, a torture that he felt personally. After several false starts he brought out the question.

The girl made no reply. She was stooping over the bed, doing mysterious things—herself a mysterious being. David could not take his eyes off her, although an old saying sounded warningly in his ears: "Go behind a lion but not behind a woman." Was this the mysterious thing of which the prophets gave warning? Blond hair, falling unconfined over her shoulder, a slender white shoulder coming out of her dress? It must be—it is—Lilith. This girl straightened herself and paused for rest, quite ignoring him. Suddenly her voice rang out high and clear. Yet she was not speaking! No, she was doing what only men should do, what no one must listen to when women do it: she was singing.

He drank in the sweet notes and it was as if each one trickled down his throat like a tear and ran right through him. And the fragrant March breeze played about his body, which suddenly began to pain him.

Then she flashed a keen glance at him. "Oh, you want your reward. A Jew does nothing for nothing."

But this time his face must have been distorted with shame and fury for the girl grasped him kindly by the hand. He tried to tear himself away. "Hand in hand you shall not escape evil." But the girl began to pet him, saying: "Why, what a fire-brand you are, Jew," and to show him how the hedges—not trees!—were clipped so that they could grow more freely and be kept symmetrical. All along the city wall there were hedges like that.

But David was not listening. Her hand weighed on him as if it were squeezing his heart. "He who passes money from his hand to a woman's hand so that he may look at her shall not escape hell fire, be he learned in the law and full of good works as the first among the prophets." But although he whispered the words as a reminder he turned so weak all at once that he could not free his hand.

"I tell you what, you shall help me to carry the chest out of the shed, then I'll give you your wages."

Happy to have his hand released he rushed over to the shed. More useful than before, he carried the heavy chest out to the bed, relieved to have the death's hand removed from his own hand and his heart.

As he came up, coughing under his load, the little beauty received him with: "Now you shall have a kiss for thanks."

She couldn't really mean it! All the same he made haste to put down the chest and escape. But the girl seized him by the head, knocking off his peaked hat—and crash went the tool chest with all its rakes and hoes. But under his hat David wore, like all pious Jews, a black silk skull cap, so that his head might never be completely uncovered; and when the girl saw this second head covering she burst into uncontrollable laughter. David wrenched his hat from her and rushed away. Into the smithy. Storming at the smith: "Where's my basket? Hand it over."

"All filled and ready," replied the smith, surveying the furious youth with placid wonder.

"Hand it over!" David thundered. He threw down his coin and

pulled the heavy basket of old iron out of the bewildered apprentice's hand. The deaf-and-dumb servant who had been sent to meet him was waiting outside the door and David handed over the load and ran home as if the devil were at his heels.

ON TO BERLIN

by SOLOMON MAIMON

MY circumstances were becoming unendurable. I was unwilling any longer to adapt myself to my ordinary occupations, and found myself therefore everywhere out of my sphere. I was also unable in Poland to satisfy sufficiently my growing inclination for the study of the sciences. So I determined to betake myself to Germany to study medicine and, as opportunity offered, other sciences also. But how was such a long journey to be made? I knew that some local merchants were soon to make a journey to Königsberg in Prussia; but I had only a slight acquaintance with them, and could not therefore expect that they would take me with them without compensation. After much deliberation I resorted to a capital expedient.

Among my friends was a very learned and pious man, who was held in great esteem among all the Jews of the town. To him I revealed my plan. I described my miserable circumstances, pointed out to him that, as my inclinations had been once directed to the knowledge of God and His works, I was no longer fit for any ordinary occupation; and I complained that I was now obliged to support myself by my scholarship alone as an instructor in the Bible and the Talmud, which, according to the judgment of some rabbis, was not altogether permissible. I explained to him, that on this account I wished to study medicine by which means I might be of service, not only to myself, but to the whole of the Jews in this neighborhood, as there was no regular physician here, and those who gave themselves out for such were charlatans, who packed men out of the world by their cures.

These reasons had an extraordinary effect on so devout a man. He went to a merchant of his acquaintance, represented to him the importance of my undertaking, and persuaded him to take me with him to Königsberg on his own vessel. The merchant could refuse nothing to so godly a man, and therefore gave his consent.

Accordingly I set out with this Jewish merchant for Königsberg in Prussia. When I arrived there, I went to a Jewish doctor, told him of my plan to study medicine, and begged him for advice and support. As his professional occupations prevented him from conveniently speaking with me on the subject, and as he could not understand me very well, he referred me to some students who lodged in his house. As soon as I showed myself to these young gentlemen, and told them what I had in mind, they burst into laughter. Certainly for this they were not to be blamed. Imagine a man from Polish Lithuania of about five and twenty years, with a tolerably stiff beard, in tattered dirty clothes, whose language is a mixture of Hebrew, Yiddish, Polish and Russian, with their several grammatical inaccuracies, who insists that he understands the German language, and that he has attained some knowledge of the sciences. What were they to think?

They began to poke fun at me, and gave me to read Mendelssohn's *Phaedo,* which by chance lay on the table. I read in the most pitiful style, both because of the peculiar manner in which I had learned the German language and my bad pronunciation. Again they burst into loud laughter. They asked me to explain to them what I had read. This I did in my own fashion; but as they did not understand me, they demanded that I should translate what I had read into Hebrew. This I did on the spot. The students, who understood Hebrew well, were exceedingly astonished when they saw that I had not only grasped correctly the meaning of this celebrated author, but also expressed it well in Hebrew. They began therefore to interest themselves on my account, procured for me some castoff clothing and board during my stay in Königsberg. At the same time they advised me to go to Berlin, where I might best attain my object. To make the journey suit my circumstances, however, they advised me to go by ship from Königsberg to Stettin, and thence to Frankfort-on-the-Oder where I should easily find means of getting to Berlin.

I went therefore by ship, and had nothing for food but some toast, herring, and a flask of whiskey. I was told in Königsberg that the journey might take ten or, at the most, fourteen days. This prophecy, however, was not fulfilled. Because of contrary winds, the voyage lasted five weeks. In what circumstances I found myself as a result, may be easily imagined. There were in the vessel besides me no other passengers, but an old woman who sang hymns all the time for her comfort. The Pomeranian German of the crew I could understand as little as they could my medley of Yiddish, Polish and Lithuanian. I got nothing warm to eat and was obliged to sleep on hard stuffed bags. Sometimes the vessel was in danger. Of course, most of the time I was seasick.

At last I arrived at Stettin, where I was told that I could make the journey to Frankfurt quite pleasantly on foot. But how was a Polish Jew in the most wretched circumstances, without a pfennig to buy food, and without knowing the language of the country, to make a journey even of a few miles? Yet it had to be done. Accordingly I set out from Stettin, and as I thought over my miserable situation, I sat down under a lime-tree, and began to weep bitterly. I soon became somewhat lighter in heart; I took courage, and continued. After I had gone two or three miles, I arrived towards evening at a ramshackle inn. It was the eve of the Jewish fast, which falls in August. I was nearly starving with hunger and thirst, and I had to fast the whole of the next day. I had not a pfennig to spend and nothing of any value to sell.

After long reflection it occurred to me that I must still have in my coatpocket an iron spoon, which I had taken with me on board ship. I brought it out, and begged the landlady of the inn to give me a little bread and beer in exchange for it. She refused at first to take the spoon, but after much insistence she was at last induced to grant me a glass of sour beer in exchange. I was obliged therefore to content myself with this, drank my glass of beer, and went off to the stable to sleep on straw.

In the morning I proceeded on my journey, having previously inquired for a place where there were Jews, in order that I might be able to go to the synagogue, and sing with my brethren the lamentations over the destruction of Jerusalem. This was done, and after the prayers and singing—about midday—I went to the Jewish schoolmaster of the place, and talked with him. He soon discovered that I was a rabbi, began to interest himself in me, and procured for me dinner at the house of a Jew. He also gave me a letter of introduction to another schoolmaster in the neighboring town, recommending me as a great Talmudist and an honorable rabbi. Here also I met with a pleasant reception. I was invited to the Sabbath dinner by the most respectable and richest Jew of the place, and attended the services in the synagogue where I was shown to the highest seat and received every mark of honor usually bestowed on a rabbi.

After the close of the service the rich Jew took me to his house and put me in the place of honor at his table, that is between himself and his daughter. She was a young girl of about twelve years, dressed in the most beautiful clothes. I began, as rabbi, to hold a very learned and edifying discourse; and the less the gentleman and lady understood it, the more divine it seemed to them. All at once I observed, to my chagrin, that the young lady began to put on a sour look, and to make wry faces. At first I did not know how to explain this; but, after a while, when I turned my eyes upon myself and my tattered suit of rags, the whole mystery was at once unriddled. The uneasiness of the young lady had a very good cause. And how could it be otherwise? Since I left Königsberg, about seven weeks before, I had never had a clean shirt to put on; and I had been obliged to lie in the stables of inns on bare straw, on which who knows how many poor travellers had slept before? Now all at once my eyes were opened to see my misery in its appalling magnitude. But what was I to do? How was I to help myself out of this unfortunate situation? Gloomy and sad, I soon bade farewell to these good people, and proceeded on my journey to Berlin, struggling continuously with every kind of want and misery.

At last I reached this city. Here I believed that I should put an end to my misfortune, and accomplish all my wishes. Alas, I was sadly deceived. In this capital, as is well known, no Jewish beggars were allowed. Accordingly the Jewish community, in order to make provision for their poor, built at the Rosenthaler gate a house in which the poor are received, and questioned by the Jewish elders about what they want in Berlin. According to the results of such inquiry, they are either taken to the city or they are sent away. I was therefore conducted to this house, which was filled partly with sick people, partly with a lewd rabble. For a long while I looked round in vain for a man with whom I might talk about my affairs.

At last I observed a man, who, to judge by his dress, was surely a rabbi. I went to him, and how great was my joy to learn from him, that he was really a rabbi, and well known in Berlin! I conversed with him on all sorts of subjects related to rabbinical lore. As I was very open-hearted, I related to him the story of my life in Poland, revealed to him my purpose of studying medicine in Berlin and showed him my commentary on Maimonides' *Guide to the Perplexed*. He listened to all, and seemed to interest himself very much in my behalf. But all of a sudden he disappeared.

At length towards evening the Jewish elders came. Each of the persons in the house was called and questioned about his wants. When my turn came, I said quite frankly that I wished to remain in Berlin in order to study medicine. The elders refused my request point-blank, gave me a pittance and went away. The reason of this conduct towards me in particular was nothing else than the following.

The rabbi of whom I spoke was a zealot in his orthodoxy. Accordingly, when he had discovered my sentiments and purposes, he went into town and informed the elders about my heretical thinking. He told them that I was going to issue a new edition of the *Guide to the Perplexed* with a commentary, and that my intention was not so much to study medicine, but mainly to devote myself to the sciences in general and to extend my knowledge. This the orthodox Jews look upon as something dangerous to religion and good morals. They believe this to be specially true of the Polish rabbis, who, having been delivered from the bondage of superstition by some lucky accident, suddenly catch a gleam of the light of reason and set themselves free from their chains. And this belief is to some extent well-founded. Persons in such a position may be compared to a man, who, after being famished for a long time, suddenly comes upon a well-spread table, will attack the food with violent greed, and even overstuff himself.

The refusal of permission to stay in Berlin came upon me like a thunderclap. The ultimate object of all my hopes and wishes was all at once removed beyond my reach, just when I had seen it so near. I found myself in the situation of Tantalus, and did not know where to turn for help. I was especially pained by the treatment I received from the overseer of this poorhouse, who, by command of his superiors, urged my speedy departure, and never left off till he saw me outside of the gate. There I threw myself on the ground and began to weep bitterly. It was a Sunday, and many people were taking their customary walk outside of the city. Most of them never turned aside to a whining worm like me, but some compassionate souls were very much struck with the sight, and asked the cause of my wailing. I answered them, but, partly on account of my unintelligible language, partly because my speech was broken by frequent weeping and sobbing, they could not understand what I said.

I was so deeply affected by this vexation that I fell into a violent fever. The soldiers, who kept guard at the gate, reported this at the poorhouse. The overseer came and carried me in. I stayed there over the day, and enjoyed the hope of becoming thoroughly sick so as to enforce a longer sojourn in the place, during which I thought I might form some acquaintances, by whose influence I hoped to receive protection and permission to remain in Berlin. But alas! in this hope I was deceived. The following day I arose quite lively again, without a trace of fever. I was therefore obliged to go. But whither? That I did not know myself. Accordingly I took the first road that I came upon and surrendered myself to fate.

KABBALISTS

by LION FEUCHTWANGER

I. RABBI GABRIEL

THREE peasant crofts lay quite high with a small wooden chapel beside them. Further up cattle were grazing. Beyond that was nothing but rocks and ice.

The stranger clambered up the ravine. Beneath him ran the mountain stream, small and noisy; one could see clearly where it welled up among glacier ice and boulders. On the other side stone-pines crawled up the hillside, stunted and tough, choked by rocks. Peaks shining white, so that the snow-glare hurt the eye, cut sharp and bizarre notches in the shimmering blue, and shut in the high valley with their rigid circle. The stranger climbed circumspectly, carefully but not very skilfully, but steadily. He crossed torrents, slippery ice, and sliding slopes. At last he stood on a spur facing the enclosing arch of icy walls. Below him a glacier stretched its naked broad creviced tongue, and another opened beside him; everything ended in rubble and desolation; a wild confusion of granite boulders lay in mysterious, rigid, and shattered lines. High over all, sunny and unattainable, glittered mockingly the noble and delicate sweep of the snowy summit.

The stranger crouched and gazed, cupping his large pale cleanshaven face in his hand. Above the small flat nose troubled grey eyes looked out, which were much too big for the short, massive head; they were full of a suffocating and hopeless sadness. The forehead, broad, heavy and not high, pressed upon thick eyebrows. His elbow on his knee, his cheek on his hand, he crouched and gazed.

Was it here, what he sought? One thing flowed into another from the upper world to the lower; every human face must have its correspondence with some part of the earth. He sought a part of the earth which would look at him with a human face but bigger, more legible, more significant, the face of that man in whom he was imprisoned. He sought the stream which united that man, and therefore himself, with his star, the Word, and infinity.

He crouched lower, and declaimed, in an obscure, unpleasantly broken and rumbling voice, half chanting, verses from the secret revelations. Skin, flesh, bones, and blood vessels are a garment, a shell and not the

man himself. But the mysteries of the highest wisdom are in the organization of the human body. As in the firmament enclosing the earth there
are stars and constellations which interpret deep and hidden mysteries,
so there are on the skin of our bodies lines and wrinkles and symbols
and signs, and they are the stars and constellations of the body, and they
have their mystery, and the wise read and interpret them.

Come and behold! The spirit chisels the countenance, and the wise
man recognizes it. When the spirits and souls of the upper world take
shape, they have their form and their certain outline, which later mirrors
itself in the faces of men.

He fell silent. One should not think. These things cannot be thought
of; thought only destroys them. They must be contemplated or left
alone. Was this the countenance that he sought? Waste land, ice and
boulders, the mocking blue glitter above it, and a small rill trickling out
of it with difficulty? Blocks of granite, or icy crevasses, falling into meaningless and gloomy patterns, was this the countenance that he sought?

He sank more profoundly into himself. He annihilated every activity
which was remote from what he sought. Three furrows, sharp, deep,
short and almost vertical above his nose cleft his forehead; and they
formed the sacred letter Shin, the first letter of God's name, Shaddai.

The shadow of a great cloud obscured the glaciers; the peaks in their
unending and delicate line of shimmering snow glittered unattainably in
light mockery. A vulture floated in the blue haze, circling peacefully
above the petrified chaos of this upper valley.

The man crouching on the projecting ledge, a tiny speck in the immense landscape, absorbed its configuration, the rock, the waste land, the
creviced ice; the delicate mocking glitter, the cloud, the bird's flight, the
gloomy meaningless caprice of the boulders, the hint of human beings
lower down and of grazing cattle. He scarcely breathed; he looked,
seized and comprehended.

At last, nearly staggering after such tense immobility, he rose up
exhausted, smoothing the furrowed symbol from his brow, in deep and
composed sorrow. Then he descended to the valley toilsomely, still half
disabled.

II. ISAAC LURIA

By the Lake of Tiberias the Master of the Kabbala, Rabbi Isaac Luria,
walked with his favourite pupil, Hayyim Vital Calabrese. The men drank
out of the Fountain of Miriam, fared out on the Lake. The Master spoke
of his wisdom. The Spirit brooded over the waters, the skiff stood still.

It was a marvel that it did not sink, for heavy with the lives of millions was the Rabbi and his word.

Back to the Fountain of Miriam the men returned again. And again they drank. Then suddenly the fountain changed its course. It formed a bow in the air, with two vertical rays, a cross ray above them. Into the bow strode the Rabbi to be a third vertical ray. So out of him and the Fountain came the character Shin, the beginning of the most exalted of the names of God, Shaddai. And the character waxed, and spanned itself over the lake, and spanned itself over the world. When the pupil Hayyim Vital returned out of his trance, the fountain flowed as before, but the Rabbi Isaac Luria was no longer there.

But this middle column in the sacred character was the only thing he had written down of his learning. For the words of his wisdom fell from his lips and were like snow. They were there, they were white and glittered and were cooling; but no one could catch hold of them. So his wisdom fell from his mouth and no one could lay hold upon it. The Rabbi did not write it down and did not even suffer that others should write it. Because what is written is changed, and becomes the death of the spoken word. Therefore, even the Scriptures are not the word of God, but a mask and a distortion, what wood is to the living tree. Only in the mouth of the wise does it rise up and live.

Yet after the Rabbi had gone, his pupil could not refrain from setting down his wisdom on paper in the vain and lying symbols of the written word. And he wrote the Book of the Tree of Life, and he wrote the Book of the Metamorphoses of the Soul.

Oh, how wise had been the Master in that he had not soiled his knowledge with the written word, in that he had not twisted his wisdom by means of the evil magic of letters! Elias, the prophet, had appeared to him by day, Simon ben Jochai by night. The language of birds had been revealed to him, of trees, of fire, of stone. The souls of the buried he could see and the souls of the living when on Sabbath Eve they soared to Paradise; also he could decipher the souls of men on their brows, draw them to him, speak with them, and then release them again to return to their places. The Kabbala had opened itself widely before him, so that the bodies of things were like glass to him; he saw in One, body, spirit and soul; air, water and earth were full of voices and shapes, he saw God's shuttle weaving the world, the angels came and held discourse with him. He knew that over all there was mystery, but for him mystery opened its eyes, fawned on him like an obedient dog. Marvels bloomed on his way. The Tree of the Kabbala entered into him and broke through him, its roots were deep in the bowels of the earth, its crest in Heaven fanned the countenance of God.

But oh, how this wisdom was changed in the books of his pupil! In wild confusion foolishness and wisdom sprouted from them. False prophets and Messiahs grew out of the characters; magic and thaumaturgy, wonders and miracles and harlotry and ostentation and falseness flowed from them into the world. The pallid countenance of Simon ben Jochai looked out of these characters, and in the thicket of his silvery beard lay snared and destroyed myriads of saints and holy men; and out of the symbols of these books gleamed naked and impudent the breasts of Lilith, and at her nipples hung lisping and babbling and with drunken senses the children of lust and of power.

And this is one passage from the secret wisdom of Rabbi Isaac Luria Ashkinasi:

"It may happen that in one human body more than one soul may suffer a new incarnation, and that at one time two, yea several souls, may unite themselves by means of this body in a new earthly fate. It may be that the one is balsam, the other poison; it may be that the one is an animal's, the other a priest's or devoted anchorite's. Now they are confined in one place, belonging to one body as the right and the left hand. They interpenetrate, they bite into each other, they impregnate each other, they flow into each other like water. But though ever bruising each other, recreating each other, always this union is the means by which one soul aids another, that the guilt might be expiated on whose account they suffer the new incarnation."

These are a few sentences from the secret wisdom of the Rabbi Isaac Luria, the eagle of Kabbalists, who was born in Jerusalem, for seven years mortified himself, alone, on the banks of the Nile, brought back his wisdom to Galilee and performed miracles among the people, never defiled his wisdom with writing and paper, and mysteriously vanished on the Lake of Tiberias in the thirty-eighth year of his life.

III. RABBI GABRIEL AND RABBI EYBESCHÜTZ

It was already late in the evening when Our Teacher Rabbi Gabriel Oppenheimer van Straaten arrived at the house of his friend, Our Teacher Rabbi Jonathan Eybeschütz in Hamburg. The house was full of people who had come to see the Rabbi, to pay him honour, to seek his advice, and although his pupils perpetually explained that the Rabbi was among his books, in meditation, that there was no prospect he would receive them, they would not give in, and always hoped at least to have a glimpse of him. Many had come from a distance to see him, from communities where he had been before, Cracow, Metz, Prague; but many, too, had come from still farther, from Provence, yes, from the Black Sea. For the name of Rabbi Jonathan Eybeschütz, Rabbi of Hamburg, was held in humble reverence in many lands.

But he was also hated and combatted with the sharpest weapons in many lands. Ah, how Our Teacher Rabbi Jaakob Hirschel Emden, Rabbi of Amsterdam, had jeered at him, had torn him to pieces in icy scorn, branded him, held him up to ridicule, as the enemy of Israel, of the Talmud, of the Rabbis, and of the true Word! Rabbi Jonathan Eybeschütz: the name split the whole of Jewry asunder; in every school and synagogue, at every synod, there was strife over this name; it was greeted with blessings and paeans, with jeers and maledictions.

Who was this man? Was he a learned Talmudist, zealous, quarrelsome, furious at any neglect of the rites, venomously angry over an iota, defending word by word the lofty table of the law with jealous and wild vituperation? Or had his philosophical, historical, mathematical, astronomical erudition gnawed away his belief in the true faith, proved by the Word and by works, and turned him into a mocker and contemner of Rabbinical ritual? Did he really believe in the teaching of the Kabbala and practise it, he the secret pupil and disciple of the Messiah Sabbatai Zewi, blessing, cursing, working miracles in the name of that redeemer? But why then did he publicly curse the followers of Sabbatai, and solemnly put them in ban? And why again did he send his sons to the Frankists in Poland, to the fanatical disciples of that enigmatical Messiah? Did this zealous, orthodox Talmudist really write letters to the French cardinals, to the Jesuit fathers in Rome, begging them to make him censor for Hebrew books? Was it arrogance, or what did it mean, that he suffered his strict, rabbinical orthodoxy to be defended against all suspicions of this kind by the Helmstatt Professor, Karl Anton, his former pupil, but now become a Christian and an apologist of the Christian evangel?

Rabbi Jonathan's scholars bowed deeply to Rabbi Gabriel when he entered. "Peace be with thee!" they said, and the closed door of the Master's room sprang open before him. In his study, in the circle of lamplight, sat Rabbi Jonathan Eybeschütz, a mild figure, the wisest and craftiest of men. Cordially, whimsically, in soft self-mockery, very pleased, he smiled out of his mighty, milky-white beard, more broad than long, and only slightly forked in the Kabbalistic fashion, to the beardless, stony newcomer. All about him was round and comfortable, and accentuated his dignity. His long elegant caftan was of a heavy silk of incalculable value; his very small hand, white and manicured, was lifted out of the wide sleeve in greeting. From out of the mighty, flowing, white beard smiled hospitably a countenance almost rosy, and hardly at all troubled by age. Only over the small, elegant nose, and the mild, sagacious, sly and yet deep eyebrows, there were cloven vertically in the white, fleshy, full brow, three furrows, representing Shin, the first letter in the holiest of names, Shaddai.

"My brother and Master will not be reproachful or angry?" he greeted his guest in Hebrew. He smiled, and there was in his smile knowledge and frailty, and coquetry, and consciousness of guilt, and even a little roguery. But above all a magical, lulling charm.

But on Rabbi Gabriel this magic missed fire. Over his tiny, flattened nose the far too large, troubled, grey eyes smouldered with sadness, and from his heavy, broad, not very high brow, went out an oppressive melancholy. But Rabbi Jonathan Eybeschütz was not willing that this melancholy should touch him. "Have you," he asked lightly, almost merrily, "have you read, Gabriel, the new polemic of the Krethi and Plethi man?" This was the most important work of that same Jaakob Hirschel Emden, Rabbi of Amsterdam, his fiercest antagonist. "Now the good man has happily let fly twelve lampoons against me, one for each tribe of Israel," he went on, and his brown, wise, crafty eyes laughed in mocking enjoyment. "Jaakob Hirschel has twelve tines on his antlers now." With his small manicured hand he turned the great pages of the polemic. "The poor, dull man," he said, pitying and amused, "all must be clear, all must be bright, all must be daylight! He does not suspect, the threadbare, arid mocker, he does not comprehend that a withered flower is only hay and good only for an ox." And, scornful and amused, he wagged his mild head with the prodigious, flowing white beard.

But Rabbi Gabriel did not enter into the other's mood. "Why have you excommunicated Sabbatai's disciples?" he asked in his surly voice. "Why do you turn and twist and shuffle and disclaim? Why do you let yourself be defended by a Goi with stupid and idiotic sophistries? Why do you not resign? Is it so important that you should be Rabbi of Hamburg, and have your rooms full of people? Why have you—" and there was accusation and menace in his voice—"why have you excommunicated yourself?"

Jonathan Eybeschütz let a little, pleasant, comfortable burst of laughter out of his beard.

"Let well alone, Gabriel," he said. "You have not become milder in these two years, nor I stricter. I might say: is it not immaterial whether one is Jew or Goi or Moslem, if one but knows of the Upper World? I might say: Certainly Karl Anton, my scholar, has been baptized; but is there not more fellowship and intimacy between him and me than there is between me and Reb Jaakob Hirschel Emden, who is a good Jew with a sharp, gifted head, but unfortunately a narrow-minded worldling, stone-blind to the Upper World, and stone-deaf to its voices? I might say: The Messiah Sabbatai Zewi himself became a Moslem, to save the principle, the idea, and his disciple Frank has been baptized: shall it not be permitted to me, then, to assume the mummery of a snuffling rabbi, and pronounce with angry lips, but laughing in my heart, empty excommunications which recoil upon myself? I might say: it is easy to be a martyr; it is far harder to endure misunderstanding for the sake of the idea.

All this I might say; but I will not say it to you, Gabriel." He stood up and came forward, splendid and hospitable in his silken caftan, to the thick-set gloomy man in his old Frankish clothes, which might have belonged to any humble official. With great charm, with almost boyish warmth, he said: "I admit I am weak and foolish and vain. The stars meant well by me, they shaped me to be the vessel for a great wisdom; I might have been a channel through which in mighty streams the breath of God might have flowed from the Upper to the Nether World. But I am an imperfect vessel, I know, and nobody can feel it more intensely in his deepest spirit, what blessed peace it is to rest in God, and that the Nether World is vanity and coloured foam and fleeting as wind. But I must plunge into it, always again. Action is foolish, action is stupid and filthy and bestial, and its aftertaste is stale and leaves a very evil flavour. But I must always plunge again into action and vanity and commotion! Let me be stupid, dear friend! Let me be filthy and bestial! Let me care more for my beard than for my soul!" And with a blasphemous jest he concluded: "My soul I will find, and wash it clean in myriads of years; but who will guarantee that I will find such a lovely beard a second time?"

These blasphemies rippled softly from the sweet, persuasive, eloquent lips of the wise, frivolous, lost Rabbi. The other heard them, melancholy, stony, unmoved. Suddenly he saw a landscape. Stone, waste, broken ice; a tender, mocking light over it, overshadowing clouds, vulture flocks, dark madness and violence, gigantic blocks cast up by the ice. Almost unmanned by the picture, he recognized the same correspondence here as there. This presentiment had driven him from the man to whom he was most bound, to this other. One lay on the insolent, naked bosom of Lilith, but he yearned and longed for the Upper World. Among the saints and prophets this other reclined, the silvery beard of Simon ben Jochai on his chin, but he thirsted after the nipples of Lilith. The same picture, uttering the same thing. But that man was nearer his fulfillment than this.

He did not reply when Jonathan Eybeschütz paused at last.

He only said: "Peace be with thee, my brother and master!" and went into the bedroom which had been prepared for him. Jonathan Eybeschütz watched the round, solid, slightly bowed back recede, and his mild, frivolous smile slowly disappeared, and in spite of his milky white beard, he looked less dignified and supercilious when he turned again to his books and parchments.

ZIPPORAH'S WEDDING

by GLÜCKEL OF HAMELN

WHEN my eldest child, my daughter Zipporah, was nearly twelve years of age, Reb Loeb, the son of Reb Anshel of Amsterdam, broached a match with Kessmann, the son of Reb Elia Cleve. My husband, of blessed memory, left six weeks earlier than usual on his half-yearly visit to Amsterdam and wrote to the matchmaker to meet him there to see what could be done. At that time there was a war in progress,[1] and Elia Cleve and his family were forced to move from Cleve to Amsterdam. On my husband's arrival in that town, rumor spread that he was about to ally himself by marriage with Reb Elia. This was on Post day when people read their letters on the Bourse. Many disputed the tale and there was much wagering, for Elia Cleve was a very wealthy man worth 100,000 or more Reichstaler. My husband was then still quite a young man, just beginning to get on nicely in business, and there was a houseful of young children, God protect them. What God proposes must indeed come to pass, however much people may dislike it. Is it not proclaimed in Heaven forty days before birth that this man's son shall wed that man's daughter?

So it came to pass that my husband joined himself through marriage with the wealthy Elia Cleve, our daughter's dowry being settled at 2,200 Reichstaler in Dutch money. The date of the marriage was fixed for

[1] Louis XIV's war against Holland, 1672.

eighteen months later, at Cleve; my husband to pay one hundred Reich-staler towards the wedding expenses.

When the time of the wedding drew very near, we left for Cleve—my husband, I with a babe at the breast, the bride Zipporah, Rabbi Meyer of the Klaus who is now rabbi in Friedburg, our man-servant Fine Shemuel and a maid—quite a handsome retinue. In company with Mordecai Cohen, Meyer Ilius and Aaron Todliche we went from Altona by boat. I cannot describe the jollity and merriment of our journey. In joy and happiness we arrived at Amsterdam three weeks before the wedding. We stayed with Reb Loeb Hamburger, whom I have already mentioned, and spent more than twelve ducats every week. But we did not mind this as during this time my husband, of blessed memory, did some business and earned more than half the dowry.

Fourteen days before the wedding, with music and hilarity, a com-pany of twenty, we travelled to Cleve and were there received with great honor. Reb Elia Cleve's house was really like a king's palace, hand-somely furnished in every way—like a lord's mansion. We had no rest all day from eminent and distinguished visitors who came to see the bride. In truth my daughter was really beautiful and had no equal. There was a great excitement in preparation for the wedding.

At that time Prince Frederick [2] was in Cleve. The senior prince, the Elector, was alive, and Frederick was yet a lad little more than thirteen. Soon after, the Elector died and Frederick became Elector in his place. Prince Maurice [3] and his court, too, were there. Their curiosity was aroused and they made it known that they wished to be present at the wedding. It may easily be imagined what preparations Reb Elia Cleve made for such distinguished guests.

On the wedding day, soon after the marriage ceremony, there was a collation of all kinds of the finest sweetmeats, foreign wines and fruits out of season. How can one describe all the excitement! How all the thoughts of Reb Elia Cleve and his family were taken up with the recep-tion and accommodation of the visitors! There was not even time to pro-duce and count the dowries, as is the custom at such times. So we put our dowry and Reb Elia his dowry into a bag and sealed it, to be counted after the wedding.

When we stood all together under the canopy with the bride and bridegroom we found that in the great excitement the Ketubah had

---

[2] Later Elector of Brandenburg, and in 1701 King Frederick I. of Prussia.
[3] Prince of Nassau.

not been drawn up! What was to be done? All the distinguished guests and the young Prince stood about waiting to see the ceremony under the canopy. Rabbi Meyer advised that the bridegroom might appoint a surety who would undertake that the ketubah would be written directly after the ceremony. In the meantime we were to continue with the marriage. And so it was, the rabbi reading the ketubah from a book.

After the ceremony all the distinguished guests were led into the great hall, the walls of which were lined with gilded leather. A long table crowded with regal delicacies stood in the center, each guest being served in order of rank. My son Mordecai was then about five years old; there was no more beautiful child in the whole world and we had dressed him neatly and prettily. The courtiers nearly swallowed him for admiration, especially the Prince who held his hand the whole time. After the courtiers and other guests had consumed the confects and enjoyed the wine, the table was cleared and removed. Masked dancers entered and presented different poses quite nicely and suitably to the entertainment. They ended with the Death Dance. It was all very splendidly done.

Among the guests there were also many Portuguese [Jews], one of whom was a jeweller of the name of Mocatti who had with him a beautiful little golden watch set in diamonds, worth 500 Reichstaler. Reb Elia asked Mocatti for the little watch, desiring to present it to the young Prince. But a good friend, standing close by, said to him, "Why should you do this? to give such an expensive present to the young Prince? It is not as if he were the Elector." But, as I have already mentioned, the Elector died soon after, and the young prince, he is still Elector, succeeded him. Thereafter whenever Elia Cleve met the friend who prevented him giving the present, he would throw it up angrily at him. And in truth, if Elia Cleve had given the present the Prince would never have forgotten it, for great people never forget such things. Well, why cry for what has gone?

The young Prince, Prince Maurice and all the courtiers enjoyed themselves and left fully satisfied. For a hundred years no Jew had had such high honor. The wedding-day ended in joy and gladness.

QUEST FOR GOD

by URIEL ACOSTA

I WAS born in Portugal [1] in a city of the same name but commonly called Oporto. My parents were of the nobility, originally descended from those Jews who were forced to embrace Christianity in that kingdom. My father was a true Christian and a man of unquestioned honor and integrity. I had a good education at home, servants always at my command, and I rode a Spanish jennet to perfect myself in horsemanship, an art in which my father was so skilled and in which I endeavored to follow his steps. At length, being grown up, and as well accomplished in the liberal arts as young gentlemen generally are, I applied myself to the study of law. As to my character and disposition, I was by nature very pious and compassionate. So much so that I could not hear the story of any person's misfortunes without melting into tears. I had so strong an innate sense of modesty that I dreaded nothing so much as to suffer disgrace. Not that I had the least degree of cowardice in my nature. When there was reasonable justification I was not free from resentment. It is for this reason that I always had an aversion to that haughty and insolent tribe of men who are inclined to despise and trample upon others, and I therefore took every opportunity to defend the oppressed and to make their cause my own.

Religion has brought incredible suffering into my life. According to the custom of the country, I was educated in Roman Catholicism. When I was but a youth the dread of eternal damnation made me anxious to observe all its doctrines punctiliously. I employed my leisure time in reading the Gospels, the Breviaries of the Confessors and other religious literature. But the more time I devoted to them, the more perplexed did I become. Little by little this caused me such difficulties, doubts and conflicts that I was overwhelmed with grief and melancholy.

Reflection led me to believe that the obtaining of a plenary absolution by the confession of sins and the fulfillment of all that the Church required was impossible. This consequently made me despair of salvation inasmuch as it was to be obtained only by such special rules. But as it was very difficult to shake off quickly a religion in which I had been educated from my infancy and which by a long unquestioning faith had taken

---

[1] In 1590. See biographical note on page 781.

deep root, I began, when I was about twenty years old, to question the teachings concerning the after life. I asked myself whether or not they were forgeries and whether belief in them was consistent with reason. My reason perpetually suggested to me conclusions that were just the contrary. Under the shadow of this doubt I continued for some time, and finally I was persuaded that salvation could not be obtained in the prescribed manner.

During this time I continued to apply myself to the study of law. When I was in my twenty-fifth year an opportunity presented itself whereby I obtained an ecclesiastical benefice as treasurer in the church. But I was unable to find the satisfaction I wanted in the Catholic church. I wanted, however, to attach myself to a religion and, aware of the great dispute between the Christians and the Jews, I made a study of the *Books of Moses* and of the *Prophets*. I found some things sharply contradictory to the doctrines of the New Testament. There seemed to be less difficulty in believing those things which were revealed by God Himself. Besides, the Old Testament was assented to by both Jews and Christians whereas the New Testament was believed only by Christians. Hence I decided to become a convert to the Law of Moses. As he declared himself to be only a deliverer of what was revealed by God Himself, being called to that mission or rather constrained to accept it, I thought it my duty to make the Law the rule of my life. Having made this decision and finding it unsafe to profess this religion in Portugal, I began to think of changing my residence and leaving my native home. In order to do this, I immediately resigned from my ecclesiastical benefice in favor of another, uninfluenced either by profit or honor, the two prevailing motives among the people of our country. I also left a beautiful house situated in the best part of the city, which my father had built. When I had concluded all the necessary arrangements, my mother, brothers and myself boarded a ship, not without danger for it is illegal for those who are descended from Jews to depart without a special permit from the king. I must tell the reader that out of natural affection, I had communicated to my family my sentiments on the falsity of our religion even though the discovery of it might have proved fatal to me—so dangerous is it in that country to speak freely on this subject, even to one's dearest friends. At the end of our voyage we arrived at Amsterdam where we found the Jews professing their religion with great freedom, as the Law directs them. We immediately fulfilled the precept concerning circumcision.

I had not been there very long before I observed that the customs and ordinances of the modern Jews were quite different from those commanded by Moses. Now if the Law was to be observed according to the letter, as it expressly declares, the Jewish interpreters are not justified in adding to it interpretations quite contrary to the original text. This provoked me to oppose them openly. Nay, I looked upon the open defense of the Law against such innovations as a service to God. The modern rabbis, like their ancestors, are an obstinate and stiffnecked race of men, vigorous advocates of the teachings and institutions of the Pharisees, not without a view to gain and, as is justly imputed to them, vainly fond of the conspicuous seats in the synagogue and greetings in the marketplace. Men of this character could not bear my differing with them in the slightest degree. They insisted that I follow unswervingly their prescribed regulations or else suffer exclusion from the synagogue and the full sentence of excommunication. But it would have been unworthy of him who had so recently left his native country and been content to forgo many other temporal advantages for liberty of conscience to be overawed and to submit to men who had no right to such power. Besides, I thought it both sinful and beneath a man to be a slave in things pertaining to the conscience. Therefore I resolved to suffer the worst they could inflict rather than recant. Accordingly they excommunicated me from their congregation. Even my own brothers who before had looked upon me as their teacher, dared not take any notice of me as they passed me in the streets, for fear of the rabbis.

This state of affairs led me to write a tract in defense of myself and to prove plainly out of the Law of Moses the vanity and the invalidity of the traditions and ordinances of the Pharisees as well as their conflict with that Law. After I had begun this work (for I consider myself obliged to relate everything clearly and circumstantially), it so happened that I entirely agreed with the opinion of those who confine the rewards and punishments proposed in the Old Testament to this life only and are little concerned with the future life or the immortality of the soul. The following argument, among others, led to this viewpoint: The Law of Moses is completely silent as to the latter problems and proposes only temporal rewards and punishments to observers and transgressors thereof. The discovery that I entertained such opinions was no small triumph to my adversaries who felt that as a result they had the Christians as their allies, who by their faith in the Gospels which expressly mentions eternal rewards and punishments, do believe and preach the immortality of the soul. It was with the idea of rendering me odious to the Christians and of silencing me completely that, even before my tract went to press, they employed a certain scholar [2] to publish a book entitled *Of the Immortal-*

[2] Samuel da Silva. The book appeared in 1623.

ity of the Soul. In it the scholar inveighed bitterly against me as one who defended the philosophy of Epicurus and who by denying the immortality of the soul disputed the very existence of God. At that very time I had, in reality, an incorrect idea of Epicurus and, prejudiced by my unsavory relations with other persons without even hearing what he had to say for himself, I did not scruple to censure him freely. But now that I have heard from impartial lovers of the truth some estimate of this philosopher and his teaching, I have found reason to change my opinion and to be sorry for the injustice I did him then when I pronounced him a ridiculous madman even though, being an utter stranger to his writings, I was far from being competent to judge his opinions.

The next step they took was to set their children upon me in the streets. They insulted me en masse as I walked along, abusing and railing at me. They cried out, "There goes a heretic, there goes an impostor." At other times they assembled before my doors, flung stones at the windows and did everything they could to disturb and annoy me so that I could not live at peace in my own house. After the above mentioned book was published, I immediately set about my own defense. I wrote an answer in which I opposed with all the power at my command the doctrine of the immortality of the soul, incidentally dealing with the deviations of the Pharisees from Mosaic institutions. No sooner had this appeared in print than the elders and officials of the Jews agreed to make a complaint against me before the public magistrate. They asserted that I had published a book to disprove the immortality of the soul in order to subvert, not only the Jewish, but also the Christian religion. As a result, I was apprehended and sent to prison from which, after a confinement of eight or ten days, I was discharged upon giving security. For the magistrate fined me three hundred florins [$120] and confiscated my recently published books.

Let me here declare my mind freely. What should hinder a man from speaking the truth without reservation, who is just about to make his exit and to leave behind him a sad though true example of human misery. Sometime after this (as age and experience are apt to bring new discoveries to the mind of man and consequently to alter his judgment of things) I began to ask myself whether the law of Moses should be considered the law of God inasmuch as there were many arguments which seemed to persuade or rather determine the contrary. At length I came to the conclusion that it was nothing but a human invention, like many other religious and legal systems in the world, and that Moses was not really its author. I noted that it contained many things contrary to the laws of nature and God who was the author of those laws could not contradict himself which he must have done, had he given to mankind rules and regulations contrary to the laws of nature. Having thus determined this point, I began to reason with myself in the following manner (I wish I had never entertained such a thought!): What can it profit me to spend all my days in this melancholy state, isolated from the society of this people and their elders, especially since I am a stranger in this country without any acquaintance among its inhabitants or even any knowledge of its language? How much better will it be for me to return to their community and conform to their ways in compliance with the proverb which directs us to do in Rome as the Romans do. These considerations led me to return to their society. Accordingly, I made a formal recantation and subscribed to such regulations as they were pleased to impose upon me, after having lived for fifteen years in a state of separation from them. I must note that a certain cousin of mine helped to mediate this reconciliation.

A few days after this I was accused by my nephew, a lad whom I kept in my house, of breaking the dietary laws. New and cruel proceedings were begun against me. My cousin, whom I mentioned before as a kind of mediator between us, thinking that my behavior brought dishonor on his mediation and being a proud, bold fellow and very hasty, declared himself openly my inveterate enemy. He won all my brothers over to his side and left nothing undone that might ruin my reputation and fortune, and deprive me of life itself. He prevented a marriage which I was then just on the point of concluding, for I had lost my wife recently. He was also the cause for one of my brothers withholding my property which was in his possession. He also put a stop to the dealings which existed between us as a result of which I suffered incredibly in my business affairs. In a word, he was a most implacable enemy to my reputation fortune and life. Besides this domestic war, if I may so call it, another of a more public nature was carried on against me by the rabbis and the people who began to persecute me with fresh hatred, behaving with such insolence to me that I justly came to abhor and detest them.

About this time a new situation arose. One day I happened to be in the company of two men, one a Spaniard and the other an Italian, who came from London to Amsterdam. Both of them were Christians and not even related to Jews by descent. They revealed to me their present situation and asked my advice concerning the possibility of their becoming converts to Judaism. I dissuaded them from any such intention, advising them rather to bear the inconveniences of their present condition rather than to subject themselves to so burdensome a yoke with which they were unacquainted. At the same time I cautioned them not to make the least mention to the Jews of what had passed between us. This they faithfully promised me. These perfidious wretches, however, induced by the hope of filthy lucre, instead of repaying me with gratitude, went and disclosed everything to my dear friends, the Pharisees. The officers of the synagogue convened, the rabbis were inflamed with resentment and the insolent rabble cried out with one voice, "Crucify him!" In short, I was asked to appear before the rabbinical court where the charges against me were read with as much solemnity and impressiveness as though I had been on trial for life. Then it was decided that if I were really a Jew, I ought to submit to their sentence; otherwise I must be excommunicated again.

O just and equitable judges who take upon yourselves the power of condemnation and punishment! But when I appealed to your authority for protection against oppression and wrong then indeed you pretend that you have not the authority to interfere in such matters and are only servants of civil power. Of what validity, then, is your judgment that I should obey it? Then my sentence was read out of a little book. It declared that I must enter the synagogue dressed in the clothes of mourning, holding a black wax taper in my hand and there to read distinctly before the whole congregation a form of recantation in which they described in the blackest of colors the magnitude of my crimes. Then I was to submit to a public whipping with a scourge made of leather thongs. After that I was to prostrate myself at the entrance of the synagogue that they might all pass over me. Moreover, I was to fast a certain number of days.

No sooner had I heard my sentence than I was fired with indignation and resentment. However, withholding my anger as well as I could, I answered only that I could not consent to undergo such a severe sentence. They consulted together and proceeded to excommunicate a second time. But not content with this, many of them spit upon me as they passed me in the streets and encouraged their children to do likewise. The only reason why they did not stone me was because they wanted power. This persecution lasted for a period of seven years, and should I relate all that I suffered it would seem incredible. For two parties violently persecuted me—the whole Jewish community and my family who sought their revenge in my disgrace. Nor would they be satisfied until they got me into their own power and jurisdiction, saying among themselves: "He is stubborn. He will do nothing until he is forced to, and therefore ought to be compelled." When I was sick nobody would attend me. If I suffered any other misfortune, it became a triumph and joy to them; if I proposed any one of them to act as judge between us the proposal was rejected. When I attempted to lay the whole case before a public magistrate, I found it very tedious and difficult, for judicial proceedings are at best both expensive and dilatory.

During these troubles they would often exhort me to submit, saying, "We are all your fathers and therefore you need not fear that we shall act unfairly or unkindly toward you. Only say that you are ready to perform whatever we ask of you, leave the rest to us and all shall be made easy." This was the very point in dispute, and I understood how disgraceful it would be to surrender out of discretion and depend upon their mercy. Yet I wanted to put an end to this long affair and after much reluctance I prevailed upon myself to submit to their terms and to test their honor. For I argued with myself thus: If they deal dishonorably with me they will stand convicted by their own behavior and exhibit their implacable enmity towards me and how little they are to be trusted. At length this execrable and detested people did plainly show what their religion and principles are by treating men of honor and character as though they had been the vilest slaves. In a word, I said to them, "I depend upon your mercy and I am ready to undergo whatsoever you are pleased to impose upon me." Now let every man of truth and humanity observe my situation and judge the sentence which a particular set of people, under foreign jurisdiction, passed upon an innocent man.

I entered the synagogue which was filled with curious spectators of both sexes. At the appointed time I walked up to the reading desk which was in the center and with a clear voice read aloud the form of confession which they had drawn up for me, namely, that I deserved to die a thousand deaths for the crimes I had committed such as the profanation of the Sabbath, the breach of my religious vows, etc., which I had carried so far as to dissuade others from being converts to Judaism. To atone for these violations I submitted to their sentence and was ready to undergo whatever they wished to lay upon me, promising not to be guilty of similar crimes in the future. When I had finished the reading I stepped down from the desk. The chief elder came up to me and, whispering in my ear, bid me go to a certain corner of the synagogue. When I had done his, the doorkeeper asked me to strip. Accordingly I stripped myself down to the waist, tied a kerchief about my head, pulled off my shoes and, holding up my arms above my head, clasped a kind of pillar in my

hands, to which the doorkeeper tied them with a rope. Having thus prepared myself for my punishment, the verger stepped forward and with
a scourge of leather thongs gave me nine and thirty stripes, according to
the Jewish custom (it was a legal commandment that the number of
stripes shall not exceed forty) for these very scrupulous and pious gentlemen take due care not to offend by overstepping their bounds. During
the period of my whipping they sang a psalm. Then I was ordered to sit
down on the ground whereupon an elder came forward and absolved
me from my excommunication. So now the gates of heaven which were
doubly locked and barred against me were suddenly flung wide open. O
the ridiculous ideas and conceits of mortals! After this I dressed and went
to the entrance of the synagogue where I prostrated myself. The doorkeeper held up my head while everyone, both young and old, passed over
me, stepping with one foot on the lower part of my legs and making
ridiculous gestures, more like monkeys than human beings. After they
had all done this I got up and, being washed and made clean by a man
who stood near me for that purpose, I went home.

Now let nobody say that they did not do me honor, for if they
scourged me yet they lamented over me and stroked my head. O shame-
less race of men! O detested fathers! You from whom I had nothing
dishonorable to fear! You who said, far be it from us to abuse you in-
decently! Now let anyone who has heard my story judge how decent a
spectacle it was to see an old man, a person of no mean rank, and one
who was by nature exceedingly modest, strip naked before a large
assemblage of men, women and children and scourged by order of his
judges and those who deserved rather to be called abject slaves. Let him
imagine the confusion and anguish such a one must suffer by being
obliged to lie at the feet of his bitterest enemies and to be trampled upon
by those who had already loaded him with injuries and insults. Think
of him seeing his own brothers (O monstrous, inhuman and shameful
treatment!) who were educated in the same house, joining in an unnatural confederacy with his persecutors and unmindful of that great
affection with which I always loved them; and all this, regardless of the
many good deeds I had done them, requiting all my kindness and tenderness with shameful injuries and disgrace.

My detestable persecutors said in their own defense that they only
made me a public example in order to deter others of their faith from
open violation of religious ordinances and from writing books against
their rabbis. O wicked wretches and fathers of untruth! With how much

more justice could I have made *you* a public example of punishment in order to deter you from practicing similar abuses on men who are sincere lovers of truth, haters of deceit and invariably the friends of all mankind. Of such men you are the common enemies, esteeming all others but as the beasts of the field and scum of the earth while you arrogantly extol yourselves with vain praises as the only favorites of Heaven. In reality, you really have nothing to boast of unless you regard it as praiseworthy to live as outcasts, isolated from the society of men, despised and hated by all for your absurd customs by means of which you distinguish yourselves from the rest of the world. . . .

Permit me at this point to propound the following question: If the groundless fears which you instill into the minds of men are contrived on purpose to restrain the natural evil which is inherent in them and thus to keep within the bounds of their duty those who would otherwise lead immoral lives, must you not at the same time reflect that you yourselves are men of similar passions, naturally averse to good, prone to evil, without compassion or mercy? But I can see every one of you filled with rage at so insolent a question and cleverly justifying his own conduct. "What, are we not all pious and merciful and followers of truth and justice?" My answer is that what you so boastingly say of yourselves is patently false. Your accusation of all other men whose natural inclination to evil you pretend to correct with your terrors is outrageously unjust. How impiously you reflect upon the majesty and goodness of God whom you represent as a tyrant and destroyer. How you distort human nature in supposing it to be subjected to so deplorable a fate, just as if the ordinary calamities of life were not a sufficient portion of misery for human beings. Granting that the natural corruption of man is great, which I readily allow (you yourselves are sufficient proof of it for otherwise you could not be capable of such scandalous falsities) you ought to search for a more effective remedy to heal this general disorder without introducing a worse one in its place, and to put aside those impositions which are likely to frighten only children and simple folk. On the other hand, if the disorder is incurable then cease from your vain, delusive pretenses and do not act like impudent quacks in promising men health which you are unable to give them. Be content with establishing among yourselves just and reasonable laws which provide rewards for the good and suitable punishments for the bad. Defend the cause of the downtrodden against the violence of the oppressor so that there be no complaint that justice is not executed in the earth and that there is none to deliver the weak from the hands of the strong. In sum, if men would follow the dictates of reason and live according to the laws of nature they would all mutually love one another. Everyone would then contribute his utmost to the relief of his neighbor or at least no man would injure another for that would be acting contrary to human nature. Indeed many of the evils in life arise out of the fact that men have invented laws directly contrary to those of nature and thereby create the cause for one man injuring and persecuting another. Then, too, many men easily deceive the unsuspecting by their extraordinary pretense to piety. They use religion as a cloak in order to prey upon those who are superstitious. These may aptly be compared to a thief in the night, who treacherously attacks us when we are off our guard and do not suspect any danger. Yet these are the men who continually vaunt their honesty and patriotism: "I am a Jew, or I am a Christian. You do not doubt my integrity? Rely upon me, I will not deceive you." Infamous wretches! He who pretends to be neither of these and only calls himself a man is far preferable to you. If you do not believe him you may at least stand upon your guard. But who can defend himself against you, hypocrites, who under the mask of sanctity, like a thief in the night, come in by stealth and murder us in our sleep?

There is one thing beyond many others that puzzles and surprises me. How is it that the Pharisees, living in a Christian country, enjoy so great a degree of liberty as to exercise judicial power and authority? I may safely declare that if Jesus of Nazareth whom the Christians worship were to preach today in Amsterdam and the Pharisees, like their forefathers, decided to scourge him for opposing and condemning their tradition and hypocrisy they might do it with impunity. Such freedom is a matter of reproach and ought not to be tolerated in a free city which professes to protect men in the peaceable enjoyment of their liberty. Where a man is not permitted an advocate to defend his cause or a judge to punish the injuries inflicted upon him, it should not be a cause of wonder if, as a result, he takes every opportunity to defend and revenge himself.

I have here given a true account of my life. I have laid before you fairly the part that I acted on the vain stage of this world during the course of a checkered and unsettled life. Now, readers, judge impartially and render your opinion on what I have written with freedom and truth, like brave and honest men. If there is anything in my story which arouses your compassion let it teach you to pity me and to lament the miserable state of mankind in which you yourselves have an equal share. In order that it may be known who the author of this account was, let me note that while I lived as a Christian in Portugal, I was called Gabriel Acosta; but when I joined the Jewish fold (would that I never had done it!) my name was changed to Uriel.

AMONG THE MARRANOS

by DAVID REUBENI

THENCE we went with a good wind westward to the King of Portugal through the Mediterranean. We arrived close to Cadiz, in the Kingdom of the Emperor, and I sent Tobias, my servant, to the magistrate with the Pope's letter to ask him to allow us to leave the ship and stay in his city for one day, but the magistrate was not willing. Tobias said that the men of the city spoke evil things of us to the magistrate and said that the Jewish King had sent to the King of Portugal, who was of small account (compared with the Emperor). They thought we were going against the Emperor and advised him to come and arrest me and get horses to send me before the Emperor, but I was emboldened in my mission and rejoiced in all that God had done, for it would be for my good and the good of Israel to appear before the Emperor, but my servants were afraid and terrified, and I said to them, "Do not fear or be terrified." After that the ship captain came to me and said, "Better that you should leave this ship for another ship belonging to the King of Portugal," so we left that ship at midnight and left all our stuff in the cabin and closed it, and got into a little boat, which took us to the King of Portugal's ship, on which we embarked.

The captain of that ship was asleep, but when he heard that we had come on board he got up from his bed and we came to him to his cabin and showed him the letter of the King of Portugal [John the III] and our ship's captain spoke with the captain of the King's ship at length as to the words of the magistrate and the nobles in the city of Cadiz and we stayed there till dawn. Then we went to the City of Elmira, and the two ship captains went before the magistrates and notables, and my servant Tobias with them, and Tobias returned and said that the magistrates and notables had quarrelled with the captains because they wanted to arrest us. Afterwards our ship captain asked permission for us to go to Tavira, which is at the extremity of the Kingdom of Portugal, and gave us the stuff, which they had brought from the big ship to the other ship belonging to the King of Portugal, and I paid seventy-five ducats to the captain of the first ship for his trouble, and he left. We stayed in the King's ship until midnight and then entered a ship, laden with wheat, which was going by sea to Tavira and I sent, by my servant Tobias, the Pope's letter and that of the King to the Judge of Tavira, who is an officer of the King of Portugal. Immediately Tobias returned with two servants from the Judge on a mule, and I left the ship and went on shore.

And when all the people of the city heard that I had reached the shore, notables came to me, Christians and Marranos, with women and children, and I rode to that city on a mule, and all the road was full of men and women, too numerous to count, and we arrived at the city of Tavira at the house of a Marrano, and they prepared the house for us, and beds and tables. The Marrano is an honourable man and his wife very honourable, and the magistrate of the city came to me and rejoiced over us greatly, and said to me, "I am ready and prepared to do anything thou wishest at thy command and for thy service." He came twice to see me and that magistrate wrote to the King to tell him that we had arrived in Tavira and I wrote a letter to the King of Portugal and sent it by the hand of David the Rumanian, and I stayed in the house of the Marrano to wait for the King's answer. The Marrano and his wife showed me much kindness and would not allow us to spend anything from our pocket, for they wished to pay all expenses, and we stayed in their house forty days until the messenger from the King of Portugal reached me in Tavira.

In those days a priest came from Spain, who spoke with Rabbi Solomon Cohen Du Porto, and Rabbi Solomon was angry with him for the priest said that there was no Jewish King and that we had no sons of royal seed. He was standing before a big window, and I was zealous for God's sake and took hold of him and threw him from the window to the ground outside before all the Gentiles, and they laughed at the priest and feared to speak against me, and the great magistrate heard of this and was greatly rejoiced. When the messenger returned to me, he brought two letters from the King and in one he wrote that I should come to him in all honour and that he would do my will, and the second he wrote to all the magistrates in his kingdom that they should honour me and advance me from city to city, that they should prepare for me a bed, a table and a light in every place to which we came. The said messenger said that the King had commanded that I should set out to visit him tomorrow, and he gave me five hundred ducats and a scribe of the King's scribes, who should superintend the expenditure.

In the morning they gave me horses for me and my servants to ride to the King. We journeyed from Tavira, and the magistrate and all the notables of the city went out with me and returned, but I went on with two notables and the King's scribe and a number of men who came with me from Tavira, and at every place the King's Scribe went to the magistrates so that they should prepare for me a house and a table and a chair and candle according to the King's command. We arrived at a city called Beja and came before the magistrates on horseback, and all the notables of that city, Marranos and Christians, came out three parasangs to meet me, and when we approached the city, men, women and children also came. We arrived at the city and entered the house of a Marrano and stayed there that night and, in the morning, we journeyed on and came to a great city, Evora. On Friday, the eve of Sabbath, the magistrates and many men came to meet me two parasangs outside the city; and I entered the city and it is very big, and the King's palace is there and also a community of many honoured Marranos. We stayed at the house of a Marrano on the Sabbath and Sunday. And in every city we entered Marranos came, men and women, great and small, and kissed my hand, and the Christians were jealous of me, and said to them, "Show him great honour, but do not kiss his hand but only the hand of the King of Portugal alone." Some were of stout heart, because they believed in me with a perfect faith, as Israel believed in our Master, Moses, on whom be peace! And I said to them in every place we came to that I am the son of King Solomon, and that I have not come to you with a sign or miracle or mystery, but I am a man of war from my youth till now, and I have come to help your King and to help you and to go in the way he shall lead me to the land of Israel. I journeyed from Evora and the magistrates came to escort me, and with them were many honoured nobles and many men, too numerous to count, and they went with me two parasangs and returned. In every road that I passed, Marranos came to me from every side and every corner to accompany me, and they gave me presents, and some righteous Gentiles also, until I arrived two parasangs distance from the King. Now the King was residing in Almeda, for he had fled because of the plague in Lisbon, and I wrote to the King as follows: "Behold I have arrived at this place, and I will stay until thou dost let me know that I may come before thy honour," and I sent an honourable old Gentile to the King and also the King's scribe who had come with me from Tavira and was appointed over the expenses of the journey. They returned to me and said that the King has called his counsellors before him and are taking counsel over this matter. Some say this and some say that; some of them said, "Show him honour and send all the honoured notables before him to accompany him, for he has come from a distant land to seek thee and serve thee," but Don Miguel, my enemy, because I wished to slay him with a sword in Rome, stood and spoke against me before the King, and the notables and the messengers I had sent to the King. They inquired of the scribe if the Marranos showed me more honour than the Christians, and he replied that they honoured me with great honour and kissed my hand, and all the way honoured me and kissed my hand in all the way that I journeyed. Then said Don Miguel to the King, "Did I not say to thee that he is come to destroy thy kingdom and to restore the Marranos to the faith of the Jews? If thou wilt send before him notables to honour him, all the Marranos in thy country will follow him and will take counsel how the Christians are to be made Jews."

All these things said the wicked Don Miguel to the King and to his counsellors and messengers, and the King asked his counsellors what to reply to the Jewish King, and he said to him, "Reply that thy grandmother is dead and that thou art in mourning and canst not show him honour this year as is our custom, and ask pardon of the Ambassador who wishes to come before you with his servants from Tavira."

And when I heard the word of the King and his counsellors I rode with all my servants and the men who had come with me on horses, and we went before the King. We were about fifty men and fifteen horses besides mules which carried my stuff, and we reached Almeda and came to the palace and court of the King. I had been fasting from Sunday to Wednesday when I came to the King and stood before him with all my servants, each one with his sword upon his thigh, and I said to the King and to his wife, the Queen, "I am weary and fatigued from the journey, and have been fasting four days, and cannot speak to thee today, but if it seems good in thy eyes I will go to my house today and tomorrow we shall speak, I and thou," and I was not willing to kiss his hand either when I came or when I left, because of the anger in my heart which the wicked Don Miguel had caused me. Afterwards I took leave of the King and went to Santarem to the house of a Marrano, which they had prepared for me. It was a big house and the master of the house was quite wicked, but his wife was much honoured. A Marrano came to me who speaks Arabic and had come in the ships of the King, who had sent him once for two years to the land of the blacks [Abyssinia]. He told me that he went to an island in the sea a half-day's journey and stayed an hour in that place, and stood near a big mountain from which fire burnt day and night and from which fire and smoke went up to heaven. Near to that mountain the old King of Portugal sent the young children of the Marranos and left them there until this very day. They are near to a tribe in the island who eat men's flesh. That Marrano was learned in astrology. There also came to me one of the captains of the King's ships. He told me that he had journeyed to the capital of our kingdom from Formosa and stayed there one year, in the days of my lord, my father (On whom be peace!), twenty years ago. He had heard that there was a king over the Jews whose name was King Solomon and this ship captain told all this before the King of Portugal. He is an honoured man and the King loves him, and he became my friend in Portugal and I also loved him. He asked me to write my name down as a sign that it should be a memorial between me and him until the hour arrived, and so I did, and it was a secret between me and him. He was a real Christian and loved all the Jews. I fasted continuously six days and nights, and all the Christians and Marranos came to see me by day and by night. The King sent to summon me on Wednesday eight days after I had arrived here, and I went before him, I am old Solomon Cohen and Benzion, my servants, and we came before the King, and the King called a Marrano, an old physician, who was interpreter between me and the King in Hebrew. That old man was somewhat deaf and, when he spoke to the King he was in fear and terrified, and the King said, "I have heard of thee that thou speakest Arabic well, and I have an old servant who can speak Arabic well, and he will hear your words from beginning to end and tell them to me." The King called that lord and said, "Speak with that Ambassador in Arabic," and I spoke in Arabic to that lord, and he interpreted my words to the King, and I placed in the King's hand all the letters, and I spoke with him on the matter of my mission, and I told him all my journey, which I had travelled from the wilderness, until I came before him, and I also said to the King, "King Joseph, my brother, asks me with reference to the artificers of weapons for his kingdom." The King was greatly pleased with my words and his heart rejoiced within him, and he said, "The matter is of the Lord. I am willing to do so and it shall be my desire." The matter was good in his eyes, and in the eyes of all his lords. Then said the King to me, "Return from Santarem to Almeda, which is near me." The King ordered the old lord to prepare for me a house near to the Palace, and so the old man did, and I sent all that I had in my house, beds and linen and all household furniture, from Santarem to the house which they prepared for me in Almeda, near to the Palace.

Afterwards a great Moslem lord, a Judge of the King of Fez, came to me. He had been sent by this King to the King of Portugal, and is an honourable man, a friend of the Jews. He has ten servants. This Judge came to my house because the King of Fez had heard about me and ordered him to go first to the King of Portugal, and then to come and see me, and he gave me letters from the Jews of Fez and from Rabbi Abraham ben Zimori of Asfi-Safi and a third letter from the Captain of Tangier. Then the Judge asked me about my country, whether many Jews were there. And I answered that it is the wilderness of Habor, and that there are thirty myriad Jews in my country, and King Joseph, my brother, rules over them and has seventy counsellors and many lords, and I am a military lord over ways and war. And the Judge said to me, "What seekest thou from this kingdom that thou hast come from the east to the west?" I answered that from our youth we are trained in war, and our war is with the sword and lance and bow, and we wished to go, with God's help, to Jerusalem to capture the land of Israel from the Moslems, for the end and salvation has arrived, and I have come to seek wise handicraftsmen who know how to make weapons and firearms that they should come to my land and make them and teach our soldiers. The Judge was much amazed at this, and said to me, "We believe that the kingdom will return to you this time, and if you return will you do kindness to us?" I said to him, "Yes, we will do kindness to you and to all who do kindness to Israel, which is in captivity under Ishmael and Edom," and I said to the Judge, "Do you also believe that the kingdom of the land of Ishmael will return to us?" And he replied to me, "In all the world they believe this." I said to him, "We are kings, and our fathers were kings from the time of the destruction of the temple till this day, in the wilderness of Habor. We rule over the tribes of Reuben and Gad, and half tribe of Manasseh in the wilderness of Habor, and there are nine and a half tribes in the land of Ethiopia and other kings. The nearest to us are the tribe of Simeon and the tribe of Benjamin, and they are on the River Nile, above the Kingdom of Sheba, and they reside between the two rivers, the blue river and the black river, which is the Nile. Their country is good and extensive, and they have a king and his name is Baruch, the son of King Japhet, and he has four sons, the eldest Saadiah, and the second Abraham, the third Hoter, and the fourth Moses, and their numbers are as ours in the wilderness of Habor, thirty myriads, and we and they take counsel together." The Judge said to me, "Dost thou wish to write for me a letter to the King of Fez?" I answered, "I need not write, but you can say all this to him by the word of mouth and give him from me a thousand greetings and say to him that the Jews under his rule should be protected by him, and that he should honour them and this will be the beginning of peace between us and him, between our seed and his seed." The Judge also asked me, "What will you do with the Jews in all the lands of the west, will you come to the west for them and how will you deal with them?" I replied that we shall first take the Holy Land and its surroundings and that then our captains of the host will go forth to the west and east to gather the dispersed of Israel, and whoever is wise among the Moslem Kings will take the Jews under his rule and bring them to Jerusalem, and he will have much honour, greater than that of all the Moslem Kings, and God will deliver up all the kingdoms to the King of Jerusalem. Further, the Judge asked me, "Is it true that the Jews in Fez and its neighbourhood say, and the Moslems also, that you are a prophet and the Messiah?" and I answered, "God forbid, I am a sinner before the Lord, greater than any one of you, and I have slain many men, and on one day I killed forty enemies. I am neither a prophet nor the son of a prophet, neither a wise man nor a Kabbalist, but I am a captain of the host, the son of Solomon the King, the son of David, the son of Jesse, and my brother, the King, rules over thirty myriads in the wilderness of Habor. Moreover, the Marranos in the Kingdom of Portugal, and all the Jews in Italy and all the places that I passed also thought me to be a prophet, wise man, or Kabbalist, and I said to them, "God forbid, I am a sinner and a man of war from my youth till now." Afterwards the Judge began to write to the Jews of Fez, and to Rabbi Abraham ben Zimori of Asfi-Safi, and I wrote to them and handed the letters to him and he went on his way in peace.

Moreover, Marranos came to me of great importance and said to me that they saw four standards in the heavens, and many men, Christians and priests and Marranos stood by and told this matter to me and to Solomon Cohen, and I found two small boys of the Marranos, who fasted on Mondays and Thursdays with piety and believed in the salvation of the Lord, and I said to them, "Trust in the Lord and do good, for the great and fearful day of the Lord is approaching," and I made peace between the Marranos in all places where I went, and they listened to my voice, and among the Marranos are strong and warlike and wise men and artificers in firearms, and I saw that they were stronger and better than all the Jews that I had seen before. And the Signora in Naples had a daughter in Lisbon who fasts every day, and this daughter has a son and daughter who fast on Mondays and Thursdays and she is much esteemed and very charitable and does good deeds like her mother. (May she be blessed of the Lord!) All the Marranos believe in God, except one physician, who was Lazoa, who came to me and spoke against our religion, and I stood up to smite him but Carbalia the Marrano from Tavira, held my hand and then he repented.

After all these things, four Marranos were taken in custody from my house and placed in prison. The King's lords did this without his knowledge. I wrote to the King that they were taken, and when the King heard of it he ordered them to be let out, and those Marranos came to me. After that the King called us before him in the Queen's room and said, "I am glad that thou hast come to help me, but I hear that thou hast also come to restore the Marranos to the Jewish religion, and the Marranos pray with thee and read in thy books day and night, and thou hast made for them a Synagogue. I was angry with him and said to him, "I am come from the east to the west only to exalt thy kingdom and to help thee. I have not come for the sake of the Marranos, and all that the slanderers have told thee about me is falsehood and not at all true," and the King said to me, "If their words are true, do not so from henceforward if thou wishest to do me kindness."

After that the King pacified me with good words, because he saw that I was angry and he spoke with me as to my journey and as to large and small firearms, and promised to give me four mills in ships to take to our country, and I left the King and went home. After this the Emperor sent for his wife, the sister of the King of Portugal, men and horses at their head. The Emperor's ambassador came to my house and spoke with me and said that the Emperor had heard about me and was pleased with the matter and wished to see me. I stood before the Ambassador for two hours, and Judah, above-mentioned, was interpreter between him and me. The Duke also came from his country to Almeda to the King, his kinsman, and the King spoke to him about me and on the second night the Duke came to me in disguise with four servants, and I was sitting at table and eating. He took leave of me and they went away and, after I had retired, Marranos came to me and said he was the Duke and had come to see me in disguise. Next day the Queen departed to go to her espousals with the Emperor, and her brother, the King, accompanied her and the Duke with him, and I also went on horseback to accompany the Queen, and a renegade who had become a Moslem and afterwards a Christian, named Aldeka, from Asfi-Safi, came to see me. After I had accompanied the Queen three parasangs, I took leave of the King and his sister, the Queen, and returned home and arrived at night. The King returned the day after and the Jews told me that Aldeka was a renegade and a wicked man, but, as I saw that he was a strong man and that his face seemed that of a man of dignity, I called him before me that evening and said to him, "I have heard that thou hast become a Moslem and then a Christian, but I believe thee and in thy words that thou desirest to serve me, but it is better that thou shouldest go and leave my house." Aldeka replied, "Be kind to me for the sake of Israel, but not for my sake, for I have sinned and transgressed, and done more evil than the men have told you about me, but I wish to return with thy help and repent, and I swear by the Law of Moses that I wish to repent if thou wilt receive me. God accepts the repentant and I will stand before thee until I die and serve thee, with all thy horses, with all my heart, and will do all that thou biddest me." He placed the Pentateuch on his neck and took oath upon it and stayed in my house. I have a nice horse, better than any of the King's horses, the horse on which I rode. Aldeka was a strong man and every day attended to the horse, fed him and washed him and removed its excrement, and did everything in my house and was efficient. If the Jews went to buy anything in the market, Aldeka went with them and, with the same money bought twice as much. But the Jews quarrelled with him and gave me an ill report of him, and I said, "I cannot turn him out of my house because he is efficient and attends to the horse and to the needs of the house, and you cannot do what he does or the work he does for me." Those Jews were weak and did not do work for me. Their only strength was in their tongue. They were asking of me every day requests and petitions, and if they came with me before the King they were timid and weak-hearted and had no manners. The man that spoke Arabic told me these Jews who came behind have no manners and are not fit for thy honour, they are proud and do not remove their hat from their head, either in my house or in the Palace, and the Gentiles speak against them and despise them, for no one of them can wear a sword on his shoulder; they are a disgrace to us. Those Jews, who came from Asemur and Asfi-Safi without safe conduct, were taken into custody on their arrival at Tavira, and had to give surety in four hundred ducats in case they did not send their safe conduct to the King, and the magistrate of Tavira wrote about them to the King that they had come without a safe conduct. The King summoned me and I went to him with Judah and the man who speaks Arabic, and the King asked me how came the Jews to the country without safe conduct, and I replied to the King, "I wrote that they should come to me and they have come to be my servants. I pray thy Majesty to write to the magistrate in Tavira to cancel the sureties he had received from them and for my sake give them a safe conduct and let no harm come to them in Tavira." The King ordered his scribe to write thus to the magistrate. The King summoned me four times in two days about the Marranos, and wished to know what I was doing with them and said to me, "I have heard that thou hast circumcised my Secretary," and I replied, "God forbid, it is not true, I have not come to do these things; do not open thy ears to slanderers for I have only come for my business and thy service." The King dropped this subject and spoke with me with regard to the journey and the ships, and I left the King and stayed four days at home. Then the King summoned me and told me in the presence of Judah, and the man who spoke Arabic, "I am pleased with thee that thou hast come to help me, but thou art ruining my kingdom, for all the Christians say that thou hast restored the Marranos to Judaism, and they all kiss thy hand and that when thou sittest at table all the sons of the Marranos bow to thee." I replied to the King in anger and said to him, "I am come from the east to the west to serve thee until thou lettest me go in peace; the door of my house is open to every man, Christian or Marrano, and I do not know whether they are Christians or Marranos; do not listen to the voice of the slanderers, whose every word is falsehood and lies." Then the King gave me his hand and said to me, "Do me the favour not to allow any man to kiss thy hand." And the King promised to give me in the month of Nisan eight ships with four thousand large and small firearms, and I believed him and left and came home and stayed until night. The scribe, who had been secretly circumcised, came and spoke to me that night, and I was angry with him and said, "See what thou hast caused us; go thou to Jerusalem and be not seen here or they will burn or slay thee," and he left me. This secretary had come to me before he was circumcised and told me a dream that he had been circumcised and asked me to circumcise him or to order my servant Solomon to circumcise him, and I was angry with him and said, "Stay in thy duties before the King until the Almighty opens the door. He knows the thoughts of man and that thou hast good intentions, but beware of doing this thing at this time, for thou and I and all the Marranos will be in great danger." He left me after this talk between us about circumcision. He was secretary and honoured by the King, and the matter was known to the King of Portugal and all his lords, and all the Christians and Marranos knew that he had circumcised himself and fled and gone away, and the King and his lords said that I had caused the secretary to circumcise himself, although they knew that I had not done it myself. Afterwards the King sent for me, when I was at home, and next day he sent again his servants to accompany and guard me, and he also

sent his officer on horseback to accompany me, and that day I went to
the King and he spoke to me, saying, "I have many matters to attend to
and shall be unable to send the ships with thee to the east either this year
or next year; if thou wilt go to thy country go in peace, for I give thee
leave and bless thee for all the days that thou hast come from thy country to serve me and help me. Go to the Emperor, if thou wilt, and tell him
all. Or if thou wilt, return to Rome or go to Fez, choose that which thou
desirest." I was wrath now unto death about this matter, and replied to
the King of Portugal in great anger, and said to him, "Thou didst promise me the ships and to let me go in the month of Nisan, why hast thou
changed thy heart? It is not now my desire to go to the Emperor or to
Fez, but to Rome, to the Pope." And the King said to me, "Think the
matter over for eight days." I left the King and returned home, and the
King afterwards sent for me and said, "What dost thou intend to do, and
what way wilt thou go?" And I replied, "I wish to return to Rome to the
Pope. Pray write him letters and let them be a testimony between me and
thee, for King Joseph, my brother, that I had reached thy kingdom, and
write me a letter of safe conduct for all Christians." The King replied, "I
will do what thou wishest," and he called Antonio Carnieri, his secretary,
and, in my presence, ordered him to write the two letters, and a third
letter he wrote for me to Tavira that they should give me three hundred
ducats, and said to me, "Follow me to Santarem and receive the letters
and I will send men with thee to escort thee to Tavira." I left the King
and returned home. That day the King went to Santarem with the
Queen, for they sought there remedy for their son who was sick. And I
stayed three days longer in Almeda and then journeyed with all my stuff
to Santarem to a fine house near the river, and Aldeka attended to all my
work in the house and outside; and a report reached me that the Christians had made an effigy like me and mocked the effigy, and when the
Marranos heard this they rose up against the Christians and smote them
and took the effigy from them against their will, and the magistrates arrested two of the Marranos and put them in prison. And they sent to me
to help them, and I at once went to the King and said to him, "Is it right
in thy eyes that the Christians should make an effigy of me and mock me,
and that, when the Marranos rose up against them and took the effigy
from them, the magistrates arrested two of the Marranos and put them
in prison? Now, if I find favour and kindness before thee, write to the
magistrates that they should let the prisoners go." The same hour the
King ordered that they should write this letter, and he signed the letter
in my presence, and the King laughed and I said to him, "I beg thy

Majesty to give me this letter and to send one of thy servants to go with me to let the prisoners free," and it was done accordingly. And the King asked me about my banners and said, "I have heard that thou hast beautiful banners, what dost thou wish to do with them?" I replied that they are our sign between me and the tribes, and I unfurl them when I go with the army. The King said, "Good," and I left the King and stayed two days in my house. And the Cardinal, the King's brother, sent for me, and I went to him with the man who spoke Arabic, and the Cardinal showed me great honour and asked me about the banners and the journey. I replied that the banners were my sign and I was going to Rome, and the Cardinal said, "Wilt thou join my faith and I will make thee a lord?" I replied, "Wouldst thou make me like the raven that Noah sent from the Ark which never returned? This matter would not be good in the eyes of the kings, my forefathers, for I am the son of a King of the seed of David, the son of Jesse; they would thrust me from my inheritance. I have not come from the east to the west to do this thing, but I am come in God's service and to make me a name everlasting for doing the meritorious act I have come to do. How can thy heart compel thee to ask this matter of me?" And I further said, "If I were to tell thee to join my faith wouldst thou be willing?" And the Cardinal answered, "No." And I said to him, "It is better that thou remainest in thy faith and I in my faith: thou sayest that thy faith is true and I that my faith is true, it is the faith of Moses and Israel." And I was angry with him. After this he spoke kind words to me and I left him and returned home. Next day the Queen sent to me and asked me about the banners and how I intended to journey, and I replied that the banners are my sign and that I am going to Rome, with God's help. And the Queen rejoined, "Go in peace and return to thy country in peace. The King has said to me that his heart is well inclined to thee and I have heard that he has written letters for thee to the Pope, God bless him!" I took leave of her and left her, and all the Marranos came to my house by day and night, and they were grieved that I was leaving and their children came to kiss my hand in the presence of the Christians, until I left Santarem; but the Almighty saw to it that I did no harm to the Marranos in all the kingdom of Portugal. Thank God! The King was very good and was wrath with the slanderers and said to them that they should say no more about the Ambassador who should do what he wished. After that the man that spoke Arabic came to me with the letters written in beautiful writing on paper by Antonio Carnieri, and he, in the innocence of his heart, had written good things with much honour in those letters. And the man who spoke Arabic said,

"Let us go and give thanks to the King and take leave of him and then I will hand the letters to thee in his presence." And when I came before him I was angry and said that the Pope had written letters for me on parchment and these letters were on paper, and I have come from east to west for the service of the King, but if these letters were on parchment they would remain as a testimony between us and our children's children after us, and they would know that I had been to his kingdom. The King replied, "It is not our custom, like the Pope's, to write on parchment," and I said to the King, "I ask thee as a favour to write them this time on parchment, for I wish the letters to be a memorial," and he replied that he would do so for love of me. Then the King told Don Miguel to write them on parchment and he did so, but they were without the expressions of honour which Antonio Corenzi had written. Nevertheless my wrath was diminished, for the Elders and King Joseph, my brother, had charged me not to be angry; and when I was in Pisa in the house of Rabbi Jechiel, his old grandmother Sarah, who was a wealthy and wise woman, had told me, "I see that thou art angry all thy days; if thou wilt avoid this anger thou wilt prosper in all thy days," and she gave me a great Bible as a gift, and wrote at the beginning of the book "Anger not and thou shalt prosper." But I have not been able to conquer my spirit from this anger and it had caused my quarrel with Don Miguel and brought me to this point, and the man that spoke Arabic always went as a spy before Don Miguel and told him everything that I spoke to the King and all that I spoke with him in my house. After that the man who spoke Arabic gave me the letters in parchment but did not tell me Don Miguel had written them. And I sought for the letter that I have to receive the money in Tavira, for he gave me two sealed letters, one for the Judge in Tavira and one which the man who spoke Arabic said was the writing in which the King had ordered me three hundred ducats; but this was falsehood and lies, for the true letter Don Miguel had taken and the letter he had sent to me was false and I could not examine the letter because it was sealed, but I took his letters and believed his word. Afterwards I went with the man who spoke Arabic to take leave of the King, and the King said, I send with thee the man who speaks Arabic to accompany thee on the journey to Tavira, and I have written that they should give thee three hundred ducats, and if thou needest anything write to me."

LAUGHTER
THROUGH TEARS

To the Jew have been ascribed various talents, but not the gift of humor. Religion and tragedy have been his métier, and they are not congenial to the funny bone. This was the opinion of Ernest Renan and so many of his successors who lacked his erudition and insight. He admitted that the Jews had enjoyed seasons of joy and gladness, but these were "periods of forgetfulness when the people of God allowed their infinite hopes to slumber . . ." and when they "forgot the religious mission they had been called upon to fulfill." This estimate is borne out by the portrait of the Jew in general literature until recent years.

Yet, among Jews, the enjoyment of humor is unquestionable. A few researchers—Adler, Kohut and Chotzner—have traced it back to Biblical times. The Hebrew volumes of Durianov exhibit ample evidence of it. Historians of literature call our attention to the trenchant satire of the medieval poets Alharisi and Ibn Zabara and the incisive parodies of Perl and Erter.[1] Within the last century it has found brilliant expression in the writings of Sholem Aleichem, Heine, Zangwill and Asch, and in the pungent, self-critical folktales about Joseph Loktsch, Mottke Habad, Hershele Ostropoler and the Wise Men of Helm. To these we may add the skillful stories in Anglo-Yiddish dialect, from Montague Glass and Milt Gross to Arthur Kober and Leonard Q. Ross.

Has Jewish humor a distinctive quality? One cannot fail to feel an extravagant emotionalism underneath the obvious differences of nuance and climate. One of Sholem Aleichem's characters pointedly remarks: "Our feasting and our rejoicing have always found their most adequate expression in tears and weeping. Through an excess of joy, our hearts melt. . . ." It is laughter mingled with tears. Another peculiar quality has stemmed from the Jews' long experience in argument. Yiddish has a word for it—*hutzpah*. The best translation for it is Joseph Jacobs' "iridescent insolence," and good examples of it are Zangwill's Grobstock (in *The King of Schnorrers*) and Heine's matchless salvos. *"Shalet,"* wrote Heine, "is a delicious dish. I deeply regret that the Church, indebted to the Synagogue for so much that is good, has failed to take over *shalet*. This should be her concern in the future. If ever she falls on evil times, if ever her most sacred symbols lose their appeal, then the Church may resort to *shalet,* and the faithless people will crowd into her arms with renewed appetite. The Jews will then join the Church from conviction, for it is clear that it is only *shalet* which keeps them in the old covenant. Börne assures me that renegades who have accepted the new dispensation feel a homesickness for the Synagogue when they but smell *shalet* so that it may be called the Jewish *ranz-des-vaches."*

The warm humanity and the enormous vitality of the Jew are fully revealed in his humor. Here is an avenue to the psychology of the Jewish people, that deserves the attention of the genius of a Freud.[2]

[1] See *Parody in Jewish Literature* by Israel Davidson (1907).
[2] Freud has touched upon this subject in his *Wit and Its Relation to the Unconscious.*

THE KING OF SCHNORRERS

by ISRAEL ZANGWILL

SHOWING HOW THE WICKED PHILANTHROPIST WAS TURNED
INTO A FISH-PORTER

IN the days when Lord George Gordon became a Jew, and was suspected of insanity; when, out of respect for the prophecies, England denied her Jews every civic right except that of paying taxes; when the *Gentleman's Magazine* had ill words for the infidel alien; when Jewish marriages were invalid and bequests for Hebrew colleges void; when a prophet prophesying Primrose Day would have been set in the stocks, though Pitt inclined his private ear to Benjamin Goldsmid's views on the foreign loans—in those days, when Tevele Schiff was Rabbi in Israel, and Dr. de Falk, the Master of the Tetragrammaton, saint and Cabbalistic conjuror, flourished in Wellclose Square, and the composer of "The Death of Nelson" was a choir-boy in the Great Synagogue; Joseph Grobstock, pillar of the same, emerged one afternoon into the spring sunshine at the fag-end of the departing stream of worshippers. In his hand was a large canvas bag, and in his eye a twinkle.

There had been a special service of prayer and thanksgiving for the happy restoration of his Majesty's health, and the cantor had interceded tunefully with Providence on behalf of Royal George and "our most amiable Queen, Charlotte." The congregation was large and fashionable —far more so than when only a heavenly sovereign was concerned—and so the courtyard was thronged with a string of *schnorrers* (beggars), awaiting the exit of the audience much as the vestibule of the opera-house is lined by footmen.

They were a motley crew, with tangled beards and long hair that fell in curls, if not the curls of the period; but the gaberdines of the German Ghettoes had been in most cases exchanged for the knee-breeches and many-buttoned jacket of the Londoner. When the clothes one has brought from the Continent wear out, one must needs adopt the attire of one's superiors, or be reduced to buying. Many bore staves, and had their loins girded up with coloured handkerchiefs, as though ready at any moment to return from the Captivity. Their woebegone air was achieved almost entirely by not washing—it owed little to nature, to adventitious aids in the shape of deformities. The merest sprinkling boasted of physical afflictions, and none exposed sores like the lazars of Italy or contortions like the cripples of Constantinople. Such crude methods are eschewed in the fine art of *schnorring*. A green shade might denote weakness of sight, but the stone-blind man bore no braggart placard—his infirmity was an old established concern well known to the public, and conferring upon the proprietor a definite status in the community. He was no anonymous atom, such as drifts blindly through Christendom, vagrant and apologetic. Rarest of all sights in this pageantry of Jewish pauperdom was the hollow trouser-leg or the empty sleeve, or the wooden limb fulfilling either and pushing out a proclamatory peg.

When the pack of *schnorrers* caught sight of Joseph Grobstock, they fell upon him full-cry, blessing him. He, nothing surprised, brushed pompously through the benedictions, though the twinkle in his eye became a roguish gleam. Outside the iron gates, where the throng was thickest, and where some elegant chariots that had brought worshippers from distant Hackney were preparing to start, he came to a standstill, surrounded by clamouring *schnorrers,* and dipped his hand slowly and ceremoniously into the bag. There was a moment of breathless expectation among the beggars, and Joseph Grobstock had a moment of exquisite consciousness of importance, as he stood there swelling in the sunshine. There was no middle class to speak of in the eighteenth-century Jewry; the world was divided into rich and poor, and the rich were very, very rich, and the poor very, very poor, so that everyone knew his station. Joseph Grobstock was satisfied with that in which it had pleased God to place him. He was a jovial, heavy-jowled creature, whose clean-shaven chin was doubling, and he was habited like a person of the first respectability in a beautiful blue body-coat with a row of big yellow buttons. The frilled shirt front, high collar of the very newest fashion, and copious white neckerchief showed off the massive fleshiness of the red throat. His hat was of the Quaker pattern, and his head did not fail of the periwig and the pigtail, the latter being heretical in name only.

What Joseph Grobstock drew from the bag was a small white-paper packet, and his sense of humour led him to place it in the hand furthest from his nose; for it was a broad humour, not a subtle. It enabled him to extract pleasure from seeing a fellow-mortal's hat rollick in the wind, but did little to alleviate the chase for his own. His jokes clapped you on the back, they did not tickle delicately.

Such was the man who now became the complacent cynosure of all eyes, even of those that had no appeal in them, as soon as the principle of his eleemosynary operations had broken on the crowd. The first *schnorrer,* feverishly tearing open his package, had found a florin, and, as by electricity, all except the blind beggar were aware that Joseph Grobstock was distributing florins. The distributor partook of the general consciousness, and his lips twitched. Silently he dipped again into the bag, and selecting the hand nearest, put a second white package into it. A wave of joy brightened the grimy face, to change instantly to one of horror.

"You have made a mistake—you have given me a penny!" cried the beggar.

"Keep it for your honesty," replied Joseph Grobstock imperturbably, and affected not to enjoy the laughter of the rest. The third mendicant ceased laughing when he discovered that fold on fold of paper sheltered a tiny sixpence. It was now obvious that the great man was distributing prize-packets, and the excitement of the piebald crowd grew momently. Grobstock went on dipping, lynx-eyed against second applications. One of the few pieces of gold in the lucky-bag fell to the solitary lame man, who danced in his joy on his sound leg, while the poor blind man pocketed his half-penny, unconscious of ill-fortune, and merely wondering why the coin came swathed in paper.

By this time Grobstock could control his face no longer, and the last episodes of the lottery were played to the accompaniment of a broad grin. Keen and complex was his enjoyment. There was not only the general surprise at this novel feat of alms; there were the special surprises of detail written on face after face, as it flashed or fell or frowned in congruity with the contents of the envelope, and for undercurrent a delicious hubbub of interjections and benedictions, a stretching and withdrawing of palms, and a swift shifting of figures, that made the scene a farrago of excitements. So that the broad grin was one of gratification as well as of amusement, and part of the gratification sprang from a real kindliness of heart—for Grobstock was an easy-going man with whom the world had gone easy. The *schnorrers* were exhausted before the packets, but the philanthropist was in no anxiety to be rid of the remnant. Closing the mouth of the considerably lightened bag and clutching it tightly by the throat, and recomposing his face to gravity, he moved slowly down the street like a stately treasure-ship flecked by the sunlight. His way led towards Goodman's Fields, where his mansion was situate, and he knew that the fine weather would bring out *schnorrers* enough. And, indeed, he had not gone many paces before he met a figure he did not remember having seen before.

Leaning against a post at the head of the narrow passage which led to Bevis Marks was a tall, black-bearded, turbaned personage, a first glance at whom showed him of the true tribe. Mechanically Joseph Grobstock's hand went to the lucky-bag, and he drew out a neatly-folded packet and tendered it to the stranger.

The stranger received the gift graciously, and opened it gravely, the philanthropist loitering awkwardly to mark the issue. Suddenly the dark face became a thunder-cloud, the eyes flashed lightning.

"An evil spirit in your ancestors' bones!" hissed the stranger, from between his flashing teeth. "Did you come here to insult me?"

"Pardon, a thousand pardons!" stammered the magnate, wholly taken aback. "I fancied you were a—a—a—poor man."

"And, therefore, you came to insult me!"

"No, no, I thought to help you," murmured Grobstock, turning from red to scarlet. Was it possible he had foisted his charity upon an undeserving millionaire? No! Through all the clouds of his own confusion and the recipient's anger, the figure of a *schnorrer* loomed too plain for mistake. None but a *schnorrer* would wear a home-made turban, issue of a black cap crossed with a white kerchief; none but a *schnorrer* would unbutton the first nine buttons of his waistcoat, or, if this relaxation were due to the warmth of the weather, counteract it by wearing an over-garment, especially one as heavy as a blanket, with buttons the size of compasses and flaps reaching nearly to his shoe-buckles, even though its length were only congruous with that of his undercoat, which already reached the bottoms of his knee-breeches. Finally, who but a *schnorrer* would wear this overcoat cloakwise, with dangling sleeves, full of armless suggestion from a side view? Quite apart from the shabbiness of the snuff-coloured fabric, it was amply evident that the wearer did not dress by rule or measure. Yet the disproportions of his attire did but enhance the picturesqueness of a personality that would be striking even in a bath, though it was not likely to be seen there. The beard was jet black, sweeping and unkempt, and run up his cheeks to meet the raven hair, so that the vivid face was framed in black; it was a long tapering face with sanguine lips gleaming at the heart of a black bush; the eyes were large and lambent, set in deep sockets under black arching eyebrows; the nose was long and Coptic; the brow low but broad, with straggling wisps of hair protruding from beneath the turban. His right hand grasped a plain ashen staff.

Worthy Joseph Grobstock found the figure of the mendicant only too impressive; he shrank uneasily before the indignant eyes.

"I meant to help you," he repeated.

"And this is how one helps a brother in Israel?" said the *schnorrer,* throwing the paper contemptuously into the philanthropist's face. It struck him on the bridge of the nose, but impinged so mildly that he felt at once what was the matter. The packet was empty—the *schnorrer* had drawn a blank; the only one the good-natured man had put into the bag.

The *schnorrer's* audacity sobered Joseph Grobstock completely; it might have angered him to chastise the fellow but it did not. His better nature prevailed; he began to feel shamefaced, fumbled sheepishly in his pocket for a crown; then hesitated, as fearing this peace-offering would not altogether suffice with so rare a spirit, and that he owed the stranger more than silver—an apology to wit. He proceeded honestly to pay it, but with a maladroit manner, as one unaccustomed to the currency.

"You are an impertinent rascal," he said, "but I daresay you feel hurt. Let me assure you I did not know there was nothing in the packet. I did not, indeed."

"Then your steward has robbed me!" exclaimed the *schnorrer* excitedly. "You let him make up the packets, and he has stolen my money— the thief, the transgressor, thrice-cursed who robs the poor."

"You don't understand," interrupted the magnate meekly. "I made up the packets myself."

"Then, why do you say you did not know what was in them? Go, you mock my misery!"

"Nay, hear me out!" urged Grobstock desperately. "In some I placed gold, in the greater number silver, in a few copper, in one alone—nothing. That is the one you have drawn. It is your misfortune."

"*My* misfortune!" echoed the *schnorrer* scornfully. "It is *your* misfortune—I did not even draw it. The Holy One, blessed be He, has punished you for your heartless jesting with the poor—making a sport for yourself of their misfortunes, even as the Philistines sported with Samson. The good deed you might have put to your account by a gratuity to me, God has taken from you. He has declared you unworthy of achieving righteousness through me. Go your way, murderer!"

"Murderer!" repeated the philanthropist, bewildered by this harsh view of his action.

"Yes, murderer! Stands it not in the Talmud that he who shames another is as one who spills his blood? And have you not put me to shame —if anyone had witnessed your almsgiving, would he not have laughed in my beard?"

The pillar of the Synagogue felt as if his paunch were shrinking.

"But the others—" he murmured deprecatingly. "I have not shed their blood—have I not given freely of my hard-earned gold?"

"For your own diversion," retorted the *schnorrer* implacably. "But what says the Midrash? There is a wheel rolling in the world—not he who is rich today is rich tomorrow, but this one He brings up, and this one He brings down, as is said in the seventy-fifth Psalm. Therefore, lift not up your horn on high, nor speak with a stiff neck."

He towered above the unhappy capitalist, like an ancient prophet denouncing a swollen monarch. The poor man put his hand involuntarily to his high collar as if to explain away his apparent arrogance, but in reality because he was not breathing easily under the *schnorrer's* attack.

"You are an uncharitable man," he panted hotly, driven to a line of defense he had not anticipated. "I did it not from wantonness, but from faith in Heaven. I know well that God sits turning a wheel—therefore I did not presume to turn it myself. Did I not let Providence select who should have the silver and who the gold, who the copper and who the emptiness? Besides, God alone knows who really needs my assistance—I have made Him my almoner; I have cast my burden on the Lord."

"Epicurean!" shrieked the *schnorrer*. "Blasphemer! Is it thus you would palter with the sacred texts? Do you forget what the next verse says: 'Bloodthirsty and deceitful men shall not live out half their days'? Shame on you—you a *gabbai* (treasurer) of the Great Synagogue. You see I know you, Joseph Grobstock. Has not the beadle of your Synagogue boasted to me that you have given him a guinea for brushing your spatterdashes? Would you think of offering *him* a packet? Nay, it is the poor that are trodden on—they whose merits are in excess of those of beadles. But the Lord will find others to take up his loans—for he who hath pity on the poor leadeth to the Lord. You are no true son of Israel."

The *schnorrer's* tirade was long enough to allow Grobstock to recover his dignity and his breath.

"If you really knew me, you would know that the Lord is considerably in my debt," he rejoined quietly. "When next you would discuss me, speak with the Psalms-men, not the beadle. Never have I neglected the needy. Even now, though you have been insolent and uncharitable, I am ready to befriend you if you are in want."

"If I am in want!" repeated the *schnorrer* scornfully. "Is there anything I do not want?"

"You are married?"

"You correct me—wife and children are the only things I do *not* lack."

"No pauper does," quoth Grobstock, with a twinkle of restored humour.

"No," assented the *schnorrer* sternly. "The poor man has the fear of Heaven. He obeys the Law and the Commandments. He marries while he is young—and his spouse is not cursed with barrenness. It is the rich man who transgresses the Judgment, who delays to come under the Canopy."

"Ah! well, here is a guinea—in the name of my wife," broke in Grobstock laughingly. "Or stay—since you do not brush spatterdashes—here is another."

"In the name of my wife," rejoined the *schnorrer* with dignity, "I thank you."

"Thank me in your own name," said Grobstock. "I mean tell it me."

"I am Manasseh Bueno Barzillai Azevedo da Costa," he answered simply.

"A Sephardi!" exclaimed the philanthropist.

"Is it not written on my face, even as it is written on yours that you are a Tedesco? It is the first time that I have taken gold from one of your lineage."

"Oh, indeed!" murmured Grobstock, beginning to feel small again.

"Yes—are we not far richer than your community? What need have I to take the good deeds away from my own people—they have too few opportunities for beneficence as it is, being so many of them wealthy; brokers and West India merchants, and—"

"But I, too, am a financier, and an East India Director," Grobstock reminded him.

"Maybe; but your community is yet young and struggling—your rich men are as the good men in Sodom for multitude. You are the immigrants of yesterday—refugees from the ghettoes of Russia and Poland and Germany. But we, as you are aware, have been established here for generations; in the Peninsula our ancestors graced the courts of kings, and controlled the purse-strings of princes; in Holland we held the empery of trade. Ours have been the poets and scholars in Israel. You cannot expect that we should recognise your rabble, which prejudices us in the eyes of England. We made the name of Jew honourable; you degrade it. You are as the mixed multitude which came up with our forefathers out of Egypt."

"Nonsense!" said Grobstock sharply. "All Israel are brethren."

"Esau was the brother of Israel," answered Manasseh sententiously. "But you will excuse me if I go a-marketing, it is such a pleasure to handle gold." There was a note of wistful pathos in the latter remark which took off the edge of the former, and touched Joseph with compunction for bandying words with a hungry man whose loved ones were probably starving patiently at home.

"Certainly, haste away," he said kindly.

"I shall see you again," said Manasseh, with a valedictory wave of his hand, and digging his staff into the cobblestones he journeyed forwards without bestowing a single backward glance upon his benefactor.

Grobstock's road took him to Petticoat Lane in the wake of Manasseh. He had no intention of following him, but did not see why he should change his route for fear of the *schnorrer,* more especially as Manasseh did not look back. By this time he had become conscious again of the bag he carried, but he had no heart to proceed with the fun. He felt conscience stricken, and had recourse to his pockets instead in his progress through the narrow jostling market-street, where he scarcely ever bought anything personally save fish and good deeds. He was a connoisseur in both. Today he picked up many a good deed cheap, paying pennies for articles he did not take away—shoe-latchets and cane-strings, barley-sugar and butter-cakes. Suddenly through a chink in an opaque mass of human beings, he caught sight of a small attractive salmon on a fishmonger's slab. His eye glittered, his chops watered. He elbowed his way to the vendor, whose eye caught a corresponding gleam, and whose finger went to his hat in respectful greeting.

"Good afternoon, Jonathan," said Grobstock jovially, "I'll take that salmon there—how much?"

"Pardon me," said a voice in the crowd, "I am just bargaining for it."

Grobstock started. It was the voice of Manasseh.

"Stop that nonsense, da Costa," responded the fish-monger. "You know you won't give me my price. It is the only one I have left," he added, half for the benefit of Grobstock. "I couldn't let it go under a couple of guineas."

"Here's your money," cried Manasseh with passionate contempt, and sent two golden coins spinning musically upon the slab.

In the crowd sensation, in Grobstock's breast astonishment, indignation, and bitterness. He was struck momentarily dumb. His face purpled.

The scales of the salmon shone like a celestial vision that was fading from him by his own stupidity.

"I'll take that Salmon, Jonathan," he repeated, spluttering. "Three guineas."

"Pardon me," repeated Manasseh, "it is too late. This is not an auction." He seized the fish by the tail.

Grobstock turned upon him, goaded to the point of apoplexy. "You!" he cried. "You—you—rogue! How dare you buy salmon!"

"Rogue yourself!" retorted Manasseh. "Would you have me steal salmon?"

"You have stolen my money, knave, rascal!"

"Murderer! Shedder of blood! Did you not give me the money as a free-will offering, for the good of your wife's soul? I call on you before all these witnesses to confess yourself a slanderer!"

"Slanderer, indeed! I repeat, you are a knave and a jackanapes. You —a pauper—a beggar—with a wife and children. How can you have the face to go and spend two guineas—two whole guineas—all you have in the world—on a mere luxury like salmon?"

Manasseh elevated his arched eyebrows.

"If I do not buy salmon when I have two guineas," he answered quietly, "when shall I buy salmon? As you say, it is a luxury; very dear. It is only on rare occasions like this that my means run to it." There was a dignified pathos about the rebuke that mollified the magnate. He felt that there was reason in the beggar's point of view—though it was a point to which he would never himself have risen unaided. But righteous anger still simmered in him; he felt vaguely that there was something to be said in reply though he also felt that even if he knew what it was, it would have to be said in a lower key to correspond with Manasseh's transition from the high pitch of the opening passages. Not finding the requisite repartee he was silent.

"In the name of my wife," went on Manasseh, swinging the salmon by the tail, "I ask you to clear my good name which you have bespattered in the presence of my very tradesmen. Again I call upon you to confess before these witnesses that you gave me the money yourself in charity. Come! Do you deny it?"

"No, I don't deny it," murmured Grobstock, unable to understand why he appeared to himself like a whipped cur, or how what should have been a boast had been transformed into an apology to a beggar.

"In the name of my wife, I thank you," said Manasseh. "She loves salmon, and fries with unction. And now, since you have no further use for that bag of yours, I will relieve you of its burden by taking my salmon home in it." He took the canvas bag from the limp grasp of the astonished Tedesco, and dropped the fish in. The head protruded, surveying the scene with a cold, glassy, ironical eye.

"Good afternoon, all," said the *schnorrer* courteously.

"One moment," called out the philanthropist, when he found his tongue. "The bag is not empty—there are a number of packets still left in it."

"So much the better!" said Manasseh soothingly. "You will be saved from the temptation to continue shedding the blood of the poor, and I shall be saved from spending *all* your bounty upon salmon—an extravagance you were right to deplore."

"But—but!" began Grobstock.

"No—no 'buts,'" protested Manasseh, waving his bag deprecatingly. "You were right. You admitted you were wrong before; shall I be less magnanimous now? In the presence of all these witnesses I acknowledge the justice of your rebuke. I ought not to have wasted two guineas on one fish. It was not worth it. Come over here, and I will tell you something." He walked out of earshot of the bystanders, turning down a side alley opposite the stall, and beckoned with his salmon bag. The East India Director had no course but to obey. He would probably have followed him in any case, to have it out with him, but now he had a humiliating sense of being at the *schnorrer's* beck and call.

"Well, what more have you to say?" he demanded gruffly.

"I wish to save you money in future," said the beggar in low, confidential tones. "That Jonathan is a son of the separation! The salmon is not worth two guineas—no, on my soul! If you had not come up I should have got it for twenty-five shillings. Jonathan stuck on the price when he thought you would buy. I trust you will not let me be the loser by your arrival, and that if I should find less than seventeen shillings in the bag you will make it up to me."

The bewildered financier felt his grievance disappearing as by sleight of hand.

Manasseh added winningly: "I know you are a gentleman, capable of behaving as finely as any Sephardi."

This handsome compliment completed the *schnorrer's* victory, which was sealed by his saying, "And so I should not like you to have it on your soul that you had done a poor man out of a few shillings."

Grobstock could only remark meekly: "You will find more than seventeen shillings in the bag."

"Ah, why were you born a Tedesco!" cried Manasseh ecstatically. "Do you know what I have a mind to do? To come and be your Sabbath-guest! Yes, I will take supper with you next Friday, and we will welcome the Bride—the holy Sabbath—together! Never before have I sat at the table of a Tedesco—but you—you are a man after my own heart. Your soul is a son of Spain. Next Friday at six—do not forget."

"But—but I do not have Sabbath-guests," faltered Grobstock.

"Not have Sabbath-guests! No, no, I will not believe you are of the sons of Belial, whose table is spread only for the rich, who do not proclaim your equality with the poor even once a week. It is your fine nature that would like its benefactions. Do not I, Manasseh Bueno Barzillai Azevedo da Costa, have at my Sabbath-table every week Yankelé ben Yitzchok—a Pole? And if I have a Tedesco at my table, why should I draw the line there? Why should I not permit you, a Tedesco, to return the hospitality to me, a Sephardi? At six, then! I know your house well—it is an elegant building that does credit to your taste—do not be uneasy—I shall not fail to be punctual. *A Dios!*"

This time he waved his stick fraternally, and stalked down a turning. For an instant Grobstock stood glued to the spot, crushed by a sense of the inevitable. Then a horrible thought occurred to him.

Easy-going man as he was, he might put up with the visitation of Manasseh. But then he had wife, and, what was worse, a livery servant. How could he expect a livery servant to tolerate such a guest? He might fly from the town on Friday evening, but that would necessitate troublesome explanations. And Manasseh would come again the next Friday. That was certain. Manasseh would be like grim death—his coming, though it might be postponed, was inevitable. Oh, it was too terrible. At all costs he must revoke the invitation (?). Placed between Scylla and Charybdis, between Manasseh and his manservant, he felt he could sooner face the former.

"Da Costa!" he called in agony. "Da Costa!"

The *schnorrer* turned, and then Grobstock found he was mistaken in imagining he preferred to face da Costa.

"You called me?" enquired the beggar.

"Y-e-s," faltered the East India Director, and stood paralysed.

"What can I do for you?" said Manasseh graciously.

"Would you mind—very much—if I—if I asked you—"

"Not to come," was in his throat, but stuck there.

"If you asked me—" said Manasseh encouragingly.

"To accept some of my clothes," flashed Grobstock, with a sudden inspiration. After all, Manasseh was a fine figure of a man. If he could get him to doff those musty garments of his he might almost pass him off as a prince of the blood, foreign by his beard—at any rate he could be certain of making him acceptable to the livery servant. He breathed freely again at this happy solution of the situation.

"Your cast-off clothes?" asked Manasseh. Grobstock was not sure whether the tone was supercilious or eager. He hastened to explain. "No, not quite that. Second-hand things I am still wearing. My old clothes were already given away at Passover to Simeon the Psalms-man. These are comparatively new."

"Then I would beg you to excuse me," said Manasseh, with a stately wave of the bag.

"Oh, but why not?" murmured Grobstock, his blood running cold again.

"I cannot," said Manasseh, shaking his head.

"But they will just about fit you," pleaded the philanthropist.

"That makes it all the more absurd for you to give them to Simeon the Psalms-man," said Manasseh sternly. "Still, since he is your clothes-receiver, I could not think of interfering with his office. It is not etiquette. I am surprised you should ask me if I should mind. Of course I should mind—I should mind very much."

"But he is not my clothes-receiver," protested Grobstock. "Last Passover was the first time I gave them to him, because my cousin, Hayyim Rosenstein, who used to have them, has died."

"But surely he considers himself your cousin's heir," said Manasseh. "He expects all your old clothes henceforth."

"No. I gave him no such promise."

Manasseh hesitated.

"Well, in that case—"

"In that case," repeated Grobstock breathlessly.

"On condition that I am to have the appointment permanently, of course."

"Of course," echoed Grobstock eagerly.

"Because you see," Manasseh condescended to explain, "it hurts one's reputation to lose a client."

"Yes, yes, naturally," said Grobstock soothingly. "I quite understand." Then, feeling himself slipping into future embarrassments, he added timidly, "Of course they will not always be so good as the first lot, because—"

"Say no more," Manasseh interrupted reassuringly, "I will come at once and fetch them."

"No. I will send them," cried Grobstock, horrified afresh.

"I could not dream of permitting it. What! Shall I put you to all that trouble which should rightly be mine? I will go at once—the matter shall be settled without delay. I promise you; as it is written, 'I made haste and delayed not!' Follow me!" Grobstock suppressed a groan. Here had all his manoeuvring landed him in a worse plight than ever. He would have to present Manasseh to the livery servant without even that clean face which might not unreasonably have been expected for the Sabbath. Despite the text quoted by the erudite *schnorrer,* he strove to put off the evil hour.

"Had you not better take the salmon home to your wife first?" said he.

"My duty is to enable you to complete your good deed at once. My wife is unaware of the salmon. She is in no suspense."

Even as the *schnorrer* spake it flashed upon Grobstock that Manasseh was more presentable with the salmon than without it—in fact, that the salmon was the salvation of the situation. When Grobstock bought fish he often hired a man to carry home the spoil. Manasseh would have all the air of such a loafer. Who would suspect that the fish and even the bag belonged to the porter, though purchased with the gentleman's money? Grobstock silently thanked Providence for the ingenious way in which it had contrived to save his self-respect. As a mere fish-carrier Manasseh would attract no second glance from the household; once safely in, it would be comparatively easy to smuggle him out, and when he did come on Friday night it would be in the metamorphosing glories of a body-coat, with his unspeakable undergarment turned into a shirt and his turban knocked into a cocked hat.

They emerged into Aldgate, and then turned down Leman Street, a fashionable quarter, and so into Great Prescott Street. At the critical street corner Grobstock's composure began to desert him; he took out his handsomely ornamented snuff-box and administered to himself a mighty pinch. It did him good, and he walked on and was well nigh arrived at his own door when Manasseh suddenly caught him by a coat button.

"Stand still a second," he cried imperatively.

"What is it?" murmured Grobstock, in alarm.

"You have spilt snuff all down your coat front," Manasseh replied severely. "Hold the bag a moment while I brush it off."

Joseph obeyed, and Manasseh scrupulously removed every particle with such patience that Grobstock's was exhausted.

"Thank you," he said at last, as politely as he could. "That will do."

"No, it will not do," replied Manasseh. "I cannot have my coat spoiled. By the time it comes to me it will be a mass of stains if I don't look after it."

"Oh, is that why you took so much trouble?" said Grobstock, with an uneasy laugh.

"Why else? Do you take me for a beadle, a brusher of gaiters?" enquired Manasseh haughtily. "There now! that is the cleanest I can get it. You would escape these droppings if you held your snuff-box so—" Manasseh gently took the snuff-box and began to explain, walking on a few paces.

"Ah, we are at home!" he cried, breaking off the object-lesson suddenly. He pushed open the gate, ran up the steps of the mansion and knocked thunderously, then snuffed himself magnificently from the bejewelled snuff-box.

Behind came Joseph Grobstock, slouching limply, and carrying Manasseh da Costa's fish.

BENJAMIN'S FIRST JOURNEY

by MENDELE MOCHER SEFORIM

THIS, my dear friends, is the story of how one of our brothers traveled far into distant lands, and gained thereby fame and honor in the world.

Excited accounts of the remarkable journey that Benjamin, a Polish Jew, had made to remote countries somewhere far in the East first appeared in the English and German papers last year. "To think," they marveled, "that a Jew, without means and without machines, with only a sack over his shoulders and a prayer-shawl and phylacteries under his arm, should have penetrated regions that the great and famous English explorers have never reached! Unless Benjamin accomplished his ends not with ordinary human power, but by means of a power the mind cannot understand." But, however it came about, the world is indebted to Benjamin, he that is Benjamin the Third, for the marvels that have been revealed through him, marvels that have completely changed the map of the earth. "Benjamin," they all chorused, "is richly deserving of the medal awarded him by the London Geographical Society."

The Jewish press flaunted the news of Benjamin's travels on their

front pages during the whole of last summer, as the readers of these publications will well remember. They enumerated all the great men in Israel
from the days of Adam, proving thereby how wise is Israel. They printed
lists of all the explorers and travelers in history, beginning with Benjamin
the First, who lived some seven hundred years ago; to the last of the
famous of the present day. And in order to stress the importance of the
travels of our own Benjamin they meanwhile, as is the custom amongst
Jews, nullified the importance of the other travelers, and said that the
entire group of modern explorers are no more than a band of beggarly
wanderers, ignorant wayfarers, whose travels amount to nothing, to less
than nothing, to futile and aimless vagabondage like that of nomadic
beggars. They are, surely, as monkeys compared to the present Benjamin,
compared to Benjamin III, the only true and worthy traveler. Concerning him, and the record of his travels, these papers spoke in the ancient
phrase: "Such fragrant herbs have not grown in Israel before!"

Blessed will be the man, all these papers agreed, who will take the
great treasure of Benjamin's travels, to be found in all foreign tongues,
and present it in the Holy Tongue, Hebrew, so that our Jews might also
be able to taste of the honey that overflows from the Jewish Bee-hive.

So I, Mendele, who have all my days aimed to do all in my power
for my brethren insofar as I am able, said to myself:

Before the Hebrew writers—whose little fingers are broader than my
loins—before they awake to translate the books of Benjamin's travels in
Hebrew, I shall meanwhile try to give a brief account of Benjamin's
travels in ordinary Yiddish. So, old and sick as I was, I tightened the
cord about my loins like a giant, and strove to grasp from the great
treasure such things as are good for the Children of Israel, and retell them
freely in my own way. This I felt I was driven to do by an angel from
above who came and said: "Wake up, Mendele, and crawl out from behind that stove! Fill your hands with the fragrant herbs gathered by Benjamin, he that is Benjamin III, and prepare with them such delicacies as
your brothers delight in." So I did as I was told, and prepared this food
as best I could. And here it is. May it, dear readers, agree with you!

I

"All my days," these are the words of Benjamin III, "all my days,
that is, until my great journey, I lived in Tuneyadovke. There I was
born, there I was raised, and there, in a lucky hour, I was married to my
chosen one, my wife, the virtuous Zelde, long may be her days."

Tuneyadovke is a small town in a remote nook on the other side of nowhere, so apart from the large world, that if a stranger happens to arrive, windows are thrown open, and people appear in the doorways to look in wonder at the newcomer. Through the open windows, neighbors ask one another: "Who can this stranger be? Where suddenly did he come from and why did he come expressly to our town? What may such as he want here? There must be a reason! Just so one does not come! There must be something wrong, and one must find out. . . ."

So old folks relate stories, citing other strangers who have come to their town on such and such a year in the past. The town wits are reminded of not altogether proper anecdotes. Men smooth their beards and smile; older women half seriously reprimand the humorists; young married women steal glances from lowered eyes and snicker. The speculations about the stranger travel from house to house, growing like rolling snowballs, until finally they reach the synagogue—where all matters capable of discussion are rediscussed; be they private secrets, personal affairs, family trouble, politics in Stamboul, money matters, Rothschild's fortunes as compared with the fortunes of other rich men, news about government decrees, the Red Jews, or what not.

A committee of respectable citizens are always gathered in the synagogue, remaining there through the day and late into the night, admirably sacrificing their interests and those of their families for the public weal, wholeheartedly giving their entire time to these world affairs, receiving no compensation for their labors but what they may receive hereafter in Heaven. Once the committee decides a matter, all the kings of the East and the West could not change it. The Turks once nearly lost their kingdom in the synagogue. If several respectable citizens had not been looking out for the Turks' interest, who knows where they would have been by now? Rothschild once lost about ten to fifteen millions in that way. But the good God helped him the following week, when he was granted, in the bath-house, about 150 million rubles clear profit!

Though they deal in millions, the dwellers of Tuneyadovke are, God save you, terribly poor. But to tell the truth, they are not unhappy; they are laughing beggars, and orthodox in their faith. Ask a Tuneyadovke Jew suddenly: "How do you make a living and from what do you support a family?" At first he will look greatly disturbed, not knowing what to answer. But later, on regaining his composure, he will answer earnestly: "I? How do I earn a living, you ask? There is a God in Heaven, I tell you, who does not desert his creatures! He sends them what they need and will continue to send them what they need, I tell you!"

"But what precisely do you do for a living? Have you a trade or a little business?"

"Praised be the Blessed Name! I have, praised be the Name, as you see me, I have a present from God who is above us. I have a singing voice. So I sing in the synagogues in the villages during the holidays. I have a light hand, I have, and can perform circumcisions. Sometimes I am a matchmaker. Besides, I have a wineshop that sometimes brings in something. I also have a goat that gives us milk. And not very far from here I have a rich relative that in time of need can also be milked a little. Beside all these things, I tell you, God is our father and the Children of Israel are compassionate, the Sons of the Compassionate, I tell you!"

It is an added credit to Tuneyadovke's citizens that they are never dissatisfied with what God gives them. In food and clothing they are not particular. If their Sabbath clothes are old, worn, and in spots so threadbare that the skin beneath can be seen, that is nothing to worry them. Who would stop and look so closely? No one is ashamed of torn shoes—if the soles of the feet do show through, what are they but skin of the human body? As for food—bread and soup, if they only have it, is not a bad dinner. And if they have white bread and stewed meat, on a Friday—whosoever can only afford it—what else could one wish for? Once a year they taste carob-pods. That is a fruit! Looking at it one is reminded of Jerusalem, and with a sigh one prays: Lead us, O God, to our land where the goats eat carob-pods!

Once, by mere accident, dates were brought to Tuneyadovke. How the crowds gathered to look at them! A Pentateuch was opened and it was found that dates were mentioned in the Holy Book! Think of it, dates! Dates that grow in the Land of Israel! Looking at the dates they imagined the Holy Land was before them. Here one passes the Jordan; there is Rachel's Tomb; over there is the Wailing Wall; one bathes in the water of the Tveryoh, eats his fill of carob-pods and dates, then fills his pockets with the soil from the Holy Land to take along to the grave. Looking at the dates people sighed, and tears were in their eyes.

"In those days," these are the words of Benjamin III, "the whole of Tuneyadovke lived—in their talk—in the Land of Israel. For a new Chief of Police ruled the town with terror. Two Jews he ordered to take off their skull caps. One Jews he punished because he went at night without a passport. From another he took away his only goat just because it ate a hole in the new straw roof of a neighbor. The committee in the synagogue discussed the new ruler, may his name and memory be effaced, and yearned for Zion. One day, the talk drifted to the Ten Lost Tribes, how happy they must be in those distant lands where they enjoy health and wealth and honor. Followed then stories of the Sons of Moses, the Red Jews, of their lives and strength. Those days were greatly responsible for the journey I later made."

Before that Benjamin might have been likened to a chick in the egg, or a worm in the horseradish. He thought that the world ended on the other side of Tuneyadovke.

"I thought," so Benjamin relates in one place, "that one could not wish to be richer than our Aaron Arendar. Think of it! He had a home all his own; four pairs of brass candlesticks; one hanging lamp; two copper pots and at least five copper pans; two silver goblets; a Hanukkah lamp; a watch; two cows and a calf; and other such riches. I thought that the wisest man in the world was Reb Isaac Dovid Reb Aaron Yossele Soroh Zlate's. He would have been a governor if luck were with him. And who, I thought, could be a greater doctor than ours, who, it was told, learned his medical wisdom from a gypsy—a direct descendant of the wise men of Egypt?"

In short, life in his home town seemed very good and beautiful to Benjamin, though he lived in want and poverty, and his wife and children were dressed in rags. But were not Adam and Eve, when they were still in the Garden of Eden, naked and barefoot?

Yet the wonderful stories of the Ten Tribes had sunk deep into Benjamin's heart, and from then on the town became too small for him, and he felt drawn toward far away places, like the hands of small children toward the moon. Come to think of it, what did it matter to him: dates, a Chief of Police, a skull cap, a goat, a straw roof? But all were directly influential on Benjamin and led eventually to his now famous journey, which so tremendously enriched the world. How often do small causes lead to great events! To be sure, it is quite probable that Benjamin was born with the spark of a traveler. But the spark would have been extinguished if favorable winds had not conspired to blow upon it. And Benjamin would have become no more than a water-carrier or a coachman.

I have myself in my life met many coachmen who were as capable of being travelers as Benjamin III himself. But that is not what I started out to tell you.

From that time forth Benjamin thought continually of Raboh Bar Honoh's travels over sea and desert. Later came into his hands the *Travels of Benjamin I,* wherein are described the wanderings of Benjamin the First, some seven hundred years ago. He also read *The Shadow of the*

World, where in seven pages are explained the Seven Wisdoms and all the marvels and wonders of the world with all its strange creatures. These works created a great unrest in him.

"From these wondrous tales," these are the words of Benjamin III, "I became greatly enthusiastic! Often I cried out in my enthusiasm: 'If God only helps me to see with my own eyes only one hundredth part of all this I will be satisfied!' And my imagination carried me far, far. . . ."

From then on Tyneyadovke became too small for him, and, like a chick breaking his shell, he began to see the bright world outside.

II

By nature our Benjamin was a great coward. At night he was afraid to leave the house. He would not sleep alone in a room for any consideration; to go out unaccompanied any distance from town he considered equal to risking his life—who can tell what might happen? And the smallest dog he feared with the fear of death.

"Once," Benjamin relates somewhere, "once on a hot mid-summer day our Rav went to bathe in the lake at the outskirts of the town. I and two other boys followed him, at a respectful distance, so that no ill might befall us, and we might return safely home, in the protection of the Rav. As the Rav—the respected of the entire world, whose title alone claimed the greater half of a page of paper—began to undress at the lake, a farmer's boy with his dogs came over the hill. The scoundrel loosed his dogs on the Rav, and our protector began to run, holding his pants with one hand and the rest of his clothes in the other. If the Leviathan is caught in the net, what should the minnows in the mud do? We undoubtedly turned and ran like frightened deer, and arrived in town some minutes ahead of the Rav."

So when Benjamin, he that is Benjamin III, resolved to make his great journey to distant lands, he vowed to rid himself of his fear and cowardice. He steeled himself to go out alone expressly at night, he slept alone in a room, and left the city to walk alone in the woods as often as was only possible. What though his health suffered, what though he lost weight from fright and began to look like a ghost.

His strange behavior at home and in synagogue, the paleness of his face, and his disappearance daily for several hours, were on everyone's tongue. Opinions, as always, differed. Some said: "Not otherwise, but Benjamin has gone insane. First, Benjamin was always foolish, lacking a stave in his head. And secondly, it was some time since there had been a madman in Tuneyadovke, and was it not expressly written: 'Each city with her wise man, and each city with her madman'? Especially during the hot summer months!" But there were others, with Reb Isaac Dovid Reb Aaron Yossele Soroh Zlate's as their leader, who said: "Te, te te! And again—te! True, Benjamin is dull, very dull. But from that we need not conclude that he is also insane. For the question might be asked: Why now and not before? Why not last summer and the summer before, when the heat was much greater? What then is the conclusion? The conclusion is: Take for instance—take our lake. Our lake, as you know, has taken one life each year from the beginning of time, and yet, for the last two or three years, it has taken no victims. On the contrary, the lake itself has dropped in these few years and now there are places in it one can pass on foot. . . . But what about Benjamin you ask? Bah!"

But the greater number, and amongst them the women, said: "Benjamin must be dealing with Them. . . . He undoubtedly has something to do with Him. . . . With the Evil One. . . . Or else why does he wander around after nightfall? Where then does he disappear each day? Why then does he sleep alone in the woodshed?" Zelde, his own wife, told that when she listened at night, she heard someone knocking in the woodshed, as of feet against the wall. . . .

No agreement being reached, it was decided as a temporary means that a group of respectable citizens, with the Holy Writer at their head, be sent out to inspect the parchments on the doors of every house. Perhaps they could discover a clue. . . . And because such an undertaking was a communal affair, done for the good of the town, it was therefore decided to cover the expenses of the inspection by raising the price of meat.

Tuneyadovke has this proverb: All talk leads to the topic of death, and all public discussions end with a tax on meat. Thus the Creator made the world, and as He made it so it must be, and must be good. Only heretics ask questions.

Soon afterwards an event occurred whereby Benjamin gained fame in his town.

One hot summer day he left home and walked into the woods at the outskirts of Tuneyadovke. In his pockets he carried the travel-books without which he did not leave the house. And when he tired of walking he seated himself in the shade of a tree and his thoughts soon carried him away to those far-off lands at the end of the world. He imagined himself wandering over mountains and valleys, through deserts and wastelands, as in the books. He wandered in the footpaths of Alexande of Macedonia, Eldad Hadani, and their like. Before him arose the terrible Piepernoter, the lindenworm, quadruped birds, reptiles with wings, vipers, vermin as large as cats and dogs, rattlesnakes, cocatrices, basilisks, and other monstrosities. But he passed them all in peace and in the end he reached the Red Jews, and talked mouth to mouth with the Sons of Moses. . . .

Benjamin sighed. How and when should he start out on the great journey?

And as he sat there planning his travels, night came. Benjamin arose, hastily murmured the Prayers for the Departing Day, stretched himself, and started towards home. He walked and walked and walked, but he could see no end to the woods. He walked an hour, two, three, four, but still no end. The further he went the darker it became. Suddenly a storm arose and a heavy rain began to pour down upon him, amid lightning and thunder. And the sound of the trees in the wind was terrible. Benjamin stopped, his teeth chattering with cold, wetness, and a panicky fear. In the light of the flickering lightning he imagined he saw the Maatul, which, according to *The Shadow of the World,* is a large long creature with two enormous hands wherewith it can throw down an elephant. Benjamin began to pray loudly and piously, from the depth of his heart.

With the help of God day came, and our Benjamin set out again. He walked and walked until he finally came to a narrow path. He followed this path for an hour or two when he suddenly heard a human voice in the distance. Far from rejoicing, Benjamin turned pale with fear. Not otherwise, he thought, but that was the voice of a murderer! In great panic he turned and began to run until he was out of breath. But then he stopped and said to himself:

"Shame, Benjamin! You want to wander over oceans and deserts inhabited by scorpions, monsters, wild tribes, and man-eaters, and here you are frightened by the voice of an ordinary murderer! Fie, Benjamin, you should be ashamed of yourself. Did Alexander of Macedonia run away like you? Was Alexander of Macedonia chicken-hearted like you when he rode on his eagle and the meat on the end of his sword, with which he steered the bird, was gone? No! Alexander cut off a piece of his own flesh, put in on the sword, and steered the eagle again! Take heart, Benjamin, God only wants to try you. Happy the moment when you pass the trial! For then, Benjamin, you are a man and worthy before the Blessed Name to be granted your wish and to reach the Sons of Moses. If you walk back towards that voice, then you shall conquer all fear. You shall become a vessel of Solomon, a benediction in Israel, and an honor to Tuneyadovke! Tuneyadovke and Macedonia—these two places shall be equally famous on account of Alexander of Macedonia and Benjamin of Tuneyadovke!"

Our Benjamin returned with a steeled heart and great faith, until he came in view of the murderer—an old farmer driving a load drawn by a team of oxen.

"A good day!" Benjamin called in a strained voice as he neared the wagon. His greeting had many meanings: it was both a cry and a plea, as if saying: "Here I am, do with me as you please!" Also: "Have mercy on me and my wife and children at home!"

Having stammered out his greeting, Benjamin felt as if someone were choking him. His head began to whirl, his eyes went dim, his feet failed him. Then he fell to the ground.

When he came to he found himself lying in a wagon on a large sack of potatoes, covered with a heavy piece of canvas. Near him lay a rooster that looked at him angrily from the corner of one eye. Further down, the wagon was crowded with sacks of onions, garlic, and other greens. The farmer sat smoking his pipe peacefully, and calling to his oxen: *"Sop, heita, sop!"* The oxen hardly moved, and the wheels screeched with a discord that pierced the ears. The rooster, disturbed also by the whistling shriek of the wheels, with every revolution scratched Benjamin with his tied feet. Benjamin lay there with every member of his body numb. A Turk had caught him in the desert and was now leading him into slavery!

I hope, so Benjamin thought, I hope he sells me at least to a Jew. There will be some chance of salvation and redemption then. But if, God forbid, he sells me to a Prince, or, what is worse, to a Princess of the foreign nations, then I am lost, lost forever. And when the story of Joseph and Potiphar's wife came to his mind, Benjamin sighed with an exceeding great sorrow.

The farmer turned, hearing Benjamin's sigh, and asked:

"Well, Jew,—do you feel a little better?"

Now Benjamin could speak hardly a word of Russian. How was he to answer the farmer, how could he find out whither he was being taken?

Benjamin tried to sit up, but in vain. His feet were in great pain.

"You feel a little better?" The farmer asked again, and ended with: *'Sop, heita, sop!"*

"Better. But my—ai-ai-ai-!" Benjamin pointed to his feet.

"Wherefrom are you, Jew?—*Sop, heita, sop!"*

"Wherefrom are you, Jew?" Benjamin repeated in a sing-song. "Why, I—I, Niomka, Binyomka from Tuneyadovke—"

"You are from Tuneyadovke? Tell me then, why do you look at me as if you were crazy? Or maybe you are crazy, the devil take you!— *Sop, heita, sop!*"

"I—why, I tell you from beginning," Benjamin sang half in Yiddish, half in Russian. "I tell you, I myself, Niomka from Tuneyadovke!" Here Benjamin made a pitiful grimace and spread his hands, as if pleading for mercy: "In Tuneyadovke . . . wife gives . . . Sabbath bread, and good . . . thanks you!" The farmer seemed to guess what Benjamin meant.

A few hours later the wagon rolled into Tuneyadovke's market place. Men and women surrounded the wagon.

"Do you have onions? How much the garlic?"

"Maybe you have eggs? Potatoes?"

And one man asked: "Listen, maybe you saw on the road a Jew? We lost a Jew yesterday, one Binyomka, lost him as if into the water!"

But before the farmer could answer any of the questions the women had surrounded the wagon like locusts, uncovered the piece of canvas, and in one voice screamed: "BENJAMIN!"

"He is here! Tziopoh-Krone! Breindel! Run quick to Zelde with the good tidings that her loss is found! She is no longer a widow!"

In the midst of all the hubbub Zelde came running, crying loudly and wringing her hands, and not knowing whether to pour out her bitter heart upon her chosen, or to show her joy that God had spared her from being a widow.

So Benjamin was brought home just as he lay there on the potatoes, followed by a great parade.

And later Tuneyadovke's doctor came to Benjamin, shaved his head completely, set leeches on him, and suggested that besides these remedies, if, with the aid of God, he were strong enough, he should go to synagogue the very next morning to offer the Prayer of Deliverance.

PASSOVER FUGUE

by SHOLEM ALEICHEM

I. THE GUEST

"I HAVE a Passover guest for you, Reb Yoneh, such a guest as you never had since you became a householder."

"What sort is he?"

"A real Oriental citron!"

"What does that mean?"

"It means a 'silken Jew,' a personage of distinction. The only thing against him is—he doesn't speak our language."

"What does he speak, then?"

"Hebrew."

"Is he from Jerusalem?"

"I don't know where he comes from, but his words are full of a's."

Such was the conversation that took place between my father and the beadle, a day before Passover, and I was wild with curiosity to see the "guest" who didn't understand Yiddish, and who talked with a's. I had already noticed, in synagogue, a strange looking individual, in a fur cap, and a Turkish robe striped blue, red and yellow. We boys crowded round him on all sides, and stared, and then caught it from the beadle, who said children had no business "to creep into a stranger's face" like that. Prayers over, everyone greeted the stranger, and wished him a happy Passover, and he, with a sweet smile on his red cheeks set in a round grey beard, replied to each one, *"Shalom! Shalom!"* instead of our *Sholem.* This *"Shalom! Shalom!"* of his sent us boys into fits of laughter. The beadle grew very angry, and pursued us with slaps. We eluded him, and stole deviously back to the stranger, listened to his *"Shalom! Shalom!"* exploded with laughter, and escaped anew from the hands of the beadle.

I am puffed up with pride as I follow my father and his guest to our house, and feel how all my comrades envy me. They stand looking after us, and every now and then I turn my head, and put out my tongue at them. The walk home is silent. When we arrive, my father greets my mother with "a happy Passover!" and the guest nods his head so that his fur cap shakes. *"Shalom! Shalom!"* he says. I think of my comrades and hide my head under the table, not to burst out laughing. But I shoot continual glances at the guest, and his appearance pleases me. I like his Turkish robe, striped yellow, red, and blue, his fresh, red cheeks set in a curly grey beard, his beautiful black eyes that look out so pleasantly from beneath his bushy eyebrows. And I see that my father, too, is pleased with him. My mother looks at him as though he were something more than a man, and no one speaks to him but my father, who offers him the cushioned reclining-seat at table.

Mother is taken up with the preparations for the Passover meal, and Rikel the maid is helping her. It is only when the time comes for saying *kiddush* that my father and the guest hold a Hebrew conversation. I am proud to find that I understand nearly every word of it. Here it is in full.

My father: "Nu?" (That means, "Won't you please say *kiddush?*")
The guest: "Nu-nu!" (meaning, "Say it rather yourself!")
My father: "Nu-O?" ("Why not you?")
The guest: "O-nu?" ("Why should I?")
My father: "I-O!" ("You first!")
The guest: "O-ai!" ("*You* first!")
My father: "E-o-i!" ("I beg of you to say it!")
The guest: "Ai-o-e!" ("I beg of you!")
My father: "Ai-e-o-nu?" ("Why should you refuse?")
The guest: "Oi-o-e-nu-nu!" ("If you insist, then I must.")

And the guest took the cup of wine from my father's hand, and recited a *kiddush*. But what a *kiddush!* A *kiddush* such as we had never heard before, and shall never hear again. First, the Hebrew—all a's. Secondly, the voice which seemed to come, not out of his beard, but out of the striped Turkish robe. I thought of my comrades, how they would have laughed, what slaps would have rained down, had they been present at that *kiddush*.

Being alone, I was able to contain myself. I asked my father the Four Questions, and we all recited the Haggadah together. And I was elated to think that such a guest was ours, and no one else's.

II

Our sage who wrote that one should not talk at meals (may he forgive me for saying so!) did not know Jewish life. When shall a Jew find time to talk, if not during a meal? Especially at Passover, when there is so much to say before the meal and after it. Rikel the maid handed the water, we washed our hands, repeated the Benediction, mother helped us to fish, and my father turned up his sleeves, and started a long Hebrew conversation with the guest. He began with the first question one Jew asks another:

"What is your name?"

To which the guest replied all in a's and all in one breath:

"Ayak Bakar Gashal Damas Hanoch Vassam Za'an Chafaf Tatsatz."

My father remained with his fork in the air, staring in amazement. I coughed and looked under the table, and my mother said, "Favele, you should be careful eating fish, or you might be choked with a bone," while she gazed at our guest with awe. She appeared overcome by his name, although unable to understand it. My father, who understood, thought it necessary to explain it to her.

"You see, Ayak Bakar, that is our Alef-Bes inverted. It is apparently their custom to name people after the alphabet."

"Alef-Bes! Alef-Bes!" repeated the guest with the sweet smile on his red cheeks, and his beautiful black eyes rested on us all, including Rikel the maid, in the most friendly fashion.

Having learnt his name, my father was anxious to know whence, from what land, he came. I understood this from the names of countries and towns which I caught, and from what my father translated for my mother, giving her a Yiddish version of nearly every phrase. And my mother was quite overcome by every single thing she heard, and Rikel the maid was overcome likewise. And no wonder! It is not every day that a person comes from perhaps two thousand miles away, from a land only to be reached across seven seas and a desert, the desert journey alone requiring forty days and nights. And when you get near to the land, you have to climb a mountain of which the top reaches into the clouds, and this is covered with ice, and dreadful winds blow there, so that there is peril of death! But once the mountain is safely climbed, and the land is reached, one beholds a terrestrial Eden. Spices, cloves, herbs, and every kind of fruit—apples, pears, and oranges, grapes, dates, and olives, nuts and quantities of figs. And the houses are all built of deal, and roofed with silver, the furniture is gold (here the guest cast a look at our silver cups, spoons, forks, and knives), and brilliants, pearls, and diamonds bestrew the roads, and no one cares to take the trouble of picking them up, they are of no value there. (He was looking at my mother's diamond ear-rings, and at the pearls round her white neck.)

"You hear that?" my father asked her, with a happy face.

"I hear," she answered, and added: "Why don't they bring some over here? They could make money by it. Ask him that, Yoneh!"

My father did so, and translated the answer for my mother's benefit:

"You see, when you arrive there, you may take what you like, but when you leave the country, you must leave everything in it behind, too, and if they shake out of you no matter what, you are done for."

"What do you mean?" questioned my mother, terrified.

"I mean, they either hang you on a tree, or they stone you with stones."

III

The more tales our guest told us, the more thrilling they became. Just as we were finishing the dumplings and taking another sip or two of wine, my father inquired to whom the country belonged. Was there a king there? And he was soon translating, with great delight, the following reply:

"The country belongs to the Jews who live there, and who are called Sefardim. And they have a king, also a Jew, and a very pious one, who wears a fur cap, and who is called Joseph ben Joseph. He is the high priest of the Sefardim, and drives about in a gilded carriage, drawn by six fiery horses. And when he enters the synagogue, the Levites meet him with songs."

"There are Levites who sing in your synagogue?" asked my father, wondering, and the answer caused his face to shine with joy.

"What do you think?" he said to my mother. "Our guest tells me that in his country there is a temple, with priests and Levites and an organ."

"Well, and an altar?" questioned my mother, and my father told her:

"He says they have an altar, and sacrifices, he says, and golden vessels—everything just as we used to have it in Jerusalem."

And with these words my father sighs deeply, and my mother, as she looks at him, sighs also, and I cannot understand the reason. Surely we should be proud and glad to think we have such a land, ruled over by a Jewish king and a high priest, a land with Levites and an organ, with an altar and sacrifices—and bright, sweet thoughts enfold me, and carry me away as on wings to that happy Jewish land where the houses are of pine-wood and roofed with silver, where the furniture is gold, and diamonds and pearls lie scattered in the street. And I feel sure, were I really there, I should know what to do—I should know how to hide things—they would shake nothing out of *me*. I should certainly bring home a lovely present for my mother, diamond ear-rings and several pearl necklaces. I look at the one mother is wearing, at her ear-rings, and I feel a great desire to be in that country. And it occurs to me, that after Passover I will travel there with our guest, secretly, no one shall know. I will only speak of it to our guest, secretly, no one shall know. I will only speak of it to our guest, open my heart to him, tell him the whole truth, and beg him to take me there, if only for a little while. He will certainly do so, he is a very kind and approachable person, he looks at everyone, even at Rikel the maid, in such a friendly, such a very friendly way!

So I think, and it seems to me, as I watch our guest, that he has read my thoughts, and that his beautiful black eyes say to me:

"Keep it dark, little friend, wait till after Passover, then we shall manage it."

IV

I dreamt all night long. I dreamt of a desert, a temple, a high priest, and a tall mountain. I climb the mountain. Diamonds and pearls grow on the trees, and my comrades sit on the boughs, and shake the jewels down onto the ground, whole showers of them, and I stand and gather them, and stuff them into my pockets, and strange to say, however many I stuff in, there is still room! I stuff and stuff, and still there is room! I put my hand into my pocket, and draw out—not pearls and brilliants, but fruits of all kinds—apples, pears, oranges, olives, dates, nuts, and figs. This makes me very unhappy, and I toss from side to side. Then I dream of the temple, I hear the priests chant, and the Levites sing, and the organ play. I want to go inside and I cannot—Rikel the maid has hold of me, and will not let me go. I beg of her and scream and cry and again I am very unhappy, and toss from side to side. I wake—and see my father and mother standing there, half dressed, both pale, my father hanging his head, and my mother wringing her hands, and with soft eyes full of tears. I feel at once that something has gone very wrong, very wrong indeed, but my childish head is incapable of imagining the greatness of the disaster.

The fact is this: our guest from beyond the desert and the seven seas has disappeared, and a lot of things have disappeared with him: all the silver wine-cups, the silver cups, knives, and forks; all my mother's ornaments, all the money that happened to be in the house, and also Rikel the maid!

A pang goes through my heart. Not on account of the silver cups, the silver spoons, knives, and forks that have vanished; not on account of my mother's ornaments, or of the money, still less on account of Rikel the maid, good riddance! But because of the happy, happy land whose roads were strewn with brilliants, pearls, and diamonds; because of the temple with the priests, the Levites, and the organ; because of the altar and the sacrifices; because of all the other beautiful things that have been taken from me, taken, taken, taken!

I turn my face to the wall, and cry quietly to myself.

II. Elijah

It is not good to be an only son, to be fretted over by father and mother—to be the only one left out of seven. Don't stand here. Don't go there. Don't drink that. Don't eat the other. Cover up your throat. Hide your hands. Ah, it is not good—not good at all to be an only son, and a rich man's son into the bargain. My father is a money changer. He goes about amongst the shopkeepers with a bag of money, changing coppers for silver, and silver for copper. That is why his fingers are always black, and his nails broken. He works very hard. Each day, when he comes home, he is tired and broken down. "I have no feet," he complains to mother. "I have no feet, not even the sign of a foot." No feet? It may be. But for that again he has a fine business. That's what the people say. And they envy us that we have a good business. Mother is satisfied. So am I. "We shall have a Passover this year, may all the children of Israel have the like, Father in Heaven!"

That's what my mother said, thanking God for the good Passover. And I also was thankful. But shall we ever live to see it—this same Passover?

Passover has come at last—the dear sweet Passover. I was dressed as befitted the son of a man of wealth—like a young Prince. But what was the consequence? I was not allowed to play or run about, lest I catch cold. I must not play with poor children. I was a wealthy man's son. Such nice clothes, and I had no one to show off before. I had a pocketful of nuts, and no one to play with.

It is not good to be an only child, and fretted over—the only one left out of seven, and a wealthy man's son into the bargain.

My father put on his best clothes, and went off to the synagogue. Said my mother to me: "Do you know what? Lie down and have a sleep. You will then be able to sit up at the *Seder* and ask the Four Questions!" Was I mad? Would I go asleep before the *Seder*?

"Remember, you must not sleep at the *Seder*. If you do, Elijah the Prophet will come with a bag on his shoulders. On the first two nights of Passover, Elijah the Prophet goes about looking for those who have fallen asleep at the *Seder* and takes them away in his bag." . . . Ha! Ha! Will I fall asleep at the *Seder?* I? Not even if it were to last the whole night through, or even to broad daylight. "What happened last year, mother?" "Last year you fell asleep soon after the first blessing." "Why did Elijah the Prophet not come then with his bag?" "Then you were small, now you are big. Tonight you must ask father the Four Questions. Tonight you must say with father—'Slaves were we.' Tonight, you must eat with us fish and soup and *matzo* balls. Hush, here is father, back from the synagogue."

"Good *'Yom-tov'!*"

"Good *'Yom-tov'!*"

Thank God, father made the blessing over wine. I, too. Father drank the cup full of wine. So did I, a cup full, to the very dregs. "See, to the dregs," said mother to father. To me she said: "A full cup of wine! You will drop off to sleep." Ha! Ha! Will I fall asleep? Not even if we were to sit up all the night, or even to broad daylight. "Well," said my father, "how are you going to ask the Four Questions? How will you recite *Haggadah?* How will you sing with me—'Slaves were we'?"

My mother never took her eyes off me. She smiled and said: "You will fall asleep—fast asleep." "Oh, mother, mother, if you had eighteen heads, you would surely fall asleep, if someone sat opposite you, and sang in your ears: 'Fall asleep, fall asleep'!"

Of course I fell asleep.

I fell asleep, and dreamt that my father was already saying, "Pour out thy wrath." My mother herself got up from the table, and went to open the door to welcome Elijah the Prophet. It would be a fine thing if Elijah the Prophet did come, as my mother had said, with a bag on his shoulders, and if he said to me: "Come, boy." And who else would be to blame for this but my mother, with her "fall asleep, fall asleep." And as I was thinking these thoughts, I heard the creaking of the door. My father stood up and cried: "Blessed art thou who comest in the name of the Eternal." I looked towards the door. Yes, it was he. He came in so slowly and so softly that one scarcely heard him. He was a handsome man, Elijah the Prophet—an old man with a long grizzled beard reaching to his knees. His face was yellow and wrinkled, but it was handsome and kindly without end. And his eyes! Oh, what eyes! Kind, soft, joyous, loving, faithful eyes. He was bent in two, and leaned on a big, big stick. He had a bag on his shoulders. And silently, softly, he came straight to me.

"Now, little boy, get into my bag and come." So said the old man to me, but in a kind voice and softly and sweetly.

I asked him: "Where to?" And he replied: "You will see later." I did not want to go, and he said to me again: "Come." and I began to argue with him. "How can I go with you when I am a wealthy man's son?" Said he to me: "And as a wealthy man's son, of what great value are you?" Said I: "I am the only child of my father and mother." Said he: "To me you are not an only child." Said I: "I am fretted over. If they find that I am gone, they will not get over it, they will die, especially my mother." He looked at me, the old man did, very kindly and he said to me, softly and sweetly as before: "If you do not want to die, then come with me. Say good-bye to your father and mother, and come." "But how can I come when I am an only child, the only one left alive out of seven?"

Then he said to me more sternly: "For the last time, little boy. Choose one of the two. Either you say good-bye to your father and mother, and come with me, or you remain here, but fast asleep for ever and ever."

Having said these words, he stepped back from me a little, and was turning to the door. What was to be done? To go with the old man, God-knows-where, and get lost, would mean the death of my father and mother. I am an only child, the only one left alive out of seven. To remain here, and fall asleep for ever and ever—that would mean that I myself must die . . .

I stretched out my hand to him, and with tears in my eyes I said: "Elijah the Prophet, dear, kind, loving, darling Elijah, give me one minute to think." He turned towards me his handsome, yellow, wrinkled old face with its grizzled beard reaching to his knees, and looked at me with his beautiful, kind, loving, faithful eyes, and he said to me with a smile: "I will give you one minute to decide, my child—but no more than one minute."

I ask you. "What should I have decided to do in that one minute, so as to save myself from going with the old man, and also to save myself from falling asleep for ever? Well, who can guess?"

BEFORE I WAS BORN

by JOSEPH COTLER

THERE's no denying it was high time for me to be born. But the devils and angels of the Heavenly Kingdom had taken such a fancy to me that they were loathe to part with my company. So when the time came for me to be brought to earth, they placed all sorts of hindrances in the way, and it all came to nought.

Not that I complained. After all, it was not a bad sort of life up there. If I were so inclined, I could even call on the devil himself at his home. To be sure, he was mostly away, being busy with affairs on earth, while his wife was forever taken up in the kitchen with baking leaden *homon tashen* for the household. But there were always the little devils to play with, and I can remember how they, being rude little devils, used to butt me with their sharp horns. I would run and hide under the oven, where they could not reach me. Then, as soon as they turned around, I would reach out with a cautious hand and grab one by the tail. Whereupon he would set up the most terrific howl, and his brothers would all try to get at me with such droll anger that it was a sight to see, even in the other world.

Once I plaited together no less than eleven little devils by their tails, and they set up such a din that the devil's wife herself rushed out with a poker in her hand and drove me from the house.

"Get out!" she cried in shrill anger. "Go, get born. A lusty rascal like you should have been born ages ago, and not allowed to grow so large among us, to come here twisting the tails of my little imps. Get out!" she screamed.

I shrank a little under my humiliation. "Just for that I shall leave," I said. "I shall leave, and visit Angel Samuel instead, and play with his little seraphim, and with the heavenly crockery that lies scattered all over his house."

When I entered the home of Angel Samuel he was flying with his great silver wings outspread, above the heads of his little ones, giving them his blessing. As soon as he caught sight of me, he greeted me kindly: "Well, get under here and I will give you a blessing, too."

"It can't do any harm," I thought, and placed myself in the shadow of his wings. The blessing over, we all lifted up our voices in song, and after that Angel Samuel took me in his arms. "Do you know, Joseph," he said, "it is quite possible that tomorrow morning you will be born." He seemed promptly to regret his words, and began nervously to rustle his wings. "After all," he reconsidered, "it might not be such a pleasant thing to be born on a cold winter morning. Another thing," he said, "I must tell you that an older brother, who is very anxious to be born, has gotten in ahead of you. And how would it be regarded on earth if a younger brother should be born ahead of an older brother? People will point their fingers at you."

I could not help seeing the truth of his words. And, when all was said and done, it would hardly be fair to my brother. So I agreed to wait a while longer.

One afternoon, as I was playing with the Angel Samuel's grandchildren, I wondered how they would look with the feathers plucked out of their wings. So I set to work, and left not a feather. Whereupon there was quite a hullabaloo, and desperate quest was begun to find a mother who would give birth to me in haste, and thus rid Angel Samuel's house of my presence. For my part, I refused to be born in that casual fashion. My own mother was already in childbirth (with my older brother, Hayyim), and to boot, I had been so long delayed that it was already time for me to have the measles. I then learned that they sought to force me to be born somewhere in Turkey, which didn't please me in the least. I fled. By then it was night, and pitch dark. I ran, and ran, leaping over moon and stars in my flight; and again I ran, and ran. And at the end of the sky, where it abruptly slopes downward, I began to fall, and went on falling.

Falling is not a comfortable occupation, believe me. I was in a yellow nothingness, falling, falling endlessly, without a respite. Yet what else could I have done? Better anything than to be born a Turk!

Time passed, a long time, and I began to find myself. What do I mean, "find myself"? Well, to mention one thing: I learned to fall in a standing position, and when I grew tired of that, I would assume a sitting posture, this even while I was falling. Or if I were sleepy, I could stretch out lengthwise, and catch a nap. But always I kept on falling, falling.

Sometimes I became terribly lonely and homesick for the little devils and the little angels. But what could I do? At other times I felt so exhilarated that I wanted to dance. Yet how could one dance in mid-air, continuously in the act of falling? The thought persisted, "Now if I could only manage just a little jump." I simply couldn't do it. I was wholly occupied with falling.

I had been falling for what must have been years, when one day I felt something tickling my cheek. I touched it—lo! I had grown a beard! A beard! I stroked my beard; I twisted it into points; I spread it out so the wind might rush through it. And my plight was more bearable.

I must mention that my beard was of gold and accordingly very heavy, so that I began to fall with yet greater speed. By now I was past caring. I had long since become used to falling. What mattered it if I fell a little faster.

How long I went on falling, I do not know. Ages it seemed, until suddenly my beard caught in something, and there I hung, my fall at an end. Yet as I was unaccustomed to not falling, my head swam miserably, and I was almost minded to release myself and to resume falling.

On the other hand I thought to myself: "What purpose is there in forever falling?" I looked about me and saw that I hung from a great earthen wall, covered with twisted roots, in which my beard was caught. I released my beard and began to claw my way up the wall, higher and higher, until finally I reached the cover of the world.

This was the very first time I had ever felt anything firm under my feet. For, naturally, in Heaven I trod only upon clouds and blue ether. And while falling I rested on nothing, which is also a kind of softness. Hence, I found the earth rather hard for my tender feet.

I looked about me. All was earth and sky. The world was strange to me. What should I do now?

"I must at once seek out my mother," I thought, "and ask her to give birth to me as soon as she can, that I might become a man like all men."

I tried to walk, but walking was beyond me. I stumbled and fell, and began to crawl on all fours over waste-land, over rocks and mountains, with no idea at all as to where I was going. Which way should I turn? "Well," I thought, "what must come, must come." I placed my trust in my beard. Where my beard pointed, there I would drag myself.

Time passed, and I came upon a tall lean old man, clad in leather skins. He sat on the branch of a tree, and awaited the rising of the sun.

"Why do you await the rising of the sun?" I called up to him.

And in response, he shouted down that he had been long worshipping the sun, but was becoming disgruntled. Things weren't going very well in spite of all his worship.

"Who are you?" he asked. "Are you perhaps a god? If so, then I will worship you for a while, and see what comes of it."

I informed him that far from being a god I was as yet scarcely simple flesh and blood. "Perhaps," I said, "you can direct me to the world of men."

"That world is far off," he said. "And, besides, I must inform you that in the world of men it is by no means customary to put in an appearance before one is born. Yet since your beard is of gold," he reflected, "the people of the earth may find you fair, and do you honor."

"Tell me the way!" I said.

"Well," he answered, "follow such and such a way, until you reach a blazing sea of molten copper which boils without cease. As soon as you reach its fringe, your beard of gold will shame the sea of copper and the sea will cool down and you will be able to pass in safety. Then you will reach a town where the streets are lopsided, even as its stones are; its people, likewise, are lopsided. Stick out your beard, the people will bow before it and, cringing, turn aside in fear. Thus shall you pass in safety.

"Then push on yet further, until you reach a blazing sea of molten gold which boils without cease. This time your golden beard shall hardly put the golden sea to shame, and you shall have great trouble in passing."

"How?" I asked. "Is there no easier path to the world?"

He answered: "If you will take the trouble to turn to your right, you will find not far away a broad smooth highway leading straight to the world."

"Why didn't you tell me that before?" I asked indignantly.

Whereupon he began to excuse himself and finally confessed that, living so far away from the world of men, he was really not so very wise.

As soon as I discovered that he was not very wise, and, being already tired of his company, I left him, and crept along until I landed in a dark forest of pepper trees. Under one of the trees I stretched myself out to rest. While I was lying there and wondering as to the outcome of my adventure, a man with a long black beard and a yellow skull-cap came driving along in the woods.

The man jumped down from his wagon, sack in hand, and began to shake the pepper tree under which I was lying. And the hard peppers ringing against my golden beard played there a merry tune, upon which the man tucked up the skirts of his coat and began to dance. When the peppers ceased to fall and the tune came to an end, he took the sack, and began to stuff it with the hard black peppers lying on the ground.

And seeing my beard, he was all for stuffing that into his sack also. I protested.

"Who are you?" he asked.

"I am one unborn, and I go into the world to seek out my mother's address, that she may give me birth."

"Do you know what?" said he. "Come with me to my wife who is barren and would gladly bear a child, especially one with such a fine beard."

"It shall not be said of me," I said with dignity, "that I was born of a barren woman. Yet since I am a stranger, take me with you to the world, and there I will find the way for myself."

"Tu," he answered. "Seeing that your beard is of gold, better crawl into my sack. For though you are invisible to men, being unborn, your beard is not invisible. So crawl into my sack, that you may not be robbed of it on the way."

Nevertheless, I was uneasy. The idea of crawling into a sack seemed absurd to me. I persuaded him to let me ride on the seat with him until we should be within a brief distance of the world of men. "Then," I said, "I will hide face down in your wagon, that my beard may not be seen."

So we both climbed into the wagon, and rode and rode. The wagon pitched and tossed, and I was thrown about until I fell asleep.

When I awoke I found that all my wandering and adventuring was, in the manner of speaking, a dream.

As always at dawn, I found myself high in Heaven, with the moon under my head, and a few white clouds under my side.

I lay under my bedclothes, trying to make up my mind whether it was time to get up. But soon I buried my face in the moon and fell asleep again, content to leave the difficult undertaking of being born for a more propitious occasion.

A POT STORY

by s. j. agnon

For all that folks has the habit of calling me the Brod waggoner I ain't a Brod man nor I wasn't born in Brod, but I'm of Boisk and it's in Boisk I was born and that's good enough for me, seeing as a man ain't born in two different places. Well then, so why do they have to call me the Brod waggoner? But that's the way o' the world to catch hold o' the lie, seeing they enjoys the lie more than the truth; because if they'd ha' liked the truth better they wouldn't call me the Brod waggoner but the Boisk waggoner.

Boisk's a tiny place just like a goyish pancake. What's the difference between their pancakes and our pancakes? Like this, that ours is full of meat or cheese or taters or semolina or fruit, while theirs ain't got no meat and no cheese and no potatoes and no semolina and no fruit only dough folded over; and even if you go biting into them all day long you won't find nothing only dough inside them.

And that's what Boisk's like, into a group of houses and out of a group of houses and you never get further than from one group of houses to another. It's on a river so it has a lot of bridges, and there's a big trade there in boards and earthenware and flax; and there's a real ancient palace there as old as the hills, only not a single Jew ever gets any benefit out of it.

And now let's forget the palace and the river and the bridge and everybody in Boisk excepting one man, as is the cause of all my troubles and please God may there soon be an end of him together with all my troubles, not wishing him no evil; like that that palace should tumble down onto him and bury him underneath so that at last there should be some good come out of it to two Jews at once. And who's that there man? Well, I just now told you how the Boisk folk sells earthenware goods and flax, and in Boisk it's their habit when they sends flax, they cover it over with earthenware so's the highwaymen shouldn't pay no attention to it.

So once the fellow I'm telling you about hires me to take his goods to Brod and doesn't tell me it's flax, and seeing as how the waggon's loaded with earthenware I reckons it's earthenware. I goes and harnesses my horses, takes the reins in my hands and starts off. The countryside's thick wi' standing corn and the trees are in full fruit and the sun's shining and the heart's satisfied and the horses pulls like horses, not dashing like this here "We'll Run" and not dragging and crawling like that there "Pull Me," but going like real horses ought to go. And I sits me like a lord singing "for behold as the clay in the potter's hand," while the earthenware answers me a chorus back. Passersby greets me and I greets them, some of them great goyim big as giants wi' hair like wild beasts and great sticking-out eyes what looks at the waggon and goes their way.

And if it hadn't been for two drops of water I drunk I'd of reached Brod and gone off back to Boisk without nothing going wrong; only on the way I sees a fountain wi' water from the hills, and I gets down to have a drink.

I finishes my drinking and I has a look round for something to carry water in for the way. I takes one vessel and it's busted, I takes another and it's busted; every one I takes in my hand is busted. When your flax-man sends his wares he ain't particular to cover them wi' good pots, but wi' busted ones as ain't worth nothing.

Seeing I'd uncovered all the top layer there was the flax open to view. Along comes a robberman what hits me over my head till my hat falls off. Not that he wants me to break the Law and go about bare-headed God forbid, because he rightaway claps a pot on my napper, ties it round by the two ears so's it shouldn't fall off, and ties my two hands to a tree. Then he cracks me another one just to show there's no illfeel-ing like, and off he goes; and my two horses with him of course, seeing as how horses is useful when you're in a hurry.

And all this while where's Neta? May the like never befall any traveller, Neta's standing slipping into the ground because it had started to rain and the whole ground was thick and sticky. And there I was dancing fit for a king to see, trying to drag myself out of the muck, and my head would whack against the top o' the pot and back I'd slip deeper than before.

Only God always fixes up a cure before you're even sick, because if it hadn't been for that there pot I'd have sunk into the ground arms and shoulders and head and all, like old Korah in the Bible. While I'm standing dancing like that, along comes a waggonload of Hassidim what sees a pot dancing; and they says, do you reckon that there pot's danc-ing all on its own? Then I gives a yell out of the pot, it's me Neta what's tied up under the pot. So they comes along and has a look at me and drags me out and gives my head a cover with something and sits me down in the waggon and takes me into Brod.

So that's the trouble what I has coming to me out o' drinking; but it ain't nothing yet to what comes to me out of eating.

In short the Hassidim sat me down in the waggon and brought me to Brod and left me at an inn. It was the eve of Sabbath and the missus was standing in front of the oven taking out all kinds of bakings. Well, and then I says to myself, I says, Neta, I says, supposing you was offered some o' them there cakes would you say no to them? Why, I says, nothing's come your way since leaving Boisk only water and a walloping. If they hadn't knocked off my dough on the way I could have ordered something, only now I haven't a farthing wi' me I daren't even ask.

Seeing my guts was grumbling all the same I says to them I says, a fine set o' Jews you are, I says. Who's ever heard of a Jew eating before he says his prayers, I asks them. So before you starts shouting for a bite to fill you let's ask for a pair of tefillin and say my prayers. Well, the guvnor lends me his tallis and his tefillin; and when he notices as I don't put the tallis on he says, what's this, you're a singleman? Yes, says I to him. He makes his missus a sign and says, give the young man a bite of something. Before I'd ever a chance of finishing my prayers even they'd brought me some business in a pot. Them days I was shy alright and never looked a woman in the face, so I don't even know who brought it, the missus or the daughter.

Then he invites me to stay and eat wi' them over the Sabbath. While I'm eating wi' them he asks me what he asks and I answers what I answers. Then he shoves his hand on my shoulder and, Neta, never you worry, he says, pointing to the second female woman, do you see this here one, he says, your life, she's your saviour. The same time they brings in some business in a pot. I says to myself, before you pays any attention to what he's talking about, eat. So I nods my head out o' politeness and I goes on eating.

When the Sabbath is over his kinsfolk and friends gives a come in and asks to hear the story o' the pot. They hears me out and then they laugh and says, all our lives we never heard no better story. Your life there ain't none better even in the book o' the Brod town council, seeing what's a pot to do with a top? Then they claps me on the shoulder and says, all the troubles are in order now, you're meant for better things. And just then I was saying my prayers thanking God for getting me out of a mess and bringing me to the house of such a fine fellow, and I wished all kinds and manners of blessings upon him; and before I knew where I was I was saying to myself, God Almighty, I was saying, how else can I bless him seeing I've already wished him everything I can think of. Only what? Sure enough You know there ain't no man what ain't got some trouble, and if this here fellow has some trouble at home he can't get rid of, please God he'll soon get rid of that there trouble because of the way he did Your will and was real hospitable.

And I sees at once how my blessing makes an impression because the same night they wrote an engagement contract for his daughter. And was I glad then for them! I looks round at everybody there like each one's the bridegroom. When they sees how glad I am they all begins to like me twice as much and sits me down at the head. The guvnor gets up and says to me, good luck, Neta, mazel tov! I nods my head back and says to him, good luck, in-law, mazel tov, like you does to a man as is marrying off a child. Then everybody jumps up at once and shouts out mazel tov, good luck, good luck, Neta, and the womenfolk begins smashing plates and calling out good luck, good luck, mazel tov, mazel tov. I searches all round and looks into all the corners to try and find the bridegroom and wish him mazel tov; and everywhere I turns there's someone as grabs my hand and shakes it and says mazel tov, Neta. And then I understand from that as it's me that's bridegroom.

Not that I'd made up my mind whether I wanted her, mind you; only after the business with the pots how could I turn round and say no I don't want her thank you; particularly thinking how well I'd come out of it. So I says to myself I says, there you are, greedyguts, I says, if that pot had smashed Friday night so's you couldn't eat the business cooked in it they wouldn't be smashing all the pots and pans and plates this Saturday night.

And then I knew it was all over and done with; so I makes up my mind to put up wi' whatever might be coming to me and I says Neta, I says, if you're a silly hoss, take the bridle on your head and the bit in your mouth. I suppose up in Heaven they arranged you should take flax and reckon it's earthenware and have a pot planted on your napper, so's you'd come to a bloke as would feed you some stuff from pots and finish up wi' smashing a lot of pots and pans and plates.

And there ain't never a day what I ain't brought to mind o' the business with the pot, seeing what do all them there pots count against the pots my old woman smashes over me when she gets going. God forbid I should complain against my old woman, believe me; because before I complain against her I ought to complain against myself and my hurry to feed my face wi' stuff out o' pots.

MENDEL MARANTZ—HOUSEWIFE

by DAVID FREEDMAN

"WHAT is a landlord? A bore! He asks you one question all the time—Rent! What is rent? A fine you pay for being poor. What is poverty? Dirt—on the surface. What is riches? More dirt—under the surface. Everybody wants money. Money! What is money? A disease we like to catch but not to spread. Just wait, Zelde! The time will come! I'll be a landlord on Riverside Drive! We'll have our own home—"

"In the cemetery!" Zelde said bitterly.

"Not so fast," Mendel replied, sipping his tea. "Cheer up, Zelde! What is pessimism? A match. It burns the fingers. What is hope? A candle. It lights the way. You never can tell yet! What is life? A see-saw. Today you're poor and tomorrow—"

"You starve!" Zelde muttered, as she rubbed a shirt vigorously against the wash-board.

With a sudden impulse she slapped the shirt into the tub, dried her hands on the apron, and, resting her fists on her hips, turned to Mendel.

"Why shouldn't I be mad?" she began, replying to a previous question. "Here I stand like a fool scrubbing my life away, from morning till night-time, working like a horse, cooking, washing, sewing, cleaning and everything. And for what? For this I eloped with you from a rich father? Did you marry me—or hire me?"

"I stole you. Now I got to pay the penalty. What is love? A conquest. What is marriage? An inquest. Don't worry; your father was no fool. He made believe he didn't see us run away. We felt romantic and he got off cheap! What is romance? Soap-bubbles. They look nice, but taste rotten."

"Never mind! Mister Mendel Marantz, I know you too good. You talk a lot to make me forget what I was saying. But this whole business must come to a finish right here and there!

"You talked into yourself you're a great man, so you don't want to work and you don't want to listen. Sarah sweats in the factory, Hymie peddles papers, Nathan works by the telegrams. And what do you do? You sit like a king and drink tea and make jokes—and nothing! I betcha you're waiting Jakie, Lena and Sammy should grow up so you'll send them to work for you too!"

Mendel shrugged his shoulders.

"What's a woman's tongue? A little dog's tail. It wags too much!"

"I know what I talk. You hate work like poison. You like better to smoke a cigaret and close your eyes and invent schemes how to get rich quicker. But you'll get crazy quicker!"

"Zelde, you're a old woman. You don't understand. All I need is one drop of luck and that drop will sweeten our whole ocean of troubles. If only one of my inventions succeeds, none of us will have to work. Then Sarah will have dowry. What is dowry? Every man's price. And we'll move out of the fish-market. What is success? Fifth Avenue. What is failure? Fifth floor.

"Some day, you'll see. I'll be president of the Refillable Can Company and save the world millions in tin. Just wait!"

"And who'll buy bread in the meantime? Mendel, remember what I tell you. Knock out this craziness from your head. Forget about this can business!"

Mendel's dignity was roused.

"Crazy! That's what you all are! You and all your relatives think I got water on the brain!" He pointed with conviction to his brow. "But up here is the refillable can. Zelde, you see it? It's in the brain, the whole scheme. Up here is full with ideas, plans and machinery. Thinking, scheming, planning all the time. It don't let me sleep. It don't let me eat. It don't let me work. And I should forget it—ah?

"You're all jealous because God was good to me. He gave your brother Morris a shoe factory, your cousin Joe He gave a real estate, your sister Dora a rich husband. But God gave me *brains*—and that none of you got!"

Mendel paced the floor excitedly.

Zelde stood silent and bit her lip. For years she had heard the same flow of rhetoric, the same boast of intellect, and the same trust in luck. The net result was always an evasion of work, and the responsibility shifted back to her and the children.

Mendel Marantz had brains, all right. Otherwise, how could he have existed so long without working?

He always confused her with clever phrases and blurred the issue by creating fictitious ones. And he always succeeded in infecting her with his dreams, until she let him dream on while she did the work. It was that way when they had the candy-stand which her brother Gershon bought for them; it was that way when they kept a vegetable-store which sister Dora financed and later reduced to a push-cart; and it was that way now when they had nothing.

By trade a mechanic, by inclination an inventor, and by nature a dreamer, Mendel abhorred the sordid commonplaces of labor and dreaded the yoke of routine. He had been everything from an insurance agent to a night watchman in rapid succession, and had invented at least a hundred different devices for the betterment of civilization while changing jobs. None of these inventions had as yet received proper recognition, least of all from Zelde. But that could not discourage him to such a point as to drive him to work.

He really believed in his powers. That was the tragedy of it. All geniuses have an unalterable faith in their greatness. But so have most cranks. And Zelde was not sure as to which of the two species Mendel belonged.

She was sure of one thing: the family was hovering perilously near the brink. A single feather added to its burdens and it would topple over. Mendel might take it lightly, but she knew better. She had seen families in that neighborhood crumble to ruin over night. She had known many who—like Mendel—started as harmless dreamers, hopeful idlers, and ended—God forbid—as gamblers, drunkards, and worse.

"How was it with Reznick? Every day he had a scheme to make millions while his wife got sick working in the shop. She died working, and the children went to a orphan asylum and he still wanted to make millions. So he made a corner on the coffee-market and he lost everything what everybody else had, and the only way they could stop him from signing checks with Rockefeller's name was to send him to Bellevue.

"Or Dittenfass? Wasn't he the picture of Mendel? Didn't he hate work like poison, and didn't he pay for it? He thought he was smarter from the rest. Didn't his wife used to told him, 'Dittenfass, look out!'? But he laughed only. He looked out for himself only. And one day she threw in his eyes vitriol! That's what she threw in his eyes, and then he couldn't look any more!

"You can't be too smart. Didn't Karneol try? And it's two years she's waitin' already with swollen eyes he should come back. But he's got to serve three more.

"The best smartness is to do a day's work. If you wait it shall happen miracles—it happens! But the wrong way!"

Zelde knew. She wished she didn't know.

"Maybe you can invent something to make you work," she offered as a possible solution. "Somebody else with your brains could make a fortune. Why don't you make at least a living?"

"Brains make ideas; fools can make money. That's why your relatives are rich. What is business. Blind man's bluff. They shut your eyes and open your pockets!"

"Again you mix me up," she said warily, sensing this new attempt to befuddle the issue. "What's the result from all this? You joke and we starve. It's lucky Sarah works. If not, we would all be thrown out in the street, already."

At this moment Sarah entered. She was pale and tired from the climb of stairs. She dropped her hat languidly on the couch and sank into a chair.

Zelde was too surprised to speak. It was only one-thirty. She never expected Sarah before six. An ominous thought flitted through her mind. She looked anxiously at her daughter. Sarah's gaze shifted to the floor.

An oppressive silence gathered over them. Then Sarah tried to mumble something. But Zelde understood without hearing. Her heart had told her.

"It's slack! Everybody laid off. Sarah, too!"

What she had dreaded most had happened. The family of Marantz was now over the brink. Zelde stood crushed by the thought of the morrow. Sarah sat staring vacantly, her chin against her clenched hand. Mendel stopped smoking to appear less conspicuous.

Four female eyes detected him, however, and scorched him with their gaze.

The handwriting on the wall was unnecessarily large.

Mendel Marantz knew that his crisis was at hand.

Zelde spoke.

"That settles it. Either tomorrow you go to work or go altogether! Yessir! You, I mean, mister!"

Mendel had faced crises before. Some he had overcome with a jest, others with a promise, still others with a pretence at work until the novelty wore off. But there was a grimness in Zelde's manner this time that looked fatal. Nothing but a permanent job and lifelong drudgery could save him now. But that would also destroy him.

Tying him down to a position was like hitching a lion to a cart. His mind could not travel on tracks. It was too restive and spirited. He could never repeat an act without discovering how much easier it might be done by machinery, and immediately he set himself to invent the necessary machine. That was why he could not be a tailor. After he once threaded a needle, he started to devise a simple instrument for doing it, and in the meantime lost his job. And that happened in every case.

His head was so full of ideas that he often had to stand still to keep his balance. His mind sapped all of his powers and left him powerless for work. In order to work he would have to stop thinking. He might just as well stop living. Idleness was as essential a part of his make-up as industry was of Zelde's.

"I wasn't made for work," he said with finality. "I mean—for just plain work. Some people work with their feet, others with their hands. I work with my head. You don't expect I shall sit like Simon, the shoemaker, every day, and hit nails till I get consumption. One—two—three, I invent a machinery which hits nails, cuts leather, fits heels, makes patches, and I sit down and laugh on the world. I can't work like others, just as others can't work like me!"

"You can make me believe night is day and black is white, but it won't help you. It's a new rule in this house from today on—those who work, eat; those who don't, don't. If you think you can invent food, go ahead. So long I live my children is not going to starve. From today on I'm the father from this family. If you don't want to go to work—I will!"

Mendel was skeptical.

"What is a woman?" he thought. "A lot of thunder, but a little rain."

Still, the shower was more drenching than he supposed.

"Tomorrow morning I go back to be a dressmaker by fancy dresses. Sarah, you come with me. I learn you a real trade."

Then she turned to Mendel with a sneer.

"You thought I play around in the house, didn't you? All right! Now you stay home and play like I did. You want to eat? Cook, yourself. You think in the house it's easy? You'll find out different. Send the children to school, go up on the roof to hang clothes, run down with the garbage five floors, buy groceries, wash underwear, mend stockings, press shirts, scrub floors—go on! Have a good time, and I'll pay the bills."

Mendel admitted that Zelde had worn for some time the family trousers, but he believed that he still wore the belt. However, her inexorable decision disillusioned him. He admitted having been caught slightly off his guard. He had never suspected that a type of work existed so near him, into which he might be forced out of sheer necessity. Not that he intended to do it! But still—

"What is a woman?" he reconsidered. "Lightning. It's nice and bright till it hits you."

The next morning Mendel discovered perpetual motion. The children had taken possession of the house. He dodged flying pillows, tripped over upset furniture, slipped on greasy garbage from an overturned can, found salt in his coffee and something sharper on his seat. He kept constantly moving to avoid falling objects and fell into others. He had planned to have nothing to do with the house, but the house was having a great deal to do with him.

The youngsters seemed to be under the impression that with Zelde all law and order had passed away. Mendel found it hard work to change their minds. It was monotonous to spank Lena, then Jakie, then Sammy. Then over again. It would be better to send them off to school. But they had to be dressed and fed and washed for that!

He was tempted to snatch his hat and coat and leave the house. But what would he do in the streets?

He hesitated, gritted his teeth, and set to work by scrubbing Jakie's face till it resembled a carrot.

"What's a wife?" he muttered, and Lena started at the question. "A telescope! She makes you see stars!" And some soap got into his eye.

"Sammy, don't you never marry!" he exclaimed with a profound look of warning at the frightened little boy. "What is marriage? First a ring on the finger and later—on the neck. Lena, stop pulling Jakie's hair. She's like her mother. Don't do that, Sammy. A table-cloth ain't a handkerchief! Ai! Little children, little troubles; big children, big troubles. What is children? Life insurance. Some day they pay you back —when you're dead. But you like them anyhow. Such is life! You know it's tough, but you try it once, anyway.

"After all, what is life? A journey. What is death? The goal. What is man? A passenger. What is woman? Freight.

"Jakie, you bad boy! Don't cry, Lena. He didn't mean it. Here's an apple. Go to school. Sammy, get off the bannister! Look out, children! It's a step missing down there! Who's crying? Jakie, give her back the apple! Did you ever hear such excitements? My goodness!"

Mendel, perspired, exhausted, sank into a chair.

"I'm working after all," he noted with surprise. "If this lasts, I don't."

But the trials of Mendel Marantz had only begun. The sensation of womanhood did not thrill his bosom, and the charms of housekeeping failed to allure him. A home like a warehouse on moving-day tumbled about him. The beds were upset, the table and floor were littered with breakfast leavings, the cupboard was bare, the dishes were piled in the sink, the dust had gathered already as if cleaning were a lost art, and the general atmosphere was one of dejection, confusion, chaos. The magic touch of the housewife revealed itself by its absence.

Zelde had now proved to him conclusively that her presence and service were essential to his comfort. As if he had ever questioned the fact. Why did she go to all this trouble to drive home a point?

"Zelde, a glass of tea," he used to say, and the tea stood steaming hot before him. "Zelde, it's a draft. Shut up the window," and presently the draft was gone.

"Zelde—" he would call, leaning back in his chair, but why torture himself with things that were no more?

That night when Zelde arrived, masculine and business-like, through with work and ready for supper, she beheld a pitiful spectacle.

The house was in hopeless disorder. The children had managed that. The cat was on the table and Jakie was under it, while Lena kept him there with her foot. Sammy's eye had been darkened by a flying saucer which Hymie let go in a moment of abandon. Everything was where it should not be. The kitchen furniture had been moved into the dining room and the feather beds were in the wash-tub.

Mendel was nowhere within the range of Zelde's call.

"Where is papa?" she asked sharply, after calming the youngsters with her two convincing hands. "Everything is upside down. I betcha he didn't do a thing all day. My goodness, that man will make me crazy!"

A crashing sound as of dishes in hasty descent issued from the next room.

Zelde and her retinue rushed to the scene of disaster. With one foot in the sink and the other on the wash-tub Mendel Marantz was poised on high, searching through the closet. Dishes, pans, bottles and rags lay scattered in ruined fragments beneath him.

Zelde blazed.

"Gozlen!" she almost shrieked. "What do you want up there!"

Mendel steadied himself. His heart having missed a beat, he waited a moment, then answered quietly, "Iodine."

"What for iodine, what for?" She was still furious, but also a little anxious.

"A small scratch," he explained without moving. "My finger got caught—under the meat-chopper."

"Oi! You clumsy! And what's all the rags and the water on the floor?"

"To put by my side and my leg. I—slipped and—the gas-range fell on me. My ankle turned around. The soup was good and hot. Maybe you got something for burns?"

Zelde was a little less furious and a little more anxious.

"Then what are you climbing on the walls for? Go in bed. Go—you look broken in pieces!"

She sighed heavily and shook her head.

"After all, he's only a man," she soliloquized. "What can you expect? He don't know if he's alive!"

She continued to scold, but nursed him tenderly.

"How is it? You're a inventor, and you don't know how to light the gas without blowing up the house? A man who can't help nobody else can't help himself!"

After a pause she said, "Maybe I should stay home? Ah?"

"Maybe," he murmured weakly.

Zelde vacillated.

"So what'll be if I stay home?" she prodded.

"It'll be better."

"That I know, but what'll be with you?"

"I'll get well."

"And—?" She expected him not only to recover, but to reform.

"And if I get well I'll feel good. What is health? A garden. What is sickness? A grave. What is a good wife? A gardener. What is a bad wife? A grave-digger."

"He's as bad as ever," she thought.

She finally resolved, "It's not such a terrible! He won't die from it and we can't live from it. He'll learn a lesson and I'll earn a living."

And the experiment continued.

It was very hard on Mendel. It was harder on Sarah and hardest on Zelde. But time subdued Mendel's protests and improved his work.

Zelde was surprised at his altered attitude of gradual submission. It almost alarmed her. She had never really intended this radical change to last. She had expected Mendel to rebel more and more violently as time went on and finally to make a break for his freedom and exclaim, "I'm sick and tired of this slavery. I'm going to work!"

Instead he was getting actually to like it. By degrees Zelde found less to do in the house after her return from the shop. True, his work was crude and slovenly to her practiced eye. She never would have cleaned dishes as he did, with a whisk-broom, or swept dirt under the table, or boiled soup in a coffee-pot, or wiped the floor with a perfectly good skirt.

But withal, Mendel was doing things, and as his domestic craftsmanship improved, Zelde grew more disappointed and depressed. She felt that he was planning to displace her permanently. She pictured him bending over the wash-tub as she used to do; or arranging the dishes in the closet, which was once her favorite diversion; or scouring the pots and pans as only she knew how, and a genuine feeling of envy and longing seized her.

"Thief!" she was tempted to cry. "Go out from my kitchen! Give me back my apron and let alone my housework!"

For she had become nothing more than a boarder in that home, to be tolerated merely because she earned the rent. She saw the children only at supper-time, and they looked curiously at her as if they hardly recognized her.

At table all eyes were turned to pa.

"Papa, Sammy took my spoon!"

"Take his," Mendel decreed.

"Pa, I want some more meat!"

"Take mine."

"Pop, Lena stole my bread!"

"Take hers."

"Pa-ah! The thoup ith too hot. I tan't eat it!" Jakie complained, and turned a bruised tongue to his father.

"Take some water from the sink," was Mendel's motherly advice.

Zelde felt like a stranger. They did not seem to know that she was present. She tried to interfere.

"Don't put water in soup, Jakie! Better blow on it."

But the little boy slipped down from the chair without noticing her, wriggled out from under the table, and soon returned, gaily carrying a cup of sink-water.

Her maternal instinct rebelled.

"No!" she said warningly, as Jakie tilted the cup over the plate of bean-soup.

But the child, with his eyes fixed on Mendel, poured the contents bravely.

Zelde slapped his hand, and the cup fell with a clatter. It was not a hard blow, but an impulsive one. It created a strained and awkward silence. Jakie burst into tears. He ran to Mendel and buried his little face in daddy's lap. Lena began to whimper in sympathy.

Something snapped in Zelde. Her appetite was gone. She rose and went into the bedroom and shut the door behind her.

She did not want them to hear her sobs.

It had all turned out so different!

Instead of driving Mendel to work she had driven herself into exile. Mendel the housewife was now further from ever getting a man's job than Mendel the idler had ever been. Zelde felt she had made a grave mistake. Rather should she have permitted him to idle and mope —he would have tired of it eventually—than that he should be wrongly occupied and contented.

If only she could undo what she had done, she'd be satisfied.

"After all, a house to manage is for a woman," she began, bent upon re-establishing the old order. "A man should do housework? It can make him crazy yet!"

"I believe you," Mendel conceded.

"It don't look like housework should agree with you," she observed.

"Looks is deceiving."

There was a pause. A good deal of understanding passed between them.

"Mendel, hard work will kill you yet," she insisted.

"So will idleness—in the long run. What is death? An appointment. You got to keep it some time."

"But you don't look good."

"I don't feel bad."

Zelde became a little dizzy. Did he mean to say that he intended to stick to housework? She tried to tempt him.

"Wouldn't you like, like you used to, to have nothing to do, and sit and cross your legs, and, without you should move, somebody should bring you hot tea?"

Mendel blew rings of smoke at the ceiling.

Zelde continued, scarcely breathing.

"And wouldn't you like to lie on the couch with your hands together behind your head and look on the sky from the window and dream what a great inventor you are?"

An impressive silence followed. On Mendel's face were fleeting traces of an inner struggle.

"And—I'll clean the house," she added softly to clear any doubts that he might still have.

Mendel shook his head.

"It'll be too hard for you," he said gallantly.

"It's not such a terrible!"

"I haven't the heart to let you," he complained feebly.

"You'll get over it."

His tone became firmer.

"No! Housework is not for a woman. Like the Masora says, 'Be good to your wife and give your children to eat.' That means a man should clean the house and cook for his children. What is a wife? A soldier. Her place is on the field. What is a husband? A general. His place is at home!"

Zelde was chagrined.

"So this is the future what you aimed for?" she chided. "To be a washerwoman and a porter! Pooh! You ought to be ashamed to look on my face! Think what people say! They don't know which is what? If I am the husband or if you are the wife or how!"

Mendel carefully rolled a new cigarette. There was a plaintive note in her anger. He could afford to be defiant.

"Didn't you make me to stay home and work? So! I'm working! What is work? Pleasure!— If you know how!"

And he struck a match.

Zelde sat down to avoid falling down.

"Work is pleasure," echoed through her mind like an explosion. Maybe solitary confinement at home every day had gone to his head. Or maybe—maybe—! She slowly repeated to herself his sally. "What is work? Pleasure!" and "What is pleasure?" she wondered. The shock of the answer almost made her scream.

So that was it! She had suspected something, but *that* would never have occurred to her in a million years. Those floor-brushes that she found the other day under the bed, and the mop and the tin pail. They did not belong to the house. To whom *did* they belong? She had certainly seen them somewhere before. Now she knew! At the janitor's!

"No wonder he likes to stay home," she muttered to herself. "I should have knew; it's a bad sign if Mendel likes work all of a sudden!"

Her suspicions were still hypothetical, but fragments of evidence were fast falling in to shape an ominous and accusing picture.

One day, upon her return from work, Zelde found Mendel sitting near the window, restfully smoking a cigarette. His legs were crossed under his apron and his arms were folded over his lap. He gazed wistfully out upon the city.

Zelde looked about her in astonishment. The house was tidy, the kitchen spick and span, the wash dried and ironed, the floor freshly scrubbed. A model housewife would have envied the immaculate perfection of the work.

Zelde gasped. So early in the day and already through with all his work! And what work!

"Sarah, I wonder who did it," she finally said to her daughter when she had regained her composure.

Her groping suspicions now became a startling conviction. Evidence fairly shrieked at her from every corner.

"Only a woman could do this," she thought, overcome by the shock of the revelation.

"Who do you think?" Sarah asked innocently.

"Did you see the way she looks at me?" Zelde exclaimed with mounting fury. "No wonder she laughs in my face. No wonder she tells all the neighbors, 'Such a fool! She works and he plays!' No wonder!"

"What are you talking about?" Sarah inquired, bewildered.

"Never mind! Your father knows what I mean! She did it. Rifke! The janitor's wife! I know her, all right. She made eyes to Mister Mendel Marantz lots of times! She's older from me by four years, but she paints up like a sign and makes her hair Buster Brown and thinks the men die for her. Ask your father. He knows!"

Mendel sat dumofounded. His eyes opened like mouths.

"Don't make believe you're innocent. I know you men too good," Zelde broke out violently. "I slave like a dog and that dirty old—" Tears of rage stifled her. But with a swift change of tone she added, her finger shaking under Mendel's nose, "Mister Marantz, remember, you'll be sorry for this." And she walked out of the room.

Mendel was sorry for her. He turned a puzzled face to Sarah. "When the house was upside down she said I made her crazy. Now when it's fixed up she tries to make me crazy! What's a wife? An epidemic. If it don't break out here, it breaks out there!"

The next day Zelde fidgeted at her work. She was prompted to fling it aside, rush home, and catch them together—Mendel and Rifke—and pull out the old vixen's hair and scratch out her eyes. But she bided her time. Mendel was, no doubt, expecting a surprise attack and perhaps had warned his paramour to stay away.

Zelde decided to be wily. She would make believe that she had forgotten and forgiven. But how could she?

That night, on the landing of the fourth floor, she met Rifke coming down from the fifth. There were only two tenants on the fifth floor— Mrs. Peril Tzvack, a widow who hated Rifke and would never let her into her house, and Mendel Marantz. From which of the two was Rifke coming?

As Zelde entered her home the same neatness, the same cleanliness and smartness stung her sight. In fact, she herself could not have done better. To be honest—not even as good. The house was a mirror of spotlessness. It was so obviously the accomplishment of the wicked woman she had met on the stairs that Zelde spent a tortured and sleepless night.

She went to work the next morning with a splitting headache, and mists swam before her eyes as she tried to sew. Weird thoughts revolved in her mind. If it were only a question of Mendel, she would not hesitate a moment to leave him forever. But the children! A daughter of marriageable age and the tiny ones! What would people say? And even Mendel. True, there was no excuse—absolutely none—for his abominable treachery. She would never forgive him! Still, Rifke, that superannuated flirt, was the kind of woman that could turn any man's head! With that double chin of hers and the shaved neck and a dimple like a funnel in her cheek! That's what the men liked!

After all, Mendel was a helpless male, all alone in a house. He probably did not know the first thing about housekeeping and would have starved or been buried in dirt if he had not appealed to somebody to help him. And Rifke was just the type to take advantage of a defenceless man in such a predicament. She doubtless opened her eyes at him like two coal-scuttles, and pursed her lips—she had a way of doing it which gave the women of the neighborhood heart failure. And Mendel must have been grateful and kind to her for her assistance, and she must have mistaken his attitude for something else. She always misunderstood kindness from men.

So that's how Mendel managed to clean the house so well! And that's why work was pleasure to him! Judging by the amount and quality of the work Rifke was doing for him, their affection for each other must have developed to an alarming degree.

Zelde visualized the hateful scenes of faithlessness in which Mendel probably danced fawningly about Rifke, the fifty-three-year-old "vamp," who cleaned dishes and washed clothes for him as a reward. She must have nudged him with her elbow while she boiled the wash and said invitingly, "Mendel, dear, why are you blind to beauty?"

And Mendel, edging closer, must have answered, "What is beauty? Wine! The older it gets, the rarer it is!" Then pressing his cheek against hers, he undoubtedly added, with tenderness, "You're so fat! It's a pleasure to hold you around! What is a man? Dynamite. What is a woman? A burning match. What is passion? The explosion!"

"Stop it! Your whiskers tickle me," she probably replied with a coquettish laugh, and slapped him playfully over the hands with a rinsed shirt.

But she was only jesting, and was perhaps ecstatic with joy when Mendel courageously kissed her on the cheek despite her protests, and exclaimed, "What is a kiss? A smack for which you turn the other cheek!" And she probably turned it.

Then Rifke amorously rested her head on his chest and looked up with those devilish eyes of hers, and, linking her plump arms about his neck, she whispered, "Love me, Mendel, love me! I am yours!"

And Mendel, planting his feet more solidly to bear her weight, and carried away by the flames of desire, must have gripped her in his passionate embrace and murmured in a throaty voice, "What is love? A broom. It sweeps you away!"

"What's the matter with you, Zelde?" cried Marcus, the tailor, biting the thread from a seam. "You stitched the skirt to a sleeve and you're sewing up the neck of the waist!

"You look white like a ghost!"

Zelde drew herself up, as out of a lethargy.

"Eh! W-where am I? Oh!"

And her face sank into her palms.

Instantly there was a tumult in the shop.

A startled group of frightened men and women gathered about her.

But Zelde regained her self-control, without aid, and pale and faint though she was, she smiled weakly to reassure them all.

"It's nothing. A dizziness. I'm better," she said. But Sarah insisted upon taking her home at once.

"That's right," Marcus advised. "Go home and take a hot tea with lemon. It'll sweat you out."

He added in an undertone to his neighbor, "It's a shame! Such a fine woman! She's got a husband who's a nix!"

Zelde refused to have Sarah accompany her home.

"We can't afford you shall lose a half day," she argued. But the real reason was that she did not wish her daughter to behold her father's infamy.

At eleven o'clock Zelde left. As she neared the house her breath became short and rapid. She stumbled several times going up the stairs. She stopped at the door.

Was it voices or was it her imagination?

No. Yes. It was. A man's voice, then a woman's laughter, then some—oh! She could stand it no longer. She broke wildly into the room and dislodged a bulky person who had been leaning against the door. Zelde stood electrified.

It was Rifke. And she was laughing in her face! And there was Mendel. And the janitor, too—Rifke's husband. And two men! With stovepipe hats and cutaways and spats! Detectives, no doubt! Brought by the janitor to catch his wife and arrest Mendel! Oh, heavens! And there was Morton, Mendel's nephew, a lawyer!

"Oi! A lawyer in the case!" she moaned to herself. "Then everything is lost!"

Zelde was ready to drop, but Mendel took her by the hand, and she heard him say, "This is my wife. It's all her fault. She drove me to it."

"We want you to come with us now," one of the strangers said to Mendel.

"What's the matter here, anyhow?" Zelde exclaimed at last.

"I got to go with these people," Mendel replied. "But you can ask—Rifke," he added significantly. "She knows all about it."

Mendel, his nephew and the two gentlemen departed before Zelde had time to protest. She turned with burning eyes to Rifke—the hussy!

"I wish they could take my husband where they take yours," Rifke began by way of explanation. "You don't know what kind of a husband you got. It's gonna be in all the papers. He did something. Those men what was here watched him, and when they seen it they jumped up like crazy."

"What did he do?" Zelde asked in great alarm. "I betcha you made him to do it."

"I? He says you made him. I only brought up the people. They knock by me in the door. They say, 'Do Mendel Marantz live here? Where is it?' So I bring them up."

"What for did you bring them up—what for? A blind one could see it's detectives!" Zelde muttered angrily.

"How shall I know it who they are? When they came in your husband turned white like milk. 'Are you the man which done it?' they ask him, and he says, shivering, 'Yes.'"

Zelde wrung her hands.

"What for did he say 'Yes'—what for?"

"Because it's true," Rifke explained.

"What's true?"

"That he done it."

"What did he done—what? You'll make me crazy yet. Why don't you tell me?"

"But I told you already!"

"When did you told me—when? You're talkin' and talkin' and it don't come out nothing! What happened here? What did they want here? Why is your husband here? Why are you here? Why were they here? What's the matter here, altogether, anyway?"

"It's a whole lot the matter—with you!" Rifke exclaimed impatiently. "Come over here and look and maybe it'll open your eyes!"

She led the dazed Zelde into the kitchen.

"You see it?" Rifke asked triumphantly, pointing out a mass of wrinkled canvas in the middle of the room.

"What shall I see?" Zelde answered skeptically. "Rags, I see!"

"But under the rags!" Rifke insisted. She lifted the canvas. Zelde stood completely bewildered. Her eyes opened wide, then her face reddened. A feeling of indignation welled up in her.

"You can't make a fool from me!" she began at last with rising momentum. "What do you show me—what? An ash-can on wheels! What's that got to do with you and my husband? Don't think I don't know. You show me this, I should forget *that!*"

Rifke began to perspire. She mopped her face with her apron as she struggled to keep calm.

"You don't know what I'm talkin' about and I don't know what you're talkin' about. It's mixed up, everything! Where do you see a ashcan? This ain't a ash-can! It looks, maybe, like it. But it ain't. All my friends should have such ash-cans! It's a wonder in the world!"

Zelde's head was reeling.

"So what is it, I'm asking you?" she gasped helplessly.

"It's a whole business!" Rifke replied. "We seen it, my husband Shmeril and me and the people which was here. Your husband showed us. He winds up the can like a phonograph and it begins to play. The dishes go in dirty and they come out clean like after a bath. You see it?

On these straps the dishes take a ride. They go in from the back and come out on the front. When it's finished the dishes, your husband opens the box—I thought a man will jump out from it—but it's only wheels and straps and wires and pipes inside! Did you ever?

"Then he pulls off the feet and the box sits down on the floor, and he takes out the straps from the back door and puts in such a board with bumps and brushes, and he turns the handle and the box rides like a automobile and washes up the floor till it shines! I tell you the people was standing and looking—I thought their eyes would fall out!

"Then your husband stands up the box and puts back the feet and takes out the bumpy board and sticks in a whole machinery with pipes and wheels and winds up the machine and pumps in fresh water and throws in all the old clothes, and you hear inside such a noise, and then the clothes come out like frankfurters, clean and washed and ready to hang! Such a business! You don't have to work no more! It works itself! I wouldn't mind to have such a box by me!"

Zelde, dumb with amazement, gazed at the mute, ugly monster before her. She recognized the wheels from the old baby-carriage; the legs were from her kitchen chair; the handle from the stove. And now she remembered the can, the brushes, and the mops that Rifke had probably discarded, and that Mendel had used in the creation of this freak.

So this was the rival she had been jealous of, the usurper of her rights!

"It makes in five minutes what I do a whole day," Rifke rambled along. "They call it such a fancy name—Combination House-Cleaner. It cleans everything. The strangers is from a company which goes to make millions cans like this.

"You're gonna be rich, Mrs. Marantz!

"Who would think from house-cleaning you could get rich! Here I'm cleaning houses for twenty-nine years and I never thought from such a scheme! You gotta have luck, I tell you!"

"And I thought all the time it was Rifke! Oi, Mendel, you must think I'm such a fool!"

"Forget it. If not for you I never would have did what I done. You made me to do it."

"I didn't, Mendel."

She added in a caressing tone:

"Your laziness did it, Mendel. You invented that machine because you were too lazy to work."

"What's a wife? An X-Ray. She knows you through and through!"

BABY MILLY AND THE PHARAOH

by BEN HECHT

I

ERMAN GERSHKY was worth around six hundred million dollars.
People who liked to quibble, and the movie industry is full of
such, put his fortune at three hundred million. There were still
others—those shrewd nonentities to be found on all curbings watching
all the parades—who were ready to argue that Mr. Gershky had very
little money of his own, but that he controlled hundreds of millions. That
is, if he had wanted to he could spend a thousand million; or if he
needed money he could raise a thousand million.

Mr. Gershky himself, who had spent his youth and much of his
maturity counting nickels, didn't know the right answer. If you had
asked Mr. Gershky point blank how much money he was worth he
might have answered with Zcar Paul (the mad one) "as much as there
is." As a matter of fact Mr. Gershky would have scratched his flat, bald
head unhappily and looked bored and said nothing, and been very embarrassed and thought you a fool.

But just because Mr. Gershky was too rich to be concerned with how
rich he was, the subject did not lack interest for others and Mr. Gershky's
little ears would have long ago been burned away if the discussion of
his bank balance had had any effect on them.

Mr. Gershky had entered the movie industry when he was in his
late forties and had puttered around like any financier, buying, selling,
and organizing and barricading himself behind more and more lawyers.
Then suddenly Mr. Gershky had changed from a financier into a sort
of a fungus bearing his name and spreading all over the world. For
some fifteen years Mr. Gershky had then sat in one office after another
and grown more and more awe-inspiring to his associates and rivals—as
he retired more and more from contact with them. And finally Mr.
Gershky had undergone another change—passing from a fungus into a
bas-relief Pharaoh—a sort of half-fabulous potentate imbedded in a new
Empire of (God forgive the word) Art.

But to return to the interesting side issue of Mr. Gershky's wealth.
Once on a train to California when he had just turned Pharaoh, Mr.
Gershky had wandered out of his private car and encountered a rather

terrifying little fat man who looked so much like himself that he had stared at him. The thought came to his mind that this squat, round-faced, flat-headed fellow passenger might well be a relative and Mr. Gershky would have risen quickly from the club chair into which he had settled himself and scurried back to his private car, but the presence or even thought of a relative always deprived Mr. Gershky of his initiative and even personality.

So he had sat full of apprehension and yet powerless—waiting for the inevitable cry of uncle or cousin from this little stuffed-looking stranger.

Mr. Gershky already had some two or three hundred relatives working for him. This did not include that inner circle of relatives whom he knew by name or at least could remember vaguely having seen somewhere or heard about—before they joined the payroll. This inner circle though numerous, numbering some thirty or forty souls, made just as good managers and vice-presidents as strangers—at least Mr. Gershky had long reconciled himself to this theory. What harassed him about relatives and made him feel helpless before this present unknown but dreadfully familiar-looking little fat man, was the strange ramifications of lineage they had to offer him. Hardly a week had passed in the last ten years that had not produced some third uncle or fourth cousin—some dubious and far-fetched claimant to the Gershky blood stream. And the greed of all these magically spawned kinsmen made an uncomfortable din in Mr. Gershky's spirit as if he were standing knee-deep in some ghostly, biological surf.

Sure enough the little fat man whom Mr. Gershky, with a deep shock to his vanity, recognized as looking almost like a twin brother, began to return his furtive eyeing and finally approached him and addressed him by name and began shaking his head contemptuously and snorting.

It developed, however, that the stranger, far from laying claim to some common Aunt Zippa in Kremetchuk, seemed to feel a great relief that despite his resemblance to the famous Mr. Gershky (a phenomenon that had not passed without comment) he was in no way related to him. For the little fat man was a Socialist, a very sincere one—and he would have looked upon such a kinsman as Mr. Gershky as a personal betrayal of his doctrines. He, the little fat man, regarded the accumulation of wealth—so he told Mr. Gershky—as a crime against civilization. And then while Mr. Gershky stared out of the train window at the endless-looking desert covered with dirty little bushes through which they were passing, the little fat man launched into an amazing flood of statistics to which Mr. Gershky's mathematically inclined mind couldn't help listening.

Finally fastening the cinema colossus with a triumphant and sneering eye, this stranger in the desert said something to Mr. Gershky about his riches that he was never to forget—and that continued to bother him for years afterward in a peculiar, irrational way.

The little fat man said, snorting now without fear of contradiction, that Mr. Gershky had so much money that if he were to stand on Brooklyn Bridge throwing it away as fast as he could in two-dollar bills it would take him ten years to get rid of it.

Day and night without stop for a second, Mr. Gershky could drop two-dollar bills off Brooklyn Bridge at the rate of one for every clock tick and it would take ten years—but Mr. Gershky, sensing some psychic shock to his nature, had risen at this point and gone hurriedly back to his private car.

Here with a pencil Mr. Gershky had sought to verify this statement about Brooklyn Bridge. He figured out 86,400 seconds in a day and 31,536,000 seconds in a year and with a deep feeling of inner distress realized that the little fat man was more or less right.

As a result Mr. Gershky, staring again at the desert, felt a peculiar disillusion with himself and with his status of Pharaoh. Far from pointing a moral in Mr. Gershky's soul about the crime of wealth accumulation, this stranger had suddenly made Mr. Gershky feel poor—or rather he had removed from his spirit the illusion that his riches were inexhaustible; which seemed to Mr. Gershky, riding through the desert in his private car, much the same thing. Ten years was such a short time. And whenever Mr. Gershky crossed the Brooklyn Bridge thereafter, an odd disquiet seized him—and the picture of a Mr. Gershky standing haggard at the bridge rail with a last two-dollar bill in his hand always darkened his mood.

2

Of the fifteen or twenty subsidiary czars who conducted the Gershky Amusement Enterprises, and with whom Mr. Gershky consulted (needlessly) from week to week, there was none but seemed physically, mentally, and spiritually superior to the Pharaoh. These production heads, studio heads, sales heads and general financial heads were as windy and phenagling, as devious, as full of guile, greed, and personality as the general military staff of a Mexican revolution. Their energies were about equally divided between the slam-bang catch-as-catch-can business of

movie-making and selling and the subtle, hoighty-toighty oriental in-
trigue involved in the keeping of their jobs.

The superiority of Mr. Gershky's group of nobles, their keener grasp
on the details of his enterprises, their handsomer faces, their more
worldly minds and more dynamic spirits were all, however, discounted
by the fact that, toil and triumph as they might, they remained Mr.
Gershky's employees.

However high they rose, however gaudy and bizarre the powers they
maneuvered into their hands, Mr. Gershky, fat, squat, bland and round-
faced, remained beyond their reach—as if he occupied, and functioned
within, another dimension. He appeared once a week in his office whose
windows overlooked the tangle and tom-tom of Broadway. He would
come sidling out of the elevator and treading softly, almost apologetically,
down the corridors to his sanctum, leaving behind in those employees
lucky enough to witness his passage a confused sense of wrong-doing.

So great, so powerful was the name Gershky in their minds that they
felt their attitude in his actual presence failed to do him justice. While
an inner backbone within them curved itself into the immemorial salute
to Pharaohdom, while their spirits postured in the ancient and poetical
obeisance before the Light of the World, being Americans they kept their
bodies straight, held their breaths, tried to look natural and at the same
time deeply infatuated with their work as Mr. Gershky moved by.

The tension he inspired was very pleasing to Mr. Gershky, pleasing
in a minor and almost childish way. For Mr. Gershky was not vain.
He lacked the imagination to understand his own greatness in the eyes
of others. He was almost entirely without that egoism which makes great
men dramatize and delight in their effect upon inferiors.

In short Mr. Gershky wasn't thrilled by himself. He was a simple
and cautious little Pharaoh. He accepted the inner awe and obeisances
of his court with a pleased but detached mind, and at heart he remained
as shy, evasive, and ineffectual a social being as in the days of his broken
accents and nickel-nursing. Now, after so many years of quite maniacal
success he would no more have been capable of arresting the attention,
let alone commanding the respect, of strangers than of leading the Symphony Orchestra in Carnegie Hall.

But this shyness made Mr. Gershky a perfect Pharaoh. For because
of it he never competed with his own greatness, of giving it any dramatic or manneristic outline. And this delinquency was, as always, a
good preservative for his reputation. Its result was that when he appeared
in the flesh he became more of a legend than ever, for he was incapable

of obtruding a human and disillusioning figure on the almost fabulous preconceptions he encountered in people's minds.

Arrived in his office, Mr. Gershky's secretaries would summon the subsidiary Czars and the weekly conference would ensue. A stranger attending these conferences would have come away with a deep conviction that Mr. Gershky was an out-and-out fool. For, surrounded by his nobles, Mr. Gershky would start talking in a mild, uninteresting voice and keep on talking and repeating himself until one would have expected his listeners to burst with ennui. Instead they sat hanging on Mr. Gershky's words as if all their fates were secretly contained in his reiterative babble—which, in a manner, they were.

The reason Mr. Gershky had grown to talk like this—he who had once been a very concise if ungrammatical financier and who socially was hardly capable of a comment on the weather—was that for a good ten years (ever since he had mysteriously rid himself of a partner) nobody had interrupted him. Also Mr. Gershky, being a shy and socially ineffectual man, found a happy relief from his general human incompetence in these hours of conference.

Here he was garrulous. Here the vague little spirit of the man, protected and coddled by this inner court, emerged and gamboled lamely about the premises for several giddy hours—a diversion which cost Mr. Gershky thousands of dollars if the accumulating salaries of his high-priced nobles were to be calculated.

The conference usually lasted until Mr. Gershky became satiated with his own reiterations. So perfect was the respect in which Mr. Gershky was held that no one ever thought of turning on him when he was finally run down, hoarse and winded with any sort of argument. Each noble, at the conclusion of Mr. Gershky's verbigeration, consumed a few minutes repeating fragments of the Pharaoh's discourse, during which the latter listened proudly and excitedly, bursting into happy exclamations of "Fine. That's right. Oke. Exactly. Puffeck."

And when each of the Czars had been patted on the head for his fine parroting, the company arose and—as on this early summer afternoon which was to usher such disturbing events into his life—Mr. Gershky found himself all too quickly alone, all too completely abandoned to his own greatness.

His court as always had obsequiously withdrawn, each member thereof eager not to seem too sycophantically interested in the Pharaoh and all of them instinctively contributing to the industry's illusion that Mr. Gershky was too vast, too imperial a figure to waste his time with any of them. But Mr. Gershky's vastness and imperialness were external qualities on which his soul nor his heart nor yet his mind could feed.

Never was there a more touching illustration of the fact that too much greatness is almost as useless to its possessor as none. For Mr. Gershky was so important that there was really nothing he could stoop to with which to occupy himself, and nobody he could speak to and no one, not even his most intimate nobles, who dared, without summons, speak to him.

There were several hundred thousand things Mr. Gershky could, as a matter of fact, have turned his hand to this afternoon. He could have called in any one of his stenographers, told her to change her name, telephoned his nobles in Hollywood, set into operation such a blistering ballyhoo as would have converted her within six months into a world figure and popular idol. Indeed there was almost nothing one could think of that Mr. Gershky couldn't do with a wave of his cinema wand. He could make stockmarket panics, create stars, order parades, throw up skyscrapers, frighten the wits out of a hundred thousand employees, his nobles included; tangle destinies, answer dreams and shower gold in a way that would have made Merlin and Aladdin gape like amateurs.

But Mr. Gershky was too sensible a man to engage in any of these sleight of hands. He left such didoes to his lesser rivals—the runner-up Pharaohs of Hollywood. The less he did the more awe he inspired—the more incalculable his powers seemed to those others whom he ruled.

So Mr. Gershky, abandoned by his court this early summer afternoon, sat twiddling his thumbs and feeling as lonely and restless as any five-dollar-a-night watchman. In a simple, unegoistic way, he felt a vague envy for the lesser mortals of the world—and his flat bald head drooped under the weight of its glittering crown.

He puttered for a time among the papers on his desk. He thought of calling up his friend Sam Meyer and taking him on for a round of golf on his private links but he remembered that Sam was sputtering in the throes of some merger and would start spouting prophecies and statistics like a maniac.

He rose from his desk and looked out of his vita-glass windows and scratched his head and wondered at his own restlessness. At sixty a man should be content to sit back and be Pharaoh. But the simplicity that was the basis of Mr. Gershky's nature rebelled this afternoon against the hierarchical trappings in which he must move. Not a violent rebellion, but a wistful unformed daydream, such as disturbs the wool-gathering thoughts of a suburban housewife, stirred Mr. Gershky's heart and sent him walking or rather sidling out of the carved doors of his sanctum into the corridor.

Here he stood, irritably aware of the electricity his presence engendered in the spirits of the half-dozen hirelings who were fortunate enough to catch a glimpse of him. Scowling, to conceal just what he did not know, Mr. Gershky walked slowly down the corridor, peering into one office after another and being met each time by such frightened and confused eyes (quite as if he were a bogeyman) that he hurried on.

He turned into another corridor, bethinking himself of Chollie Frieda, his chief noble, a gentleman thrashing around in ambitions that embraced no less than the Pharaoh's own shoes. Mr. Gershky was fond of Mr. Frieda and admired the clever and unscrupulous and always smiling manner in which he had elbowed his way through his fellow nobles—hamstringing, knifing, and garroting as he went—to a position at the Pharaoh's right hand. Mr. Gershky was not beyond enjoying that thought of the assassinations and pogroms that lay behind the always deferential but amused face of this right-hand man of his.

Mr. Gershky paused. Mr. Frieda's door was open, a sign that he was not at his desk. He stood listening abstractedly to the sound of typewriters and giggles and discussions and the scurrying of feet—and the revolt that had sent his sidling out of his sanctum grew stronger, or at least his unrest and old-manish wistfulness deepened. Whereupon at this moment, as if some magician even more powerful than Mr. Gershky had heard his plaint, and answered it, his eyes lighted on an occupant of Mr. Frieda's office—an unexpected and wholly delightful occupant.

This occupant was neither standing nor sitting—but lay on the carpet stretched on its stomach, its heels in the air, its chin cupped in its hands, its eyes intent on a large picture book. Mr. Gershky smiled. The presence of a child in Mr. Frieda's office struck Mr. Gershky as a very incongruous thing. He studied the little one with an increasing sense of calm and delight.

She was hardly more than six and her pale, slightly chubby face was framed in a symmetrical casque of coal-black hair as if it had been carefully fitted into a chiseled ebony frame. She seemed very exquisite to Mr. Gershky and his simple heart contracted with a peculiar emotion—almost pity—at the spectacle of such innocence lying on the floor of Mr. Frieda's office.

Mr. Gershky was no promiscuous child-lover. It had actually been years—fifteen at least—since he had spoken to one. But such was his mood at the moment that Mr. Gershky held his ground and continued to regard the little one with an expression whose tenderness and un-sophistication would have startled the entire personnel of the Gershky Enterprises.

The occupant, aware of this scrutiny, slowly turned her eyes upward and favored Mr. Gershky with a dark, unwavering and half-sleepy stare. Mr. Gershky smiled at once as if he were about to offer it some peanuts. Then he blinked his eyes, clucked tenderly, and made a face. The occu-pant, without moving a muscle, regarded these manifestations of Mr. Gershky's favor with a Mongolian calm, and the Pharaoh, still clucking gently, as if in the midst of a strange barnyard, advanced into the office. Obeying some long repudiated set of impulses, he leaned over and placed his hand very gently on the occupant's head and patted it. There was no immediate result. The occupant continued to regard Mr. Gershky with a peculiarly concentrated aloofness that began to startle him. He found himself looking worriedly at the half-closed saucerish eyes of the child and listening nervously to see if it were breathing.

"Don't be afraid of me," Mr. Gershky finally faltered and this time was rewarded with so flashing, eager, and excited a smile that he himself chuckled automatically and once more fell to clucking—this time in a loud and self-assured manner. At these salivous sounds, however, the little one lapsed almost magically into her previous Mongolian calm. And Mr. Gershky, renowned through the industry for his ability to read char-acter (if nothing else), silenced himself at once and frowned slightly.

"Hello," the child spoke in a surprisingly full, flat voice for one so young.

"How do you do," said Mr. Gershky gallantly. "Is that a pwetty book?"

The child again fell to studying him coldly.

"I said is that a pwetty book," repeated Mr. Gershky with a slight tinge of anger to his words.

The child hesitated and then apparently satisfied that the gentleman was not attempting baby talk but lacked the ability to pronounce his words correctly (which was indeed true, Mr. Gershky substituting a W for an R whenever it was vocally possible) she nodded her head slowly.

"Yes," she said. "But I'm finished with it."

To prove this the child closed the large book with a bang and bounced to her feet and continued to bounce up and down. And ap-proaching Mr. Gershky in this manner as if she were a rubber ball, she suddenly seized him around the knees. Mr. Gershky, tackled unawares, would have toppled over but for the fact that the little one continued to hold him erect in her arms, which seemed remarkably strong. For a moment Mr. Gershky hesitated as to whether or not he should wrestle, which seemed to be the child's unexpected whim. The decision was taken out of his hands, however. His new friend released her hold and, picking up the hem of her tiny dress in one hand, planted her left toe behind her right foot and made him a pretty curtsey.

Then apparently forgetting all about the gentleman, she placed her left hand on her hip and walked with a most amazing swagger across the room, her head tilting from side to side, her large black eyes flashing about the room and her mouth spread in a giddy smile.

Mr. Gershky retreated into a large leather chair and sat watching her with a doting chuckle. He felt deeply pleased with this adventure, wondered whose delightful child this could be and for the first time in years found himself thoroughly occupied and entertained by a fellow human being. So young, so innocent, Mr. Gershky sighed, as if these were phenomena whose presence he had not suspected in the world. Just beginning life, just a little tot . . . and his heart grew warm, his spirit felt the reviving touch of childhood.

The little one had maneuvered into a position in front of Mr. Gershky and was standing with her feet spread apart in a half split and looking soulfully up at the gentleman.

"I like you," she spoke after a pause in which Mr. Gershky had the good sense not to chuckle.

"Come here," said Mr. Gershky and waved his fingers invitingly.

The words were no sooner out of his mouth than his impetuous friend had leaped on his lap and twisting and climbing all in one snake-like movement, had flattened herself against Mr. Gershky, her knees buried in his stomach, her arms encircling his head, her lips bestowing hearty, wet smacks on his cheek.

"I love you," she explained excitedly. "Do you love me?"

Mr. Gershky was for the moment out of breath. This sudden embrace, this quick surrender of a child's heart, confused him. But it was a pleasing confusion and under it was that flattered sense which only children can stir when, liking us, they give us the delicious notion that they have beheld us in some subtle and dramatic light—quite as if we were a figure in a fairy tale. Mr. Gershky, under this little one's plaster of kisses, grew a bit light-headed as if he were making his début in a Christmas school pantomime.

This was what was missing in his life, something intimate and spontaneous; something real like a child's love! Mr. Gershky floundered through several such clichés and answered finally:

"Yes, deawie. I love you. You're a vewy, pwetty little girlie."

Mr. Gershky's curious pronounciation again plunged the little one into its Mongolian calm—but only for an instant. Observing anew that this gentleman's peculiar diction was not a wanton insult to her intelligence but some sort of educational defect which he couldn't help, her arms tightened rather savagely about the Pharaoh's neck. With her head snuggled on his shoulder she lay dormant for a moment thinking up her next move, when raising her eyes she observed three hateful figures standing in the doorway. Unaware of this audience Mr. Gershky continued to assure her in the tenderest of tones that if she were a good girlie he would reward her not only with his love but with a great deal of candy.

"Hello, H. J.," said Mr. Frieda. "I see you've met Baby Milly."

Mr. Gershky tried unsuccessfully to wiggle his head out of the Baby's embrace.

"Go on away," growled the little one, her eyes angrily on Mr. Frieda. "Go on. You!"

Mr. Frieda arched his face in a critical smile and approached his desk, remarking curtly over his shoulder to the two figures poised on the threshold, "I'll send for you in a few minutes."

A hireling immediately closed the door on the two figures.

"Her dear parents," Mr. Frieda continued to the Pharaoh who was coming out of the headlock with dignified but unscientific maneuvers. "There's a pair of Tartars for you. You know what they want for that brat?"

A well-dressed youth appeared through another door. This was Mr. Frieda's secretary.

"Yes?" said Mr. Frieda, widening his mouth so that he suddenly looked very nervous and ominous, albeit still the soul of courtesy.

"I beg your pardon," the secretary answered, crisply, cool and articulate in these front-line trenches, "Mrs. Stackleback says she wants her baby."

"Her what?" inquired Mr. Frieda with nasty innuendo.

"Baby Milly," said the secretary firmly, "she says she doesn't want you and—and Mr. Gershky conferring with her behind her back."

"O.K.," said Mr. Frieda, turning on the little one loosely entwined with the Pharaoh and endeavoring futilely to glare her down. "Go on outside—your Ma wants you."

"Chollie," Mr. Gershky's voice was reproving.

Mr. Frieda so far forgot his fifteen years of diplomacy as to snort.

"Go to your mama," Mr. Gershky relayed his petulant noble's order in the persuasive, *entre-nous* tones of the superior child psychologist.

Baby Mily, continuing to glare at Mr. Frieda and forcing him to arch his eyebrows, a sure indication to those who knew him that he was exercising self-control as well as cunning, tobagganed down Mr. Gershky to the floor. She picked herself up quickly and confronted Mr. Frieda with tilted head, lips pursed, nose wrinkled, and eyes blinking rapidly.

"Yooou!" she drawled in liquid contempt. "Yooou! Hm! Oh, yooou!"

"Go on outside," said Mr. Frieda, his jaws working at both ends of his smile.

"Oh, yes!" replied Baby Milly, adding with withering mimcry. "Go on. Outside. Go on yourSELF! Yoooou!"

With this speech she tilted her head clear around to her other shoulder and fluttering her eyelids, sneered at the waiting secretary. Then with the three gentlemen regarding her she emitted a little snort and marched triumphantly back to Mr. Gershky's lap, climbing thereon with straightforward, business-like gestures. Mr. Gershky, despite his better judgment, was touched by this evidence of preference and trust.

"Now weally," he began, "your mama . . ."

"Oh, now. Shush," said Baby Milly, cuddling. "He don't know anything," and she pointed a tense upcurving finger at Mr. Frieda.

"Tell La Stackleback—God what a name—" said Mr. Frieda to the imperturbable courier, "that we will send her her child—as soon as we can scrape it off."

"O.K.," said the secretary, retiring in good order.

"Well," said Mr. Frieda, "you seem to have made a hit, H. J."

Mr. Gershky grew bland and Pharaoh-like and his chief noble accepted the rebuke contained in his manner with a patient smile, a smile, however, which gave him the look of a shy but very contemplative cobra.

"Madam Stackleback," continued Mr. Frieda, "wants twenty-five grand for her baby's services. Can you imagine that? She also wants her starred. Personally, I'm sorry we ever went into the thing at all. Although I still think it's a natural. But twenty-five grand is out of the question. And she won't take a nickel less."

Mr. Gershky, without thinking, had placed his arm around his little admirer, thrilled by the sense of peace and relaxation this contact seemed to inspire in her.

"So you are Baby Milly?" he said, ignoring Mr. Frieda's plaints. "I've heard of you. You're wery famous, indeed."

"He don't want me," said Baby Milly, again pointing the tense and curved finger at her enemy. "Him!"

"Wouldn't you like to work for me?" cooed Mr. Gershky.

"You but not him," said Baby Milly, and turning her face to Mr. Frieda added "Puh!" Then caressing Mr. Gershky's tie she inquired coyly, "What's your name?"

"That's Mr. Gershky," Mr. Frieda answered for the Pharaoh, to save him that mystic embarrassment which greatness feels when called upon for its identity. Mr. Gershky smiled modestly at the sound of his name— as if to disparage some of it.

"I didn't ask you. You!" Baby Milly waggled her finger. Toboganning down Mr. Gershky once more she went through her curtsey, smiling up at him with her lips parted and her eyes rolled coquettishly like black marbles into their corners. Mr. Gershky nodded with approval.

"Vewy nice," he smiled. "Thank you."

Mr. Frieda looked away.

The door of the office flung open and a substantial and defiant-looking Mrs. Stackleback presented herself.

"I sent for my child," she announced, and holding out her arms, added in a cornet tremolo, "Baby!"

Baby Milly remained motionless, staring at her mother with a disdain which almost equalled that she had accorded Mr. Frieda—a disdain, however, whose spontaneity and naturalness made the child seem human for the moment. Ignoring the mother's woeful bleat, she scurried back into Mr. Gershky's lap.

"You have a vewy intresting child," said Mr. Gershky.

"I told you I'd send for you, Madam, when I wanted you." Mr. Frieda lowered his head as if to hide this discourteous remark.

"Chollie!" Mr. Gershky was once more reproving. Turning to Mrs. Stackleback, he was somewhat surprised to see a completely changed woman. Her long, horselike face was thrown back happily as if she were going to whinny.

"Mr. Gershky!" She tossed the name giddily before her as she advanced. "I'm Mrs. Stackleback. Baby Milly's mothah. And Mr. Frieda sent for us. And we came over ready to do business, ready to listen and discuss. As I told Mr. Stackleback. Of course! Well! Baby Milly is a genius. A tremendous drawing card. That's very obvious! But we must remember, Mr. Gershky, that she will not be a little baby very long. Her little Innocent years are numbahed. And what she has is therefore all the more precious. All the more dear and sweet and wonderful."

"I understand," said Mr. Gershky while Mr. Frieda, his head lowered as if he were having a shampoo, remained shy but very contemplative.

"Of course you do. I knew you would," cried Mrs. Stackleback in a manner which combined languor and a college yell.

Mrs. Stackleback's child, who had been snorting unnoticed through her mother's oration, suddenly raised her voice in an unexpected and commanding English accent.

"Mothah!" it exclaimed, "Mothah deah!" And spacing her words cried out, "I—don't—care. No-o-o-o!"

"Of course you don't, sweetheart," said her understanding parent.

"I said I don't care," repeated the child roundly. "Soooh!"

"Isn't she a darling," Mrs. Stackleback yodeled. "And she's quite right. Absolutely right."

This corroboration of her child's mysterious utterance confused Mr. Gershky, who felt a growing discomfort over this trifling financial discussion. It seemed rather out of place to discuss money with a little baby and her mother.

"And if you want Baby Milly, Mr. Gershky," Mrs. Stackleback declaimed, looking up as if under the spell of a great, sacrificial mood, "you may have her."

"For fifteen thousand dollars for the first picture," Mr. Frieda interpolated firmly, "and an option for twenty thousand for the next."

"Exactly," Mrs. Stackleback thrust her head forward—but toward Mr. Gershky—with a winsome shake, "my main concern is that my child be happy, be pleased, be in the proper hands. And I can see that you, dear Mr. Gershky, have captured her little heart. And she is so indifferent to people. She is so much the little hermit. That I am amazed!"

Each of her parent's words seemed to stir in Baby Milly a new and deeper contempt but she remained silent, shutting her eyes tightly and blowing as if she were gasping for air.

"That's fine," said Mr. Frieda and pressed a button. "I'll send for your husband and we'll all sign the proper papers."

Mrs. Stackleback, with many pert little feminine gestures, began removing the glove from her right hand, and Mr. Gershky, smiling down on the little one who had opened her eyes now and was nestling with perfect confidence against his vest and actually purring, inquired blandly:

"What is the name of the pickchew?"

" 'The Brat,' " said Mr. Frieda. "It's that play I told you about."

"Hm," Mr. Gershky shook his head. "Call it 'The Little Lady.'"

"Oh! That's much nicer! That's a wonderful, MARvelous title," Mrs. Stackleback exploded. "How did you ever THINK of it?"

And Mr. Frieda stared smilingly into space as his ears turned red.

MRS. GROSS REMEMBERS

by ARTHUR KOBER

PA and Bella were on their way to work, and Ma Gross was now completely alone. She picked up the breakfast dishes, carried them to the kitchen sink, turned on the hot water, and then she sighed contentedly.

Yes, she had gone a long way since those old days in Harlem when they had the candy store, when Irving awoke at dawn to get the morning newspapers and when little Bella used to "tend on the customers" while she hurried with Pa's breakfast so that she could relieve the children.

Today they lived in a Bronx apartment with an elevator. (She was very proud of that!) Irving was happily married and had "a beyoodyful little kiddie, switt like a doll." Bella was now quite a young lady. True, she wasn't married, nor even engaged. ("Say, listen, a girl twendy-one is still a spring chicken, she can affudder to be choosy yet!")

In spite of her comparative ease and comfort Mrs. Gross missed the candy store and its activity. She remembered how much pleasure she used to get out of the marble soda fountain with its big silver spigots which she always kept so highly polished.

In those days the syrup bottles lined the top of the fountain. Each of the bottles was marked with the name of the flavor: "Strawberry," "Vanilla," "Chocolate," "Pineapple." The chocolate bottle, she recalled, had its label almost off from being used so much. She always had a difficult time keeping the syrups in their proper bottles. Vanilla and chocolate, however, were the two flavors most in demand and these were in their proper containers.

Mrs. Gross wiped a coffee cup and smiled wistfully. She remembered how she used to ask the customers when they ordered a soda, "You want a penny gless udder a two cent gless?" She would then reach for a glass—the size depended on the answer—and pour an inch of syrup.

She would lift the glass to the silver spigot, pull the knob forward until the charged water came sizzling near the top, and then push it backward for a squirt of strong fizz. A large spoon would stir the mixture, causing it to bubble so that it ran over the glass. She always had "a piece rag" under the counter and was constantly mopping the marble surface.

She was very proud of that candy store (it was in her name and purchased with money she had saved out of Pa Gross's "paychick") with its glass-top counter well stocked with penny candies. There were chocolate sponges, Hershey bars, silver-covered kisses, colored discs with mottoes on them, shoestrings (dots of speckled candies on long strips of paper), twists, Tootsie Rolls, butter-scotches. There were Indian nuts to be scooped up in a wooden container, and nine-for-a-penny which were gathered with a glass dish. Part of the counter was devoted to exposed wares: apples-on-a-stick, a wooden box containing "Halvah," a Turkish confection (Mrs. Gross always called it "Hollavah"), and charlotte russes which the patrons referred to as "charlie ruses."

She remembered the cigarette files on the left of the counter. There was a great demand for Turkish Trophies, plain and cork-tipped. There was also a call for Meccas, Hassans and Sweet Caporals. (Stored down in the cellar somewhere was the picture of the Helmar girl which adorned the wall of Mrs. Gross's candy-store.)

She thought of Mrs. Kehoe, the school-teacher, who helped to create a demand for rubber bounce balls. Once a ball fell into her garden, it was gone. She seized it, pulled out a hairpin from her head, punctured it and threw it back. She was mean and the kids hated her; Mrs. Gross felt she ought to hate her, too.

Then there were the "cockamanies"—painted strips of paper which the kids applied to their wrists and rubbed with spit until the image was transferred to their hand. Many a discussion over tattooing occurred in her store following such a sale.

Mrs. Gross had "a sizzin" for everything. May meant May parties: paper crowns for kings and queens, tissue paper, stars and ice-cream by the can. June meant a rush on the soda-fountain, calls for wax paper to be wrapped around sandwiches for hikes, rubber balls and fly-paper. July was the time to get rid of her stock of fire-crackers, sparklers, pin-wheels and cap-pistols. (The noise of exploding firecrackers used to infuriate her husband who would chase the kids out of the store the moment they had made their purchase.) In August she stocked her school supplies; pads and pencils and slates and chalk and rubber erasers and pen-points and pens and ink and rulers and brown-paper to cover school-books.

On Thanksgiving Day there was a great demand for paper-masks—Chinese false-faces with a droopy-mustache painted on them, Negro false-faces with thick red lips, Indian false-faces, multi-colored and terrifying. Halloween called for a supply of chalk. The kids would come around with their coats turned backward, for the neighborhood gangs would pelt each other with stockings filled with flour and would streak each others' clothes with chalk. Only the most heroic and hardy ventured out on that day.

Mrs. Gross dried the dishes, sat down and sighed again in contemplation of the old days, remembering the quarrels she and her husband had in that store. There was always something to fight about, always something she had done to displease him when he came home at night and helped "tend" on the customers.

"Lookit her!" he would shout when she was preparing a malted milk. "Look, look, how much milk she puts in the multed machine. Mrs. Dairy Lady! If the customer wants a gless milk let the customer go to a grossry store, not a kendy store! Where you gung to make a profit when you put so much milk in a multed?"

Another thing that used to distress Pa very much was her gullibility in accepting seltzer bottles which didn't belong to her. The kids knew she couldn't read English and so they were bringing in bottles marked with the name of another candy store and asking for the return of their deposit.

Pa Gross wasn't very popular with the juvenile patrons of Mrs. Gross's store. "Hey!" he was always shouting at them. "How many times I told you you shouldn't lean on the counter? So if you break the gless, then you'll be serresfied, ha?"

It never bothered Mrs. Gross when the kids hovered around the news-stand looking through the comic section of the *Evening Journal*. A group of them would scan the pages nightly, following Desperate Desmond and his adventures, suffering horrible nightmares with Little Nemo, watching George MacManus's "Newlyweds," absorbing the antics of Gus Mager's monks. But the moment Mr. Gross presented himself, they would quickly dissolve and disappear.

Mrs. Gross allowed her forehead to contract into a frown as she wondered about her "trust" book. Her patrons used to order five cents' worth of candy (if they had a party they'd buy five cents' worth of the stuff called "chicken corn" and get a heaping bagful) and say, "It's fa trust." "Fa trust?" Mrs. Gross would repeat. She would then take her "trust" book, thumb the pages until she found their name written in

Yiddish, and then apply the amount against her customer's credit. She had a very bad memory and lost a number of dollars because of this credit account.

Mrs. Gross was so lost in this revery that it was some time before she was aware of the ringing of the telephone. She rose with a start and rushed to the living room. "Aha!" she said as she ran, "it begins awready the larm clock ringing."

She picked up the receiver, said, "Hello," and listened. "Ha? Mr. Gross? Mr. Gross, he's in the shop awready. So who is spikking bime telephone?"

She heard a man's voice say something about a phone call he had received from Mr. Gross and about an interest in a bathhouse which was for sale.

"I dunno fomm badhouses," Mrs. Gross curtly replied. "Mr. Gross, he's at the shop. Goodbye!"

"Aha!" she reflected. "Mr. Rockefelleh, he's gung to buy badhouses awready! Where comes he to a badhouse?" She returned to her kitchen chores. "A kendy store," she mused, "that's awready a business! But a badhouse? I need it like I need a hole in head!"

MR. KAPLAN'S SO-AND-SO

by LEONARD Q. ROSS

THE spring rain slithered across the windows of the American Night Preparatory School for Adults. It was a nasty night, a night of wet feet, drab spirits, and head colds. Mr. Parkhill, indeed, *had* a head cold. He was at home, indisposed, and a young substitute teacher, bubbling with the courage of a year and a half of practice teaching, was at the desk in front of the beginners' grade. The young man could tell, by the way the students received the sad news of Mr. Parkhill's indisposition, that they really liked him and were worried by his absence. This filled the young substitute with pride in his calling.

"Is it maybe Mr. Pockheel *seryous* seeck?" asked a pleasant-looking gentleman in the front row, centre.

"No, I'm sure not. He'll be back with you Monday night, Mr.—?"

"Hymen Keplen," the man with the pleasant face said. His smile was either profoundly modest or completely automatic.

"Mr. Kaplan."

"Denks Gott isn't scryous awreddy," sighed Mr. Kaplan with relief. Many other students sighed with relief, too; the collective sighs were like a choral "Amen!" to Mr. Kaplan's touching thought. "Dat soitinly takes a beeg load off!"

"You mean, 'That takes a load off my mind!'" Mr. Parkhill's substitute corrected quickly. Nothing escaped this young man.

"A load off mine *mind?*" Mr. Kaplan repeated softly. He thought this over for a moment, nodded, and then said, "An' off mine *hot* also."

The young man saw at once that this Mr. Kaplan had a remarkable mind. (Had he known that only last week Mr. Kaplan had said, "For eatink smashed potatoes I am usink a knife an' fog!," he would have concluded that Mr. Kaplan had a remarkable use of words too.)

"Well, let us begin tonight's lesson. Mr. Parkhill suggested that we—"

"Podden me, Titcher." It was Mr. Kaplan again, Mr. Kaplan with an apologetic smile. "Can ve know plizz *your* name?"

The young man laughed boyishly. "Well, pardon me! How stupid of me. Of course. My name is Jennings."

From the look on Mr. Kaplan's face, the name might have been that of a Chinaman. "Channink?" he asked, incredulously.

"No, *Jennings.* J-e-n-n-i-n-g-s."

The young man wrote the characters on the blackboard with undismayed fingers.

"Aha!" Mr. Kaplan beamed. "*Ch*ennink! I tought you said, '*Ch*annink'!"

Mr. "Chennink" smiled feebly and decided to let well enough alone. He was a realist.

"As I was saying, Mr. Parkhill suggested that we spend the first part of the period in what he calls Open Questions." (Open Questions was one of Mr. Parkhill's happiest pedagogical innovations. It permitted students to ask questions about anything on which they sought enlightenment—grammar, vocabulary, idiom, spelling, pronunciation, anything.) "I have been told you keep notes of the questions you may wish to ask. If you will refer to them now, please, for *just* a few minutes. . . . Everybody, now!"

The students seemed a little breath-taken by this gust of energetic tutelage. (Something of the cheerleader still clung to young Mr. Jennings.) Then there were shrugs, exchanges of glances, and sighs of adjustment; the beginners' grade girded its scholastic loins for Open Questions. Notebooks, foolscap pages, envelopes, scraps of paper, even chewing-gum wrappers appeared, to be studied for the great event. A fat woman seemed to be reading the wall just above Mr. Jennings' head, seeking inspiration. She moaned as she waited for the golden light to descend. A man with a conspicuous gold tooth fumbled through his pockets. Mr. Hyman Kaplan, for whom Mr. Jennings already felt a certain respect, merely leaned his head to one side, half closed his eyes, and whispered, "So now is Haupen Quastions! My!" His whispers left nothing to be desired in the way of audibility. "Esk Titcher abot *a room goink arond.*"

"Pardon?" Mr. Jennings asked quickly. "I didn't hear what you were saying." Mr. Jennings was a very alert teacher.

Mr. Kaplan opened his eyes. "I vasn't sayink," he murmured dreamily. "I vas tinking."

Mr. Kaplan continued "tinking." "Esk Titcher," he whispered, "abot *a room goink arond!"* Mr. Jennings felt a damp sensation on his brow. "Abot *so-an'-so!* . . . Esk Titcher . . . abot *a room goink arond!* Abot *so-an'-so!"*

Horror invaded Mr. Jennings' eyes. For some strange reason a quotation flashed through his mind: "That way madness lies." Mr. Jennings fought it down.

"Esk Titcher . . . abot—"

"Let us begin," Mr. Jennings said, with calculated briskness. "We shall recite in order, starting with—with the lady in the back row, please."

That would leave Mr. Kaplan and his cryptic "room goink arond"— to say nothing of "so-an'-so!"—almost to the end. Mr. Jennings caught himself hoping that the recess bell would ring before Mr. Kaplan's turn came. This was contrary to all that Mr. Jennings had been taught in Education V (Professor Heppelhauser's Education V) and he felt ashamed of himself.

Mr. Kaplan opened his eyes with an injured air. "*Goldboig* foist," he whispered sadly. "Oi!" His expression was that of a man betrayed.

Miss Goldberg wanted to know whether "trumpet" had anything to do with bridge, "like, with my Jeck I trumpet." After this brilliant beginning, Mr. Weinstein sought aid with the orthography of "Tsintsinnati," where his married brother and "fife" children lived. (He hadn't been able to find "Tsintsinnati" in the dictionary, he said; he admitted, however, that it was a *cheap* dictionary.) Mrs. Yampolsky asked whether "Specific" was the name of the *other* ocean. Miss Mitnick, obviously a superior student, was puzzled by the difference between "beside" and "besides" and, after Mr. Jennings had analyzed the distinction, between "loan," "borrow," and "lend."

Through all these weighty matters Mr. Kaplan sat with heroic resignation. Occasionally he indulged in wistful and philosophic sighs. It was plain that Mr. Kaplan was saddened by the naïveté of his colleagues.

Miss Shirley Ziev inquired whether there wasn't something queer about the interrogative form, "When did you came, Morris?" Mr. Scymzak, confessing it was probably a silly point, asked if the "state alienist" was the officer in charge of immigration and citizen papers. Miss Caravello ventured to query what the "G" in "G-men" stood for.

Mr. Jennings treated each of these problems with profound earnestness. Mr. Jennings was, indeed, lost in the sweet delirium of the pedagogical chase. He was exhilarated by the challenge of communication. He was tasting, as never before in his year and a half of practice teaching, the simple joys of the schoolman. And before he knew it, it was Mr. Kaplan's turn, with a good ten minutes to spare.

"Mr. Kaplan," he said slowly, and something in him went taut.

Mr. Kaplan's face took on the lustre of ecstasy. "My!" he breathed, semi-publicly. "Now is commink *mine* time!" This was journey's end, Ultima Thule, the last, for which the first was made.

Mr. Kaplan rose. No other student had risen, but there was something eminently fitting, almost teleological, about Mr. Kaplan's rising. Mr. Pinsky observed every motion of the ascent with the humility of a weaker spirit. A rustle, compact of anticipation, pleasure, and anxiety, went through the classroom.

"Ladies an' gantleman," Mr. Kaplan began, in his finest oratorical manner. "Mr. Pockheel told us, a lonk time beck awreddy, dat if ve vant to *loin,* den avery place ve goink, ve should vatchink for mistakes, for Haupen Quastions. In de sopvay, on de stritt, in de alevatits—poblic or private, day an' night, alvays ve should be *stoodents!* Believe me, dat vas a fine, smot idea!" Mrs. Moskowitz nodded reverently, as if to a reading of the Psalms. "So like Mr. Pockheel said, avery place I vas goink I vas vatchink, vatchink"—Mr. Kaplan narrowed his eyes and looked suspicious, to lend authenticity to his "vatchink, vatchink"—"all de time vatchink for tings I should esk by Haupen Quastions time!"

This, Mr. Jennings sensed, was the introduction. It was.

"So de foist quastion. Vat's de minnink fro~m 'A room is goink arond'?"

" 'A room is going around?' " repeated Mr. Jennings, though he knew perfectly well what Mr. Kaplan's words had been.

" 'A room is goink arond!' " Mr. Kaplan repeated firmly, and sat down.

The beginners' grade was hushed.

"I see. 'A room is going around.' "

There was no doubt about it—Mr. Jennings was fighting for time. "Well, the meaning of the words is perfectly simple, Mr. Kaplan. As anyone can tell—" Mr. Jennings explained the meaning of the words. He treated them individually, collectively, conceptually. But he admitted that the phrase, as a phrase, seemed strange. "Of course, if one were dizzy, or faint, or *drunk*"—Mr. Jennings was not the type to mince words— "why, then one *would* say, 'I feel as if the room were going around.' "

Mr. Norman Bloom snickered. "*I* think that's a crazy quastion!"

Mr. Kaplan surveyed Mr. Bloom with a haughty glance. "Mine dear Bloom, to *som* pipple is even de bast quastions crazy!"

Mr. Bloom collapsed.

"Could you tell us exactly how you heard the phrase?" Mr. Jennings interrupted quickly, fearful of the heights to which Mr. Kaplan's scorn might ascend.

Mr. Kaplan nodded. "Fromm mine vife," he said. "She vas talkink to Mrs. Skolsky—dat's de lady livink opstairs—abot Mrs. Backer—dat's de femily livink *don*stairs. An' Mrs. Skolsky said, 'You know, I tink Mrs. Backer vill saparate Mr. Backer mit divorce!' so mine vife esked, netcheral, 'So how you know?' So Mrs. Skolsky gave enswer, "Averbody's sayink dat! *A room is goink arond!*' "

" 'A *rumor's* going around!' " cried Mr. Jennings. Meaning burst within him, like a firecracker. "A *rumor* is going around, Mr. Kaplan! Why, that's an *excellent* phrase! A rumor refers to—"

But Mr. Kaplan hardly listened. His smile was phosphorescent. He dropped rays of sweet redemption over his shoulders, right and left. For Mr. Norman Bloom, staring moodily at the floor, Mr. Kaplan had a special and triumphant radiance.

When Mr. Jennings had given his all to "A rumor is going around," Mr. Kaplan murmured, "My! Dat vas *som* quastion!" (There was always a fine objectivity in the awe with which Mr. Kaplan regarded his brain children.) Then he asked his second question.

"I hoid soch an axpression, I can't believe. Also, it sonds fonny. *Fonny.*" Mr. Kaplan repeated with a telling glance at Mr. Norman

Bloom, "not crazy. Plizz, vat's de minnink fromm *'so-an'-so,'* a 'so-an'-so'?"

It had come.

"Do you want me to explain 'so-and-so' or *'a* so-and-so'? There is a distinction, you know," said Mr. Jennings, facing the worst bravely.

"Awright, lat be *'a* so-an'-so,'" said Mr. Kaplan.

Mr. Jennings took a deep breath. Education V, and all the pedantic wisdom of Professor Heppelhauser, seemed to be far away, so abstract, so totally worthless in dealing with problems of the magnitude of "a so-and-so."

"The phrase 'a so-and-so,'" he began earnestly, "is heard quite commonly. But it's vulgar. It's used, really, instead of—well, profanity."

Mr. Jennings paused hopefully, ready to go on further. But in the eyes of the class there was no flicker of understanding of the concept "profanity." Mr. Jennings faced the task of explaining profanity without using it.

"Profanity means—well, cursing, swearing, using bad, foul, *not nice* language." Still the faces were in blank repose; still the eyes held no flame of recognition. "Let me put it this way, class. Suppose John, say, wants to—"

"Who is dat 'John'?" asked Mr. Kaplan promptly.

Mr. Jennings' hands felt scaly. "Any John, Mr. Kaplan. I use the name only as a sample."

"My!" Mr. Kaplan exclaimed, admiring Mr. Jennings' ingenuity.

"Suppose *someone,* then, wants to say something bad about someone else, wants to *curse* him, really, but doesn't actually want to use profane language. Well, he'll say, 'He's a so-and-so!' instead of—" Too late did young Mr. Jennings realize that he had gone too far. "Instead of—" The class waited expectantly, Miss Mitnick with a blush, crescendo. "Instead of—"

"Low life! Tremp! Goot-fa-noddink!" cried Mr. Kaplan impetuously.

"Yes! Fine! Exactly!" Never had Mr. Jennings been so grateful. "That's *precisely* how 'so-and-so' is used."

An "Ah!" of illumination went through the class. But Mr. Bloom glowered. "That's a bad quastion to ask with ladies in room!" he cried out.

Two hot camps of thought sprang up. The room buzzed with argument, defence, recrimination. Miss Rochelle Goldberg supported Mr. Bloom indignantly. Mr. Sam Pinsky, aided by many a sarcastic gibe from Mr. Marcus, rallied to the Kaplan banner. Mr. Jennings looked bewildered.

"Ha!" Mr. Kaplan's war cry resounded against the walls. "Who is sayink mine quastion is bed? Who? *In aducation is no bed quastions!*"

And the opposition fell into shamed silence. On Mr. Kaplan's face there shone a glow which, without a doubt, meant *"Honi soit qui mal y pense."* "De kind 'so-an'-so' *I* minn, Mr. Chennink," Mr. Kaplan said in a clarion voice, *"isn't* volgar, or de odder ting!"

"Profane," Mr. Jennings ventured.

"Or 'profane,' like you say. I minn altogadder difference, plizz."

Mr. Jennings took counsel with his soul. He had done his duty with patience and discretion. And yet, undaunted, Mr. Kaplan pursued some strange, evasive Truth. It was in a voice freighted with caution that Mr. Jennings said, "Perhaps you had better illustrate what you mean, Mr. Kaplan."

Mr. Kaplan rose for the last time that memorable night. The rain-drops did impish gavottes on the panes, and the room echoed their derision.

"Vell, lest veek I mat in de stritt mine old frand Moe Slavitt," Mr. Kaplan began, *sotto voce.* " 'Hollo, Moe!' I said. 'How you fillink dis beauriful mornink?' So Moe said, 'I got in mine had a hadake.' So I esk, 'Noo, a *bed* hadake, Moe?' So he gives enswer, 'Not a tarrible hadake, but also not *not* a hadake.' Dat Moe—alvays he's sayink yas an' no mit de same brat. So I said, 'Leesen, Moe! Don' talkink all de time in reedles! I esk a tsimple quastion, so give, plizz, a strong, plain enswer. Do—you—fill—Hau—Kay; *yas or no?'* Vell, vat Moe did? Ha! He made like dis mit his shouldiss"—Mr. Kaplan shrugged his shoulders with pro-found expressiveness—"an' said, 'I don' fill rotten, I don' fill A Number Vun. I'm just so-an'-so!' "

The recess bell rang. And the rain drops howled on the steamy windows, like madmen.

PLAYS OF A
CHANGING WORLD

In the world of drama and theater, the Jew is a virtual newcomer. There were echoes of drama in the past—the Biblical *Song of Songs* and *Job,* the Hellenistic Ezekielos and several less significant morality plays in the 17th and 18th centuries—but it was only after they entered Western culture in the 19th century that Jewish dramatists increased and multiplied. The selections in this section (and the productions of other playwrights like Zangwill, Bernstein and Beer-Hofmann, that have not been included) as well as the fame of institutions like the Yiddish Art Theater,[1] the Habima, the Vilna Troupe, the Ohel Theater and the Jewish Theaters of Moscow and White Russia indicate, to some extent, the considerable role played by the Jew in the modern theater.

How the European theater exploited the Jew and his trivial characteristics has been narrated in detail in M. J. Landa's *The Jew in Drama* (1926). He was presented as the incarnation of every evil,—parasite, bloodsucker, fiend. The modern theater has succeeded in almost liquidating the "stage-Jew" tradition; it is now in the process of rehabilitating the Jew as a human being and of capturing the deeper perceptions that consciousness of history and tradition create. This may be illustrated by the earliest production of a realistic play dealing with Jewish life: In 1908, while the animosities growing out of the Dreyfus case were still simmering in France, Henri Bernstein produced his *Israel* at the Rejane Theater in Paris.

Bernstein stated his case in a long interview published in *Le Temps.* "I feel certain," he declared, "that this excess of inner spiritual life which people commonly call 'temperament' and which makes a man an artist is largely due to my Jewish lineage. . . . My respect for a man invariably increases when I discover that he is not attempting to disavow himself and the inclinations of his racial spirit. There is only one thing I have in common with antisemites: I despise, even more than they do, the Jew who apologizes for the fact that he is a Jew. Every attitude a Jew of that species manifests, every relation he seeks, is a vile excuse in disguise. The frightful humiliations which would make a self-respecting person die of shame, but which this variety of snob accepts on bended knee, crawling before his insulters, have always seemed to me sufficient punishment. . . . My play *Israel* is neither an attempt to revenge nor is it an apology for the Jew. I do not intend to place the Jewish problem on the stage for a solution. It would be naive to pretend that this immense problem can be solved in a few acts. I simply wanted to have a Jew on the stage—that's all. A Jew is part of life: I want to portray life. Why should I deprive myself of one of its most stimulating ingredients?"

The selections have been arranged to throw the kaleidoscope of drama on Jewish life and history from the days of David, the son of Jesse, to our own times.

[1] For a discussion of the Yiddish drama, see *The Drama of Transition* by Isaac Goldberg, pp. 327-420.

MICHAL

by DAVID PINSKI

PERSONS

DAVID   SAUL
MICHAL   SAUL'S SUITE
JONATHAN

SCENE

A luxuriant spot in the garden of King Saul. To the right and left, various paths that wind among the thickly growing trees. In the middle of the high, rocky background, which is matted with wild growths, is a narrow path approached by a flight of steps hewn out of the rock. It is a spring morning. Sunrise.

David. [*Stands upon the top step, as if framed in foliage, leaning against his harp. His eyes are raised to the distant sky, which is gradually becoming brighter; they shine with an inspired, joyful, exalted fire. His fingers find their way instinctively to the strings of his harp and pluck, hesitantly, several strong, warm chords. Soon he begins to declaim, slowly.*] "The heavens declare the glory of God; and the firmament showeth his handiwork. Day unto day uttereth speech, and night unto night showeth knowledge. There is no speech nor language where their voice is not heard. Their line is gone out through all the earth, and their words to the end of the world. In them hath he set a tabernacle for the sun."

Michal. [*Appears at the right. She hides behind a tree and listens with bated breath, closing her eyes and clenching her fists in passionate ecstasy.*]

David. [*Is unaware of her presence. He continues to declaim undisturbed, and with greater exaltation than before.*] "Which is as a bridegroom coming out of his chamber, and rejoiceth as a strong man to run a race. His going forth is from the end of the heaven, and his circuit

401

unto the ends of it; and there is nothing hid from the heat thereof. . . ."

Michal. [*She has stepped out of hiding. Her eyes are still closed. She is quite pale and breathes heavily.*]

David. [*Feeling her presence before seeing her, his hand trembles, and his playing is abruptly terminated by a false, weak chord. He closes his eyes and stands as if in a trance.*]

Michal. [*At the sound of the last chord her eyes open. Her face assumes a hard, cold expression. She is about to withdraw.*]

David. [*Whispering*] Michal?

Michal. [*Proud and cold*] I was taking my morning walk.

David. [*Opens his eyes and looks at her. Calmly.*] The King's daughter, all alone?

Michal. Does Michal need a bodyguard? Must she be watched at every step? I like to be alone and undisturbed.

David. [*Slowly raises his harp and moves as if to leave by the narrow path behind him*] I understand. You need make your wish no clearer to me. Farewell, daughter of the king!

Michal. [*Quickly*] I did not mean you. I believe I am the intruder and that I should go.

David. You are the princess, and *I* must yield place to you. [*Bow. and is about to leave.*]

Michal. You broke off your song in the middle. Will you not sing i to the end?

David. [*Sadly, with his eyes closed*] I shall not be able.

Michal. I'll go away. I'll not disturb you.

David. My heart is no longer in my song.

Michal. You were singing the glories of the day and of the sun, th greatness of God and his splendor.

David. That was liberation,—for a moment only.

Michal. Liberation?

David. [*Hastily*] Dwell in peace, Michal! [*Turns, as if to go.*]

Michal. [*With an outcry*] David!

David. [*Stops, turns back. For awhile they look at each other i silence. As if hypnotized, without removing his glance from her, DAVI slowly descends the steps and comes over to MICHAL. Now they are clos to one another, eyeing each other with penetrating glances.*]

Michal. [*At last breaking the silence, softly and bashfully*] You saic liberation.

David. [*Very sadly*] I lay all night upon my pillow, torn wit despair.

Michal. With despair?

David. Until finally, with the first rays of dawn, I made a resolution.

Michal. A resolution?

David. And I sought my harp, and stole quietly away from my room and from the king's castle.

Michal. [*With embarrassed laughter*] Not quietly enough.

David. Did I wake you?

Michal. My sleep too—was—restless. [*Hastily.*] But tell me of your despair, and your resolution and your liberation.

David. It was still dark when I stole forth, my eyes and my feet were turned toward the West, where everything was veiled in deepest shadow. It seemed to me that I had stepped into a sea of darkness, and that black waves engulfed me. But within me it was even darker. Heavily and bitterly my spirit wept, and heavily and bitterly my harp sang back to me, its strings stirred by the gloom.

Michal. [*Turns away her head, her eyes brimming with tears.*]

David. But when I had reached this last step, and before the greater darkness of the narrow path had swallowed me, I turned my face to the East, back to the road over which I had already traveled, to the palace of your father. And what I saw made me forget my sadness.

Michal. [*With mingled curiosity and surprise*] Ah!

David. I thought to behold the same dense darkness, but my eyes were greeted by a stream of morning light. This surprised me, astounded me quite, and roused my thoughts from my sadness. I raised my eyes to heaven, and a gray cloud, faintly tipped with red, captivated my sight. At first I did not realize what I saw, and the reddened darkness was a riddle to me. I looked more sharply, and soon began to smile in happy forgetfulness and the blessed delight of the scene. On the cloud lay the first touch of the rising sun. As if in merry dance my eyes darted across the wide sky, seeking the red spots, the tokens of the day-star. With each moment they grew in number, and with every second the dark red became brighter and still more bright. And soon the sun itself appeared from behind the palace of the king in all its golden-red fiery splendor. My heart flowed over, and from my lips began to pour the song—

Michal. And then I came.

David. [*Lowers his head.*]

Michal. [*Softly; after a brief silence*] What was your resolution?

David. To leave the king's palace forever.

Michal. Ah! That is what I suspected!

David. I can remain here no longer.

Michal. I know. The king's hatred is driving you away.

David. [*Turns his face aside.*]

Michal. But David need not steal away from the king. Let him leave the king like a man.

David. Saul will be content if I never show myself again.

Michal. [*With meaning*] I believe that the king is your debtor. You have a claim upon him.

David. The king owes me nothing.

Michal. Owes you nothing? [*Laughs with embarrassment.*] Did he not, then, promise great wealth to the conqueror of Goliath?

David. I did not slay Goliath for money.

Michal. Not for money?

David. Not for the most boundless treasures and not for the freedom of my father's house.

Michal. [*Her face brightening*] Then you slew him—you slew him—[*Suddenly changing to a harsh tone.*] Why do you not claim me of the king?

David. [*Falling on his knees before her, and hiding his face in her dress*] Michal!

Michal. [*Her face again brightening; she speaks triumphantly.*] Ah! You did not desire the king's prize—you wanted my love! Ah! Why were you silent all the time? Why did you avoid me? I have loved you for a long time already,—I have loved you from the first time I saw you. I was in the king's camp when he was in the field against Goliath and the Philistines, and of all the king's daughters Saul offered me, me alone, as reward for Goliath's head. Is any of the king's daughters more beautiful than I? Am I not the youngest? Does not the king love me best of all his daughters? Am I not worth the head of Goliath, the Philistine? How it grieved me that of all the heroes of Israel none appeared against Goliath! How it affronted me that none found courage within him, although *I* was the prize! But then you came forth, young and handsome, with blond hair and cheeks so red—how wildly my heart began to beat, and what rejoicing there was within me! And I thanked God that none had come before you. And when you took your place against the giant, I fell upon my knees and prayed to God for you. Oh, how I prayed! And I won the certainty that you would conquer, because you were waging battle for me as the prize, and then you would come and claim me of my father. Oh, you should have done so! *That* you should have done! But you did not come. Ah, you did not claim me. And I was waiting for you!

David. [*As before*] Michal!

Michal. [*Bending down to him and taking his face in her hands*] I was waiting for you, and could not imagine what held you back. What a fright I had when the king offered you my sister Merab, and how I rejoiced when you refused her. And my heart became heavier than ever because you did not come and claim me as your just reward. Ah, David, how I have suffered through you! You robbed me of rest by day and of sleep by night. But it was well that I did not sleep, and that I lay listening for you. For that is how I heard you leave your room and the palace today, and at once I followed you by the tracks left by your feet. Ah! How could you have wished to run away! How could you have wished to forsake me! But now you know it! I love you! Oh, how I love you. My body and soul belong to you! Now come before the king and demand your prize! Come, David; come, my hero, my champion!

David. [*With an outburst, burying his face in his hands*] I cannot, Michal! I cannot!

Michal. [*Recoiling, in fright*] You cannot!

Jonathan. [*Comes running in*] Oh, here you are! Quickly, the king is seeking you! [*Looks at both of them in astonishment.*] What has come over you both? What's taken place?—Have you heard? The king is seeking you and he is in one of his most terrible fits of anger. They told him that both of you rose early and stole away from the palace. He fell into a fury at once—one of those raging attacks that the Evil Spirit sends to him so often these days—and berated and cursed all his servants, and then woke me from my sleep with the vilest of oaths. I must know where you are, he said, whither you had run off and what you had made up between you. And when he could learn nothing from me, because I myself knew nothing about it—convinced that I knew and simply did not wish to tell—he sent out his servants with orders to find you and bring you to him dead or alive.—Haven't you heard me?—Why do you stand there like that?

Michal. [*In her great fright she stands motionless, her eyes riveted upon* DAVID, *as if she were still waiting for him to explain his words. It seems as if she has not heard* JONATHAN's *warning—not even noticed his presence.*]

David. [*At* JONATHAN's *appearance he has slowly arisen. His head, however, is still lowered, as if he, too, has not heard* JONATHAN's *warning, not even heeded him.*]

Jonathan. In God's name, what has happened between you?

David. [*Softly, with lowered eyes*] I have just told your sister that I cannot take her as my wife.

Jonathan. You cannot?

David. [*With a deep sigh*] No.

Jonathan. You must marry the king's daughter. She was promised to him who should slay Goliath, the Philistine. Are you not he, perhaps, who has freed us from Goliath and the Philistines? Was it not *your* stone, that stretched the giant out dead? The king's daughter belongs to you.

David. Not for her sake did I go forth against Goliath, not for the sake of becoming the king's son-in-law did I slay the giant. I did it because he had blasphemed God and God's people. I fought only for God and His name.

Michal. [*Breathes heavily, clenches her fists and utters a sob of deep anguish.*]

Jonathan. But your reward is the king's daughter.

David. I dare not receive the reward. For the scoffers would come and sneer: "David said that he was battling on the side of God, but what he really meant was the king's daughter and the king's wealth."

Jonathan. What do you care? God sees your heart and knows the truth.

Michal. [*Laughs.*]

David. My deed must be as pure in the eyes of people as it is in the eyes of God. All men must know and none must doubt. Only the love of God gave strength to my arm, not the love of the king's daughter or the pursuit of wealth and honor. How will they know this if I become the king's son-in-law?

Jonathan. Will you sacrifice your love out of fear of the gossip of evil human tongues?

David. I will sacrifice it to God's name, just as I was ready to sacrifice my life to Him.

Michal. [*Sobbing, with fright in her voice.*]

Jonathan. [*After a brief pause, looking at* DAVID *with a penetrating glance*] Why then are you so sad? Why do you look so unhappy?

David. [*Turns away.*]

Jonathan. You offered your life with gladness. You went forth to meet Goliath as if to a dance. Then why should the sacrifice of your love make you so sad? You are doing it for God; you should be joyful.

David. [*Bitterly*] Ah! Do not laugh at me, and do not add mockery to my sufferings.

Jonathan. But am I not speaking the truth?

David. You have never loved.

Jonathan. Then hear me, and take Michal as your wife. Give me your hand,—give me your hands, both of you; I will unite you and speak, too, in your behalf to the king. I will say to him that his son paid the debt which he did not want to pay. [*To* DAVID.] Come and receive my blessing. Hail, great conqueror! They will not dare to speak against you. The whole people heard the king's proclamation, and yet none dared to step forth against Goliath. Only he who was armored in the love of God was possessed of the daring, and to him God gave the strength. Surely all must see this and understand.

David. You have never loved.

Jonathan, What does that mean?

David. Those who love would have found the courage within them.

Jonathan. You really think so?

David. I know it for certain. Let another Goliath appear today, and let the king offer Michal as reward; I will accept his offer and declare to him, before all the people: "My king, I love your daughter Michal and will joyfully risk my life for her."

Jonathan. So you crave still another Goliath to make you happy! Ha-ha! But I love you too much and would not wish to see you in danger before a second giant. Come; do not be obstinate. Just look at Michal— You must not let her suffer so.

Michal. Speak not of my sufferings, Jonathan. I shall suffer no more.

Jonathan. The proud Michal speaks thus. Be patient, sister, speak nothing against your love.

Michal. Michal, the king's daughter, will not share her love, not even with God!

Jonathan. Those are proud words, but what does your heart say to them? Ah, I have never loved, but I know the ways of love better far than you. God has planted a flower in your hearts. Let it not wither. Come, I am the oldest, and you must both obey me. Give me your hand, David, and let the idle tongues wag idly on. Come, sister, and let not your heart bleed from your pride. Or shall our father's pledge stay unfulfilled? The king made a promise; the king's children shall keep it for him.

Saul. [*Steals suddenly out from the right, where he has been hiding in a clump of trees. Several servants accompany him.*] Ha-ha-ha-ha-ha! You rebellious son of a rebellious mother! You told me a lie before, saying you did not know where they were and what they had conspired between them. And now again, you lie deep down in your throat when you say that I haven't kept my word.

Jonathan. You may berate me and my mother, for you are father and husband—king and ruler besides. But I told no lie. I met them here by accident and only then did I learn what was going on between them. And have you kept the word that you gave before all the people? Have you given the conqueror of Goliath your daughter to wife?

Saul. Worthless son, may your lie choke your throat like boiling lead! Did I not offer your conqueror of Goliath my daughter Merab? He refused her, and I am freed from my pledge.

Jonathan. Did you proclaim Merab the reward for Goliath's head? You offered a daughter; if he does not wish the one, you must grant him the other.

Saul. [*Furious, pointing his clenched fist at* JONATHAN] Ah-h-h-h!

MICHAL. [*Quickly*] The king is freed from his word.

[*General astonishment.*]

Saul. [*Restrains his wild outburst and turns his head slowly toward* MICHAL] What!

Michal. The conqueror of Goliath did not even accept the king's conditions.

Jonathan. Sister!

Saul. [*Turning his wild glances from* MICHAL *to* DAVID, *and from* DAVID *back to* MICHAL] He did not accept my conditions?

Michal. He fought only for God, and battled against Goliath only to avenge the insults to God's name.

Saul. [*Furious*] You lying shepherd; that wasn't your answer to me when I offered Merab to you! You crawled like a worm, bowed abjectly and spoke in utter humility. You were too lowly and unworthy, you said, and the match was altogether above you. Ah, how I hate you, you good-for-nothing slayer of ten thousands, with all your lying and deception.

David. Because Saul does not believe me, I gave him an answer that would be most flattering to his ears. But God is my witness that I love your daughter Michal with a burning, holy love and did not claim her of you. I have her love, too, yet I cannot take her as my wife. I preferred to steal away from your house, that the beloved sight of your daughter should not torture me. I slew Goliath only for God.

Michal. Give him another Goliath, and he will slay him for me.

Jonathan. [*In great fright*] Sister!

Saul. What?

Michal. He said so himself.

Jonathan. Sister, what is your purpose?

David. Yes. I said so myself. Give me even an army of Goliaths, and in the name of my love for your daughter I will go into battle against them.

Jonathan. David, speak not like that. The king owes his daughter to you.

Saul. Silence! I'll let you know at once what you owe to the king, and close your mouth for you forever. [*To* DAVID.] Do I owe you anything, harp-twanger?

David. Nothing.

Saul. Did I promise you anything and fail to keep my promise, stone-slinger?

David. You never promised anything to me in private, and what you promised in your proclamation was not for me.

Saul. [*To* JONATHAN] Do you hear what the shepherd says? Don't you claim from me what he himself doesn't claim! Ha-ha-ha! . . . [*To* MICHAL.] And you love the slayer of Goliath?

Michal. [*Breathing heavily*] No, not the slayer of Goliath.

Saul. Ah-h-h, Ha-ha-ha-ha! The proud princess! Come to my arms! You are my own true blood. Not for nothing does Saul love you best of all his children. The others are not his kind. See that worthless wretch there? His father and the throne itself are less to him than the shepherd! . . . Ha-ha-ha! . . . "No, not the slayer of Goliath." Ha-ha-ha. . . . But *him* you love, *him*! The harpist, the blond locks, the ruddy cheeks, the lithe body, the handsome fellow, the splendid mien, that worm, that viper? *Him,* him you love? Yes, you love him, you love him! Don't curl your pretty lips! Don't ask your pride! Don't turn your head away. You love him, I can see. I am old and impetuous and ill-tempered, but I remember well the signs of love and how it inflames the blood. You love— you love him. You are no better than your brother! Away from me! Ha-ha-ha! And he loves you! "With a burning, holy love" he loves you! Ha—! Do you love her, sheep-driver? Do you love her, insect?

Michal. Father!

Saul. Ha-ha-ha! That struck home! Do you love her, bear-slayer?

David. You have already heard my answer. And as to your insults, king, I have more than once answered you and our people.

Saul. How proud! The women's champion! The hero in the songs of old and wasted harlots! But soon we'll see your heroism, and what your word is worth. Hear, all of you, my word, and King Saul *keeps* his word: Jesse's son shall receive my daughter for his wife, if he brings to me, for her, the heads of a hundred Philistines as a dowry.

Jonathan. [*In great fright*] Father! [*Covers his head.*]

Michal. Ah-h!

[*Looks at* DAVID *in keen suspense. There is a murmur of amazement and fright among the men of the king's suite.*]

David. [*With enthusiasm*] I accept your challenge, my king!

Michal. [*Laughing, her entire countenance beaming.*]

Saul. And I will keep my word. The heads of a hundred Philistines, and she is yours!

David. May God bless you, king. You have given me back my peace of mind. Now I shall be happy! Must I leave you at once, my king?

Saul. At once!

David. Then I go straightway, and may God restore your joyous spirit, even as you have given me back my own. Farewell, my king! Uncover your head, my Jonathan! See, in your David every fibre sings and rejoices; your David is full of power and courage. Come, kiss me and help me chant my joy! Do you not believe in me? I will be the victor. Do you believe in me, Michal? Farewell, my bride! Give me your hand to press. But I shall long for your lips, and the Philistines will have to pay dearly for my longing. Ha-a! My love has been freed and it has won the strength of Samson! I go! Tremble, ye Philistines! [*Turns to leave.*]

Michal. [*Frightened*] David! Father!

David. [*Stops, and looks back.*]

Jonathan. [*Raises his head.*]

Saul. Who spoke those words? I do not recognize the voice.

Michal. [*Composed, resolutely*] Nothing . . . I thought—a hundred Philistines were too many.

Saul. For you?

David. A hundred Philistines too many for my Michal? It shall be two hundred! My Michal, I love you!

[*Walks off with closed eyes, breathing audibly, his arms outstretched as if for an embrace.*]

Saul. Ha-ha-ha! The liar! Ha-ha-ha! He will never return!

Jonathan. [*Despairingly*] Sister, what have you done?

Michal. [*Transfigured, exalted, with a joyful expression upon her face, she breathes heavily*] He loves—me! . . . He will conquer! . . .

THE EVERLASTING ROAD

by STEFAN ZWEIG

The great square in front of the temple. Everywhere signs of the sack are visible.

In the square we see a medley of hand-carts laden with household goods, of packhorses and other beasts of burden, and of wagons. Men and women, preparing for the exodus, are busied among these. New groups continually flock into the square from the surrounding streets, and the noise of conversation grows ever louder. The women and children, together with the men too old for work, sit apart on the steps. Chaldean warriors, fully armed, stride masterfully through the crowd, making way for themselves with their spears.

The moon shines fitfully. Gradually the dawn reddens in the east.

Voices. This is our meeting place.—How many of us are here?—Keep together, sons of Reuben.—How dark it is.—This is the best place, so that we can lead the way.

Other Voices. Don't push.—This is our place.—Our mules have been standing here since evening.—The place is ours.—The sons of Reuben always want to be first.

An Elder. Do not quarrel, children. Let Reuben lead the way, for such is the law.

Voices. There is no longer any law.—The scriptures are burned.—Who are you to order us about?—It is the priests' commandment.—There are no priests left; they have all been put to the sword.—Hananiah escaped the slaughter.—Nay, they made an end of him too.—We are leaderless.—Who shall give us the law?—Who will make the sacrifices for us in Babylon?—Who will interpret the scriptures?—All of the race of Aaron have been slain.—Woe unto us that are orphaned.—Had we but the ark and the roll of the law.—The roll of the law has been burned.—Nay, the word of God cannot be burned.—I tell you I saw it perish in the flames.—Alas, is the law burned?—Impossible, how can God's word be burned?—Has not his house been burned; has not his altar been overthrown?—Did he not deliver over his holy city to destruction?—Yea, yea, he has made us the slaves of our enemies. He has broken the covenant.—Blaspheme not.—I fear him no longer.—We are leaderless;

would that Moses could lead us as of old; would that there were still a judge among the people.—What has become of the king, him whom they blinded?—He has always been blind.—To him we owe these disasters.—Alas for the fate of Israel, the destruction of Jerusalem!

[*A disorderly rout, laughing loudly, issues from the palace. The new-comers are the princes of Chaldea, with slaves bearing torches. The princes are drunk. In the midst of the brawling crowd we see the figure of a man whom the princes are buffeting and pushing one to another, so that he totters, and is continually in danger of falling.*]

The Chaldean Princes. Are you ready for a fresh attack on Nebuchad-nezzar?—On, stormer of Babylon.—Pillar of Israel, take heed lest you fall.—He cannot dance like King David.—He cannot play the psaltery.—Enough of him, let us go back to our wine.—I would rather amuse my-self with his wives.—Let him drink darkness while we drink wine.—Come away!

[*Laughing and shouting, the princes return into the palace, leaving the man of whom they have been making sport swaying unsteadily as he stands at the top of the steps. The moon has pierced the clouds, and his shadow stretches across the stone flooring behind him. This gives him the appearance of a gigantic wraith. The crowd beneath is filled with astonishment and alarm.*]

Whispering Voices. Who is it?—Why have they cast him out from their board?—Why does he not speak?—Look how he raises his hands imploringly to heaven.—Who is he?—Don't go near him.—Yes, I will see who it is.

[*Some of the bolder spirits have mounted the steps.*]

A Voice. [*With a cry of recognition*] Zedekiah!

The Crowd. The king.—The blinded king.—God's judgment.—Zedekiah. . .

Zedekiah. [*Falteringly*] Who calls me?

Voices. No one calls thee.—For thee there are naught but curses, and God's judgments.—Where are thy Egyptian friends?—Where is Zion?

Other Voices. Be silent!—He is the anointed of the Lord, blinded by our enemies.—Reverence the king.—Have pity on his sufferings.

The First Voices. Nay, he shall not sit among us.—Where are my children?—Give me back my children.—A curse on the man who has murdered Israel.—He is to blame for all.—Why should he live when better men have died?

Zedekiah. [*To one who has taken his hand to lead him*] Who are these who rail against me? Are my foes those of mine own household?

The Guide. Lord, they are thy companions in misfortune.

Voices. Do not bring him down here, for his lot and ours shall not be mingled.—Let him sit apart.—God has punished him.—A curse lies upon him.—No longer shall he be king.—Of what use is a blind king?

Zedekiah. [*Well-nigh weeping in his helplessness*] Lead me forth. They have put out my eyes, and now they will take my crown. Hide me from my enemies.

A Woman. Rest here, Lord King. Lie down and rest.

[*A couch is extemporized for* ZEDEKIAH *at the foot of the steps. The inquisitive gather round.*]

The Elder. Keep away, keep away. Reverence the Lord's anointed. God has appointed him our leader.

Voices. How can a blind man lead us?—He cannot reign in Jerusalem, for Zion has fallen.—We are all slaves, and slaves need no leader.—Nay, we need a deliverer.—Were but Moses here to help us at this hour.—How can a man so afflicted give us help and consolation?—No one can help us.—See, the dawn comes. Let us make ready for the journey.—Alas the day!—As wanderers and exiles, we go leaderless into a far country. [*Loud chanting is heard in the distance.*] Hark, the trumpet.—Alas, the trumpet sounds.—The first signal for departure.—No, no, that is not a trumpet.—Cannot you hear singing, with cymbals and drums?—Our enemies are rejoicing.—O shame! O torment!

[*The chanting draws nearer and nearer, until individual voices and the clashing of the cymbals can be clearly distinguished. At length a group of persons is seen advancing, and thronging exultantly round a tall figure.*]

A Voice. Look! They are of our own people.

Voices. Impossible.—They are rejoicing.—How could any son of Israel exult on this day of sorrow?—They must be drunken with wine.—Assuredly they are our brothers of Israel.—Who is it in their midst?—Look at that frenzied woman clashing the cymbals!

[*The approaching singers,* JEREMIAH *in the center, advance in the pale light of dawn. Some of them are in truth ecstatic and unsteady in their movements, as if drunken; but others are of sober mien.*]

Chanting Voices. Hosanna!—A prophecy.—Jerusalem endureth for ever!—Blessed our return home.—Blessed be the consoler, and blessed the comfort he brings.—Hosanna!—Jerusalem endureth for ever!

Voices from the Crowd. [*In excitement*] They are mad.—What has happened?—Hark, how they shout Hosanna!—Who is the prophet?—

What is his message?—Let him deliver it to us also.—Who shall bring us consolation?

A Voice. Look, is it not Jeremiah whom they surround?

Voices. Yes.—No.—His face was lowering, but this man's face is radiant.—Nay, it is he.—How changed he is.—A curse upon him who breathed curses.—How can sweetness come from the bitter?

Baruch. Hearken to the message of comfort, brothers. Feed your souls with the word of God, with the bread of life!

Voices. How can comfort be brought by this man accurst?—His words are like scorpions.—His message will choke us.—We have had enough of the prophets, for they have misled us one and all.—No, no, Jeremiah gave us true warning.—I tell you he will rub salt into our wounds.—Away, away, man without bowels of compassion!

Baruch. I beseech you to hear his message. He has uplifted our hearts, and will uplift yours likewise, brothers in God.

The Wounded Man. I testify for him, I testify for him! Fevered by my wounds I lay unable to move. His words have restored my strength. Lo, on me he hath wrought a miracle.

Voices. Who is this?—Listen to what he says.—He tells of a miracle, and a miracle is what we need.—I need comfort.—Naught but Zion's valleys will comfort me.—What comfort can he give?—Can he raise the dead; can he rebuild the temple?—Let us hear his message.

The Woman. Balaam! Balaam! Balaam! Hail, for that you who came to curse Israel have blessed us thrice.

Baruch. Master, look upon their discord. Make their hearts one, their spirits fruitful. Lift them from their mourning, lift their souls to God.

Jeremiah. [*Leaving his companions and going to the top of the steps*] Brothers, in the darkness I feel you to be near me, and know that your souls are filled with darkness. But why do you despair? Why do you lament?

Voices. Hearken to the blasphemer.—I warned you against him.—He mocks us.—He asks why we lament!—He rubs salt into our wounds.—Are we to rejoice on the day of our exodus?—Are we to forget the dead?—He laughs at our tears.—Silence, let us hear him.—Let us hear his message.

Jeremiah. Hearken, brothers, give ear unto my words. Is all lost, that you should lament? There still remains the precious gift of life.

A Voice. What a life!

Jeremiah. And I say unto you, who has life, has God also. Leave it to the dead to complain of those who have led them to the tomb. We, who survive, should continue to hope. Lament not, despair not, while breath remains; neither opening your mouths in revolt, nor closing your ears to words of consolation.

Voices. Words, only words, which avail nothing.—If you would lift up our hearts, lift up the walls of Jerusalem.—Rebuild the fortress of Zion.—Alas, he cannot see our distress, he cannot recognize our suffering.

Jeremiah. Brothers, I read your suffering like an open book, and the scroll of your pain lies unrolled before me. Natheless, brothers, I see a meaning in this pain and suffering; I see God therein. The hour is sent to us for trial. Let us meet the test.

Voices. Why should God try us?—Why should he visit us, his chosen people, with affliction?—Why should he make our burden so heavy?

Jeremiah. God sends us this trial that we may know him to be God. To those of other nations, few signs are given and little recognition is vouchsafed. They fancy themselves able to see the face of the Eternal in images of wood and stone. Our God, the God of our fathers, is a hidden God; and not until we are bathed in sorrow are we enabled to discern him. He chooses those only whom he has tried, and to none but the suffering does he give his love. Let us therefore rejoice at our trials, brothers, and let us love the suffering God sends. He has broken us with affliction, that he may sink the deeper into the freshly ploughed ground of our hearts, and that we may be ready for the scattering of his seed. He has weakened our bodies that we may strengthen our souls. Let us joyfully enter the smelting furnace of his will, that thereby we may be purified. Follow the example of your forefathers, and thankfully accept the scourgings of the Almighty!

Voices. Not our will but his.—A blessing on our trials.—I must learn to stifle my complaints.—True, our forefathers likewise were in bondage.

Jeremiah. Brothers, if we believe that we shall arise, already we have arisen. What should we be without faith? Not to us, as to other nations, has a country been given to which we may cling; a home, where we may tarry; rest, that our hearts may wax fat! Not for peace have we been the chosen among the nations. Wandering is our habitation, trouble our heritage, God our home. Do not for that reason covet your neighbor's goods; do not for that reason complain. Leave to others their happiness and their pride; leave to others an abiding place. For yourselves, people of suffering, gladly accept trial. Have faith, chosen of God, seeing that sorrow is your heritage. Because it is your eternal heritage, therefore are you chosen.

Voices. True is the word.—Sorrow is our heritage.—I will shoulder my burden.—I have faith in God's mercy. He will lead us now, as he led us out of Egypt.—God will deliver us, as he delivered our fathers.

Jeremiah. Arise, then, and cease repining. Take up your faith as a staff, and you will march bravely through these trials as you have marched for thousands of years. Happy are we to be vanquished, and happy to be driven from home; for we are vanquished, we are driven from home, by God's will. Happy are we to lose all, that we may find him; happy is our hard lot, gladsome our trial. Kings who mastered us have vanished like smoke; nations which enslaved us have been scattered and their seed has been destroyed; towns wherein we served as bondmen have been made desolate, and are now the home of the jackal; but Israel still lives, ever young, for sorrow is our buttress and overthrow is our strength. Through suffering we have endured the assaults of time; reverses have ever been our beginning; and out of the depths God has gathered us to his heart. Think of our former troubles, and how those troubles were met. Think of Egypt, the house of bondage, the first ordeal. Give praise to affliction, ye afflicted; give praise to trial, ye sorely tried; praise the name of God who, through tribulation, has chosen us for all eternity!

[*A wave of enthusiasm answers his words. The confused medley of voices gradually gives place to rhythmical choruses.*]

Voices. Bondmen of Mizraim
Were our fathers,
Bridled and bitted
Were our fathers,
Israel's children.
Taskmasters cruel
Hasted our fathers,
Beat them with rods,
Scourged them with cords,
Afflicted our fathers
With manifold tasks.

Higher Voices. Ere long the darkness which encompassed us
Was pierced by Jehovah's compassionate gaze.
To save his people before it had perished,
God raised up a deliverer,
One of the house of Levi.
Moses came to our aid,
A man mighty of tongue,

A man mighty of hand.
He led us forth from the land of Egypt.
He freed us from the house of bondage.

Exultant Voices. Those who had numbered but seventy
When they entered the land of Egypt,
Went out from it numbering countless thousands,
Driving before them flocks and herds,
And bearing with them great possessions.
Before their faces went the pillar of cloud,
Before them went the pillar of fire,
And the angel of God went before the camp of Israel.
Such was the first exodus,
Such was the beginning of happiness,
When God was bringing our fathers to the land of promise.

Jeremiah. But new tribulations awaited us,
Fresh trials;
Forbear not to recall the days of bitterness,
Forget not those days!

Voices. Pursuing us,
Came the army of Pharaoh,
Horses and chariots,
And a multitude of horsemen.
With vengeful clamor
Did they follow after.
The sea barred our passage;
Death pressed at our heels.

Higher Voices. Thereupon the Lord sent the strong east wind,
Dividing the waters that the sea might be dry land.
The waters were a wall unto us,
On our right hand, and on our left.
Thus went we into the midst of the sea
Upon the dry ground.

Exultant Voices. With the clashing of arms and the roaring of chariot
    wheels,
Our foes, thirsty for blood, followed after,
On the dry ground between the walls of the sea.
They shouted in their wrath as they thought to smite us.
But Moses stretched forth his hand over the sea,

And the waters returned, and covered the chariots and the horsemen,
And all the hosts of Pharaoh that came into the sea after them;
Thus did the Lord overthrow the Egyptians in the midst of the sea!

> *Deep Voices.* Thus did the Lord deliver us out of danger,
> And lead us forth from the land of bondage.
> Thus wonderful was the beginning
> Of our happy and unhappy wanderings!

Jeremiah. Again and again did he pour over us the bitterness of death
and the waters of the cup of trial, that we might be healed for evermore.
Bethink ye of the scorching days in the desert, of the forty years of pri-
vation ere we reached the promised land.

> *Voices.* Parched were our throats,
> Blistered our lips,
> Athirst were we
> And anhungered,
> In that waterless and barren region.

> *Exultant Voices.* Then Moses lifted up his hand,
> And with his rod smote the rock twice,
> Lo, the stone was riven in sunder,
> The water gushed forth abundantly,
> The congregation drank and their cattle,
> And the wanderers laved their toilworn feet.

Higher Voices. When we were weary, the Lord gave us rest.
He sent cool breezes
To temper the burning heats of noontide.
Bitter springs did he sweeten for our sake.
The wind brought fat quails from the sea.
When our entrails were gnawed with hunger,
Lo, after the morning dews had risen,
There lay on the face of the wilderness
Manna, small and round, the bread of heaven.

Jeremiah. Albeit, never was it granted us to live in safety.
Continually did the Lord chastise us with his holy hand.
Ever and again did he renew the tribulations of his people.

> *Voices.* The nations stood
> Against us in arms;

> Greed and envy
> Closed the roads
> Of our pilgrimage;
> Cities shut their gates;
> Spears gleamed,
> Strewing our path with death.

Higher Voices. Then God forged us new weapons,
Making our hearts like sharp swords,
Giving us strength against thousands,
Victory over tens of thousands.

Exultant Voices. Trumpets blew, walls fell down;
Moab was overthrown, and Amalek.
With the sword we carved ways
Through the anger of the peoples and the times,
Until our hearts stood the test,
Until we reached the land of promise,
Canaan, where after labor we could rest.
Here was a home for the wanderers,
Now could we ungird our loins,
Doff our shoes, lay aside our staves.
These staves put forth green shoots,
Israel blossomed, and Zion arose.

All the Voices. Again and again have we been yoked to the plough,
Necks bowed; again and again enslaved;
But never has he failed to break our yoke,
To free us from captivity and exile;
From all our afflictions, all our privations,
Never has he failed to deliver us,
To summon us home at last,
To grant us a renewed flowering.

Jeremiah. Have no fear, have no fear, that the Lord will forsake us!
Mistrust him not, brothers, in days that are dark!
For when he debases us, when he afflicts us,
The suffering he sends is but sign of his love.
Then bow ye, my brothers, bend necks to the yoke,
Accept gladly the lot by Jehovah decreed.
Know, that sorrow but proves us, that trial uplifts us,
That affliction, though sore, brings us nearer to God.

Each pang that we feel is a step toward his kingdom,
Since the vanquished on earth are in heaven beloved.
Up, brothers, march onward, march onward to God.

Voices. [*Ecstatically*] Yea, now let us begin our wanderings.—Lead us forth.—We shall suffer, even as our fathers suffered.—Exodus and never-ending return.—Hasten, hasten, sunrise is at hand.—Let us march steadfastly into slavery.—Now as ever, God will deliver us.—We will all go, not one will stay behind.

Zedekiah. Alas, alas! Who will lead me? Leave me not behind! Who will carry me?

Jeremiah. Who calls?

Voices. Let him stay where he is.—He is chaff for the winnowing fan.—He is rejected of God. [*To* JEREMIAH.] Lead us, prophet.—You shall be our master.—Leave the outcast.

Jeremiah. No one is an outcast! Whoever calls for help must be heard, for all our sakes.

Voices. Not he.—He is the cause of our troubles.—He is the rejected of God.—He is one accurst!

Jeremiah. I, too, was rejected of God, and God has heard my prayer; I, likewise, was a man accurst, and God has blessed me. Who was it, crying in his distress? Let me bring him comfort, even as I was comforted.

Voices. 'Tis the man lying on the steps.—God's wrath has smitten his pride.

Jeremiah. Why lies he alone there? Wherefore does he not join us?

Voices. Look, his stars are darkened.—No longer can he find his way, for he is blind.—They have put out his eyes.

Jeremiah. [*Drawing near the recumbent figure with profound emotion*] Zedekiah! Lord King!

Zedekiah. Is it thou, Jeremiah?

Jeremiah. It is I, Lord King. I am thy faithful servant, Jeremiah. [*He kneels beside the king.*]

Zedekiah. Scorn me not! Drive me not from thee, as I drave thee from me! Thy words have burned me to ashes, man of might. Now leave me not alone in the hour of mine anguish. Be with me, as you swore before God when last we met.

Jeremiah. I am with thee, King Zedekiah.

Zedekiah. [*Groping for him*] Where art thou? I cannot find thee.

Jeremiah. I am at thy feet, thy servant and thy slave.

Zedekiah. [*Trembling*] Mock me not before the people, nor bow thyself in reverence to one abased. The oil wherewith I was anointed hath turned to blood upon my brow. My crown is dust.

Jeremiah. Thou hast become the king of sorrows, and never wert thou more kingly. Zedekiah, I stood upright before thee when I faced thee in thy strength, but I bow myself before thee now that God hath brought thee low. Anointed by suffering, lead us forth! Thou who now seest God only, who no longer seest the world, guide thy people. [*He rises and faces the multitude.*]

> Behold, behold,
> Children of sorrow, children of God,
> The Lord hath hearkened to your cry,
> He hath sent you a leader!
> One crowned with suffering,
> One scorned of men!
> Who is more fitted than he
> To reign over those that are blessed by defeat?
> God hath closed Zedekiah's eyes on earth
> That he may better see the glories of heaven.
> Brothers, has any son of the house of David
> Been so fitted as he to be king of the sorrowful?

Zedekiah. Whither would you take me? What will become of me?

> *Jeremiah.* Lift him up,
> Him who has been abased,
> Pay him all honor!
> Harness the horses,
> Make ready the litters,
> Tenderly lift him,
> Israel's guardian,
> King over Zion.

[*The king is lifted with all signs of respect, and is placed in a litter. A trumpet sounds in the distance. There is a red glow upon the walls as the day dawns. The sky has cleared. A tremor runs through the crowd at the sound of the trumpet.*]

Voices. The signal!—The first signal!—God summons us.—The day of our trial has dawned.—Soon the sun will shine over Jerusalem.—The exodus.—The exodus.—Exodus and return.—Jerusalem.—Jerusalem.

Jeremiah. [*With confident mien, strides up the steps once more. The crowd has drawn back, and he stands alone at the top, looking taller than ever in his isolation.*]

Up, ye rejected,
Up, all ye vanquished,
Brisk for the journey!
Wanderers,
Chosen of God and the world,
Lift up your hearts!
[*A surge of activity passes through
the crowd.* JEREMIAH *gazes out
over the city.*]
On Jerusalem's pinnacles
Now for the last time
Look through your tears.
Carry with you the image
Of the home you so love.
Drink your fill of the towers,
Drink your fill of the walls,
Drink your fill of Jerusalem.

Voices. Yea, yea, ere we go
Let us drink our fill of Jerusalem.

Jeremiah. Bend down a last time,
Piously caressing
Your native earth.
[*He apostrophizes the earth.*]
Earth drenched with blood and tears,
Lo, I touch you
With loving hand.
The memory of this touch
Shall go with me,
Shall be an undying hunger.
[*He addresses the people once more.*]
Unceasingly,
Wherever we wander,
Shall we be anhungered,
Shall we be athirst,
For Zion!

Voices. Unceasingly,
Wherever we wander,
Shall we be anhungered,

Shall we be athirst,
For Zion!

Jeremiah. Wanderers, chosen of God,
Filled with your hunger, your thirst,
Having now said your farewells,
Manfully turn to the journey.
Look forward, not backward.
Stay-at-homes
Have home;
Wanderers
Have the world!
God's are the ways

On which ye shall walk.
Made wise through suffering,
Wanderers, chosen of God,
On, through the world!

The People. Shall we ever see Jerusalem again?
Jeremiah. He who believes, looks always on Jerusalem.
The People. Who shall rebuild the city?
Jeremiah. The ardor of desire, the night of prison, and the suffering which brings counsel.
The People. Will it endure?
Jeremiah. Yea. Stones fall, but that which the soul builds in suffering, endureth for ever.
[*There is a bustle among the crowd as all make ready for the start. The trumpet sounds again. It is now quite light. The crowd, eager to begin the exodus, greets the second blast of the trumpet with a shout of impatience.*]
[*Raising his voice to dominate the tumult.*]
Wanderers, sufferers, march in the name
Of your forefather Jacob, who erstwhile with God,
Having wrestled the livelong night,
Strove till dawn for a blessing.
March on in the morning light
By a path like that which your forefathers trod,
When from Mizraim forth by Moses led
Toward the land of promise their way they sped.
Scatter your seeds, scatter your seeds,
In unknown lands,

Through numberless years.
Wander your wanderings, watered with tears.
On, people of God; for, wherever ye roam,
Your road leads through the world to eternity, home.

[*The march begins in silence. At the head of the procession, the king is borne in a litter. In due order, tribe by tribe, the wanderers fall into line and move towards the gate. They gaze heavenward, singing as they march, so that the exodus has the solemnity of a religious procession. There is neither haste nor lagging, but a rhythmic movement forward. The files succeed one another in an endless train. An infinite on the march.*]

First Chorus of Wanderers. In strangers' houses now must we dwell,
Eating bread salted with tears.
By an enemy's hearth, with souls full of dread,
Must we sit upon stools of shame.
The weight of the years will lie heavy upon us
When, captives and bondmen, we must serve men of might.
But from exile escaping, from bondage redeemed,
To Jerusalem homing, to Zion returning,
Our spirits shall ever be free and at rest.

Second Chorus of Wanderers. Our drink must be drawn from distant waters;
Evil their taste, bitter in the mouth.
We must shelter from the sun beneath strange trees,
Their leaves breathing fear as they rustle in the wind.
But we shall win solace from the starry skies;
Dreams of home will comfort our nights;
Our souls will find continual refreshment
In the thought of Jerusalem.

Third Chorus of Wanderers. We shall journey by unfamiliar roads;
The wind will carry us afar, through many lands;
Weary shall we be, footsore and weary,
As the nations drive us from home after home.
Nowhere at all will they suffer us to take root,
Perpetual our pilgrimage through the changing world,
Yet happy shall we be, eternally vanquished;
Happy shall we be, chaff blown by the breeze;
Kindred to none, and by none made welcome;

For through the ages our path leads unerringly,
To the goal of our desire,
Jerusalem!

[*A few Chaldeans, among them a captain, have come out from the palace. Some of them are half drunk. Their voices sound shrill in contrast with the chanting of the wanderers.*]

The Captain. The dogs are mutinous. They murmur against their fate. Beat them with rods if they refuse to go.

A Chaldean. Look, Captain, they have not waited for an order. There is no sign of mutiny.

The Captain. If they complain, strike them on the mouth.

The Chaldean. Captain, they are not complaining.

Another Chaldean. Watch them marching. They stride along like conquerors. Their eyes flash with joy.

The Chaldeans. What people are these?—Have they not been vanquished?—Can anyone have spread among them false tidings of liberation?—What are they chanting?—A strange people.—No one can understand them, whether in their dejection or in their exultation.—Their very gentleness is a danger, for it has a strength of its own.—This resembles rather the triumphal entry of a king, than the exodus of an enslaved people.—Saw the world ever such a nation?

Fourth Chorus of Wanderers. [*Here* JEREMIAH *inconspicuously joins his tribe.*]

Through ages we wander, we march through the nations,
The tale of our sufferings ever renewed;
Aeon after aeon eternally vanquished,
Thralls at the hearths where in passing we rest.
But the cities wither, and the nations
Shoot into darkness like wandering stars.
The oppressors who scourged us with many whips
Have become a hissing and a byword among the generations.
Whereas we march onward, march onward, march onward,
Drawing strength from within, eternity from earth,
And God from pains and tribulations.

The Chaldean Captain. Verily madness has seized them. We are the victors, they the defeated and the disgraced. Why, then, do they not complain?

A Chaldean. An invisible force must sustain them.

Another Chaldean. True, they believe in the invisible. That is the mystery of their faith.

The Captain. How is it possible to see the invisible, or to believe in what cannot be seen? They must have secret arts, like those of our astrologers and soothsayers. It would be well to learn their mysteries.

The Chaldean. These mysteries cannot be taught; the secret lies in faith. What sustains them, they say, is their faith in the invisible God.

Fifth Chorus of Wanderers. We wander adown the road of suffering,
Through our trials we are purified,
Everlastingly vanquished, and everlastingly overthrown,
For ever enslaved, for ever enfranchised,
Unceasingly broken and unceasingly renewed,
The mock and the sport of all nations on earth.
We wander through the eternities,
A remnant, a remnant,
And yet numberless.
We march onward to God,
To God who is the beginning and the end,
To God who is our home.

The Chaldean. See how they are walking to meet the sun. His light shines on their foreheads, and they themselves shine with the strength of the sun. Mighty must their God be.

The Captain. Their God? Have we not broken down his altars? Have we not conquered him?

The Chaldean. Who can conquer the invisible! Men we can slay, but the God who lives in them we cannot slay. A nation can be controlled by force; its spirit, never.

[*For the third time the trumpet sounds. The sun has risen, shining on the exodus of the chosen people, beginning their march athwart the ages.*]

PAUL AND GAMALIEL

by FRANZ WERFEL

The great chamber of the priests. Three entrances with white waving curtains. In a corner a raised throne-like seat. Priestly utensils. Ebbing and flowing in a wave of sound the murmur of the praying people flows into the room. It is the Day of Atonement.

[*Enter, briskly,* PAUL *and* BARNABAS. *Both wear shrouds, which every Jew, the High Priest included, must wear on this Day of Contrition.*]

Barnabas. [*Grasping* PAUL *by the arm*] I will not let go of thee, man!

Paul. Here is the chamber where Rabbenu takes rest after prayer, where he retires from the multitude. Oft have I sat at his feet here on the Day of Atonement.

Barnabas. This time thou shalt not shake me off! I must keep thee for the Kingdom of the Christ!

Paul. In the name of the Christ must I fight with Moses!

Barnabas. Long enough hast thou dwelt in Gamaliel's house!

Paul. The greatest thing is at stake. He and I had not as yet collected our thoughts. Therefore we both have kept silence.

Barnabas. The greatest thing is at stake! The High Priest has issued a warrant to seize thee tomorrow, even if it were in Gamaliel's house.

Paul. I know it. But another warrant hangs over me. Without Christ the world has two ways: in Christ one alone.

Barnabas. All the bailiffs of Jerusalem will have to search for thee this night. Now, now is the moment for us!

[*The murmur of the prayer is lifted up on a wave of sound.*]

Barnabas. The great Confession of sin! The priest has laid upon the goat the sin of the people and driven it out. Soon the scapegoat will have reached the desert ravine. All who are not halt or leprous are in Jerusalem, mourning and wailing in the inner court. Not a soul is in the streets. Let us use this hour!

Paul. Not yet!

Barnabas. Thinkest thou that the brethren will protect thee? They want to get rid of thee. With all their hearts they wish thee in Tarsus.

Paul. Lord, help me! How intractable must I be still, for them to hate me so!

Barnabas. I have prepared everything. We will steal away to Bezetha, to the house of a friend. Greek garments lie in readiness there. So away with us at once into the darkness! [*Breaking out wildly.*] How have I shaken off all this: Temple, sin, the Law, through thy assistance! Free am I, Paul! Free from this place of the rich, the oppressors, and the priests! Our Lord is the Christ of the poor! Let them dare! Let them try to take hold of thee! Him and thee will I protect. [*He goes to where the priestly utensils are and takes up a knife.*] And this sacrificial knife will I take with me!

Paul. Thou sinful man! Lay it down at once!

[BARNABAS *backs under the glance of* PAUL *and obeys.*]

Paul. Woe unto thee that thou hast grieved God's Torah! It was our stern and mighty leader to the Christ. Not for sin have we been freed, man! We are Jews of Christ. Pray, pray now, that Gamaliel's soul may be open! I shall speak. But for the truth of Christ there is no other proof than grace alone can vouchsafe. He who breathes, alone apprehendeth life. Pray, pray! Rabbenu is the purest vessel. He alone lives always near the impossible. Verily, I swear: before I go to Edom I will seek Jacob! [*Enter* GAMALIEL.]

Barnabas. For a little moment only will I leave thee, brother! [*Exit.*]

Gamaliel. Thou hast complied with the teaching: "On a holy day visit thou thy teacher!" The greatest hour of the year has arrived. This hour is ours, and I have appointed it in my heart. Now speak! [*He seats himself on the raised seat.*]

Paul. My father, thou, my more than bodily father, for thou hast begotten me into the spiritual world! [*He kisses his hand.*]

Gamaliel. This thanks is a farewell! Speak on!

Paul. [*Seats himself on a step at the feet of* GAMALIEL *and leaning forward away from the Rabbi; speaks without looking up at him*] May God help me now, Rabbenu, that thou mayest understand what no one understands. Behold, it is not long since that I was a care-free child. Yet, early did they inculcate me with the Torah. Then was the world filled with flaming angels of the Law, who beset all my paths. And all their swords blazed against me, thousands and millions of them! I scourged my body in order to keep the Law! But, alas! What is this body of feverish dream-chasing flesh, stamped with Adam's curse, able to do? Nothing, nothing! I fasted, had sleepless nights, cried to God in the night! But the prohibitions tempted, sins grew to the deadly sin, and I was immersed in it. Thus, daily and hourly my death-warrant hung over me. Who is the man who can love his own death-warrant? Listen, Rabbenu! The Torah redeemed me not, it cursed me only with the knowledge of my sin! And as I was, so is Israel now!

Gamaliel. Speak not of it!

Paul. My father brought me to thine house. I can still see they glance, Rabbenu, that pierced me as if from heaven, bringing tears of joy to my eyes. Thy soft hand, it lies still upon my youthful head. Yea, thou art great and righteous! God loves thee. And upon the angels of the Law thou springest like a lion. In thine hands sin melteth. *One* Being only the earth has held whom thou resemblest!

Gamaliel. Speak not of me!

Paul. Oh, thou great king without ill-conscience. I, slave of sin, loved thee in despair. Thou gavest me food super-abundantly. But I was starving and could not digest the king's rich food. Thou knowest how I have tormented myself to resemble thee a little! Yet, not out of myself, the accursed, could I find the means to become different. For there is on earth no will that can help! So I fled from thee! I began to be jealous of thee. Then I hated thee! For an ugly slave of sin cannot bear the free lord over sin. Alas! Have pity on me, pardon me, Rabbenu! My hatred against *thee* was a hatred against *Him*. Thus it came about that the disciple of Gamaliel led young Stephen to be stoned! For in proportion to the death in us so is the will to murder in us.

Gamaliel. Speak of that which thou shouldst speak!

Paul. [*Springing to his feet and speaking with strong excitement*] How can I speak of the moment when the Light from heaven rushed into my being, when I entered, blind, into a new world? My heart is torn when I only think of it. Can a man speak of the moment of his birth?

Gamaliel. Thou wilt speak! For I have decided that thou shouldst lead back Rabbi Jehoshua of Nazareth to Israel!

Paul. Glorious! Rabbenu! Isaiah's word is being fulfilled: "I was found of them that sought me not." Hear, O Israel! Thou has found Him!

Gamaliel. I have found a holy man of God. And I will testify of him. With thee I will stand up before the Tribunal!

Paul. And the fathers, Rabbenu? Thou wilt also be judged.

Gamaliel. He who does the deed has nothing to ask. I will stand with thee before the judges. A false verdict has been passed in Israel. An undeserved death has brought Truth into confusion. Atonement is necessary! I will offer it. I am determined to agitate. I determine upon even more! But be thou not over-zealous! For even illumination is guilty, when it is too dazzling for weak eyes. Very dangerously hath Jehoshua illumined the Law, and beside, it was too premature.

Paul. He did more, master, than illumine the Law!

Gamaliel. No Jew can do more, Saul! No Jew can live, think, or say, what is not already sealed in God's Word. For it is the blood of our souls!

Paul. The dispensation of the Word is past.

Gamaliel. Blaspheme not the Word! It is the only thing which God and man have in common.

Paul. Rabbenu! A strange Being breathes in our midst. We draw in His breath with every breath we breathe. Grasp this mystery! Every thing is now filled with His breath also. When I was the old Saul, there was between me and Creation a dead, black atmosphere—Loneliness! Death was the second name of the world. Death—all-smiling, all-filling earth-scents; jeering stinking death! And now? Why has Loneliness vanished? What is this strong exulting love in me? Whence cometh this knowledge of eternity in the heart, that consumes all fear and decay? A transformation! I tell thee, no smallest blade grows now untransformed. Even thou, also, master, art transformed! For we live now in the midst of the Kingdom of God and know it not. . . .

Gamaliel. [*Rising*] Saul! . . . Thou art in the Temple. . . . We wear shrouds. . . . Think of the atonement which I would make on this Day of Atonement! [*Quietly but firmly.*] What has the love of thy Jesus changed? It has changed nothing, as His anger changed nothing. He overthrew the money lenders' tables in the Temple, but on the next day they stood there again. *Not* He, and *not* I, can banish evil, only the Law, that mystery that we serve that we may live, the holy Tie which binds mankind.

Paul. This Tie has become rotten, Rabbenu! Like a discarded wine-skin the Word lies upon the road!

Gamaliel. [*With a deliberate composure*] *This* this man Jesus did not say!

Paul. Rabbenu speaketh of a *man!* Oh, the world is swallowed up, both Jews and Gentiles, and only thou art here, thou and He. Gladly would I be anathema from Him, if thou, Israel's hero, now, now, shouldst know Him. A man! Has ever a man conquered death and decay? Has ever a man risen bodily from the dead? The Light which spoke to me before Damascus, was it a man? Was it a man that delivered me from myself? Can a man grant God's renewing grace? No, Rabbenu! He was not merely a man! He wore Manhood as a garment, as thou and I wear these shrouds. He, the Messiah, the incarnate Shekina, God's Son, He was before the world came into being. . . .

Gamaliel. [*Coming towards* PAUL, *breathing heavily*] Saul, say that he was a man, for thine own sake and mine!

Paul. How can I? From man new birth cometh not.

Gamaliel. From man alone it cometh! For this Temple's sake, say that he was a man!

Paul. Not in the Temple, but on the Cross was the Blood of the Atonement shed. Now is the whole world the Temple of the great Sacrifice.

Gamaliel. Saul! Here I still stand before thee. Not yet has the immeasurable calamity taken place! Destroy not my work of peace! The Messiah hath not come, for the Ever-Coming is He! Thou hast never understood the Torah, bad disciple thou! Only in its star-immersing depth abides the Kingdom of God and our ability to receive it. Where the Torah ruleth not there is wilderness and chaos! Do not force a strange spirit between God and Israel's freedom! For Israel's freedom sake, say that He was a man!

Paul. Rabbenu, by the living God I implore thee. Believe! In this hour, not for anyone's sake can I lie.

Gamaliel. Woe unto thee! Knowest thou who the Messiah is? He is annihilation! For when this arrow flies the bow will break. I will not see Him. . . .

Paul. [*After an awful pause, in a whisper, jerkily*] The bow is broken, Oh Israel! And for ever!

Gamaliel. Traitor! [*As if unconsciously.*] Ten thousand crucified ones against one. . . . [*He produces a cloth.*] Here! This bloody cloth, blasphemer! 'Tis not prophets' blood! Child's blood! Children slaughtered in Alexandria! They would not be traitors to the Torah! Thou pratest of the Messiah and of love, thou cold Satan, who lovest nothing, nothing, nothing! [*Overcome, he presses the cloth to his face.*] Children, singing they died. Singing, they died for the Torah. . . .

[*The prayer of the people behind the scene increases in volume mightily. Many voices chant verses of the Psalm with groaning, wailing, or wavering altogether confusedly.*]

Gamaliel. [*With fixed eyes, muttering the penitentiary Psalm as if he had become the concentrated voice of the people*] "Hide not thy face from me. . . . For my days are consumed like smoke. . . . My bones are burnt up as with a fire-brand. . . . My heart is dried up, and withered like grass. . . . For the voice of my groaning my bones will scarce cleave to my flesh. . . . I am become like the pelican in the wilderness, and like an owl that is in the desert. . . . Even as if it were a sparrow that sitteth alone upon the house-tops. . . . Mine enemies revile me" . . . [*He falters, pulls himself together, and walks towards the priestly utensils.*]

I retract my decision concerning Jesus of Nazareth! Perhaps he was a holy prophet, but *I* call him enemy! The old contradiction is he, the rebellion in lamb's wool. The Rabbis were wise and not I. There can be no peace! And thee I tear out of my heart, thou destroyer, thou drunken apostate! And that thou mayest know who thou art, I give thee thy name: "Israel's self-hatred!" [*He grasps the sacrificial knife.*] The angel of Death between us, Saul!

Paul. [*Bowing low*] Here I am, Rabbenu! The death of Stephen has made a seer of me also.

Gamaliel. I shall not deliver thee to justice. Let no more blood be spilt over Israel! For the sake of the people I take upon myself the triple great sin: the desecration of the Sabbath, the defilement of the Temple, and murder! [*He approaches* PAUL.]

[*A long and urgent trumpet blast.*]

Gamaliel. Behold, my God, I have done everything to save this soul. His youth I have nourished; he fell away: I wounded him. I have accepted his blasphemies. I have saved him from the judgment of men. For the sake of the peace of thy Creation I wished to return this soul and its master into Thine house. Oh, I have been mocked! Can I let Thine enemy go, my God? Let him go to a strange land, him, who wishes to destroy thy inexhaustible Torah and our holy responsibility towards men, in order that he may preach his phantom gospel? Oh, they will listen to him, and the phantom will become their Law, for a shadow lies but lightly, but Thy Law lies heavily! Lord, what shall I do? Should I perpetrate the horrible sin here in thy Temple, in this breathless hour of the world? In this hour in which Thou numberest souls, should I destroy one?

[*Short trumpet blasts from all sides.*]

Gamaliel. The priests' trumpets blow on high to blast the walls of Thy Solitude! Men wail for their lives. The moment of decision has come. Never hast thou forsaken me in this moment, Lord of the world! I have always come before Thee on the Day of Atonement with my pleading, and with Thy loving voice which I know so well Thou hast shed abroad the answer in my heart. . . . Answer me now! Who is Jesus of Nazareth? . . . Answer! . . . What should I do? . . . Who is Jesus whom they call Messiah? . . . Has the Messiah come? . . . Have we profaned Thy light? . . .

[*Trumpet blasts, always shorter and wilder.*]

Paul. [*Pale, fixed, with closed eyes, as if in a trance.*]

Gamaliel. [*Stamping, imperiously*] Answer!

[*A long trumpet-blast which dies away slowly.*]

[*Deep silence, long and breathless.*]

Gamaliel. No answer! For the first time no answer! Empty am I like death!

Paul. [*Softly and fervently*] I have received the answer, Rabbenu! Here am I!

Gamaliel. [*Suddenly quite exhausted*] I know the Truth no more.
. . . Go! [*He lets the knife fall.*]

Paul. [*Suddenly falling on his knees*] Take it from me, Rabbenu!
Here is my people, here my house. What should I accomplish in the
world, I, a poor weak Jew?

[*He takes* GAMALIEL's *hand and presses it to his forehead.*] Yes, I
have seen God's answer! I was wafted into dusty streets, in harbours I
saw ships come and go; sailors sang. I stood among the throng in a great
city, and ever must I go—go—go! For the Christ is a tireless hunter.

Gamaliel. [*As though out of a far-off dream*] "Go—go—go." . . .
Was this thine answer?

Paul. Now that I know it, I wish I might sleep and be no more.

[BARNABAS *stands at the entrance.*]

Gamaliel. [*Seeming to have just awakened, and in perplexity*] Who
art thou, Jew? [*Letting his hand rest heavily on* PAUL's *head.*] Whosoever thou art, man: The Lord bless thee, the Lord keep thee, the Lord
make His face to shine upon thee. . . .

Barnabas. 'Tis the blessing of the priests.

Paul. Thou givest me the strength for the way. [*Rises, and, walking
backwards, keeps his eyes on* GAMALIEL *the whole time.*] "Setting-sun of
my people. . . ."

[*Exit with* BARNABAS.]

Gamaliel. [*His face becoming slowly distorted, calls out*] The Destruction upon us! The Destruction. . . . [*He stumbles out with a covered face, his cry dying away in the distance.*]

[*Enter* RABBI SHIMON *and* RABBI HUNA.]

Rabbi Huna. It is not true!

Rabbi Shimon. The priests hid the goat at once, but I saw it myself
with its red sin-band. It has run back to the Temple.

Rabbi Huna. Nonsense! The last guide threw it, offering of our sin,
into the ravine, just as it has been done every year. On the first rock
already the animal was shattered to pieces.

Rabbi Shimon. The animal has not been shattered but has returned.

Rabbi Huna. As long as the Temple stands . . . [*Grasping* RABBI
SHIMON.] Shimon! God has not accepted the sacrifice! It is clear. We
have not been reconciled with Him today. He sends our sins and blasphemies back to us.

[*Enter* RABBI ZADDOK *and the Priests.*]

Rabbi Zaddok. Judgment has been given.

Rabbi Huna. I saw it come, Rabbis.

Rabbi Zaddok. Ye fathers, help! The people must not know!

[*They stand whispering together.*]

[*Enter* SIMON PETER, JAMES *and* TWO NAZAREANS, *who come forward to the front of the stage, where they remain to the end.*]

Simon Peter. Seest thou now, James, that Paul is right? Every sacrifice of the Law is rejected, for the Son of God was sacrificed. Hearest thou aught?

James. The whole Mount of Olives is full of Romans. . . .

Simon Peter. Brothers, the Anti-Christ blows his trumpet!

[*Shrill military music in the distance.*]

[*All thoroughly shaken and pale.*]

[*Turmoil without.*]

[*Enter* MARULLUS *and* AULUS FRISIUS *with a company of soldiers. Behind them a crowd, surging.*]

The Rabbis. What dost thou, Roman, in the inner courts of the Temple? . . . The punishment is death! . . . Our right! . . .

The People. Back! . . . Death to the Romans!

[MARULLUS *has meanwhile ascended the steps of the raised seat, and is waving a parchment.*]

[*Enter* THE HIGH PRIEST *in his robes, assisted by priests. He can scarcely stand upright. The people fall back. At once an open space is made between him and* MARULLUS.]

The High Priest. In the name of God I command thee, Marullus, to leave the holy Temple!

Marullus. If I am not mistaken, most worthy friend, we are here on Roman ground. Why be so unpolite and "command," when the Procurator himself commandeth not, but is sincerely sorry that it has come to this, through your fault? It is getting difficult for me, dear fathers, because I am your self-sacrificing well-wisher. But I have, by higher command, to declare all the special privileges in relation to this place to be annulled! . . . Peace, I beg you. . . . Do ye want me to lose my patience also? . . . It is an edict of the divine Caesar Caligula! . . .

Shouts. The Enemy of God!

Marullus. Of course, I can wait. . . . [*There is silence—he reads.*] "To the Jewish people! Hear, thou stubborn Judea! I am a god! No nation in the wide world would ever dream of denying my divine nature, attested by miracles. Thou alone in thy superstitious blindness has striven against my effigy and against my ensigns. With the deep-seated mercy of a god I have been patient until now. But it is enough! I prohibit thee thy customary idolatry in thy Temple! Petronius, my legate, has been in structed to erect in the most holy place of· Jerusalem the statue of my true divinity. Should ye oppose it, it shall be by force of arms. Rome, in the third year of my reign of grace Caius Caesar!"

[*Martial music is heard approaching.*]

Marullus. For the divine omnipotence everything has been arranged. Petronius marches on to Jerusalem, bringing the statue of the lawful god with him!

[*Silence, then a cry from all the Jews.*]

The People. [*Casting themselves upon the ground*] Abomination of desolation! . . . Rather kill us! . . . Let's be off against the Romans! . . . Search for arms! . . . No! Let us ourselves put fire to the Temple! . . . Take torches to the Temple! . . . Who will help us? Who? Who? . . . Look at the High Priest! . . .

[THE HIGH PRIEST *reels, and is kept from falling by the other priests.*]

A Voice. Gamaliel will help us!

The People. Gamaliel! The righteous! Where is Gamaliel? [*The call becomes a yell.*] Gamaliel!

Marullus. [*To* FRISIUS] I am curious to see whether thy Gamaliel will today also play the role of being above all this.

[*A sudden dead silence.*]

[*The body of* GAMALIEL, *covered with his shroud, is brought in by Levites.*]

Rabbi Meir. [*Follows*] Here is Rabbenu!

Marullus. Frisius! This man is invincible!

[THE PEOPLE *break into subdued yet dreadful wailing which continues to the end.*]

Rabbi Shimon. [*Kneeling beside the body*] Father, why art thou so terribly silent?

Rabbi Zaddok. [*In a wild frenzy*] Listen! The catapults rumble! The storm-rams bleat! The flame roars! The plough crunches over Zion!

[*Shrill martial music, abrupt and very near.*]

Simon Peter. [*To the* NAZAREANS] The last righteous one has passed away! The Anti-Christ has come! Every promise has been fulfilled! [*With a feeble movement of the hand, trembling throughout his whole body.*] Go home! The hour of the Christ has come!

[*The wailing of the Jews continues throughout.*]

CURTAIN

SHYLOCK'S CHOICE

by JOHN COURNOS

SCENE

Night. Interior of a Venetian counting-room. The shutters are up, the doors latched and barred. Behind a counter a table piled up with papers. On the table a seven-candled candelabra, but only one of the seven candles is lit, and its light is faintly diffused on the papers and on the several objects usually found in a sixteenth century counting-room. In the penumbra, in a half-reclining attitude, is discovered, seated, the contemplative figure of SHYLOCK, *obviously in deep study. A clock on the wall, barely visible, ticks away the seconds. A knock is heard on the outer door.* SHYLOCK *shakes himself, raises his head with a start. The knock is repeated, this time louder.*

Shylock. Who knocks?

Tubal. [*From the outside*] It is I, Tubal.

Shylock. [*Rising and shuffling to the door, in his long gabardine, pushes back the bar and holds the door ajar*] Sholem aleichem, Tubal.

Tubal. Aleichem sholem, Shylock!

Shylock. What is afoot, Tubal? What brings thee at this late hour? Nothing amiss, I trust!

Tubal. Nothing, yet . . . an evil spirit hath kept me awake, would not let me rest, urged me hither.

Shylock. Come in, Tubal. Sit thee down, Tubal. We belong to a sleepless nation. The Gentile dogs, sleek in their godless vainglory, may sleep; not we. When the great Adonai chose us from among the nations, He gave us fire and fortitude and infinite patience, and above all this gift of sleeplessness, lest in our unwary slumber our foes come with their devices and destroy us. Ah, the dogs . . .

Tubal. [*Perturbed*] I have come, Shylock. . . . I could not sleep, because . . .

Shylock. [*Unheeding*] Never mind, Tubal. There is always time for sleep. The time shall come, good Tubal, when the God of Israel—blessed be His name!—brooding upon this extensive universe, whose author He is, will bethink Himself of His children and put it into their power to smite their foes with that skill and surety with which young David smote

Goliath in an open field. But until that felicitous moment doth come, we must be even as Judith, who did confound the mighty Holofernes by craft and cunning. . . .

Tubal. But, Shylock, hear me. I have come to . . .

Shylock. Oh, were but Judith my own daughter! She did use the blade well, Tubal. 'Twas a sharp blade, Holofernes' own, but not more sharp, not more firm, nor better tempered than the natural instrument which that Master Craftsman, the God of Israel, so richly bestowed upon her at very birth. We intelligent men call it mind; moreover, 'tis mind allied with spirit; 'tis delicate yet unconquerable. Mind! There's the Jew's weapon! Understand, Tubal. It saved our nation then, will save it again, and yet again. Depend on it!

Tubal. 'Tis true, Judith saved Israel.

Shylock. A Jewess, a most noble woman. Did Judith rob her father of his ducats and squander them with the connivance of Israel's enemies? Did she pollute her body in a Gentile's bed, willingly, and betray her nation in amorous caresses with an uncircumcised dog who mocked her nation? Oh, can there be baser treachery? Cursed be thou, Jessica! False to thy nation, false to thy father, false to dear Leah's memory, trebly a harlot!

Tubal. Be calm, Shylock, restrain thy righteous rage. I entreat thee, for thy own cause. There's tomorrow. Thou mayest need all thy strength tomorrow. I have been much concerned about thee and tomorrow's judgment. I have come to speak to thee anent this matter. Tomorrow's on my mind. I cannot sleep when I think on tomorrow.

Shylock. [*Springing up in great excitement from his chair and clutching* TUBAL *by the sleeve*] Tell me, Tubal, dost thou know aught about tomorrow that I do not already know? Dost thou mean thou art sleepless on my account, art in the grip of apprehension lest I, Shylock, demanding justice, shall be cheated in the Court tomorrow of an honest judgment? Tell me, tell me what thy knowledge is!

Tubal. Nothing precise. . . . Well, thou art not ignorant how they hate and mock us. . . .

Shylock. Is that all? What of that? Shall I fear, then, barking dogs? We Jews feed on mockery, it sharpens our wits. Adversity helps to preserve our nation. When trod upon, Israel doth acquire new life, new strength, develops a sturdier, fiercer growth; in that we follow the example of the hardy camomile, the plant thou hast heard me speak of. . . . Such is our nation. . . .

Tubal. Yet, Shylock, listen to a friend, a fellow-sufferer, a Jew.

Shylock. Tubal, if thou hast come to dissuade me from tomorrow's design, I will not listen. Though thou wert a thousand times a Jew and friend, nothing, nothing shall move me from my purpose. I shall have my bond. Or there is no justice in Venice, and no God in Israel. Speak, Tubal, speak, if there be pertinence in what thou hast to say. But in this my mind is made up, adamant.

Tubal. There have been murmurings today on the Rialto.

Shylock. What are murmurings to me? I am not a child to be frightened from my purpose by murmurings. Murmurings are nothing new to our nation. Ever since the Pharaohs, and again since the Dispersion, there have been murmurings, and continue they shall until the new Messiah come. What are murmurings to me, Tubal? I am a Jew.

Tubal. There have been rumours in the market-place that Antonio's friends have engaged distinguished advocates to plead his cause.

Shylock. The law is on my side, Tubal. If they engage Beelzebub himself, they cannot evade the law. Venice, for her own honour, cannot afford to have the law evaded.

Tubal. That is admitted. Yet it is also agreed there's no precedent of a Jew being granted sanction over the life of a Christian, and Antonio's friends, pending judgment, have engendered hatred and fury in the multitude. If thou dost win and exact thy bond, it may go hard with thee.

Shylock. What dost thou counsel, then, Tubal? Would'st thou have me swallow all the insults and humiliations, all the gibes and taunts heaped upon me by that paragon of Christian virtue, Antonio? Would'st have me, publicly, in the presence of the august Court, disavow the bond, release Antonio from obligation, the same that called me dog, hindered me diversely in affairs of livelihood, helped to dispossess me of my daughter, conspired to destroy me? Would'st have me bow my head in low humility and say with honeyed tongue: "Kind sir, I thank thee. Most heartily I thank thee. Come again when thou art in sore need, good Antonio. I am Shylock, thy slave, always at thy service. In the meantime, as thou art a Christian, practised in the art of Christian charity, so thou mayest spit on me, or pull my grey beard, if such be thy mood and inclination. I am but a Jew, hence thy sport, a thing for thee and thy associates to mock at, at thy pleasure!"

Tubal. I've but come to tell thee . . .

Shylock. [*Interrupting*] Ere thou proceed, good Tubal, mark thou this: When I did seal the bond with Antonio I had no premonition, nor the slightest inkling that Antonio's fortunes would go thus far astray, leaving him a beggar and a bankrupt so wholeheartedly at my mercy.

There's the hand of God in it, Tubal. The God of Israel hath long looked with a jealous and wrathful eye on this most arrogant Christian, and now God hath put him in my hand to avenge the wrong he hath done His nation. Rest assured, there's divine judgment in it. And if God Himself hath so willed it and hath decreed the punishment of this infidel, shall I, His servant, stumble and hesitate in a Heaven-imposed task? Shall I incur the wrath of the God of Israel by acquiescence, a passive violation of His sanction and command? As it is, I am living for tomorrow's enterprise. Fear not, thou shalt find my hand steady, my blade sharp. Israel's foes will be confounded. Now, what hast thou to say, Tubal?

Tubal. But this, Shylock. The Lord's ways are inscrutable. Thou mayest be right, yet I fear tomorrow. Thy coming ordeal fills me with dread.

Shylock. Not me. Tomorrow will find me firm. The prospect of tomorrow fills me with indescribable elation.

Tubal. I was going to say: there were rumours current today that Antonio's friends will offer a handsome ransom for the Christian merchant's life, twice or even thrice the original sum stipulated in the bond; perchance a greater, as circumstance dictates.

Shylock. Well! . . . What's that to me?

Tubal. Shylock, I am thy friend. As thou knowest, I have thy interest and the interest of Jewry at heart. Take my humble counsel. Accept the money the Christians offer, since they are minded to pay, and pay well. Hearken to Tubal, who means well; lest ill befall thee, which God forbid! I tell thee, Shylock, I am filled with foreboding. I could not sleep tonight for thoughts of evil which doth threaten thee.

Shylock. Fie, Tubal, thou art a craven heart. Bethink thee, Tubal, of Judas Maccabeus, the great hero whom we Jews celebrate during the Feast of Lights. Did not he and his Maccabean tribe, a mere handful of dauntless fellows, defy Antiochus most gloriously? Did they stay their blades because they feared the vengeance of doughty foes? Not they! Nor shall I fear the Christians. I am Shylock. Shylock's eminence, the house he hath built and the chattels and wealth therein, were won by the sharp and finely tempered blade of his mind. Tomorrow it shall not fail him.

Tubal. If reason were all, Shylock, then I should be expeditiously and irrevocably convinced. But tonight I am possessed of a most curious, a most inexplicable apprehension, which defies all reason, and as friend to friend and Jew to Jew I do passionately appeal: "Be circumspect. Thy enemies conspire to do thee harm!"

Shylock. Listen, Tubal. Listen! What I shall reveal now, I had not intended to reveal to a living soul. I do so but to allay thy anxiety. Thy earnest solicitude doth move me to confession. My tomorrow's enterprise is a matter of undreamt-of magnitude. It should confound the knaves, send them scurrying from the Court like the slinking curs they are, with lowered heads, and tails behind their legs! Ha! Ha! Ha! Tubal. Ha! Ha! Ha! I have a plan, a deep, a well-conceived, a diabolic plan. . . . [*Pauses, while his eyes sparkle expectantly.*]

Tubal. How? What is thy plan?

Shylock. A simple matter, Tubal. I will illustrate. [*Rising and drawing a short, slightly curved blade out of a scabbard.*] Stand up, Tubal! 'Tis a fine old Moorish blade that will not suffer in the light. Cunning craftsmen, those Moors. A thousand pities they have been worsted by the Christian dogs in Spain. [*Tries the edge with a finger, then runs the finger up and down the flat side of the blade.*] Now, this blade shall accompany me on tomorrow's enterprise. Supposing, now, they begin tomorrow's legal ceremony by offering the three thousand ducats stipulated in the bond, plus interest. I will refuse most promptly. Then, perhaps, indeed 'tis most likely, they'll offer, as thou hast heard it rumoured, twice the sum, nay thrice, or even double or treble that again! Hesitate? Not I! I shall refuse it with courteous promptness. They shall plead then for his life with hypocritical entreaties. What pleasure shall be mine to see the beggars passionately implore for a cur's life! And that, Tubal, of a despised Jew! But plead heartily as they may, I shall turn a deaf ear to their piteous whining, and remain steadfast and adamant. The court is bound to render judgment in my favour. Then the real comedy shall begin, ay surely! I promise you some rollicking fun before the session doth terminate. [*Pause.* SHYLOCK *assumes a contemplative attitude.*]

Tubal. Well . . . What then?

Shylock. [*Suddenly galvanized into life by* TUBAL's *question. His eyes blazing, knife still in his hand, he catches* TUBAL *by his gabardine. With a spasmodic movement he brings the knife within an eighth of an inch of* TUBAL's *bosom.* TUBAL *is too frightened for speech.*] What then? What then? Thus, thus, Tubal, when the judgment is rendered will I bring my knife within an ace of Antonio's bosom! Thus, thus will I stand and look unflinchingly in his affrighted eyes, while the Invisible Deity, He of the Unutterable Name, shall applaud me and give me strength to terminate my enterprise with an ultimate finality which shall leave Israel's foes breathless! For even while Antonio stands there in a state of petrifaction like a frightened hare before the enchantment of the wise serpent, will I, with a grand gesture, fling my weapon from me thus! [*Drops the knife on the floor.*] and release my clutch hold from my prey. [*Takes his hand from* TUBAL.] "Go, go, Antonio! Thy life is not worth the taking! My religion doth forbid me to touch the flesh of certain animals, while my natural courtesy will not allow me to call their names, lest it offend thee. As thou art a Christian, so thou hast surely read regarding the wise injunction in the Book of Genesis. I have enacted this play but to teach thee better manners. Go, Antonio! Keep thy ducats, and mine too! But go! Get thee out of my sight!" . . . Ah, and we, you and I, Tubal, will have a celebration. . . . My enterprise will be published far and wide, to our foes' dismay, and bring me profitable undertakings, without hinder from hypocritical Antonio and the other shamefaced Christians, who in the past have spoiled my ventures and have interfered with the enrichment of my treasury. For never, never shall Antonio look upon me again but think: "I owe my life to this Jew!" Tomorrow will be a marvellous, a memorable, an historic day! For, when I have flung the knife from me, innocent of blood it might have shed, my business will be done, and, my head high, I shall stalk out of the Court, proud, yet full of irrepressible mirth. . . . And as I shall strut past the dismayed, astonished spectators, how I shall laugh! How I shall laugh, Tubal! Ha! ha! ha! Ha! ha! ha! How I shall laugh, Tubal, good Tubal! Ha! ha! ha! . . .

CURTAIN

URIEL ACOSTA

by CHARLES REZNIKOFF

SCENE ONE

[*In the house of the Acostas in Portugal at the close of the sixteenth century.*]

Uriel Acosta's Brother

The rain will stop any day now. . . .
I was in the garden this morning. The inner leaves of the trees have
    turned brown. . . .
You have been too long over the Bible, brother.
Take the horse and splash through the puddles of the road
The way father used to. . . .

There's a puddle in father's coffin, I suppose.
Death is so trite and yet—
But we should be the happier
That father has left this bubble, Earth, for Paradise.

Uriel

And your tears, my tears. A funeral is sad.
Whatever our wish whispers—

Brother

We are too near the Jews, our grandfathers, to speak so freely.
Dominican Torquemada still listens at our hearts.

Uriel

Listen at mine: an uneven rhythm in its monotony,
As if it would speak out and dares not and would and dares not.

Brother

Dares not to me?

Uriel

Here in Oporto Mother Church takes those who grope too far,
Gently by the hands and hangs them by those hands, hangs stones upon
    their feet,
To lengthen their reach that, groping and groping,
They catch hold of truth at last;
Or else, like Moses who split a rock for water, a man's thirsty:
Mother Church lifts his head
And down his nostrils drips drop by drop. He chokes—
But if he gulped too much would he not choke?
Until he would swallow, like you and me, enough.
They have burnt a woman with a queasy intestine,
That could not put up with bacon on Mondays,
For having Jewish villi.
What must be done to cure a queasy mind?

Brother

Will you scratch at the wall of the cathedral?
Was that the servant? . . .

Uriel

You who see in this wood, the world,
Jesus walk,
Wringing, wringing his pierced hands,
Shall I tell you that he was not Christ?
Should I persuade you from your high estate,
You for whom the only son of God has died.
Who take his flesh in wafers in your mouth,
Whose priest hears out your story,
Your grave, the womb of an eternal life?
But I have come to our grandfathers' belief. . . .
Should I get to Holland, will they not rack and question you,
Truly a Christian, until you cry out, "Guilty!"
Or are condemned, too stubborn to confess.

Brother

Will you leave our house, our garden, the streets you know so well,
Your honors and office?

Uriel

Because I have to say some words and bend sometimes,
Hurt no one but myself, if at all,
Is it not mad to throw away this comfortable life,
Which ended, for us is ended always,
To thrust myself into risk of fire or twisting wheels,
And not myself only, but the dearest to me?
If only we could go on as we were,
But I am of those madmen, brother. Forgive me.

Brother

The servant . . .

Uriel

Were the clouds lifting?

Brother

The sky seemed darker and more rain.

Servant

[*Comes in.*]

I'll close the shutters against the smoke and smell.
The wind sets this way.

[*To* URIEL.] Is it not time you went down, sir? The square is crowded.
What heretics are burnt today, sir?

Uriel

A Jewess and a Moor.

Servant

Search the cracks, crush, pour in boiling water,
And think the bed clean at last. One or two are in a corner,
And make as many bugs as before.
Well, they burn hereafter.

Uriel

And here.

Servant

Amen, sir.
The Master must not find us idle servants. [URIEL *goes out.*]
[*To his* BROTHER.] Do you go?

Brother

I have some reading.
When you have closed the shutters, bring a candle.
[*The* SERVANT *does so.* URIEL ACOSTA'S BROTHER *reads until shrieking is
heard. He presses his hands against his ears.*]

SCENE TWO

One of Several Men

[*To* URIEL *and his* BROTHER.] We have been informed by Lisbon
That you ask leave to go to France.
You know that some of Jewish blood,
Free of us,
Disgorge and spit out their Christianity.
We knew your father to be Christian,
But you your fellow officers have seen
Troubled, without trouble before your father's death,
Unless—corrosion of the soul, not wrapped in faith.

Uriel

Salt in the air these days,
When the ships go down the river

To India or Brazil.
All our lives
My brother and I have duly walked
Within Oporto.

[*One of the group whispers to another.*]

Another

Why to France, near Holland?

Uriel

The French are skilled in the arts.

The Other

More so the Italians.

Uriel

The university at Paris.

The Other

A better one at Salamanca.

Uriel's Brother

Shrines—

The Other

An afterthought.

The First

We who were your father's friends,
May we not warn you not to waste his wealth
And your lives
In an idle journey,
Lucky if you can return
To this rock on which we stand.
We will say to Lisbon
That you have changed your minds.
A fancy
Of grief for a dead father in the dead man's house
And youth eager to forget. [*They go out.*]

Uriel's Brother

Will you not listen to them?

Uriel

If we have souls, mine has a running sore
With my thick flow of lies.
I know the captain of a ship.
We'll row about the harbor as if for sport,
At night, climb upon his ship
And with the tide sail out to sea.

Brother

When England exiled the Jews, the captain of their ship
Stole all they had and left them on a sand-bar in the Channel.
The tide came up and so they drowned.
If your friend should serve us so?

Uriel

I know that here is bad and there—who knows?

SCENE THREE

[*Within a synagogue at Amsterdam.*]

A Rabbi. [*To* URIEL *and his* BROTHER.]

Since we are not to boil the kid in its mother's milk,
We are not to have butter with our meat.
Nor after meat, milk; nor for milk, dishes used for meat.
                    [URIEL *makes a gesture of impatience.*]
You must unlearn the uncleanliness of Christians.
The rabbis have considered each thought and action—
How much better to do what wise men have thought out
And generations found good.

Uriel

What wisdom is such that I must
Shut eyes and gulp it, like a child medicine?
In what reasoning or belief is more than error
Certain? [*The Others leave their books to listen.*]
I have read *thou shalt not boil the kid in its mother's milk*
Was to forbid a heathen sacrifice, not food.
But if food. *not that which goeth into the mouth defileth.*

Another Rabbi

As if what hurts the body with which we are entrusted,
Does not hurt the soul whose machine it is.
My son, you are young and new among us, listen patiently;
When you are old with thought about our laws, we shall listen.

Uriel

Must I spend my life in mummeries that common sense
Tells me at once are frippery and rigmarole?

Uriel's Brother

If no man is so great that you must follow blindly,
Are you so great that you may wave aside men like these?
If prohibitions, like these of milk and meat, do not matter,
Why not obey them?

Uriel

Who shall divide what matters and what not?
Shall I, silent, see others wrong?
They are afraid that I crack open
The black doubt
In the shells of their precious laws.

Chief Rabbi

We have withstood sword and fire,
Surely words.
But the young and foolish, always with us,
Turn and listen,
Whoever pounds a drum and mounts
A stool:
Follow him into the marshes of his thoughts.

Uriel

Perhaps, he is the sanest of you all.

Chief Rabbi

Our sons shall be inheritors of his wisdom.
That we are not infected with his folly,
I forbid our congregation
To greet you, talk to you, touch you, trade with you,
Hear you, look at you, or be near you—

Uriel's Brother

Uriel, we live this way or that and die,
And surely earth is merciful, knowing us all so well.
If we leave Holland, what land is left us?
These are closest to us, friendliest. Do as they do.
Do not answer now.
[*To the Others.*] Let his blood cool in the shadows of our synagogue,
Until the evening prayer
And the first star bring us here again.
You will find, as I know him, a brother gentle and good.

[*They all go out but* URIEL.]

Uriel

This is to be my life: pray, trade, eat, wive, and sleep;
On Saturday walk along the quays after the prayers for the afternoon,
Before evening prayers;
Say what the next man says, bow when he does,
Argue if the ass be on a journey and Sabbath come, so on, so on;
Pocket my gulden with the best of them; in the end,
Wrapped in my prayer shawl, go—they know where.
They have the streets of Heaven plotted and the houses numbered
And I may have a lease forever—a long time.
The babble of their prayers cuts the knots of the world.
Is the sun too swift? Pray, Joshua.
The savages who have machines save time:
The wheel turns the praying stones and God listens. . . .
I'll send them words to stick in their livers.
How will my book begin?
The ship sinks at last into gloom and knotted seaweed,
Or falls to pieces on the white sand
That moves at every gust of wind like smoke.
Why are you afraid of truth, if you are truthful?
If what I say is false—but does the false die?
These with merchandise cross oceans or barter in an alley;
Free as a tethered goat, I must feed
Upon truth and falsehood, although it gives me colic.

SCENE FOUR

[The noise of stones flung against the closed shutters. URIEL opens the door of the room in answer to loud knocking. A soldier enters and arrests him.]

Uriel

I understand no Dutch.

One of the Jews

[Who have crowded in, to URIEL.]

The jail and gallows are easily understood:
The key in the lock squeaks, 'Stay';
And the knot, rubbing on the gallows rope, says, 'Jump!'
[URIEL is led away. Boys tear up his books and papers until driven out by the watchmen, two old Jews.]

First Watchman

Spit on, I might not spit; but to make him I'm not afraid of feel as bad,
    I spit. A dirty world.

Second Watchman

From Spain and Portugal like mice into this hole, Holland, here we creep
    along our street still as we can,
When down comes a Uriel Acosta, prints in Latin, shouts, 'The books
    of Moses are not by Moses.'
And the Dutch, 'Shelter these Jews and they destroy our religion.'
The rabbis must come to the magistrate first, 'He hurts us as much as
    you, our enemy as much as yours.'

First Watchman

If you look once, simply the moon; then, a shadow on it; and sometimes,
    it's broad as an orange or thin as a blade of grass. . . .
They've been tearing up his papers.
But unless they tear up his brain—

Second Watchman

The brain itself tears up what the brain thought.

SCENE FIVE

Uriel

[In prison.]

The lamp is now my sun and the wide night, these cellar walls; the dripping from the ceiling here, the rain, and I, God, who sees night and
sun at once.
God falls asleep and wakes; after the longest while, falls asleep and wakes
to the same universe: the sun burns in the night and the rain falls.
[He hears the jailers coming.] If I could dig my fingers into the floor,
hold like a tree. . . . *[They enter and drag him out.]*

SCENE SIX

Uriel

[In his room.]

A fine, my writings burnt—after all, nothing.
Now I am fixed within them like a weed
That torn up, trampled, grows again,
The hardier for its torments.
In someone's thoughts somewhat of me takes root—
Until the statue crumbles to a stone again. . . .
None shall talk to me,
As if I have not Plato, the prophets, Buddha. . . .
*[He sits down to a book and a stone flies through a window. He closes
the shutters, against which stones begin to drum.]*
You Jews! . . . *[He turns the papers of his book.]*
My fingers sweat acid and where I touch leave holes. . . .
*And behold, a Canaanitish woman came out from those borders and
cried, saying, Have mercy on me, O Lord, thou son of David; my
daughter is grieviously vexed . . . And he said, It is not meet to
take the children's bread and cast it to the dogs.*
But if she were the servant of a centurion—. *[He turns the pages.]*
*Verily I say unto you, This generation shall not pass away, till all these
things be accomplished. [He turns the pages.]*
Back from the dead, was this all you had to say, *Have you here anything
to eat?*
They could not counterfeit that style. . . . *[He pushes the book aside.]*
The Carpenter, despairing of his life,
Reached so surely for eternal life;

While Buddha, the king's son, satiated,
Saw himself forever rid of life. [*He takes another book and turns the
pages listlessly.*]

SCENE SEVEN

[URIEL's *room after fifteen years. His* BROTHER *comes in.*]

Uriel

So. You dared not come before the rabbis consented.

Brother

We live with others. You yourself now seek us.

Uriel

Yes.
No one to talk to, even about trifles:
I might have been buried; in my grave,
The shroud, the coffin, coffin chest and solid earth
Shutting out companionship.
If you ever walked alone in a woods, even an hour,
Or through the fields, far from houses,
And returning, met a man, a kind of animal, nearer his dog or ox
    than you,
Did you not greet him gladly in that loneliness?
I have been alone fifteen years.
My life is a frenzy of words,
Spoken to myself.

Brother

That is over. . . . Penance will be light.

Uriel

Have I not had enough to crawl back like this?

Brother

The rabbis, for the discipline of the congregation, must—

Uriel

Well, if they must. You are married, of course.

Brother

The daughter of a merchant.

Uriel

Children?

Brother

A son.

Uriel

And trade?

Brother

My share in ships to England and the Indies.
I'll tell the rabbis fully of your intention
And, God willing, shall be back at once, Uriel. [*He goes out.*]

Uriel

So I become at last a monkey among monkeys.

SCENE EIGHT

[*In a garden.*]

The Rabbi's Servant

[*Comes in with* URIEL *and his* BROTHER.]

The rabbi asks that you await him here. [*They stop at a bench. The servant goes out.*]

Uriel

I need this sun. . . .

[URIEL *and his* BROTHER *sit down.*]

Even our little walk has tired me. . . .
I did not leave the house weeks at a time.

Brother

If you were in a dungeon of the Inquisition—
We, too, suffered; you, too, must be kind.

Rabbi Manasseh

[*Comes in. To* URIEL'S BROTHER.]

My sister's daughter is here from Antwerp.
Uriel, leave your house; at your brother's

Learn the happiness in a Jewish home,
And what you did not give us time to teach.
I'll see you at the synagogue tonight.
Stay; the porter will unlock this gate.
[*He goes out.* URIEL *and his* BROTHER *glance at the* RABBI'S *niece, off stage.*]

Uriel

So quick and eager, she has no place in a room;
She belongs among trees and flowers. [*The* RABBI'S SERVANT *comes in.*]

Brother

Now to the section to buy your prayer shawl, fringes, phylacteries, and skull-cap. [*They follow the servant.*]
One phylactery is strapped to the inner side of the left arm, two fist widths from the shoulder blade;
The other, on the forehead, two fist widths from the nose's tip.
Wind the strap seven times about the arm and say, *Blessed. . . .*

SCENE NINE

[*In the house of* URIEL'S BROTHER.]

First Jewish Merchant

I do not like this Uriel in our venture.

Second Jewish Merchant

Still, not to displease his brother—

Uriel
[*Comes in.*]

Good morning.

First Merchant

So you are to become a Jew again?

Uriel

We who hold out against the world—was I not most the Jew
When I held out also against my fellow Jews?
But we are here to talk trade, I think,
Not theology. What is your matter?

Second Merchant

When we told your brother of our undertaking, he wished to have you
    share
In its certain profit. [URIEL'S BROTHER *comes in.*]

Uriel's Brother

I'd place money, Uriel, in their venture;
No profit is sure, but in this, likely.
This, too, will be distraction: rub shoulders
With enterprising men.
[*To the* MERCHANTS.] If you will, be here this afternoon,
And I'll have contract and gulden ready. [*The* MERCHANTS *leave.*]
[*To* URIEL.] You'll lose your hesitant speech, that stoop, that shamble,
Become genial like a merchant.

Uriel's Nephew

[*Comes in.*]

Uncle, two men to see you—Christians.

Brother

I'll wait for you at my desk. [*He and the lad go out. The two men
    come in.*]

One of the Two

We are students at the university, have read Rashi, Maimonides, Abar-
    banel;
Have come to think that our salvation is, perhaps, in being Jews.
We have read your book of some fifteen years ago—and learn
That you have just become a Jew again.
Should we become Jews?

Uriel

I thought my work lost,
Every copy of my book burnt.
You say you have one?

Student

We had, but lent it to a friend, he to another.

Uriel

Well, no matter. The book lives.
As to this you ask one who once was Christian, then Jew, then non-
    Jew, and now again a Jew;
Why incur the hate—at least the sufferance—
Of Christians, here the great and dominant majority,
Until both Jesus and Jehovah are with Jupiter,
Baal and Isis—
Believed in by intelligent peoples, too—
Incur this odium
To shoulder a mass of prayer and petty regulation?
But here I am a guest and my brother waits for me.
In my home we will reason the matter through seven and seventy wind-
    ings. [*The* STUDENTS *go out.*]
There I have touched companionship.

Uriel's Brother

[*Who has come in.*]

Still talking to yourself? . . . Who were your visitors?

Uriel

Students who have read my book.

Brother

I hoped that we were quit of all that.
Don't set too much upon idlers, busy to gape at a sensation.

A Crowd

[*Is heard in the street, then on the stairs. It enters and shouts at* URIEL.]

Unbeliever!

Uriel's Brother

Have you not heard of his repentance, seen him in the synagogue;
Surely you know that Rabbi Manasseh sent him here?

One of the Crowd

We heard what the two just here reported;
We know, though he apes pious men, what he speaks in his heart
Of sacred laws and the Holy One, you hypocrite! [*Turning to* URIEL.]

Uriel's Brother

[*To* Uriel.]

Answer him, tell him the truth.

Uriel

[*To his* Brother.]

He tells me that. Can I believe
In what I left behind with my blocks and dolls?
This is our parting, I suppose. Live and farewell.

[*The crowd makes way for* Rabbi Manasseh.]

Rabbi Manasseh

Uriel Acosta, did I impose a penance,
As others would? I was not wiser.
A penance would have searched you somewhat.
None shelter you, deal with you, talk or look at you,
Until you come to the synagogue in mourning clothes,
A burning candle in your hand,
Confess your errors to the congregation,
Strip to the waist to be beaten by the sexton;
. Then stretch yourself upon the threshold,
For the congregation going out to step upon.

Uriel

I had forgotten.
So stupid is the mind—at least, mine—
Now what you are comes flooding back.

[*He goes out through the silent crowd.*]

SCENE TEN

[*Seven years afterwards.* Uriel Acosta *at a window in his room.*]

Uriel

. . . How many years since they stopped throwing stones?
I suppose spinning tops became the fashion.
They no longer trouble themselves to spit,
As I pass. I am left alone, at last. . . .
I have grown so afraid of the stillness of this house . . . and of the
    night.
In a few hours it will be night again.

What though the city is wound about me mile on mile,
The street-lamps shine, eight to a block,
And I light candles until the room is yellow,
Upon me, mile on mile, leagues and leagues beyond measure,
The night—
And no one to talk to, to call, to touch. . . .
I sometimes think, Keep on
Into the fields and into new towns.
What shall I do in a strange town?
Will they not know me for a Jew?
And after a mile or two, the sun and wind become hateful.
Keeping indoors, I have become a mouse.
I know all the cracks in the walls:
Which divide and which run into the floor or stop, an inch from the
     ceiling. . . .
Most are born poor; I could have had anything,
Even here in Amsterdam. . . .
What can they do to me, if I come back?
Mourning clothes and candle in my hand.
What do I care what the masquerade costume is?
They will preach. Words.
They will have me beaten. One backache more.
The congregation going out shall step on me. And I am through.
Must I keep on like this until I die here alone?
But do we not all die alone?
No, no, to have friends about to distract the mind from pain, dying and
     living. [*He goes out.*]

THE TRIAL

by S. ANSKY

Miropol. A large room in the house of RABBI AZRAEL *of Miropol. Right,
door leading to other rooms. In middle of wall, center, door to street.
On either side of this door, benches. Windows. Left, a table almost
the entire length of the wall, covered with a white cloth. On table,
slices of white Sabbath bread. At the head of table, a great armchair.
Past the door right, a small cupboard containing scrolls of the law.*

Beside it, an altar. On the left, a smaller table near footlights. RABBI
AZRAEL, *wrapped in his prayer shawl and wearing the phylacteries, is
in the armchair. The two* JUDGES *sit in ordinary chairs.* RABBI SAMSON
stands beside the table and, at a distance MICHOEL. *They are finishing
a prayer whereby an evil dream may be turned into good.*

Rabbi Azrael, Michoel and the Two Judges. You beheld a good
dream! You beheld a good dream! You beheld a good dream!

Rabbi Azrael. We have found a solution of good to your dream.

Rabbi Samson. I beheld a good dream—a good dream I beheld. I
beheld a good dream.

Rabbi Azrael. Will you now, Rabbi Samson, take your seat with the
other judges? [RABBI SAMSON *sits down next to* RABBI AZRAEL.] Let us
now call upon this dead man to be present at the trial. First, however,
I shall draw a holy circle beyond which he may not pass. Michoel, my
staff. . . . [MICHOEL *gives him the staff.* RABBI AZRAEL *then rises and,
going to the corner left, describes a circle on the floor from left to right.
He then returns to the table.*] Michoel, take my staff and go to the
graveyard. When you get there, go in with your eyes closed, guiding
yourself with the staff. At the first grave it touches, stop. Knock with it
three times upon this grave, and repeat what I shall tell you faithfully
word for word: Pure dead, I am sent by Azrael, son of the great sage,
Rabbi Itzele of Miropol, to beg you to pardon him for disturbing your
peace, and to deliver his command that you inform the pure dead, Nissin
ben Rifke, by means known to you as follows: That the just and
righteous Rabbinical Court of Miropol summons him to be present immediately at a trial at which he shall appear in the same garb as that in
which he was buried. Repeat these words three times; then turn and
come back here. You will not look behind you, no matter what cries or
calls or shrieks may pursue you, nor will you allow my staff to leave your
hand even for one moment, otherwise you will place yourself in dire peril.
Go and God will protect you, for no harm can come to him who is
bound on a virtuous errand. But before you go, let two men come in and
make a partition which shall separate the dead man from the living.
[MICHOEL *goes out.* TWO MEN *enter with a sheet with which they screen
the left-hand corner down to the floor. They then leave the room.*] Let
Sender come in. [SENDER *appears.*] Sender, have you carried out my instructions and sent horses for the bridegroom and his people?

Sender. The swiftest horses were sent, but the bridegroom has not yet
arrived.

Rabbi Azrael. Have someone ride out to meet them and say they are to drive as fast as they can.

Sender. Yes, Rabbi.

[*Pause.*]

Rabbi Azrael. Sender, we have sent to inform the pure dead, Nissin ben Rifke, that the Rabbinical Court summons him to appear in his cause against you. Are you willing to accept our verdict?

Sender. I am.

Rabbi Azrael. Will you carry out our sentence?

Sender. I will.

Rabbi Azrael. Then step back and take your place upon the right.

Sender. Rabbi, it begins to come back to me. . . . It may be that the trial which Nissin ben Rifke has summoned me to, concerns an agreement upon which we shook hands one day many years ago. But in that matter I am not to blame.

Rabbi Azrael. You will have an opportunity to speak of this later on, after the complainant has made known his grievance. [*Pause.*] Very soon here is personally to appear in our midst, a man from the True World, in order to submit to our judgment a case between himself and a man of our Untrue World. [*Pause.*] A trial such as this is proof that the laws set forth in the Holy Scriptures rule all worlds and all people, and unite both the living and the dead within their bonds. [*Pause.*] A trial such as this is difficult and terrible. The eyes of all the worlds are turned towards it, and should this court deviate from the Law by so much as a hair's breadth, tumult would ensue in the Court on High. It is with fear and trembling, therefore, that we are to approach the trial at issue . . . with fear and trembling. . . .

He looks anxiously around him and as he does encounters the partition in the left-hand corner. He ceases to speak. There is a silence of awe.]

First Judge. [*In a frightened whisper to the* SECOND JUDGE] I believe he's come.

Second Judge. [*In the same tone*] It seems so.

Rabbi Samson. He is here.

Rabbi Azrael. Pure dead Nissin ben Rifke! You are commanded by this just and righteous court to stay within the circle and partition assigned to you, and not to go beyond them. Pure dead Nissin ben Rifke, you are commanded by this just and righteous court to state your grievance and the redress you seek against the accused, Sender ben Henie.

[*Awestruck pause. All listen as though turned to stone.*]

First Judge. I believe he is answering.

Second Judge. It seems so.

First Judge. I hear a voice but no words.

Second Judge. And I words but no voice.

Rabbi Samson. [*To* SENDER] Sender ben Henie, the pure dead Nissin ben Rifke makes demand saying that in the years of your youth you and he were students in the same *yeshiva,* comrades, and that your soul and his were bound together in true friendship. You were both married in the same week, and when you met at the house of the Rabbi, during the Great Holidays, you made a solemn pact that if the wife of one of you should conceive and bear a boy and the other a girl, those two children should marry.

Sender. [*In a tremulous voice*] It was so.

Rabbi Samson. The pure dead Nissin ben Rifke makes further demand, saying that soon afterwards he left for a place very far away, where his wife bore him a son in the same hour as your wife gave you a daughter. Soon thereafter he was gathered to his fathers. [*Short pause.*] In the True World, he found that his son had been blest with a noble and lofty soul, and was progressing upwards from plane to plane, and at this his paternal heart overflowed with joy and pride. He also found that his son, growing older, had become a wanderer from province to province, and from country to country, and from city to city, for the soul to which his soul had been predestined was drawing him ever onward. At last he came to the city in which you dwell, and you took him into your house. He sat at your table, and his soul bound itself to the soul of your daughter. But you were rich, while Nissin's son was poor, and so you turned your back on him and went seeking for your daughter a bridegroom of high estate and great possessions. [*Short pause.*] Nissin then beheld his son grow desperate and become a wanderer once more, seeking now the New Paths. And sorrow and alarm filled his father's soul lest the dark powers, aware of the youth's extremity, spread their net for him. This they did, and caught him, and tore him from the world before his time. Thereafter the soul of Nissin ben Rifke's son roamed amidst the worlds until it entered as a Dybbuk into the body of his predestined Nissin ben Rifke claims that the death of his son has severed him from both worlds, leaving him without name or memorial, since neither heir nor friend remains on earth to pray for his soul. His light has been extinguished forever—the crown of his head has rolled down into the abyss. Therefore, he begs the just and righteous court to pass sentence upon Sender according to the laws of our Holy Scriptures, for his shedding of the blood of Nissin's son and of his son's sons to the end of all generations.

[*An awestruck pause.* SENDER *is shaken with sobs.*]

Rabbi Azrael. Sender ben Henie, have you heard the complaint brought against you by the holy dead, Nissin ben Rifke? What have you to say in answer to it?

Sender. I can't speak . . . I have no words to say . . . in justification. But I would ask you to beg my old comrade to forgive me this sin, because it was not committed in malice. Soon after we had shaken hands upon our pact, Nissin went away, and I did not know whether his wife had had a child, either boy or girl. Then I received news of his death, but none about his family. And gradually the whole affair of our agreement went out of my mind.

Rabbi Azrael. Why did you not inquire about him? Why did you make no inquiry?

Sender. It is customary for the bridegroom's father to make the first advances, not the bride's. I thought that if Nissin had had a son, he would have let me know.

Rabbi Samson. Nissin ben Rifke asks why, when you received his son into your house and had him sit at your table, did you never ask him whence he came and of what family?

Sender. I don't know. . . . I don't remember. . . . But I do swear that something urged me continually to take him for my son-in-law. That was why, whenever a match was proposed, I always made such hard conditions that the bridegroom's father would never agree to them. Three marriages fell through in this manner. But this time the bridegroom's people would not be put off.

[*Pause.*]

Rabbi Samson. Nissin ben Rifke says that in your heart of hearts you were aware of his son's identity and therefore feared to ask him who he was. You were ambitious that your daughter should live in ease and riches, and for that reason thrust his son down into the abyss.

[SENDER *weeps silently, covering his face. There is a heavy pause.* MICHOEL *returns and gives the staff back to* RABBI AZRAEL.]

Rabbi Azrael. [*After a whispered conference with* RABBI SAMSON *and the* JUDGES, *rises and takes the staff in his hands*] This just and righteous court has heard both parties and delivers its verdict as follows: Whereas it is not known whether, at the time Nissin ben Rifke and Sender ben Henie shook hands upon their agreement, their wives had already conceived; and whereas, according to our Holy Scriptures, no agreement whatsoever which involves anything not yet in existence can be held valid in law, we may not therefore find that this agreement was binding upon Sender. Since, however, in the Upper World, the agreement was accepted as valid and never canceled; and since the belief was implanted in the heart of Nissin ben Rifke's son that the daughter of Sender ben Henie was his predestined bride; and whereas, Sender ben Henie's subsequent conduct brought calamity upon Nissin ben Rifke and his son; Now, therefore, be it decreed by this just and righteous court, that Sender give the half of his fortune in alms to the poor, and each year, for the remainder of his life, light the memorial candle for Nissin ben Rifke and his son as though they were his own kindred, and pray for their souls. [*Pause.*] The just and righteous court now requests the holy dead, Nissin ben Rifke, to forgive Sender unreservedly, and to command his son in filial duty to leave the body of the maiden, Leah, daughter of Channah, in order that a branch of the fruitful tree of Israel may not be blighted. In return for these things, the Almighty will make manifest his grace to Nissin ben Rifke and to his lost son.

All. Amen!

Rabbi Azrael. Pure dead Nissin ben Rifke, have you heard our judgment? Do you accept it? [*Pause.*] Sender ben Henie, have you heard our judgment? Do you accept it?

Sender. I accept.

Rabbi Azrael. Pure dead, Nissin ben Rifke, the trial between you and Sender ben Henie is now ended. Do you return therefore to your resting place, and in going we command you to do no harm to man nor other living creature whatsoever. [*Pause.*] Michoel, water. . . . And have the curtain taken away. [MICHOEL *calls in* TWO MEN, *who remove the sheet* RABBI AZRAEL *traces a circle in the same place as before, but from right to left. The* MEN *return with basin and ewer, and all wash their hands.*] Sender, have the bridegroom and his people arrived?

Sender. There has been no sign of them.

Rabbi Azrael. Send another rider to meet them, and say they are to press on with all the speed their horses can make. Have the canopy raised and the musicians in readiness. Let the bride be dressed in her wedding gown so that the moment the Dybbuk has been cast out you may lead her under the canopy. What is now about to be done—will be done.

[SENDER *goes out.* RABBI AZRAEL *takes off his prayer-shawl and phylacteries, folding them up.*]

Rabbi Samson. [*Whispering to the* JUDGES] Did you notice that the dead man did not forgive Sender?

Judges One and Two. [*In low, frightened tones*] Yes, we did.

Rabbi Samson. Do you know the dead man did not accept the verdict?

Judges One and Two. Yes, we realized that.

Rabbi Samson. He failed to say Amen to Rabbi Azrael's sentence—you felt that too, no doubt.

Judges One and Two. Yes, distinctly.

Rabbi Samson. It is a very bad sign—

Judges One and Two. Extremely—

Rabbi Samson. Rabbi Azrael is terribly agitated—look at him. See how his hands are trembling. [*Pause.*] We have done our share—we can go now.

[*The* JUDGES *slip out unobtrusively, and* RABBI SAMSON *prepares to follow them.*]

Rabbi Azrael. Rabbi, please remain until the Dybbuk has been cast out—I should like you to perform the wedding ceremony. [RABBI SAMSON *sighs and sits down again, with bowed head. An oppressive pause.*] God of the Heavens, marvelously strange are Thy ways, and secret, yet the flame of Thy Divine Will illuminates with its reflection the path I tread. Nor shall I stray from that path forever, either to the right or to the left. *He raises his head.*] Michoel, is everything prepared?

Michoel. Yes, Rabbi.

Rabbi Azrael. Let the maiden be brought.

[*Enter* SENDER *and* FRADE *with* LEAH, *in her wedding-gown, a black cloak over her shoulders. They seat her on the sofa.* RABBI SAMSON *takes his place behind* RABBI AZRAEL.]

Rabbi Azrael. Dybbuk, in the name of the Rabbi of this city, who is present, in the name of a holy community of Jews, in the name of the great Sanhedrin of Jerusalem, I, Azrael ben Hadassah, do for the last time command you to depart out of the body of the maiden Leah, daughter of Channah.

Leah (Dybbuk). [*Firmly*] I refuse!

Rabbi Azrael. Michoel, call in people to witness the exorcism—bring the shrouds, the horns and the black candles. [MICHOEL *goes out and shortly returns with* FIFTEEN MEN, *among them the* MESSENGER. *The shrouds, trumpets and candles are brought.*] Bring out the scrolls. MICHOEL *gives a scroll each to seven, and a trumpet each to seven others.*] Stubborn spirit—inasmuch as you have dared to oppose our power, we deliver you into the hands of the Higher Spirits which will pull you out by force. Blow *Tekiah!* [1]

[*The horns are blown.*]

Leah (Dybbuk). [*Leaves her seat and struggles violently as against invisible assailants*] Let me alone—you shall not pull me away—I won't go—I can't go—

Rabbi Azrael. Since the Higher Spirits cannot overcome you, I surrender you to the Spirits of the Middle Plane, those which are neither good nor evil. I now invoke *their* power to drag you forth. Blow *shevarim.*

[*The horns are blown again.*]

Leah (Dybbuk). [*Her strength beginning to fail*] Woe is me! The powers of all the worlds are arrayed against me. Spirits of terror wrench me and tear me without mercy—the souls of the great and righteous too have arisen against me. The soul of my own father is with them—commanding me to go— But until the last spark of strength has gone from me, so long shall I withstand them and remain where I am.

Rabbi Azrael. [*To himself*] It is clear that One of Great Power stands beside him. [*Pause.*] Michoel, put away the scrolls. [MICHOEL *does so.*] Hang a black curtain over the altar. [*This is done.*] Light the black candles. [*This, too, is done.*] Let everyone now put on a shroud. [*All, including the two* RABBIS, *do so.* RABBI AZRAEL *stands with both arms upraised, an awe-inspiring figure.*] Rise up, O Lord, and let Thine enemies be scattered before Thee; as smoke is dispersed so let them be scattered. . . . Sinful and obstinate soul, with the power of Almighty God and with the sanction of the Holy Scriptures, I, Azrael ben Hadassah, do with these words rend asunder every cord that binds you to the world of living creatures and to the body and soul of the maiden, Leah, Daughter of Channah. . . .

Leah (Dybbuk). [*Shrieking*] Ah! I am lost!

Rabbi Azrael. . . . And do pronounce you excommunicated from all Israel. Blow *teruah.*

Messenger. The last spark has been swallowed up into the flame.

Leah (Dybbuk). [*Defeated*] Alas!—I can fight no more. . . .

[*They begin to sound the horns*

Rabbi Azrael. [*Hastily raising his hand to silence the horns*] Do you submit?

Leah (Dybbuk). [*In a dead voice*] I submit—

Rabbi Azrael. Do you promise to depart of your own free will, from

---

[1] Certain shrill notes sounded on the *shofar,* the sacred ram's horn.

he body of the maiden, Leah, daughter of Channah, and never return?

Leah (*Dybbuk*). [*As before.*]

Rabbi Azrael. Dybbuk—by the same power and sanction which leputed me to place you under the ban of anathema, I now lift from ou that ban. [*To* MICHOEL.] Put out the candles—take down the black urtain. [MICHOEL *does so.*] Put away the horns. [MICHOEL *collects them.*] And dismiss the people—let them take off their shrouds before they go. *Exeunt the* FOURTEEN *with* MESSENGER *and* MICHOEL.] [RABBI AZRAEL rays *with upraised arms.*] Lord of the world, God of charity and mercy, ook down upon the suffering of this homeless, tortured soul which the rrors and misdeeds of others caused to stray into the bypaths. Regard ot its wrongdoing, O Lord, but let the memory of its virtuous past and s present bitter torment and the merits of its forefathers rise like a soft, bscuring mist before Thy sight. Lord of the world—do Thou free its ath of evil spirits, and admit it to everlasting peace within Thy man- ons. Amen.

All. Amen.

Leah (*Dybbuk*). [*Trembling violently*] Say *kaddish* for me! The our of my going was predestined—and it has come!

Rabbi Azrael. Sender, say *kaddish.*

[SENDER *begins the prayer as the clock strikes twelve.*]

Sender. Yisgadaal—ve—yiskadeesh—shmeh raboh! [2]

Leah (*Dybbuk*). [*Springs up*] Aie! [*Falls swooning upon the sofa.*]

Rabbi Azrael. Bring the bride to the wedding canopy.

Michoel. [*Rushing in, greatly agitated*] The last rider has just come ack. He says a wheel has come off the wagon so the bridegroom and his arty must walk the rest of the way. But they are at the hill, so they will e here soon—they've been sighted already.

Rabbi Azrael. [*Profoundly astonished*] What was to be, shall be. [*To* ENDER.] Let the old woman remain here with the bride. We will go—all us—to meet the bridegroom. [*He traces a circle round* LEAH, *from left* right, *takes off his shroud, which he hangs up near the door, and goes* t carrying his staff. SENDER *and* MICHOEL *follow him.*]

[*A long pause.*]

Leah. [*Waking—in a faint voice*] Who is here with me? Granny—is at you? Oh! I feel so strange, Granny—so weary. Rock me in your ms.

Frade. [*Caressing her*] No, little daughter—you mustn't feel that

2 "Magnified and sanctified be His mighty Name!" First line of prayer for the ad.

way. My little child must not be sad. Let the Black Cat be sad. My little
one's heart must be as light as dawn, as light as a breath, as white as a
snowflake. Holy angels should embrace her with their wings.

[*Wedding music is heard.*]

Leah. [*Frightened and trembling, seizes* FRADE's *hand for protection.*]
Listen! They are beginning to dance round the holy grave to cheer up
the dead bride and bridegroom.

Frade. Be calm, my darling. No harm can come to you now—a
mighty power is standing guard over you on every side. Sixty giants, with
drawn swords, protect you from evil encounter. The holy fathers and
holy mothers ward off the evil eye. [*Little by little she drifts into a chant*

Soon they'll lead you under the canopy—
A blessed hour—a happy hour—
Comes your mother—the good and virtuous—
From the Garden of Eden—the Garden of Eden.
Of gold and silver are her robes.

Angels twain go out to meet her, go out to meet her—
Take her hands—one the right hand, one the left hand,
"Channele—Channele mine,
Why do you come decked out so fine?"

So Channele answers the angel:

"Why should I not come robed in state?
Is this not a day of days?
For my bright crown, my only daughter,
Goes to her wedding and luck goes with her."

"Channele, as in robes of state you go,
Why is your face all wan and pale with woe?"

So Channele answers the angel:

"What should I do but sorrow, on this day that my daughter's a bride
For she's led to the altar by strangers, while I must stand mournin
    aside?"
Under the canopy stands the bride, and old and young bring her thei
    greetings and good wishes.

And there stands the Prophet Elijah,
The great goblet of wine in his hand,

And the words of his holy blessing
Roll echoing over the land.

[FRADE *falls asleep. Long pause.*]

Leah. [*Her eyes closed, sighs deeply—then wakes.*]

Voice of Channon. I.

Leah. I hear your voice, but I cannot see you.

Voice of Channon. Because you are within a magic circle which I may not enter.

Leah. Your voice is as sweet as the lament of violins in the quiet night. Who are you? Tell me.

Voice of Channon. I have forgotten. I have no remembrance of myself but in your thoughts of me.

Leah. I remember—now—the star that drew my heart towards its light—the tears that I have shed in the still midnight—the one who stood before me ever—in my dreams—was it you?

Voice of Channon. I—

Leah. I remember—your hair, so soft and damp as if with tears—your sad and gentle eyes—your hands with the thin tapering fingers. Waking and sleeping I had no thought but of you. [*Pause—sadly.*] You went away and darkness fell upon me—my soul withered in loneliness like the soul of a widow left desolate—the stranger came—and then— then you returned, and the dead heart wakened to life again, and out of sorrow joy blossomed like a flower. . . . Why have you now once more forsaken me?

Voice of Channon. I broke down the barriers between us—I crossed the plains of death—I defied every law of past and present time and all the ages. . . . I strove against the strong and mighty and against those who know no mercy. And as my last spark of strength left me, I left your body to return to your soul.

Leah. [*Tenderly*] Come back to me, my bridegroom—my husband— I will carry you, dead, in my heart—and in our dreams at night we shall rock to sleep our little children who will never be born. . . . [*Weeps.*] And sew them little clothes, and sing them lullabies— [*Sings, weeping.*]

> Hush—hush, little children—
> No cradle shall hold you—
> In no clothes can we fold you.
>
> Dead, that the living cannot mourn;
> Untimely lost and never born. . . .

[*The Music of a wedding-march is heard approaching.*]

Leah. [*Trembling*] They are coming to take me to a stranger under the canopy—come to me, my true bridegroom; come to me.

Voice of Channon. I have left your body—I will come to your soul.

[*He appears against the wall, white-robed.*]

Leah. [*With joy*] Come, my bridegroom. The barrier between us is no more. I see you. Come to me. . . .

Voice of Channon. [*Echo*] Come to me.

Leah. [*Crying out with joy*] I am coming. . . .

Voice of Channon. [*Echo*] And I to you. . . .

[Voices *outside.*]

Voices. Lead the bride to the canopy.

[*Wedding march is heard.* Leah *rises, dropping, as she does so, her black cloak onto the sofa, and in her white wedding dress, to the strains of the music, she goes towards* Channon, *and at the spot where he has appeared their two forms merge into one.*]

[Rabbi Azrael *enters, carrying his staff, followed by the* Messenger. *They stand on the threshold. Behind them,* Sender, Frade *and the rest.*]

Leah. [*In a far-away voice*] A great light flows about me . . . predestined bridegroom, I am united to you forever. Now we soar upward together higher and higher. . . .

[*The stage grows darker.*]

Rabbi Azrael. [*With lowered head*] Too late!

Messenger. Blessed be a righteous judge.

[*It is now completely dark. As if from a great distance, singing is heard, scarcely audible.*]

CURTAIN

PROFESSOR BERNHARDI[1]

by ARTHUR SCHNITZLER

CHARACTERS

Professor Bernhardi, *Professor for Internal Medicine and Director of the Elizabethinum*

---

[1] This adaptation was authorized and approved by the author. It was first published by Paul Elder and Company in San Francisco in 1913, and is dedicated by the adapter to the memory of her son, Austin Ramon Pohli.

DOCTOR EBENWALD, *Professor of Surgery, Vice-Director*
DOCTOR CYPRIAN, *Nerve Specialist*
DOCTOR PFLUGFELDER, *Eye Specialist*
DOCTOR FILITZ, *Diseases of Women*
DOCTOR TUGENDVETTER, *Skin Specialist*
DOCTOR LOEWENSTEIN, *Specialist on Children's Diseases*
DOCTOR SCHREIMANN, *Throat Specialist*
DOCTOR ADLER, *Pathological Anatomist*
DOCTOR OSCAR BERNHARDI ⎱
DOCTOR KURT PFLUGFELDER ⎰ *Assistants to Bernhardi*
DOCTOR WENGER, *Assistant to Tugendvetter*
HOCHROITZPOINTNER, *Student of Medicine—Interne*
SISTER LUDMILLA, *a nurse*
DOCTOR·FLINT, *Minister of Education*
PRIVY-COUNCILLOR WINKLER, *Department of Education*
FRANZ REDER, *Priest at the Church of Holy Florian*
DOCTOR GOLDENTHAL, *Attorney-at-Law*
KULKA, *a Reporter*

Vienna—in 1900

TIME AND PLACE

Fifteen years before the opening scene, Professor Bernhardi, with the help of Professor Tugendvetter and Professor Cyprian, founded the medical institution named Elizabethinum, after the Empress of Austria. Now, owing to his skill as a physician, his mental gifts and his energy, the hospital and clinic are among the best in Vienna, with Professor Bernhardi at its head as President.

ACT I

In the Elizabethinum—The opening scene is laid in a large ante-room of the Elizabethinum, with several doors, one leading to a ward, another to a private sick-room, and large folding doors opening into a vestibule.

All the furnishings are white; along the walls are large bookcases filled with medical works, and glass cases where the latest surgical instruments and appliances are assembled.

In an open wardrobe are seen the white operating coats of doctors. There is also a long table covered with charts, diaries and other documents.

SISTER LUDMILLA, *a nurse, about twenty-eight years old, is occupied arranging medical instruments. She has large blue eyes, weak and watery.*

HOCHROITZPOINTNER *enters from the ward. Young man twenty-five years old, medium height, fat, pale face with scars, small moustache, eyeglasses, and oiled smooth hair. Type of student who attends all lectures and has never succeeded in passing an examination.*

Hochroitzpointner. Professor has not come yet? They are a long time at it today. That's the third autopsy in a week, and only twenty beds in the ward. And tomorrow we'll have another one.

Sister. Do you think so, Doctor? That septicaemia case?

Hochroitzpointner. Yes. By the way, did you make a report?

Sister. Of course, Doctor.

Hochroitzpointner. Well, we could not prove it, but it was surely a case of malpractice. I tell you, Sister, there are all kinds of things happening in the world. Ah! here are the invitations to the ball—under the patronage of the Princess Stixenstein. Well, Sister, are you going to the ball?

Sister. I guess not, Doctor.

Hochroitzpointner. Dancing forbidden?

Sister. [*Smiling*] No, Doctor, we are not a religious order. Nothing is forbidden us.

Hochroitzpointner. [*With a sly look*] Nothing?

[DOCTOR OSCAR BERNHARDI *enters. Twenty-five years old, elegantly dressed, handsome, pleasing appearance, but diffident manner.*][2]

Oscar. Good morning! Father will be here directly. [*At the table.*] Oh! here are the invitations to the ball. Why do they send them here?

Hochroitzpointner. The ball for the benefit of the Elizabethinum promises to be the most elegant affair of the season. The papers are full of it. I hear that you have composed a waltz for the occasion.

Oscar. [*Deprecatory gesture and pointing to sick-room*] Anything new in there?

Hochroitzpointner. That septicaemia case is near the end.

Oscar. [*Regretfully*] Oh, well! there was nothing to be done.

Hochroitzpointner. I gave her a camphor injection.

Oscar. Yes, the art of prolonging a doomed life is one secret that we have solved.

[*Enter* PROFESSOR BERNHARDI. *Type of a man of the world, distinguished,*

---

[2] The tender relations between Bernhardi and his son Oscar are a tribute to the affection that existed between Professor Schnitzler and his son Arthur.

gray hair, fine eyes. He is accompanied by his assistant, DOCTOR KURT
PFLUGFELDER, *twenty-seven years old. They come from the dissecting
room.*]

Kurt. I could not help it, Professor. Doctor Adler would have liked
it much better if Professor Ebenwald's diagnosis had been correct.

Bernhardi. But, my dear Doctor Pflugfelder, you suspect treason
everywhere.

Hochroitzpointner. I just heard from Doctor Oscar that we were
right.

Bernhardi. Yes, but at the same time, *we* were wrong! Or don't you
attend Professor Ebenwald's courses?

Oscar. Doctor Hochroitzpointner attends nearly all the courses.

Bernhardi. [*Laying his hand on* HOCHROITZPOINTNER's *shoulder,
kindly*] Well, anything new?

Hochroitzpointner. That septicaemia case is very bad.

Bernhardi. Poor girl! Still alive?

[*Enter* PROFESSOR EBENWALD.]

Ebenwald. [*Vice-president, tall, slender, spectacles; with exaggerated
Austrian accent*] Good morning! Ah, there you are, Professor!

Bernhardi. How do you do, Doctor.

Ebenwald. Have you a second for me?

Bernhardi. Now?

Ebenwald. [*Approaching him*] If it were possible. It is in regard to
the appointment of a successor to Professor Tugendvetter.

Bernhardi. Is there any hurry for that?

[*The* SISTER *gives* BERNHARDI *a document to sign.*]

Excuse me one moment, we have a case of septicaemia there, [*pointing to door*] a young girl, absolutely conscious; she wants to get up, take
a walk, believes herself perfectly well. You cannot count the pulse any
more. It may be over before an hour is gone.

Ebenwald. [*Pompously*] That occurs not infrequently.

Hochroitzpointner. [*Eagerly*] Shall I give her another camphor injection?

Bernhardi. You might have spared yourself the first one—never
mind, you gave her perhaps the happiest hour of her life, though, I suppose, unintentionally.

Hochroitzpointner. Do you consider me a mere butcher?

Bernhardi. I do not remember having uttered a reproach of that kind.

[HOCHROITZPOINTNER *and* EBENWALD *exchange a look.*]

Bernhardi. [*To* SISTER] Has she relatives?

Sister. Nobody has called.

Bernhardi. Not her lover?

Oscar. Trust him! He won't dare. She hasn't even mentioned him. Perhaps she doesn't know his name.

Bernhardi. And that is what they call "love's happiness."

Sister. [*Who has been standing near, whispers to* HOCHROITZPOINT-NER] I'll go now and get his Reverence to come.

Hochroitzpointner. Yes, you might go. If you get there too late, it is no misfortune.

[SISTER *goes out.*]

Ebenwald. [*Displaying impatience*] Well, the case is this, Doctor: I have received a letter from Professor Hell, from Graz. He is inclined to accept an appointment as successor to Tugendvetter.

Bernhardi. Ah! he is inclined!

Ebenwald. Yes, sir.

Bernhardi. Did anyone ask him?

Ebenwald. I took the liberty, as his old friend and classmate.

[*Enter* PROFESSOR TUGENDVETTER. *About fifty years old, gray, "side-chops," affects jovial, humorous manner. Of uncertain demeanor, tries to win applause.*]

Tugendvetter. Good morning! I have to talk to you, Bernhardi. His Excellency—I have just come from His Excellency—sends his regards to you.

Bernhardi. Who sends his regards?

Tugendvetter. Flint, the Minister. Oh! we talked about you. He thinks a great deal of you. He remembers with pleasure the time when you were assistants together at Rappenweiler's. Ah! he is a winner! First time in Austria a clinical professor ever rose to be a Minister.

Bernhardi. He was always a good politician, your latest friend Flint. By the way, did he approve your acceptance of this municipal hospital appointment? Lucky we have someone to take your place.

Tugendvetter. Little Wenger? Yes, quite capable. You will not let him fill my place for any length of time?

Ebenwald. I have just mentioned having received a letter from Professor Hell, who is willing—

Tugendvetter. Oh! he has also written to me—

Bernhardi. Well! there is certainly nothing slow about the gentleman.

Tugendvetter. [*Looking at* EBENWALD] Say, Bernhardi, your institution would have a splendid acquisition in Hell.

Bernhardi. Then he must have developed remarkably in Graz. When he was in Vienna, we considered him absolutely incompetent.

Tugendvetter. Who, for instance?

Bernhardi. You, for instance.

Tugendvetter. I think that Wenger is too young.

Bernhardi. Well, one of them has to be elected, and I hope that you take sufficient interest in the future of your department to vote for the better man.

Tugendvetter. Well, I should say so! Aren't we the founders of it, Bernhardi, Cyprian and I. How long ago was it?

Ebenwald. Fifteen years ago, dear Tugendvetter.

Tugendvetter. Fifteen years, a-hem—a beautiful time. By Jove, it will not be easy for me. Say, Bernhardi, could it not be arranged for me to remain here?

Bernhardi. Absolutely not. The day you take your place there I shall appoint your former assistant to fill your place until the election.

Ebenwald. Then I wish to ask that the election take place within the next few days.

[BERNHARDI *shows resentment at the interference of* EBENWALD, *who leaves in apparent indignation. All exit. As they leave,* DOCTOR ADLER *enters; small, dark, lively, about thirty years old.* KURT *enters. He and* ADLER *engage in conversation about the slow progress the science of medicine has made.*]

Adler. All that you can do is to experiment.

Kurt. What are we to do? We must try the new remedies if the old ones fail.

Adler. And tomorrow the new is old; that is why I chose Pathological Anatomy. There, at least one knows what he is doing, and is the master.

Kurt. You forget, Doctor Adler, there is One above you.

Adler. And He hasn't time to bother about us, He is too busy with the spiritual department. [*Looks over the record.*] Also Roentgen? Do you really use that in such cases?

Kurt. We are obliged to try everything, Doctor Adler, especially where there is nothing more to be lost.

[CYPRIAN *enters, an elderly man with long, blonde hair. He is looking for the janitor.*]

Cyprian. Can't find him. I am sure he is in a saloon. The same thing will happen here that occurred in Prague, where we had a janitor who was addicted to liquor. That fellow actually drank even the alcohol out of the specimen jars.

[BERNHARDI *enters.*]

Oscar. [*From the sick-room*] Oh, father, if you want to speak to her—

[BERNHARDI *exits.*]

Adler. [*To* CYPRIAN] A dying patient!

[PRIEST *enters. Young man, twenty-eight years old, with an energetic, intelligent face. The Acolyte remains standing at the door.* ADLER *greets him.*]

Priest. Good day, gentlemen. I hope that I am not too late?

Kurt. No, Your Reverence, the professor is with the patient now.

Priest. Then you have not given up hope?

Kurt. Yes, it is a perfectly hopeless case!

[HOCHROITZPOINTNER *offers the* PRIEST *a chair.*]

Priest. I will wait until the professor has left the patient.

Cyprian. Your Reverence, if only we could help all of these patients; but sometimes we cannot do anything better than to comfort them.

Kurt. And lie to them.

Priest. You use a very hard word there.

Kurt. Pardon, Your Reverence, I was referring to the physician; still that is sometimes the most difficult and noblest part of our professional duty.

[BERNHARDI *is seen at the door; the* PRIEST *rises. There are now present in the room:* HOCHROITZPOINTNER, ADLER, KURT, CYPRIAN, OSCAR, PRIEST *and* BERNHARDI. *The* SISTER *follows* BERNHARDI *in from the sick-room.*]

Bernhardi. Oh, Your Reverence!

Priest. [*Shakes hands with him*] We take each other's places, Professor. Will I find the patient still conscious?

Bernhardi. Yes, you might say—in a heightened state of consciousness; she is in a state of absolute euphoria. She is, you might say—well, she feels well.

Priest. Oh! that is perfectly beautiful. Only the other day I had the joy of seeing a young man on the street, who, fully prepared to die, had a few weeks previously received from me the last ointment.

Adler. Who knows whether it was not Your Reverence who gave him back the strength and courage for the new life.

Bernhardi. [*Turning to* ADLER] His Reverence has misunderstood me. I meant to say that the patient has no conception of her true condition; she is going, but imagines that she is recovering.

Priest. Really?

Bernhardi. And I almost fear that your appearance, Your Reverence—

Priest. Fear nothing for your patient; I have not come to pronounce the death sentence. When may I prepare the patient? It would be best to prepare her.

[*At a glance from the* PRIEST *to the* SISTER, *unnoticed by* BERNHARDI, *the* SISTER *enters the sick-room.*]

Bernhardi. That would not help matters. As I have told you already, the patient has no idea that she is going to die; she expects anything else rather than this visit. On the contrary, she is in the happy belief that in the next hour someone that is near to her may come to take her with him into life and into happiness. I believe, Your Reverence, that it would be wrong to awaken her from this last dream.

Priest. Is there a chance that my appearance might bring about a change for the worse, Professor?

Bernhardi. It is not impossible that the end might be hastened, possibly by only a few minutes, but at all events—

Priest. Can your patient still be saved? Does my appearance in that sense, mean danger? Then, of course, I would be ready to retire.

Bernhardi. She is hopeless. There is no doubt about it.

Priest. Then, Professor, I see no reason—

Bernhardi. Excuse me, Your Reverence, I am still here performing my professional duty, which demands that, if it is not in my power to save my patient, it is at least my duty to let her die happily.

[CYPRIAN *shows impatience and disapproval.*]

Priest. To die happily? Probably we have different conceptions of what that means, and from what I learned from the Sister, your patient is more in need of absolution than others.

Bernhardi. [*With an ironical smile*] Are we not all sinners?

Priest. That is neither here nor there; you do not know whether in the depth of the soul, into which God alone can look, there may be just in this last moment, a longing to free itself from sin by absolution.

Bernhardi. Must I repeat again, Your Reverence, that the patient does not know that she is lost; she has hope, she is peaceful, and she feels no repentance.

Priest. All the more culpable would I be, if I left this place without having administered the consolation of our holy religion to this dying one.

Bernhardi. Your Reverence, every earthly judge will absolve you from this guilt. [*After a gesture of the* PRIEST's.] Your Reverence, as her physician, I cannot permit you to go near my patient.

Priest. I was called here. I must beg—

Bernhardi. Not by me. I can only repeat, Your Reverence, that as her physician, to whom the happiness of the patient is confided to the last minute, I must forbid your entering that room.

Priest. You forbid me?

Bernhardi. [*Touching his shoulder lightly*] Yes, Your Reverence.

[*The* SISTER *hurries in from the sick-room.*]

Sister. Your Reverence—

Bernhardi. Were you in there?

Sister. It will be too late, Your Reverence—

[KURT *quickly enters the sick-room.*]

Bernhardi. [*To* SISTER] You told the patient that His Reverence is here?

Sister. Yes, Doctor.

Bernhardi. Answer me quietly. How did the patient take the message? Did she say anything? Speak! Well—!

Sister. She said—

Bernhardi. Well—?

Sister. She was a little bit frightened.

Bernhardi. [*Not angrily*] Well, speak! What did she say?

Sister. "Must I really die?"

Kurt. [*From the sick-room*] It is all over—

Bernhardi. Do not be disturbed, Your Reverence. It was not your fault; you only wanted to do your duty, the same as I. I am more than sorry that I did not succeed.

Priest. It is not for you, Professor, to give me absolution. That poor soul has gone hither as a sinner, and without the solace of her religion; and that is your fault.

Bernhardi. I am perfectly willing to accept the responsibility.

Priest. It will remain to be seen whether you are able to do so. Good day, gentlemen.

[PRIEST *leaves. The others are stirred and embarrassed.* BERNHARDI *looks at all of them in turn.*]

Bernhardi. Well, Doctor Adler, tomorrow the autopsy.

Cyprian. [*Aside to* BERNHARDI] It was not right.

Bernhardi. Why, not right?

Adler. I would be insincere, did I not say right now that in this affair I cannot take your side, Professor.

Bernhardi. And it would be insincere on my part if I did not assure you that I was certainly aware of that.

[CYPRIAN *and* ADLER *leave.* OSCAR *bites his lips.*]

Bernhardi. I hope this will not hurt your career.

Oscar. Oh, father!

[BERNHARDI *lays his hand tenderly upon* OSCAR's *head.*]

Sister. Professor, I thought—

Bernhardi. Well, what did you think? Well, what is the difference? It is all over now.

Sister. [*Stammering, and pointing at* HOCHROITZPOINTNER] Well—well—the doctor—

Hochroitzpointner. Well, I, of course, did not forbid her.

Bernhardi. Oh, of course not, Doctor. You undoubtedly are as zealous an attendant at church as at the lectures.

Hochroitzpointner. Professor, we live in a Christian state.

Bernhardi. [*Looking at him steadfastly*] Yes, God forgive them, they know too d—d well what they do.

[BERNHARDI *leaves with* KURT *and* OSCAR.]

Hochroitzpointner. [*To* SISTER] Why did you excuse yourself, child? You only did your duty. Why did you cry? Look out that you do not get one of those attacks again.

Sister. [*Weeping*] Professor was so angry!

Hochroitzpointner. Suppose he was angry; the Professor, our President, he will not last much longer—this will break his neck.

CURTAIN

ACT II

Office of PROFESSOR BERNHARDI. [*Bookcases, writing-desks, medical appliances, pictures, and statuary busts of scientists.* OSCAR *is seated at his father's desk. A bell rings and a servant brings a card.*]

Oscar. [*To servant*] Admit the gentleman.

[*Enter* FILITZ. *Handsome, blond, about forty years old. Pince-nez.*]

Filitz. Good morning, Doctor Oscar! Where is your father?

Oscar. Good morning, Professor! Father is with Prince Constantin. I expect him at any moment.

Filitz. I cannot wait. Give your father a message from me, which will be of some interest to you also. My wife has been refused admission today by the Princess Stixenstein.

Oscar. Oh! maybe the Princess was not at home.

Filitz. My wife has been asked, in her capacity as President of the Ball Committee, to appear before the patronesses of the Board of Directors. I think this is significant.

[*Enter* LOEWENSTEIN. *Medium height, small eyes, spectacles, hanging shoulders, bent knees. Excited manner. He carries a letter.*]

Loewenstein. [*Handing letter to* OSCAR] Here, read it! The Princess Stixenstein has withdrawn from the Advisory Board of the Ball Committee.

Oscar. Without explanation?

Loewenstein. She did not consider it necessary to give any.

Filitz. It is too evident to everyone.

Oscar. Why? Has that story about the priest become public within a week?

Loewenstein. I knew, as I heard of the scene, that it would be "nuts" for certain people. No one would have tried to exaggerate the harmless incident into an affair if Bernhardi were not a Jew.

Filitz. If a Christian had acted like Bernhardi, it would have been an affair just the same.

[*Enter* BERNHARDI *with his customary smile.*]

Bernhardi. Well, gentlemen! What's the matter? Are we burnt out, or did someone leave us a million?

[OSCAR *hands him the letter.*]

Oscar. The Princess has resigned from our Ball Committee.

Bernhardi. Well! We will find another patroness.

Filitz. I came here to tell you that the Princess did not receive my wife today. You need not play the innocent. I want to know what reparation you intend to make for the insult to my wife?

Bernhardi. Say! really you are not in earnest? [*Enter* CYPRIAN.] Are you also coming to me because the Princess has resigned?

Cyprian. The ball is a second consideration—

Filitz. Excuse me, I have no time. I ask you once more—

Bernhardi. Tell your charming wife, dear Filitz, that I consider her far too intelligent to believe for one moment that her feelings would be hurt, because the salon of a princely goose is closed to her.

Filitz. That kind of an answer relieves me at once. I have the honor, gentlemen—

[*Exit* FILITZ.]

Cyprian. You should not say such things, Bernhardi. The Princess is no fool, but a very intelligent woman, and you'll see that the entire Board of Directors is going to resign.

Bernhardi. You are entirely mistaken. Prince Constantin told me that the Bishop sympathizes.

Cyprian. Did he tell you what the Bishop said? His words were—"That man Bernhardi pleases me, but he will have to pay for this."

Bernhardi. Who has given you all this information?

Cyprian. Counselor Winkler, whom I saw just now, intimated to me that the entire Board might resign.

Bernhardi. And all this because I did my duty as a physician.

Loewenstein. It's monstrous! It's a disgrace! Well, let them resign, let the institution go, and we'll build up another, without the Ebenwalds, Filitzs and their clan. Ah, Bernhardi, how I warned you not to trust those people.

Cyprian. Let me say a word! Loewenstein, you do not give anyone a chance. So far, only the Princess has resigned, and I think Bernhardi can find a way to explain this unfortunate incident in a manner satisfactory to all.

Loewenstein. He shall not apologize!

Bernhardi. I really do not care to play the hero, *a tout prix,* I have sufficiently proven that I have the manhood to carry through anything that I sincerely want.

Cyprian. [*Slightly ironically*] You will find the way, I am sure. Your smile would be sufficient; one need only to bring that to the Princess.

[*Exit* CYPRIAN. BERNHARDI *is left alone. After walking up and down, he sits at his desk, takes a sheet of paper, and with his ironical smile playing about his lips, he writes. A servant brings a card, and is directed to admit the visitor.* EBENWALD *enters and shakes hands.*]

Ebenwald. I consider it my duty to inform you that there are things preparing against you—against our institution.

Bernhardi. Oh! you mean the resignation of the Board? That will be arranged.

Ebenwald. I have just come from Parliament, where my cousin informed me that an indictment is going to be prepared against you. You will have to demonstrate that your actions were not prompted by anti-Catholic feelings.

Bernhardi. Is it necessary to tell that to the people?

Ebenwald. Tell it to them? No; you will prove it to them.

Bernhardi. How? This is getting interesting. What kind of a proof would you furnish?

Ebenwald. It lies in your hands. Tomorrow Tugendvetter's successor is to be appointed.

Bernhardi. Ah!

Ebenwald. [*Coldly*] Yes; there are two candidates.

Bernhardi. [*Decidedly*] One who deserves the place and one who does not. I tell you to your face why you work for Hell, because he—is not a Jew.

Ebenwald. Then I reply to you, that your preference for Wenger—

Bernhardi. You forget that three years ago I voted for you, Professor Ebenvald.

Ebenwald. I think you understand me, Doctor, that it will be best for you to consider this matter before the meeting tomorrow. I need not say that it is entirely confidential between us.

Bernhardi. There is no occasion to ask for your discretion, Professor. Tell the gentleman who sent you—

Ebenwald. Eh!

Bernhardi. That I do not lend myself to business of that kind.

Ebenwald. I was sent by no one; but I do not feel inclined to share the responsibility of your conduct towards His Reverence. I came in your interest and in that of our institution; but you have scorned the hand of a friend, Professor.

Bernhardi. And you leave as my enemy. I like it better so. It is more honest.

Ebenwald. As you choose. I have the honor—

[BERNHARDI *is alone again. He walks up and down. Takes up the paper he has written and tears it. Servant enters and hands him a card.*]

Bernhardi. What! His Excellency himself!

[*Enter* FLINT. *Tall, slender, about fifty years old. Face and figure of a diplomat. Very amiable.*]

Bernhardi. Your Excellency! Be seated.

Flint. You are surprised to see me here?

Bernhardi. Yes, pleasantly surprised. And I shall profit by this occasion to offer you my congratulations upon your new dignity.

Flint. I have not come for the purpose of accepting your congratulations. I have come for the great work of reform—reform of medical education, of social hygiene, of general public education, for which my position offers me opportunity to work; I come to you, Bernhardi, to ask if I may count on you for assistance?

Bernhardi. I wish you would have the kindness to explain in what particular field you want my assistance. Is it social hygiene—reform of medical education—have I forgotten something?

Flint. You are just the same; but that is why I set my special hopes on you. There may be something between us—though I do not really know—

Bernhardi. [*Very seriously*] The friendship of our youth and what became of it afterwards.

Flint. Are you holding that against me? I know that I fought against your enterprise. I did not believe in your institution; but that was my conviction at that time; we all make mistakes; but there is one thing, I never act against my conviction—

Bernhardi. Are you so sure of that?

Flint. Bernhardi!!!

Bernhardi. Let me tell you. I am thinking of a case—when you acted directly against your conviction.

Flint. Now this is too much!

Bernhardi. Wait! [*Walks up and down the room a few times, and suddenly stands still.*] We were both assistant physicians at Rappenweiler's. A young man was a patient in our clinic. I see him lie before me now; I even know his name, Engelhart Wagner. Our chief—we all—had made a false diagnosis of his case. The autopsy revealed the fact that another treatment would have saved him. And as we stood there, when the fact was made clear, you whispered to me: "I knew it." You knew what was the matter with the patient; you had the correct diagnosis.

Flint. The only one.

Bernhardi. Yes, you were the only one. Yet you carefully avoided, while he was alive, making it known. And why you did it is a question you may answer yourself. I do not suppose it was conviction.

Flint. By Jove! you have a good memory. I remember the case, and I'll admit that I considered the other treatment the right one; and I will also admit that I kept silent because I did not want to hurt the chief's pride by showing that one of his assistants knew more about the case than he did. You have reason to reproach me with sacrificing a human life. But the motive, the deeper motive, you do not understand. What was one victim compared to the hundreds of other human lives which would be entrusted later to my skill?

Bernhardi. And you think that Rappenweiler would have turned against you?

Flint. That is very probable. You overrate humanity. You do not know how narrow-minded people are. It might have meant a long delay in my career, and I had to advance rapidly to gain the proper sphere of action for my capacities, which even you cannot deny. Therefore, my dear Bernhardi, I permitted Engelhart Wagner to die, and I am unable even to regret it. For it does not matter much, my dear Bernhardi, whether or not you may act correctly, or even be true to your convictions in some immaterial detail, the thing is to serve the one main idea of your life with faithfulness. It is interesting to me that you bring this poor Engelhart Wagner out of his oblivion; for suddenly I am enabled to recognize the essential differences in our two natures. You will be astonished, Bernhardi, to learn of their capacity to supplement each other, as it were. You, Bernhardi, are probably much more than I what the world calls "a respectable man." But whether you are more capable than I to do more for the general good seems very doubtful to me. You lack the eye for that which really counts, the universal viewpoint. For it is not the question whether you do right here and do right there, but whether you accomplish really big things. And to give up the possibility of doing some really big things, for the poor miserable satisfaction of having done the right thing in some non-essential, some unimportant matter, is a matter of indifference to me I must confess, and does not only seem small, but immoral, yes, immoral to me, my dear Bernhardi.

Bernhardi. Well, now you might let me know the real purpose of your visit here?

Flint. Yes, for the matter which brought me here is, I believe, already attracting wide-spread attention. You have forgotten to look a bit further in your dealings with His Reverence. You forgot one trifle, namely, that we live in a Christian community. Why are you smiling?

Bernhardi. I am thinking of an article you were going to write, long ago, when we were both young men—"Churches versus Hospitals."

Flint. Ah! one of the many articles I wanted to write, and which were never written. At any rate, since you committed the imprudence of forcibly preventing His Reverence—

Bernhardi. Forcibly?—!!

Flint. Well! I understand that you pushed him from the door, so it is told—

Bernhardi. What is told?

Flint. Well—you pushed him away rather violently.

Bernhardi. That is a lie! You'll believe me?

Flint. Then you did not push him?

Bernhardi. I barely touched him. To speak of force— They are inveterate liars!

Flint. Do not get excited. Officially, nothing has been done. A simple declaration from you and that indictment will not be brought against you.

Bernhardi. Is it for *my sake* that you want to save yourself from that indictment before Parliament?

Flint. Certainly! There is so little that can be done in such a case. No matter what your intentions were, your behavior towards His Reverence was not wholly correct.

Bernhardi. My dear Flint, you have no idea how you overrate your power.

Flint. A-hem!

Bernhardi. You evidently imagine that it lies with you to prevent that indictment.

Flint. It lies with you, I assure you.

Bernhardi. With me, yes. You have no idea how right you are. A half an hour ago I could have turned the danger of that indictment from your head and from mine.

Flint. How is that?

Bernhardi. Oh, very simple! Tugendvetter's vacancy is to be filled, you know. Tomorrow we have a meeting. If I had pledged my vote for Hell, instead of for Wenger, everything would have been all right.

Flint. Pledged yourself? How? To whom?

Bernhardi. Ebenwald was here just now. He was sent to me with that proposition.

Flint. [*Walking up and down*] Ebenwald is very friendly with his cousin, who is the leader of the clerical party, and if he did not want the indictment it would not be made. Well, how did you deal with his proposal?

Bernhardi. Flint!!!

Flint. My dear Bernhardi, politics—

Bernhardi. What do I care for politics, Flint. Even if you are a Minister now, you are also a physician, a man of science, a man of truth. What did you say a moment ago—to consider the essential—well, what counts here? Don't you see that the most capable man must be put at the head of this department; the man who can render the best service to humanity, to science. That, to my mind, is the important thing that counts in this situation. What does it matter if we save ourselves from an indictment which, after all, can be met with a proper defense.

Flint. Tell me, Bernhardi, can you write me a letter, a statement of the whole affair? Then I could make a defense for you; for they listen to me, just as the students did in the clinic; they listen, and when they listen to a speaker who is in earnest they cannot entirely disagree with him.

Bernhardi. That is right.

Flint. This would be an opportunity to touch on the general situation. I consider this case a symbol of our political conditions.

Bernhardi. I suppose that is what it is.

Flint. These things always occur to me. No matter how unimportant the case, for me, it is transformed into a symbol. That is how I have come to be destined for the political career.

Bernhardi. Ah! Churches—versus Hospitals!

Flint. You smile— Ah! I cannot make light of such matters.

Bernhardi. Well, my dear Flint, from all that you have said just now I get the impression that you are inclined to be on my side in this affair; but I want you to consider one thing. The party that you have to oppose is very strong, very obdurate; it is a question whether you will be able to rule without it, and if you care for your office—

Flint. Not more than for you.

Bernhardi. Than the truth—that is the important thing—as for me, do not risk anything for me.

Flint. For you, no. I won't do that; but for the truth, for the great cause—yes. Whatever happens, I cannot think of a more beautiful death, than for a just cause; for someone, who, confess—was only an hour ago—my enemy.

Bernhardi. I was not your enemy, and if I did you a wrong, I am willing to ask your pardon. But let me tell you now, Flint, even if this matter should not end favorably for you, my conscience will not prick me. You know where justice lies in this case, and I decline to admire you for doing your duty.

Flint. I do not expect you to do that. [*Stretching out his hand.*] Farewell! I looked for a man; I have found him. Au revoir!

Bernhardi. Good-bye, Flint. [*Hesitatingly.*] I thank you.

Flint. You must not do that. Our sympathy rests on firmer ground

[*Exit* FLINT.

Bernhardi. [*Stands lost in thought*] Well—we shall see.

CURTAIN

ACT III

Conference room in the Elizabethinum—Long green table, electric lights, pictures on walls. A portrait of the Empress Elizabeth over the door. It is the evening after the ball. HOCHROITZPOINTNER *sits at the table, writing. Enter* DOCTOR SCHREIMANN, *tall, bald, with martial black moustache. He is a baptized Jew. Enter* EBENWALD.

Ebenwald. [*To* HOCHROITZPOINTNER, *who rises with signs of great respect*] Do you know where you danced last night, Hochroitzpointner? On a volcano!

Hochroitzpointner. It was hot, Professor.

Ebenwald. [*To* SCHREIMANN] May I depend upon you when we meet afterwards?

Schreimann. I told you before that I could not look at that affair from a religious standpoint. Even if I were a Jew, I would have to be against Bernhardi; and I assure you, that for one of my race, it takes more courage to profess Christianity than to keep the faith in which you were reared. I should have led an easier time as a Zionist.

Ebenwald. Probably, you might have had a professorship in Jerusalem.

Schreimann. [*With a gesture*] Bunk!!

[*Enter* DOCTOR PFLUGFELDER. *About sixty-five years old. Type of a scientist. Wears spectacles.*]

Pflugfelder. Good evening, gentlemen! Do you know that our Advisory Board has resigned in a body?

Ebenwald. You seem to be astonished; we were prepared for that.

Pflugfelder. Astonished? No, but disgusted! You must agree that the persecution instituted against Professor Bernhardi has no foundation whatever.

Ebenwald. I know of no persecution.

Pflugfelder. Oh, you don't; and that your cousin, Ottocar, is the leader? I suppose you don't know that either.

[*Enter* FILITZ, *the handsome. General greetings.*]

Filitz. Good-evening, gentlemen! I'll tell you at once what I intend to do. I follow the example of the Advisory Board and resign.

Ebenwald. I beg your pardon! There is another way to demonstrate that we do not countenance the act of our principal. We cannot leave our institution; we must try to get the Board to reconsider this resignation.

Filitz. That will never be done as long as Bernhardi is at the head.

[*Enter* ADLER.]

Adler. Have you seen the evening paper?

Ebenwald. What is the matter?

Adler. The indictment!

Schreimann. Affair Bernhardi?

Ebenwald. We have read nothing.

[WENGER *enters. Small, uncertain, depressed, sometimes too loud. Wears spectacles. Is carrying the evening paper.* SCHREIMANN *pulls it out of his hand. All crowd around.*]

Pflugfelder. Let Filitz read it.

Filitz. [*Reading*] "The undersigned consider it their duty to inform the Government of the following:

"His Reverence, Franz Reder, Priest of the Church of the Holy Florian, was called by Sister Ludmilla to the death-bed of Philomena Beier, maiden, to give her the holy sacrament of the last ointment. In the ante-room he was met by several physicians, amongst them, Professor Bernhardi, Director of the Elizabethinum, who in a rough manner, asked His Reverence to desist from his purpose, as the dying patient might suffer from the excitement."

Pflugfelder. No, no!

[*The others cry "Silence."*]

Filitz. [*Continuing his reading*] "Professor Bernhardi, who professes mosaic faith, was told by His Reverence that he had come to fulfill a sacred duty, all the more important because the patient was dying from the result of her own act. Professor Bernhardi insolently asserted his rights as Superintendent of the institution, which, of course, was erected through the charitable gifts of noble donors. When His Reverence, refusing further discussion, attempted to enter the sick-room, Professor Bernhardi placed himself in front of the door, and the moment His Reverence seized the knob to enter the room to perform his sacred function, Professor Bernhardi dealt him a blow—"

Adler. An absolute falsehood!

Pflugfelder. Infamous!

Ebenwald. There were witnesses.

Pflugfelder. I know that you were a witness.

Schreimann. Go on! Read!

Filitz. [*Reading*] "During the scene in the ante-room, the patient died without having received the consolation of her faith, which, as Sister Ludmilla testified, she longed for. In bringing this incident to the attention of the Government, we desire especially to inquire how His Excellency, the Minister of Education, intends to make reparation for the severely injured feelings of the Christian population of Vienna, and what means His Excellency will take to prevent a repetition of such a revolting scene. Finally, if His Excellency does not deem it advisable in the future to disregard the claims of such persons to appointment of public offices, who, by reason of their origin, education and character, are not capable of understanding the religious feelings of our Christian population.

Signed:"

[Great commotion.]

Ebenwald. Now we are in a fine position—

Wenger. Why "we"? Nothing has been said against the institute—

Pflugfelder. And our Director? This interpellation is nothing but a political maneuver of the clerical and anti-Semitic parties.

Filitz. Nonsense!

Schreimann. I object—

[Enter BERNHARDI. He immediately takes his place at the head of the table. The others seat themselves.]

Bernhardi. Good evening, gentlemen! Please excuse me for being a little late. I hope that the gentlemen have passed the time pleasantly. We will open the meeting. Before reading the minutes, I take the liberty of welcoming our new member, Doctor Wenger, in the name of the Elizabethinum.

Wenger. Mr. President, Gentlemen! It would be inconsiderate on my part, were I to take up your valuable time—

Ebenwald and Schreimann. Correct.

Wenger. Permit me to express my heartfelt thanks for the greatest honor—

[Noise.]

Schreimann. [Rising] In consideration of the lateness of the hour, I move that we proceed with the business of the meeting.

Bernhardi. Gentlemen! I took the liberty of calling this special meeting. I consider your presence here a proof of the great—let me say—patriotic interest you all take in our institution. It is a proof of the fraternal fellowship that unites us all, in spite of some occasional differences of opinion which cannot be altogether avoided amidst the staff of a big institution. But when it comes to vital questions, we have always been of one mind to the joy of our friends and the dismay of our enemies; we also have those!

Gentlemen! You all know why I have called you together; nevertheless, it is my duty to read to you the letter I received this morning by special delivery.

Filitz. Hear! Hear!

Bernhardi. [*Reading*] "To the Honorable—

I take the liberty of announcing to you that the members of the Advisory Board, etc., etc., have decided to resign from their honorary positions. In communicating this decision to you, Mr. President, I request that you notify the Board of Directors and the Staff.

Signed:

Counselor Winkler, *Secretary.*"

Ebenwald. I would ask our President if the cause of this action is known to him?

Bernhardi. I shall answer the question of the Vice-President in all brevity. Yes, I know the cause; and it lies in the same incident of which you have just now read with more or less pleasure, in the form of a so-called indictment in the evening paper. As a certain party misrepresents this case—

Filitz. Which party?

Pflugfelder. The anti-Semitic—clerical party.

Bernhardi. I, as President of this institution, desire to ask you how we should deal with this resignation? [Cyprian *rises.*] Professor Cyprian has the floor.

Cyprian. We all know the cause, or rather the pretext for this resignation. We all know that Bernhardi fulfilled his duty as a physician when he refused admission to the priest. We all know that we would have acted as he did—

Filitz. O-ho!

Schreimann. No!

Cyprian. [*Continuing*] There is only one answer to this attack, and that is to express our implicit confidence in our President, Professor Bernhardi.

Pflugfelder. Bravo!

[Ebenwald *rises.*]

Bernhardi. Vice-President Ebenwald has the floor!

Ebenwald. Gentlemen! Do not be deceived. This resignation of the Committee would mean disaster for our institution. I am sorry, but Professor Bernhardi alone should have the responsibility of his action, of which we do not approve. I move that we request the reconsideration of this resignation on that ground.

[Enter Loewenstein, *looking very pale.*]

Loewenstein. Gentlemen! I come from Parliament. The indictment has been answered, and you, Bernhardi, will be prosecuted for religious disturbance.

[*Great commotion.*]

Pflugfelder. Impossible! Tell us all about it.

[*Amidst the great excitement* BERNHARDI *stands unmoved.*]

Loewenstein. What is there to tell? It's a disgrace! [*Looking at* EBENWALD.] You have succeeded. You'll read it in the papers tomorrow morning.

[*Great commotion. All are shouting.*]

All in Unison. Tell us! What happened?

Loewenstein. Well, at first, Flint took Bernhardi's part, and spoke of his great merits, and you felt sure that his accusers would be completely routed. Then there were cries of "Too much Jew." Somehow, the Minister lost his theme; got angry, confused, and then, to his own surprise, I am sure, he wound up that the law should take its course. That that would be the best way of clearing up the matter.

Bernhardi. [*Composedly*] Gentlemen, let us resume.

Ebenwald. I withdraw my first motion, and move for the suspension of President Bernhardi from the Elizabethinum, until the law has dealt with his case.

Pflugfelder. You ought to be ashamed of yourself, Ebenwald.

Loewenstein. Bernhardi is the President of the Elizabethinum. No one can suspend him.

Filitz. He is no longer that to me.

Bernhardi. I wish to put a question to the Vice-President.

Ebenwald. Please—

Bernhardi. Is it known to you that I could have prevented this indictment?

Schreimann. [*Calling out*] Do not answer.

Bernhardi. If you are a man, Ebenwald, you will answer.

Ebenwald. Oh! I expected this question. You know, gentlemen—that the Elizabethinum has always had enemies. There are many people who do not think it right in an institution with a Prince and a Bishop on its Advisory Board, and eighty-five per cent of its patients Catholics, that the majority of the physicians of the staff should profess another religion. And that is why I moved for the appointment of a Catholic, Doctor Hell, instead of Doctor Wenger. [*Looking at* WENGER, *who professes* BERNHARDI'S *religion.*] I beg your pardon for this.

Wenger. Perfectly correct.

[*Laughter.*]

Bernhardi. You do not expect me to defend myself for not making this deal, though it might have saved ourselves all this trouble. But I am willing to lay down my office as President of this institution.

Cyprian. What is the matter with you?

Loewenstein. Never!

Pflugfelder. Put it to a vote.

Bernhardi. What for? Professors Ebenwald, Filitz, Adler and Schreimann will vote for my suspension. I would like to save Doctor Wenger a conflict. He might vote for me out of gratitude. But to such a motive I should not like to owe the questionable honor of being further your President.

Ebenwald. As Professor Bernhardi has just now resigned from his position as President, I shall, according to Article Seven of the By-Laws, take the chairmanship of this meeting.

Loewenstein. Infamous!

Filitz. The first question will be: Who shall take charge of Professor Bernhardi's department?

Bernhardi. Gentlemen! Even though I am no longer your President, I still am at the head of my department.

Schreimann. He is suspended!

Bernhardi. [*Losing his composure*] No one can suspend me. I shall take a leave of absence until my affair is settled, and I entrust my assistants, Doctor Kurt and Doctor Oscar, with my department.

Adler. Professor, I would be unhappy if you misinterpret my conduct; I wish to express to you in this hour, my admiration.

Bernhardi. Whosoever is not for me, is against me, gentlemen. Good evening, gentlemen.

[*Exit* BERNHARDI.]

Pflugfelder. How can you let him go, gentlemen? Come to your senses! Think how this whole thing began—you must come to your senses! A poor young creature lies sick unto death in the hospital, paying for her youth and happiness and sin—if you want to call it so—with torture, agony, and even with her life. The last hours bring euphoria; she is well, happy, has no thought of death; dreams that her lover is coming to take her away from the place of suffering and misery, back to life and happiness. It was perhaps the happiest moment of her life, her last earthly dream, and from this dream, Bernhardi did not wish to awaken her to a terrible reality. That is his fault, the crime that he committed. He asked the priest to let the girl go peacefully to sleep. He asked him, you all know it. Had he even been less polite than he was, everybody would have to forgive him. What enormous hypocrisy it is, to look at this event other than as a purely humane action. Where does the creature exist, whose religious sentiments could in reality be hurt in any way by Bernhardi's action? And if snobdom, graft and villainy were not at the bottom of it all—in short—vile politics, would it be possible, anywhere, to construe this case into a serious affair? Ah! I protest, gentlemen. This is the act of climbers, good-for-nothings! But we, gentlemen, *we* do not want to belong to any of these classes. Why should we, for petty political reasons, leave this man in the hour of his trial, when he has only done his duty? Far be it from me to praise him, or to represent him as a hero, simply because he has acted as a man! And from you, gentlemen, I ask nothing more than that you prove yourselves worthy of this modest title. Annul the actions of today's meeting, and ask Professor Bernhardi to again accept the position which cannot be filled by a worthier representative. Call him back, gentlemen; I implore you, gentlemen, call him back.

Ebenwald. Permit me to ask Professor Pflugfelder if he has finished his tirade. If so, we will proceed with the business of the meeting.

Pflugfelder. [*Starting to leave*] Good-bye!

Loewenstein. You are insane!

[*Exit* CYPRIAN *and* LOEWENSTEIN. *As* PFLUGFELDER *opens the door,* HOCH-ROITZPOINTNER *enters.*]

Pflugfelder. Ah! this happens opportunely. Doctor Hochroitzpoint-ner, please come in; walk right in. Fine company. Have a good time.

[*Exit* PFLUGFELDER.]

Ebenwald. Close the door. Call the meeting to order, gentlemen.

CURTAIN

ACT IV

Salon at BERNHARDI's *home.* [*Enter* PFLUGFELDER, *followed by* LOEWEN-STEIN.]

Behind the scene.]

Loewenstein. [*Breathless*] Professor Pflugfelder?

Pflugfelder. Ah! Loewenstein—

Loewenstein. I have been running after you.

Pflugfelder. Were you not in court?

Loewenstein. I was called to a case, while they were debating about he term of punishment.

Pflugfelder. Two months.

Loewenstein. In spite of the testimony of the priest?

Pflugfelder. His testimony, that he felt only a slight touch on the shoulder, caused the prosecuting attorney to represent His Reverence a an example of Christian forbearance and kindness.

Loewenstein. Then Bernhardi has been convicted solely on the tes timony of that hysterical Sister Ludmilla, and that rascal Hochroitz pointner. For all the other witnesses testified in his favor; I must apolo gize to Adler, for he acted splendidly, also Cyprian—not to mention you son.

[*Enter* CYPRIAN.

Pflugfelder. Where is Bernhardi?

Loewenstein. Do you suppose they kept him at court?

Cyprian. He will come with Goldenthal.

Loewenstein. Goldenthal acted like a scrub. Well, what could yo expect!

Cyprian. What do you mean?

Loewenstein. Those baptized ones!! His wife wears a cross—so big— his son is being educated by the Jesuits. That's the kind. With anothe counsel for the defense, this case would have had a different ending.

Cyprian. I doubt that very much; perhaps with another defendant.

[*Enter* KURT.

Pflugfelder. [*Embracing him*] Kurt!

Loewenstein. [*To* CYPRIAN] What means this touching scene?

Cyprian. Don't you know? Kurt called Hochroitzpointner a liar, an was fined two hundred crowns for contempt of court.

[*Enter* GOLDENTHAL, BERNHARDI's *attorney. Fat, about forty-five years ol Curly black hair streaked with gray; side-chops. Very pompous.*]

Goldenthal. Gentlemen! I desire to talk seriously with you. I am gla that I advised Bernhardi to leave court through the side doors. I want yo all to assist me. Our dear Professor Bernhardi, is—what shall I say—a littl stubborn. You know, his idea was to have His Excellency, the Ministe subpoenaed; and now he plays the insulted, and refuses to avail himse of the privileges the law offers him.

Pflugfelder. [*To* GOLDENTHAL] You want him to appeal?

Goldenthal. Why, most certainly!

Pflugfelder. One ought to appeal to the people.

Loewenstein. And in the interest of the cause, Bernhardi should ser his two months' term.

Pflugfelder. That would show up the infamy committed against hin

[*Enter* BERNHARDI *and* OSCAR

Bernhardi. Excuse me, gentlemen, for letting you wait.

Cyprian. Did you receive an ovation?

Bernhardi. Yes! They yelled, "Down with the Jews"—"Down with the Masons!"

Loewenstein. Just think of that!

Bernhardi. Gentlemen! I hope you will stay to supper. Oscar, please see that we are sufficiently provided. My housekeeper has left; her confessor declared that she could not stay in my house without danger to her soul's salvation. It will be a frugal meal. But what can you expect from the larder of a prospective jailbird? Oscar! why, the boy has tears in his eyes! Don't be sentimental, Oscar.

Oscar. I am only furious.

[*Enter* ADLER.]

Bernhardi. Welcome, Doctor Adler. There is more rejoicing over one repentant sinner than over ten just men.

Adler. I was never a sinner, Professor. The trial of this case seemed a necessity to me from the beginning. Of course, I could not foresee that the court would rather believe the testimony of Mr. Hochroitzpointner than Professor Cyprian's and mine.

Pflugfelder. One ought to get rid of Flint.

Goldenthal. I always respect the convictions of my adversaries.

Loewenstein. The convictions of Flint?

Goldenthal. He has to protect the convictions of others. Believe me, gentlemen, there are things one should not touch, and which should not be permitted to be touched.

Pflugfelder. Why—if I may ask? It is only because someone has had the courage to touch those things, that the world's progress is accomplished.

Goldenthal. I think that our friend, Bernhardi, will gladly admit that he had no intention of contributing to the progress of the world.

Loewenstein. Some day it may be shown that he has done just that thing.

Pflugfelder. As matters stand now, your affair has to be handled from a general standpoint. The prosecuting attorney was not a bit bashful in beginning that way. Did you notice that, Doctor?

Goldenthal. It is not my duty to do politics, but to defend—

Pflugfelder. If you had accomplished that task—

Bernhardi. But I shall not permit—

Goldenthal. Never mind, Professor. This is getting interesting. So you think that I did not defend my client?

Pflugfelder. According to my idea—no. Why, listening to you, one got an idea that all the religious sentiments of the whole world, from the Pope down to the humblest parish priest, had been deeply hurt by Bernhardi's wrong against the Church. And instead of contending that every physician should have acted as Bernhardi did, you blandly excused it as an act of carelessness. You treated those idiots in the jury-box, who, from the very first moment they entered it, were ready to convict Bernhardi—you treated them like the salt of the earth; and the judge presiding at the trial, who did everything to convict Bernhardi, you looked upon as the embodiment of human justice. Even that scoundrel, Hochroitzpointner, and Sister Ludmilla, you handled with kid gloves, and gave the impression that you really believed them. First a polite nod toward your client, and then a deep bow toward the side of the enemy; the representative of calumny and hypocrisy! If Bernhardi is satisfied with that, Doctor Goldenthal, that is his business; as for me, I do not understand that kind of a defense.

Goldenthal. I am glad that you have devoted your great gift to medicine, and not to the law; for with your temperament—your conception of the dignity of the court—you would have landed the most innocent of your clients in jail.

Loewenstein. You seem to manage that easily in spite of your lack of temperament.

Goldenthal. [*To* Bernhardi] My dear Professor, you are lucky to call such friends your own. But of course I shall offer no further advice, and leave it to you—

Bernhardi. Doctor, what is the matter with you?

Pflugfelder. If anyone leaves, *I* go. I beg your pardon, Bernhardi, I permitted myself to go too far. I cannot take anything back—not another word, Bernhardi.

[*Exit* Pflugfelder.]

[*The doors of the dining-room are opened. A servant enters and whispers to* Bernhardi, *who shows great embarrassment.*]

Bernhardi. I beg your pardon, gentlemen; a visitor whom I have to receive. Please dine—Oscar, have the kindness—

[*All enter the dining-room.* Bernhardi *closes the door and pulls the portière. Enter* Priest.]

Priest. Good evening, Professor!

Bernhardi. A visit of condolence, Your Reverence?

Priest. Not exactly that, but I had a great desire to talk to you today.

Bernhardi. I am at your disposal, Your Reverence.

[Bernhardi *offers a chair. Both seat themselves.*]

Priest. In spite of the unfavorable ending of your trial, it must be clear to you that I am guiltless of your conviction.

Bernhardi. If I should thank you for having told the truth on the witness stand, I might hurt your feelings.

Priest. I did not come to get your thanks, Professor, though I did more than my duty as a witness. You will kindly remember that I gave expression to my belief, in my testimony, that your behavior towards me was not prompted by hostile feelings towards the Catholic Church.

Bernhardi. Thereby Your Reverence surely executed the measure of your responsibility; but perhaps the effect which this testimony produced, might be some reward.

Priest. I doubt, Professor, if its effect will be favorable to me outside of the court-room. But you can imagine, Professor, that I did not come here for the purpose of recapitulating my testimony before the court. That which prompts me to call upon you at this late hour, is the fact that I have a further admission to make to you.

Bernhardi. A further admission?

Priest. Before the court, I expressed my conviction that you did not act with hostile intentions towards me or my church. Now I feel myself prompted to admit that in this special case—understand, Professor, in this special case—you acted correctly in your capacity as a physician, and that you only obeyed your duty as I did mine.

Bernhardi. Do I understand you aright? You admit that I could not have acted differently?

Priest. Not as a physician.

Bernhardi. If this is your real opinion, Your Reverence, I must say that you had a better opportunity, or perhaps the only proper chance, to admit it a few hours ago.

Priest. I need not assure you that it was not lack of courage that sealed my lips; otherwise should I then be here, Professor?

Bernhardi. What then?

Priest. I will tell you. That which silenced me in court was the conviction which came to me by holy inspiration, that one word more might cause infinite damage to a truly sacred cause; the most sacred in the world to me.

Bernhardi. I cannot imagine, that for a courageous man like you, Your Reverence, there could be anything more sacred than the truth. Nothing.

Priest. What! Nothing more sacred than the intangible truth for which I might have stood until the end in this single case? You don't mean that. Should I have acknowledged that you had the right to send me away from the death-bed of a Christian—a sinner—the enemies of the church would certainly have abused such a declaration far beyond my responsibility. The slight truth that I had uttered would have been twisted and misinterpreted, so that it would have become a lie. And what would have been the result of that? I should have appeared as a renegade, a traitor, not only before those to whom I owe obedience, but even before my God.

Bernhardi. Then why do you do it now?

Priest. Because at the very instant I received that inspiration, I pledged myself to make the confession to you personally, something which the public would have misunderstood and misconstrued.

Bernhardi. I thank you for this, Your Reverence, and let me express the hope that you will never again be put into the position to have to testify publicly in a cause where greater things are at stake than my humble self. For it might happen, that what appears to me in this instance as your own personal scruple, might strike you as being a message from on high—a holy inspiration—and that a higher grade of truth might be injured than that which you believe to have protected now.

Priest. There exists nothing higher for me than my church, and the law of my church, which is obedience, by reason of which infinite blessing is radiated over the whole world, and without which my whole sphere of usefulness might be lost.

Bernhardi. It seems to me, Your Reverence, that priests have existed who only found their true sphere of activity, when they excluded themselves from the community, and spread that which they considered truth and justice, regardless of trouble and danger.

Priest. And if I were one of them—

Bernhardi. Well—?

Priest. Then God would have made me tell before the court today what you alone are now hearing within these four walls.

Bernhardi. Then it was God who sealed your lips in court today, and now it is the same God who sends you to me to tell me, eye to eye, what he prevented you from saying in court. I must say that he makes it easy for you, your God.

Priest. Pardon me, Professor. I did not come here to discuss matter which you and I will never understand the same way.

Bernhardi. So you close the door, as it were, in my face, Your Reverence. Well, I do not consider this as proof that you are in and that am on the outside. There is nothing further left for me to do than to regret that you took the trouble of coming here in vain. For I cannot absolve you as completely as you may have expected, after such an extraordinary step.

Priest. Absolution! That is not what I wanted from you. I think that I have made a mistake; I see it now. The true reason you denied me admission to that death-bed, was not your sense of duty or responsibility—that was only a pretext. The real reason lies much deeper—it is—how shall I put it—an antipathy—an uncontrollable antipathy—nay, it is hostility—

Bernhardi. You speak of hostility. Does not all that has happened to me justify the feeling you call hostility? Yes, I cannot deny that in the last weeks, I may have felt antipathy, not against you personally, but against the crowd that surrounds you. But I can assure you in perfect truth, that when I refused you admittance at the door, there was not a shadow of hostile feeling in my soul. I stood before you there in my capacity as a physician, with as clear a conscience as that of anyone of your vocation performing his holy rite at the altar; not less clear than yours when you came to bring the last consolation to my patient. You knew that when you entered the room now. You confessed it to me. You cannot suddenly change your opinion, because you feel the same as I do, and perhaps never felt it stronger than at this hour, that a certain something separates us, which even under the most favorable circumstances, we cannot deny.

Priest. And you never felt this stronger than at this moment?

Bernhardi. Yes, at this hour, in the presence of one of the most liberal of his cloth. But "hostility"—that seems too small a word for that which separates us perhaps for all time—it is higher, loftier, more hopeless.

Priest. I think you are right. I have had occasion to have had similar conversations with men of your circles, scientists, and "enlightened" people; but it never seemed so utterly impossible to reach any kind of an understanding or agreement.

Bernhardi. And what about you, Your Reverence? Do you feel yourself free from all feelings of hostility towards men of my class? Can you find no milder word for the feeling you accuse me of?

Priest. [*Suppressing anger, but collecting himself with a slight smile*] I know myself to be free from it. My religion, Professor, commands me to love those who hate me.

Bernhardi. [*With feeling*] And mine, Your Reverence, or that which

I possess in its stead, teaches me to understand even those who do not or will not understand me.

Priest. I do not doubt your good-will, but understanding has its limitations. Wherever the human mind rules, there is error, there is deception. That which does not deceive, that which cannot deceive men of my kind—let me choose a word to which even you cannot have any objection—is the "innermost feeling."

Bernhardi. Let us call it so, even if this "innermost feeling" as you call it, flows from different sources in my soul, I also try to trust in it. What is there left for all of us to do? And if it is not so easy for us as it is for men of your calling, God Almighty, who created us both, surely this incomprehensible God has his reasons for it.

[*The* PRIEST *looks at him for a long time. Then in sudden decision stretches out his hand.*]

Bernhardi. [*Hesitatingly, smiling a little*] Over the abyss, Your Reverence.

Priest. Do not let us look down for a moment—
[BERNHARDI *takes his hand.*]

Priest. Farewell, Professor!

[*Exit* PRIEST. BERNHARDI *stands for a while, lost in thought; then makes a movement as if to shake off something, draws the portière and opens the door. Company at table, smoking.*]

Cyprian. At last!

Adler. We have just arrived at the cigars.

Cyprian. [*Going up to* BERNHARDI] What was the matter? A patient today—so late?

Oscar. Here are some telegrams for you, father, but won't you first have some supper?

Bernhardi. [*Opens one and reads*] Ah! that is nice. A poor patient assures me of his sympathy.

Cyprian. [*Receives the next telegram from* BERNHARDI, *and reads aloud*] "We assure the noble fighter for liberty and free thought of our admiration. He will always find us ready to support him.
Doctor Reiss, Walter Koenig."
[*Enter* SERVANT *with card.*]

Bernhardi. What next?

Oscar. [*Reading*] A deputation from "Brigittenau," the organization for free thought—

Bernhardi. [*To* SERVANT] Tell the gentlemen that I am not at home.

Goldenthal. But why?

Bernhardi. I am already in prison—I have been sentenced.

Servant. [*Enters with card and hands it to* GOLDENTHAL] The gentleman insists.

Goldenthal. Show him in.

[*Enter* KULKA. *Reporter.*]

Kulka. Ah, Doctor Goldenthal! If I am not mistaken?

Goldenthal. That is my name—we know each other. Mr. Kulka, Professor Bernhardi is a little fatigued—

Kulka. [*Taking out his note-book*] If you will have the kindness—may I ask, Doctor Goldenthal, if Professor Bernhardi intends to take an appeal?

Goldenthal. I took the liberty—

Bernhardi. With whom have I the pleasure—?

Kulka. Kulka of "The Latest News." My chief, Professor, offers you our paper. We will give expression to your just feelings against the Minister.

Bernhardi. I do not want the protection of any paper. My regards to your chief.

Kulka. I thank you—I have the honor—

[*Exit* KULKA.]

Cyprian. I do not think that was necessary—

Goldenthal. I must say, Professor—

Bernhardi. I want to get through with this whole thing. This last month was lost for my work, my profession. It was bad enough as a law case, but I shall save myself from a political battle, if necessary in prison. It is my business to make people well, or at least make them believe that I do it. And I want to do that as soon as I am able.

Loewenstein. And your revenge—Flint, Ebenwald—are you going to let them go free?

Bernhardi. I want no revenge. Their time will come.

Cyprian. No matter how you intend to carry on this matter, whether legally, politically or privately, you should not have been so short with Kulka.

Goldenthal. The friendship of such a newspaper—

Bernhardi. My dear Doctor, you have to take your enemies how and where you find them. I prefer to choose my friends.

CURTAIN

ACT V

Office in the Minister's Palace—comfortably furnished. PRIVY COUNSELOR
WINKLER, *forty-five years old. Slender, young-looking, small moustache, short, blonde hair streaked with gray, sparkling blue eyes—*

[*The telephone rings.*]

Winkler. [*At the telephone*] Yes, Counselor Winkler— Yes, Judge—
What is that?—you don't say! Sister Ludmilla—what a strange coincidence. Well, because today he gets out—Professor Bernhardi—yes, just
think of it! Of course, I must tell this to His Excellency, but, if you don't
want me to—well, good-bye.

[*He seems much moved. Enter* MINISTER FLINT.]

Winkler. Permit me to tender my congratulations. Yesterday's
speech—

Flint. The speech—a few words improvised! I did not expect you
among the congratulants. I was afraid of you. Are you not an anarchist,
Counselor? Let me tell you, that is a dangerous condition of mind to be
in. I tell you, I have made concessions. Everybody has to. Even anarchists
like you, Counselor, else you could not have become Counselor. Or do
you think it was easy for me to sacrifice my old friend Bernhardi to the
people?

Winkler. It must have been a satisfaction to you when the police
broke up the meeting where Pflugfelder roasted you and the Archbishop.

Flint. Why the Archbishop?

Winkler. Because he transferred the priest, Reder, to a remote parish
on the Polish border.

Flint. And now the liberal papers are lauding Bernhardi—as a kind
of a martyr, a political victim; as a medical Dreyfus. Did you read the
article in "The News"? Sort of a festive greeting to Bernhardi to celebrate his liberation from prison? That's too much.

Winkler. Bernhardi cannot help that.

Flint. I don't know. He likes the part. You know, when in the third
week of his imprisonment, you were commissioned to ask him to request
his Majesty's pardon?

Winkler. I tried to convince him, but on the whole, I liked it that he
did not desire any pardon.

Flint. Well, the Government will not tolerate any spirit of that kind.
I should be very sorry though, for Bernhardi acted foolishly and has

given us nothing but trouble. But, I still feel a certain sympathy for him; can't get rid of it.

Winkler. Friendship of early days, I presume.

Flint. Yes, that is it, but we should be free from such sentimentality. In our position, we should have no recollections, no heart; yes, my dear Counselor, no heart.

[*Enter* EBENWALD.]

Ebenwald. Good morning, Excellency!

Flint. Good morning, Professor, or Director?

Ebenwald. Not yet. It is possible that Professor Bernhardi may be reelected; he has only been suspended; just now he has been triumphantly escorted from prison to his home by a number of students.

Flint. Let us discuss your request for the Elizabethinum in my private office.

[*Exit* MINISTER *and* EBENWALD.]

[TUGENDVETTER *enters. A* SERVANT *brings a card to* WINKLER.]

Winkler. [*Astonished*] Ah!

Servant. The gentleman wishes to see His Excellency.

[BERNHARDI *enters.* WINKLER *shakes his hand.*]

Winkler. I am very glad to see you again, Professor.

Bernhardi. I am very glad to see you.

Tugendvetter. Why, my dear Bernhardi, I had entirely forgotten that your punishment is over today. How quickly two months pass.

Bernhardi. Especially under the open sky.

Tugendvetter. But you look splendid. Doesn't he? If you had been on the Riviera, you could not look better—rejuvenated.

Winkler. Suppose you try a little blasphemy. Then I could guarantee you such a cheap, healthful vacation.

[*Enter* FLINT *and* EBENWALD.]

Flint. You wanted to see me, Bernhardi?

Bernhardi. I shall only trouble you for a moment.

Flint. I am glad to be able to offer my congratulations. I shall be delighted to be of some use to you, now that the affair is settled.

Bernhardi. [*Very amiably*] I want a favor of you. Prince Constantin is very ill and has sent for me. But since I disturbed religion, and have been in jail, I have lost my license to practice. Therefore, I come to you, my old friend, who, as has been shown in other cases, has such influence with the Minister of Justice; I want to ask you to have the matter hurried, so that the Prince will not be compelled to wait too long.

Flint. Ah! you come here to make fun of me?

Bernhardi. Why, I am only doing the correct thing.

Flint. What you ask is granted. I take the responsibility. You can obey the call of the Prince at once. I give you my word that there will be nothing further necessary. Is that sufficient?

Bernhardi. It may be, since in this instance, the keeping of your word does not involve any personal trouble for you.

Flint. Bernhardi?

Bernhardi. Your Excellency—

Flint. Ah, now I know you. So you think that I am guilty of breaking my word.

Bernhardi. Yes, my dear Flint.

Flint. I never break my word. For I never gave you any other than this—to stand for you. I could not have prevented the indictment; and by putting your case in the hands of the law, I did the best I could for you. And let me tell you, Bernhardi, there are higher ethics than the mere keeping of a pledge. Always keep your goal before your eyes. And I never felt that stronger than in that remarkable moment when the suspicions, the dismay, the anger of Parliament, came rushing up to me, as it were, like an angry wave. And when I succeeded in quieting the storm and pacifying the waves, and became master of the situation by a lucky turn—

Bernhardi. Turn! That's right.

Flint. My dear Bernhardi, I had the alternative of plunging down into the abyss with you, to commit a sort of a crime against my mission in life, or to surrender a man already lost.

[BERNHARDI *looks at him and then applauds.*]

[*Enter* WINKLER.]

Winkler. I beg your pardon, Your Excellency, for taking the liberty, but I have just now received a very important message from the Minister of Justice, and, as it concerns the affair of Professor Bernhardi—

Bernhardi. My affair?

Winkler. Yes, just imagine! Sister Ludmilla, the chief witness in your case, has made an affidavit wherein she admits giving false testimony at the trial of your case.

Bernhardi. She, herself?

Winkler. Why, yes. And of course you can demand a revision at once.

Bernhardi. A revision? Never! I do not think of it. I am through with the entire business. I do not want to go through that farce again.

What good would it do me to have her and her accomplice locked up? I want my peace. This matter is closed for me.

Flint. Bernhardi, it will be necessary to take steps now; and it is perhaps good that one's ammunition has been saved.

Bernhardi. What is that?

Flint. A letter which will do service in this impending battle.

[*Enter* SERVANT.]

Servant. Counselor Berman of the Department of Justice wishes to speak to His Excellency.

Flint. Bernhardi, please wait for me. Please, dear Counselor, keep him for half an hour.

[*Exit* FLINT.]

Winkler. Prince Constantin has already called you today. That looks like him.

Bernhardi. I shall ask him to dispense with my medical advice in the future. I shall get away from here; from all that is likely to develop now.

Winkler. In course of time, you'll be proud of it.

Bernhardi. Proud? You have no idea how ridiculous it all seems to me. This morning the reception at the prison, the article in "The Latest News"! All my plans have vanished.

Winkler. Plans? You mean your book?

Bernhardi. When I started to write that, my wrath melted. From the accusations against Flint and consorts, I drifted into Austrian politics; then into philosophy and ethical responsibility, revelation and freedom of the will.

Winkler. That is always the case, if you go to the root of the thing. It is better to put on the brakes sooner, for some fine day you begin to understand—to pardon everything—and then where is the charm of life, if you cannot love or hate any more?

Bernhardi. Oh, one goes on loving and hating; but when I stood opposite Flint, really, my last vestige of resentment vanished. You should have heard him. I could not be angry with him.

Winkler. The Minister always liked you, I assure you.

Bernhardi. And now this confession of the Sister's, this revision. I have to flee from all this noise that is being made around me, simply because the people are beginning to realize that I was right.

Winkler. Professor, what are you thinking of? That is only your imagination—that you were right.

Bernhardi. Have the kindness to explain? According to your idea, I should have let His Reverence—

Winkler. Certainly you should have, my dear Professor. You were not born to be a reformer—

Bernhardi. Reformer?

Winkler. As little as I. For we both do not feel ready to go to the bitter end and risk all, even our life, for our convictions. That is why the only decent thing for us to do is not to mix in such matters. There is nothing in it. What would you have gained in the end, if you had saved that poor thing that last fright on her death-bed. Seems like solving the social problem by presenting a villa to some poor starving devil.

Bernhardi. But you forget that I did not want to solve a problem. I only did what I considered right in a special case.

Winkler. That was just the mistake you made. If one always did the right thing—that is, in the abstract sense—began early in the morning and continued to do so all day long, without taking into consideration the surrounding circumstances, one would surely land in jail before nightfall.

Bernhardi. And let me tell you, my dear friend, you would have acted exactly as I did.

Winkler. Possibly—and then I would have been—excuse me—just such a fool as you.

CURTAIN

IN THE DARK

by PEREZ HIRSCHBEIN

PERSONS

FAIVA, *a man who lives from hand to mouth*
PESHKA, *his daughter*
FEIGA, *Faiva's blind mother*
BEINISH, *an old street porter*
ABRAM, *a young chimney sweep*

A winter evening in Faiva's cellar. Two long, narrow rooms. When the curtain rises, one can see an oven in the room in the foreground. On the floor are blackened pots. To the left, windows buried in the

*walls. Pieces of broken furniture. In the background another room.
From a little iron stove in rear room long black pipes lead to the
oven in the front room.*
The stage is dark, and for a while remains empty. One can hear old
FEIGA's *footsteps in the backroom, accompanied by groans and sighs.*

Feiga. [*Fumbles for something*] She's out of the house, it seems. I
just nodded a little, and she's out already. . . . The oven is cold. It grew
cold before it had time to warm up. . . . Hu-hu-hu. . . . It's dark. I can't
see a thing burning. [*She gropes about.*] Peshka. . . . Ha? . . . She's
gone out. Didn't she leave the door open? . . . How cold. . . . No, it's
closed. . . . This is life, this is. . . . Hu-hu-hu. . . . God be thanked the
whole of me isn't in the earth yet. . . . [*The door opens and someone
comes in.*] Who is this? . . . Who is this? . . . Beinish?

Beinish. Good evening. It's me.

Feiga. Beinish?

Beinish. It's me, all right. Why are you in the dark yet?

Feiga. What good is light to me? . . . I'm looking for Peshka. She
was in the house a minute ago. I just fell asleep. . . . Is it very dark?

Beinish. Very dark. It's cold here. And I thought I'd warm my bones
a little.

Feiga. It's very cold. What d'you say?

Beinish. Fearfully cold. No one can bear it.

Feiga. Did you make anything?

Beinish. I didn't even take the rope off my neck. It's cold. I suppose
you didn't start the oven today?

Feiga. Of course I started it.

Beinish. With sticks, I suppose?

Feiga. With thick logs. I sawed them with my hands, myself.

Beinish. It's awfully cold out.

Feiga. Isn't it a little too dark for you?

Beinish. Dark—pitch dark.

Feiga. There must be a little lamp on that table there. [*They go into
the other room.*]

Beinish. Ah, here it is. Now, where are your matches?

Feiga. Look near the chimney.

Beinish. Near the chimney?

Feiga. They're there sometimes. . . . She doesn't want to be in the
house for a minute. Perhaps she's sleeping somewheres here. Take a look,
will you?

Beinish. Who?

Feiga. Peshka. She stays in the house, and walks without shoes.

Beinish. There's no one here. It's dark as a prison.

Feiga. I fell asleep not long ago. I'm sleepy nowadays. Sometimes my lids just drop of themselves. When I could see I was used to open my eyes at everything. . . . But it's dark now. . . . You haven't found her?

Beinish. I don't know where to look. . . . It was fearfully cold today. When one doesn't make a cent it grips one by the heart.

Feiga. She's not here. She can't stay in the house. In the daytime someone was here. They whispered to each other. Could it be Abram? I couldn't find out.

Beinish. O, I would have found out, all right. What does Faiva say? And the rope?

Feiga. It hurts to twist a rope into a young skin. She's too young for the rope. She don't like to work. She don't want to drag the yoke. Must I hang it on her? . . . I don't see what goes on on the earth. . . . It's thirty years soon. Perhaps the streets look different now.

Beinish. But how does the girl leave you in the dark? I'd tell Faiva, I would. I'd lend him my rope.

Feiga. He's got his own rope. . . . Hu-hu-hu. . . . Blind and yet one needs fire. Hu-hu-hu. . . . To beat a grown child is like beating yourself. . . . I know a mother who used to beat her children before they were born. She used to hit herself with her fists. She couldn't bear the life in her bowels. Her man used to nag her. She didn't know at whom to vent her anger. . . . What's the child guilty of? A young girl wants to have some fun, and do a little mischief.

Beinish. And I'd tear strips from her skin for that.

Feiga. Who ever whipped Faiva? He was a born mischief. And what a mischief! It was hard to give him birth. He wanted to jump out before his time. Stood on his head and beat my heart with his feet. It was hard to give him birth. . . . He was born—and his yoke was ready for him. It was ready before his birth.

[*It suddenly becomes light in the other room.* Peshka *comes in with a burning match.*]

Beinish. She's here. I didn't know it.

Peshka. Let's see your rope, Beinish. In how many knots is it twisted? [*The light goes out.*] You want to lend the rope to father? You can't even untie it from your neck.

Feiga. I thought you went out somewheres. Light the lamp, child.

Peshka. Where could I go barefooted in a frost like this?

Beinish. I bet she hid under the table. . . . I looked for her everywhere. Hua-ha-ha. She's heard it all. Well, it was the truth, anyway. Your father pities you too much.

Peshka. Yes, he pities me, he pities me.

Beinish. Then he's a fool. You must beat children. Whip 'em!

Peshka. You must feel good, Beinish, you must feel good.

Beinish. I only teased you. Believe me, I only teased you.

Feiga. Oh, no. You didn't tease her. One could tell that, but you yourself know it's foolish.

Beinish. One mustn't be a burden on his own father. A father can beat the child if it's a dead weight on his shoulders.

Peshka. You think I don't know that you spoke with father? He thinks that he'll help my father with his ropes.

Feiga. You better light a candle.

Peshka. Oh, I can sit in the dark as well. [*She lights a match.*] If you had your own children, you'd talk in another way.

Beinish. I wouldn't spare them. If they lit matches for nothing I'd break their fingers. I'm laughing, you fool.

Peshka. It's the same to me if you laugh or not. My clothes on the wall are rotten with damp. How long will I have to sit here? Till my sides begin to rot? I don't want to rot alive, and I won't. [*She lights a match.*]

Feiga. Don't light them for nothing. When you're young you've got no sense. You just want to be wise, that's all. Foolish child. Your mother bore you in a cellar, no? It was a lot damper than this, too. The walls were just covered with damp, and hung with gunnysacks near the bed. The sacks were rotten. You laughed, kicked your feet and laughed. Some children start to laugh early, in the second week, while they're still with the mother. But when they begin to talk, they don't laugh any longer. They weep.

Peshka. I won't weep. No more.

Beinish. You'll blubber in your fists yet. Dig your head into a pillow and blubber. Well, it's warmer at home. Good night. [*He goes out. There is a pause.*]

Peshka. He hasn't enough brains to crack a decent joke, even. He wants to set father on me.

Feiga. Father isn't so bad now. Suffering makes anyone hard. He's angry at himself, and it hurts. Isn't his child part of his own flesh?

Peshka. He can't forgive me if I lift my head up now and then.

Feiga. His own head is ten feet under earth. Does he ever laugh? I never heard it. Never. Trouble just likes to gnaw at him. We live in a grave. You think I don't see, because it's dark in my eyes all the time. Does it make any difference where I sit? Above or below? It's just the same, it seems. No? But no. I see with my blind eyes that I lie in a hole. I can't get up. Well, what of that? Oh, but it's cold. You're right, child; you're right. [*Her voice trembles.*] Come here, child. I see that you are right, I see I will protect you with my hands. He won't touch you. I won't let him. I'll tell him.

Peshka. What can you tell him? I don't know if he beats me from love or hate.

Feiga. I'll tell him, child: "She's a grown-up girl. You let her go. You'd better treat her with respect." He don't see that you've got nothing to do. When a man is drowning it's too hard for him to hold a straw up on his back. Where are you, child?

Peshka. Here. [*She lights a match.*]

Feiga. When you light fire it seems to me that I see the whole cellar.

Peshka. You see nothing, granny, you see nothing. Not one of us sees it. [*The match goes out.*]

Feiga. Well, it's grown dark again, hasn't it?

Peshka. I'll make it light again. [*She lights another match.*]

Feiga. It's a pity to light it. Of course I see. I see all. I can even see you. [*Pause.*] The house is empty. There isn't even any warm water here. He'll come frozen from the street.

Peshka. Ah, you with your warm water. What will come of it? Let be what will be. I couldn't, granny, I couldn't, any longer. It's better to die of hunger than to rot alive. O, granny, granny, granny. [*She throws herself on the neck of the old woman.*]

Feiga. You're so long from the factory, and you smell of tobacco yet.

Peshka. I'll keep on smelling while I live. [*Pause. Suddenly, in a louder, angry tone:*] Tell me, granny, why am I so sad? Granny, I'm lonely. Something gnaws inside of me. Perhaps I'll die of loneliness. Let father come and stripe my skin with a rope. Perhaps I'll be happier then.

Feiga. You're seventeen, child, and I'm seventy. It's hard to close the eyes for the last time. But if they're closed, a stone drops from the heart. You're lonely, and I'm so in the dark.

Peshka. You think, granny, that I'm too lazy to work? I'm not lazy, granny. I'd do anything to have things just a little better. [*Pause.*]

Feiga. Find a way to get out of this, child. I was suspicious a little while ago. Someone was talking here, it seemed. I think Abram was here. Perhaps he'll take you out of here. I told it to Beinish. Why did I tell it to him?

Peshka. Ah, granny, if you knew how it hurts. My heart is torn by iron claws. My skin grows cold and hot again. In my eyes it's darker than in yours at times. Mama used to tear my hair. I was small then. I didn't know why. I used to cry. I didn't know why. And she used to tear my hair. Tell me, did she feel better when she hurt me?

Feiga. She tore her own heart. I know how she loved you, child. But trouble. Trouble. She died from hunger. She used to give you potatoes and swallow spittle herself. Swallow tears. [*Pause.*] Your father will come home soon, hungry, and you've nothing ready for him. He'll get angry quick enough. A mother bears many things, but not a father. A mother can die before her time. You didn't hear your mother cry when you had smallpox and measles and trouble with your throat. You didn't hear. I heard it, child. I, with my blind eyes. And my heart burned in me. The tears seared my eyes. A blind one can't weep. No, she can't. Wasn't she my daughter-in-law? A little bit of light, just a little bit. And I saw with my blind eyes how she went out like a candle. Hu-hu-hu. You're lonely? Well, why not? I can't see. I'm blind. If my eyes opened I'd cry like a little child. I'd see your father, and not know him. His face must be different now. If he beats his grown-up girl, his face must be black with torture. When he tears the hair of my only child . . . Girl, he must be tortured.

Peshka. I went to the factory and just rotted there. Yellow faces, green faces, on all sides of me. Silent faces. Not a word, but all rot. . . . And I keep still, too. And my heart breaks in me . . . breaks in me. . . . A horrible fear fell on me. . . . Granny, I'm lonely. . . . O, it's terrible. A candle goes out, melts away. . . . And when people melt and go out, bend and fall. O, it's terrible, terrible. . . . Tell me, granny, am I wrong if I run from the fire because I'm afraid I'll go out like a candle? When I see a face go yellow like a leaf in autumn, I'm afraid. . . . I can die. . . . I think that my face grows all wrinkled in a second. . . . And my eyes. . . . O, granny, I'm afraid to say it. . . . And here it's even worse. . . . Tell me, granny, don't you feel at all, sitting in the cellar here, that a stone lies on your head, lies and crushes the bone and the brain together? . . .

Feiga. [*Kisses Peshka*] Youth. . . . Ah, youth. . . . I feel it. . . . I see its sufferings. . . . When I was a young girl, and my eyes could see, I felt everything. . . . It hurt. Pitiless tortures. . . . They broke my bones. . . . I bit my lips to blood from pain, and kept still. I was strong then. Strong enough to keep still. . . . Children haven't that strength

now. . . . Hu-hu-hu. . . . Tortures. . . . Tortures. . . . And no strength. . . .
[*Pause.* ABRAM *comes in.*]

    Abram. Why are you sitting in the dark? Who's here?

    Peshka. Come here, Abram.

    Feiga. We started to talk, and forgot to light the fire.

    Abram. In the dark you can't see my sooty face. . . .

    Peshka. Is it cold on the street?

    Abram. A cracking frost. Up near the chimneys it's still worse. The wind blows from everywhere.

    Peshka. You can fall down sometimes, too. The wind can push you off.

    Feiga. You can die quicker on the open road.

    Abram. It's fine to stand on top of a roof and look down on the street, and see the people shrink down there. . . . They shrink together and run as if someone chased them with a long whip.

    Peshka. Here. Light the lamp. It's on the table. My feet are cold. I haven't any shoes.

[ABRAM *lights the small lamp and puts it on the table. The cellar is filled with shadows.*]

    Feiga. It's light already?

    Abram. Why do you squeeze together like that?

    Peshka. [*Frees herself from the old woman. Her face is pale without a hint of light about it.*] We were trying to keep warm. . . . O, but you're black. . . . Wash off that soot. [*She shakes his hand.*]

    Abram. [*Looks into her eyes*] I'll wash. . . . [*He washes himself.*]

    Feiga. You can light the stove, anyway. He may bring something from the street.

    Abram. Well, am I white enough now?

    Peshka. You're still black with soot. [*She embraces his neck. For a time there is silence.*]

    Feiga. Are you lighting the stove?

    Peshka. [*Whispers something to* ABRAM. *Looks at the old woman.*] It's very cold outside?

    Abram. A frost and a strong wind.

    Feiga. Are you putting anything into the oven? If your father comes it will quiet him.

    Peshka. [*Says something to* ABRAM. *He trembles. She frees herself, and stands absent-mindedly.*] An empty house. An empty house.

                    [ABRAM *goes to her and takes her hand.*]

    Feiga. Abram went away?

Abram. I'm here. [*He whispers something to* Peshka.]

Peshka. [*Shakes her head as if saying no. Talks loudly to the old woman.*] They melted like candles before the fire. I don't want to go before my time. . . . I want to live yet. . . . My heart will bloom, bloom. . . . I awoke and saw my clothes rotting on the wall. . . . [*She buries her head on* Abram's *shoulder. Her body trembles with sobs.*]

Feiga. Father will come right away.

Peshka. The later one realizes what's happening about him the better.

Feiga. [*Interrupting*] Don't curse, child. You're young yet. But I . . . I'm afraid Faiva will come.

Peshka. Oh, let him come. Let him come. Let him trample me underfoot.

Abram. No one ought to let another trample him underfoot. I'd fight my own father.

Peshka. [*Draws him to herself, and kisses him*] No. No. No. . . . It isn't right. Mama left me, just like that. . . . She ought to get up out of her grave, with the shards on her eyes, and help me now. . . . She didn't want to quarrel with father. . . . I don't want to quarrel with anybody. [*She cries. They remain in a close embrace.* Abram *wipes his eyes.*]

Feiga. Don't cry. Don't cry. People who have light in their eyes mustn't cry. I saw mothers whose cheeks were yellow because they cried too much when they were young. . . . Spots remain on their faces. . . . For life . . .

Peshka. No yellow spots will remain on my cheeks, granny.

Feiga. Abram, you support your mother. Your mother loves you. When one has a mother who loves him, it's enough. . . . When one rests his head on his mother's heart, it's enough. . . . Both feel better. . . . Mothers suffer even when they lie in the earth. . . . They never rest. . . . They are tortured. . . .

Peshka. [*Kisses* Abram. *They still embrace each other. She makes a sign to him to go away. Talks loudly.*] Father will come soon. [*She goes to the stove and looks at* Abram *with great pain on her face.*]

Feiga. Who is crying in the stillness? Who is crying?

Abram. [*Gathers himself together, and winks at* Peshka] Good night. I may come in again pretty soon. [*Remains for a while near the door.*]

Feiga. Go in health, my boy. [Peshka *stands near the oven absentmindedly.* Abram *goes slowly out, without taking his eyes from her. Pause.*] Hu-hu-hu. . . . Youth, youth. . . . Sweet, beautiful youth. [*Pause.*] Child, you are hungry. Light the stove.

Peshka. No, granny, I'm not hungry.

Feiga. It's in your voice, child. It trembles there.

Peshka. No, granny. I'm not hungry.

Feiga. Youth. . . . Hu-hu-hu. . . . Sweet, beautiful youth. . . .

[*Oppressive silence.* FAIVA *comes in. He is blue with cold. He puts a small piece of black bread on the table. Walks about the two rooms.*]

Feiga. Faiva? [FAIVA *is silent. He sits down near the table. Leans his head on his hands.* PESHKA *looks at him from her place near the stove.* FEIGA *gets up.*] Faiva, you're here, aren't you? Peshka, your father's come, hasn't he?

Peshka. Yes.

Feiga. Light the fire, Peshka. You've brought something, Faiva? You're hungry? . . . She's also hungry.

Faiva. The bread's on the table.

Feiga. The bread—the bread. . . . What's the use if you're . . . There's enough of bread, but . . .

Faiva. Let me rest, mother.

Feiga. Mother's blind eyes hurt. Her old heart hurts. You're shedding your young blood. . . . She's dying gradually.

Peshka. You shouldn't worry, granny.

Feiga. You've brought bread, all right. . . . Why didn't you bring a happy face with you? . . . A couple of good words. . . . Hu-hu-hu. . . . Bread without them is poison.

Faiva. Don't poison my blood, mother.

Feiga. The bread's on the table. . . . Why don't you eat it? [*She goes to* FAIVA *and puts her hands on his shoulder.*] You're keeping still, still. . . . I'm afraid. Why are you still? . . . A house full of people, and they're still. . . . It's hard to bear it where people are. . . . [*She moves back a little.*] Smile, won't you? . . . Don't make the bread bitter. . . . The table's an altar, and the bread is sacrifice. . . . Don't make it bitter. . . . [FAIVA *looks at her angrily.*] Why are you still? What should I say to you? What's in your heart tonight? When you cry I know well enough. . . . When you beat, I know. . . . But when you're still . . . But don't you dare to let it out on the girl. . . . She's had enough. . . . Peshka, where are you? [*She comes near to* FAIVA, *and caresses him.*] Let your bitter heart out on me. . . . On me. . . . [FAIVA *hides his head in his arms.*] Your heart's more bitter than it is always. Pity the girl. Let her go her way. . . . Faiva, answer me. . . . I'm your mother. . . . Remember, you used to sit in my lap long ago. I used to cry over you. You used

to cry and laugh, always in my lap. Tell me now, what's the trouble.
I'd like to hear you, to hear you. . . . If you can, I'll cry with my blind
eyes. . . .

Faiva. [*Suddenly arises. Cries out with great pain:*] Mama! . . .
Mama! . . . [*He remains standing with lowered head.*]

Feiga. [*With trembling voice*] You used to cry like that when my
eyes could see you. . . . When I carried you in my arms. . . . Go on.
Tell me all. . . . You didn't know more than 'Mama,' then. . . . You
didn't know. . . . Tell me all. Tell me all. . . .

Faiva. [*Gathers himself together. Takes a long breath:*] No. I
can't. . . .

[*He goes out of the cellar.*]

Feiga. Where are you going, my child? [*She remains in the middle
of the room.* PESHKA *goes out on the street, and quickly re-enters.*] Who
is this?

Peshka. It's me. [*Pause.* PESHKA *finds a rope, and while the old
woman talks passes it across the chimney-pipes near the door of the
second room. She makes a noose. Her hands tremble.*]

Feiga. The bread is on the table. . . . It's poisoned. . . . It's sprinkled with gall. . . . Who can eat it now? . . . I feel that the ceiling is
coming down on my head. . . . What are you doing, Peshka?

Peshka. I'm dreaming, granny.

Feiga. What, my child?

Peshka. That life is lighter and easier. [*She embraces the old
woman.*]

Feiga. You're trembling, child.

Peshka. [*Kisses her*] I'm dreaming, granny. . . .

Feiga. [*Kisses* PESHKA] What, my child?

Peshka. That my youth won't be tortured like this always. [*They
stand in a close embrace. Pause.*]

Feiga. Why is your heart beating so fast, child? So fast and unquiet
like?

Peshka. From joy, granny. [*Pause.* PESHKA *frees herself from the
embrace of the old woman. Goes silently to the table, and begins to turn
down the light slowly, trying not to let the old woman notice anything.*]

Feiga. [*In the middle of the house. As if to herself*] The light goes
out. . . . The light goes out. . . . The light goes out. . . .

[*The* CURTAIN *descends slowly.*]

THE SEER LOOKS AT HIS BRIDE

by HARRY SACKLER

SOURCE OF THE PLAY

Itsikel, the protagonist of this play, was Reb Jacob Isaac Horowitz, famous among Hasidim as the "Seer of Lublin." He was born about 1745, since it is recorded that he was about fifteen years old when the Baalshem, the founder of Hasidism, died.

This miniature play recounts the sad story of the Seer's first marriage. His "light had not yet shone forth" and he was at that time a mere disciple of the renowned Zaddik, Reb Elimelech of Lizensk. The principal episodes were culled from a "Maaseh Norah," an Awesome Tale, which may be heard, even in our own day, at the consecrated gatherings, or "sittings," of the faithful.

> THE ZADDIK OF LIZENSK
> ITSIKEL (*later in life "The Seer of Lublin"*)
> REB AVROHOM, *Itsikel's father, rabbi at Yosefov*
> REB KOPEL, *his maternal grandfather*
> BERKE, *the rich innkeeper of Krasnibrod*
> LUBA, *his daughter*
> THE MARRIAGE BROKER
> A WEDDING GUEST

SCENE I

The inn near Krasnibrod. A room with two doors.

Berke. Brother, you must not leave me now. You see, I am a little flustered. The three of them might come in any minute and, in the presence of learned men, I feel lost.

Marriage Broker. Calm yourself, Reb Berke. As soon as they come in, offer them your congratulations and then lead them to the guestroom. It is really very simple.

Berke. Yes, it is simple. I only hope I don't make some ugly break. It's hard on an ignorant innkeeper to associate . . .

Marriage Broker. Now, now, Reb Berke, you have no reason to worry. The father, the grandfather and even the bridegroom himself, know all about you. I am a marriage broker of experience and I take care of such matters in advance. I told them plainly: The father of that girl is a plain person, an innkeeper. He is a God-fearing Jew, though not a learned man.

Berke. No, not a learned man. No—to my sorrow.

Marriage Broker. And I must say that they were very sensible about it. There is no dearth of learning in their family. Itsikel, the bridegroom, is famous for his knowledge of revealed and secret lore, though he is barely eighteen. All he needs is someone to take the burden from his slender shoulders. And that you promised to do.

Berke. And so I shall! And so I shall!

A Wedding Guest. [*Poking his head through door, right*] Oh, here is Berke. Host, the wedding guests are looking for you high and low. And they wonder whether the bridegroom is ever coming. No trouble, I hope.

Berke. Trouble? Why should there be trouble? Oh, God!

Marriage Broker. Of course there is no trouble. There never is where I am the marriage broker. The bridegroom and his folks only arrived a little while ago.

Berke. [*Eagerly*] And a very hard journey it was too. They were stiff with the cold when they came.

Wedding Guest. So they are still thawing out. I see.

Marriage Broker. Yes, thawing out and resting up. They will be with us in a little while. You tell the guests to make merry in the meantime. You will see the bridegroom soon and you will admit that I secured a rare jewel for Berke's daughter.

Wedding Guest. I am glad to hear that. [*Shouting.*] Hey, there! Fiddle up! The bridegroom isn't ready yet.

[*Off, shutting door behind him. Subdued strains of a country-dance are heard.*]

Berke. Do you see? When you are with me, everything is well. You know what to say and how to say it. Trouble! Why did he think that there might be trouble? Is it because Berke, the innkeeper, is climbing too high? It is no small matter to have the famous Itsikel as one's son-in-law. He looks to me like a living Scroll of the Torah.

Marriage Broker. A living Scroll of the Torah?

Berke. Oh, God, have I said something that is forbidden? Well, I could not help saying it. The first time he looked at me, I shivered. His eyes seemed to bore right through me.

Marriage Broker. I am not surprised. They say that he is blessed with wonderful vision and his master, the Zaddik of Lizensk, calls him the Seer. But what of it? He will get used to you and you to him. You may be sure about that. But just now I wonder how long they are going to keep us waiting. [*Listening at door, left.*] I think I am going to knock.

Berke. Would you? [*Restraining him.*] They might think it disrespectful of me.

Marriage Broker. Just leave it to me. [*Knocks gently.*]

Reb Kopel. [*Opens door and enters. His wrinkled face is wreathed in smiles.*] Ah, the marriage broker knocking! And the bride's father waiting for us!

Berke. [*Timidly*] And, with your permission, so are the guests.

Reb Kopel. [*Heartily*] And so is the bride, no doubt. But the two young ones with me are taking a long time to warm up. A journey in mid-winter is a hard task for a rabbi and his son.

Marriage Broker. [*Ingratiatingly*] The study of the Torah reduces a man's strength, Reb Kopel. So it is written.

Berke. Do I expect my son-in-law to split rails? I can do that and so can any peasant. But piety and learning . . .

Reb Kopel. Never fear, Reb Berke. Itsikel will give you a full measure of that. Speaking of his piety, I must tell you the story of the veiled eyes. He was twelve then. Suddenly he appeared with a kerchief tied around his forehead and so draped that he could only see a few paces ahead of him.

Berke. Was he doing penance for some trivial sin?

Reb Kopel. [*Laughing heartily*] No, Reb Berke. You know the boy was blessed with an unusual vision from his very infancy. All of a sudden he realized that sin and wickedness were staring at him at every turn and so that young Seer of mine goes to work and shuts the world clean out from his sight.

Marriage Broker. I heard that story before but I must admit that I considered it—a story.

Reb Kopel. Oh, no! It was a serious business. He kept it up for two and a half years till he came to the Yeshiva at Richivel. There he had to remove that kerchief because the head master, the great Reb Shmelke, ordered him to do so. Later, when he came for the first time to the Zaddik of Kizensk, the Zaddik looked at him for a moment, extended his hand and said: Peace be with you, young Seer. Be careful of your great gift.

Berke. [*Ecstatically*] Wonderful! He said this to my Itsikel?

Reb Kopel. That is what he said. And more than that. . . . Ah! Here they are! [*To* ITSIKEL *who has entered with* REB AVROHOM.] Itsikel, I think we have kept Reb Berke waiting long enough. You cannot have a Bridegroom's Feast without the bridegroom.

Itsikel. I am sorry. Reb Berke will forgive me. But then he might have used the time to great advantage.

Reb Avrohom. [*Curtly*] For instance?

Itsikel. [*Smiling faintly*] Well, he might have offered his evening prayers, while waiting for us.

Berke. [*Confused and stammering*] And that's right, too. I clean forgot.

Reb Kopel. [*Laughing merrily*] Was it written on his forehead, Itsikel? Well, well! Reb Berke, with this young Seer around, you will never again forget your evening prayers. Be sure of that.

Marriage Broker. [*Whispering*] Reb Kopel, the guests are waiting.

Reb Kopel. The marriage broker is right. We have kept the guests waiting all too long. They are pining to see you, Itsikel.

Itsikel. Yes, they are probably curious to look at me. But they will see very little of me, I am afraid.

Berke. [*Alarmed*] Does he refuse to show himself to my guests? Oh, he despises me and mine! Good God!

Reb Avrohom. [*Severely*] Son, do not distress this good man for no reason at all.

Reb Kopel. [*Heartily*] Come, Itsikel. No more delay! [*Starts towards door, right.*]

Itsikel. [*Raising his hand*] Grandfather.

Reb Kopel. [*Turning around sharply*] Well?

Itsikel. Forgive me, grandfather, but I cannot go in yet.

Reb Avrohom. Why not?

Itsikel. [*Hesitatingly*] Well, it just occurred to me that I have not fulfilled a command of our Sages.

Reb Kopel. [*Nettled*] And what command of the Sages is that?

Reb Avrohom. Eh? Let me see. "One must not marry a woman unless he sees her first." Is it this command you are thinking of?

Itsikel. [*Nods his head silently.*]

Reb Kopel. A queer request! Come, now. The bride will step into the guest-room. You need not trouble the girl to come here for the purpose of being gazed at. [*Pause.*] Do you insist?

Itsikel. [*Quietly*] I do.

Berke. If this is all, then all is well. Luba will be here in a minute.

[*Off to guest-room; door remains slightly ajar.*]

Reb Kopel. [*Glowering*] Itsikel!

Reb Avrohom. [*Evenly*] It's a command of the Sages, father-in-law.

Marriage Broker. [*Near door*] Now, what's this? She shakes her head violently. I think she is refusing to come.

[*Off, shutting door behind him.*]

Itsikel. [*Stands motionless, his eyes half closed. Long pause.*]

Marriage Broker. [*Rushes in breathless*] She finally consented. They are coming.

[*Several matrons, in festive garb, file in slowly.* LUBA, *head and face completely hidden by the bridal veil, is led in by* BERKE *and an elderly woman. A group of curious faces fills the doorway.*]

Reb Kopel. Well, Itsikel?

Itsikel. [*Perturbed*] The lifting of a veil is very painful. I dare not do it.

Reb Kopel. But I am an old man and I will. [*Steps quickly towards* LUBA *and gently lifts the veil.*]

Luba. [*Stares at the group of men in front of her, a defiant smile playing at the corners of her fresh lips.*]

Itsikel. [*With a half-suppressed moan*] But who is this? Who—?

Reb Avrohom. Evidently, your bride.

Itsikel. [*An imperceptible shudder running through him*] Yes, yes, this is my bride. But that other—that shadow— [*Shields his eyes with his hands.*] Lower that veil! Please!

Berke. [*Who is nearest* LUBA, *makes an attempt to do so.*]

Luba. [*Forestalling him, lowers the veil quickly. She rushes towards door, a ripple of girlish laughter trailing after her. The other women follow quickly.*]

Reb Kopel. [*Testily*] Now that you have complied with the law, we may proceed with the festivities. I would like to see that wedding over.

Itsikel. There will be no wedding.

Reb Avrohom. Did you say there will be no wedding?

Berke. [*Aghast*] Oh, where will I hide my shame?

Itsikel. She is not my bride. I cannot marry her.

Berke. [*Lamenting*] I climbed too high and I fell. I deserve it.

Reb Kopel. [*Wroth*] What is the reason of all this? I bid you speak.

Itsikel. [*With a gesture of helplessness*] Not now, not in the presence of her father. I cannot.

Reb Kopel. Reb Berke, will you leave us alone for a moment? Don't worry now. The wedding will take place tomorrow afternoon, as we agreed upon.

Marriage Broker. Leave it to Reb Kopel. He is just and he is wise. Come. We will wait in there.

[*Off with* BERKE *through door, left.*]

Reb Kopel. Now, what does all this mean, Itsikel?

Itsikel. One cannot marry a stranger. This girl is not destined to be mine.

Reb Avrohom. When you say that she is a stranger, I understand. All brides are strangers. But who can peer behind the veil of destiny?

Itsikel. I could not help peering. Just now when I looked at her—

Reb Kopel. Well, what did you see?

Itsikel. The face of another.

Reb Avrohom. Eh—of another?

Itsikel. Yes, of another, of someone who is not even of our own people. He passed like a ghost between that girl and me. [*Pause; supplicatingly.*] I beg of you, take me home again.

Reb Kopel. What? Take you home again? No, Itsikel! You heard me promise that poor innkeeper that he shall not be shamed. And he shall not.

Itsikel. Is that reason enough to make my wedding-day a day of mourning? The shadow of that other is still flitting before my eyes. Grandfather, I cannot, I cannot!

Reb Kopel. [*Quizzically*] I wonder whether that shadow of yours is not the mere whim of a young Seer. Eh?

Itsikel. [*Firmly*] I do not lie!

Reb Avrohom. No, you do not lie. Still, there is going to be a wedding tomorrow afternoon.

Itsikel. [*Pained*] But, father, there is a barrier—a chasm—

Reb Avrohom. Is there? Then the wedding will soon be followed by a divorce. It is a tradition more potent than a law.

Itsikel. I—I may not be strong enough to do that. She is so beautiful to look at. No. Take me home now. Now! If you will not—then I shall go myself. [*Turns towards door, left.*]

Reb Kopel. [*Vehemently*] Rabbi of Yosefov, assert your authority. You are a rabbi and a father.

Reb Avrohom. [*Calmly*] Son!

Itsikel. [*With an agonizing cry*] Don't, father, don't!

Reb Avrohom. Son, I bid you stay!

Itsikel. [*Bends his head in silence.*]

Reb Kopel. [*Opening door, left*] Reb Berke—

Berke. [*Rushes in followed by* MARRIAGE BROKER] And—what—?

Reb Kopel. Come, lead us to the wedding guests. Itsikel will deliver a fine oration, I am sure.

Berke. Thank God for his mercy!

[*He and the others file out slowly through door, right.*]

CURTAIN

SCENE II

The bridal chamber. A door leading to corridor.

Luba. [*In white smock and cap, reclining on low sofa. A brazier, filled with live coals, diffuses a ruddy glow over her face and half-bared arms. A pause. Suddenly the sound of steps is heard from the corridor. She listens intently, her eyes riveted on the door. As no one enters for a moment, the smile of assurance changes quickly to a frown of impatience.*]

Itsikel. [*Opens door after a while and enters timidly. It is evident that he is laboring under a great strain, which he is vainly trying to shake off.*]

Luba. [*Shifts her position imperceptibly and measures him with a cool and deliberate glance. A moment of intense silence.*]

Itsikel. [*Stammering*] I want to—to speak to you.

Luba. [*Mockingly*] Well, do. [*Pause.*] Why did you hesitate so long in front of the door? It is very cold in the corridor tonight.

Itsikel. [*Helplessly*] Yes, it is very cold. But I was undecided. There was your door and there was another—the one leading to the snow-covered road.

Luba. [*Laughingly*] You seem to have chosen the wrong door after all.

Itsikel. I don't know, Luba.

Luba. Oh, you know my name, too. I thought you didn't.

Itsikel. Why not?

Luba. You looked at me once on Thursday night. Why, this is only Saturday night and we are not married yet two full days!

Itsikel. I cannot be angry with you for mocking me. You feel hurt.

Luba. [*Calmly but curtly*] I do not feel hurt and I dislike being pitied. [*After a pause.*] This is your room as well as mine. You may sit down, since you have chosen to come in. Or you may—oh, well.

Itsikel. [*Sits down on the edge of a chair some distance from the sofa; hesitatingly*] Do you know, Luba, that I was about to go away from here on Thursday evening, after I had looked at you?

Luba. Father told me about it. It would have been queer.

Itsikel. Queer? It would have been a disgrace to both of us and a calamity to your father. Heaven be praised that my father stopped me.

Luba. Was it really your father that stopped you? [*With a half muffled laugh.*] Really, I was not afraid for one moment. You would have been the first man that ever ran away from me—and I have seen many in my father's inn.

Itsikel. [*Groaning*] Oh, God!

Luba. [*Rising, her face darkening*] Are you going to pray to God to enlighten you? I shall not disturb you then. [*Turns to leave the room.*]

Itsikel. [*Rising*] Luba, don't go now.

Luba. [*Turning back*] What is your pleasure, husband? [*Pause.*] I see you are shivering with cold. Come, sit down on the sofa. I kept the brazier hot for you.

Itsikel. [*Sits down alongside of her*] Luba, I find it very hard to talk to you. Your words sound so strange as if you were not one of us. I am all confused. If God, in His wisdom, has decreed that we become as one, why has He placed a barrier between us—a barrier which I cannot tear down?

Luba. I didn't know that there was a barrier. Are you sure there is?

Itsikel. I was sure then—when the veil was lifted for the first time. [*Haltingly.*] Oh, I found you more beautiful than the rising sun, Luba. Your eyes gladdened my heart and your smile brought joy to my soul. But then—I saw a shadow glide between us—and I could see you no longer. It was the shadow of a stranger—and I knew that you were not to be mine. That shadow will not let you. No, he will not! [*Pause; quietly.*] Tell me, Luba. Who is he?

Luba. [*Walks over to window and peers into the darkness for a moment*] The blizzard is growing worse. It is terrible to be on the road in a night like this.

Itsikel. Luba, my heart is heavy within me. Will you—?

Luba. [*Vivaciously*] Yes, but let me put some more coal in the brazier. [*Busies herself with brazier.*] I am really glad, Itsikel, that you are not abroad tonight. [*Merrily.*] It was not half so bad last Thursday. Still, when you arrived, your ears were frost-bitten.

Itsikel. [*Indignantly*] You have not answered me, Luba. I must know who he is.

Luba. Must you? [*Turns sharply and faces him.*] Then you shall. Did you see the Manor House on the outskirts of Krasnibrod? There it stands, in a cluster of giant oaks, which screen it off from the highway. Massive pillars support its broad balconies and there is strength in these pillars. The halls are spacious and cool and sombre and there is peace in those halls. [*With a faraway look in her eyes.*] When Luba was little, she dreamed of becoming its mistress.

Itsikel. Is there someone in the Manor House who—?

Luba. [*Savagely*] There is. You boast that you saw his shadow glide between us—so you know already that there is. Why must you tear it out of me as if I had robbed you of something that was yours? It was my dream and his and it was I who was afraid of the dream coming true and I bruised myself into wakefulness. But I cannot stop his shadow from prowling around when you stare at me with those terrible eyes of yours. I cannot and I would not if I could.

Itsikel. [*Breathing hard*] I hoped to find you waiting for me—for me only—pure and unalloyed.

Luba. [*Enraged*] If I were not, you would see now more than his shadow. [*Laughs bitterly.*] The great Seer does not see far enough.

Itsikel. You do not understand, Luba. It is because I want all of you, your heart and your innermost thoughts and your loving care, that I am so terribly distressed. I know that there, in that Manor House, stalks a stranger, a gentile, who thinks all the time of my Luba. With all his might, he draws you to himself in an adulterous embrace. Shall I share your soul with him? [*His voice breaking.*] Merciful Father in Heaven, what have I done to deserve this torture?

Luba. [*Approaches him quietly and begins to pet his heaving shoulders*] I am sorry for you, Itsikel. I feel that my words and my ways are strange to you. I am not meek and I am not decorous, as the daughters of our people are wont to be. If you feel that you cannot—

Itsikel. But you are strong and you are truthful and you are—beautiful to behold. If you had only waited for me—

Luba. And where were you when spring came to our valley? Why did you not come to me when the sap was running in the trees and the blind flowers opened their eyes to the sun? The young squire came day after day, riding his handsome roan. His hand was so strong and so intoxicating to touch.

Itsikel. And so you came to love him. [*Shivering.*] You still do.

Luba. Maybe I did. I really don't know. I always wanted to be loved, though. He knew it and he came to me with a song of love on his lips.

[*Harshly.*] If you had not come to me peering and sulking and hunting for shadows, if you had instead taken me in your arms and crushed me to your heart, I might have loved you no less.

Itsikel. [*Pensively*] I fear that every minute that I remain near you, I commit a grave sin. The lure that comes from you, staggers me, makes me fear for the salvation of my soul. [*Raising his eyes heavenward.*] Lord of the World, the keen sight you gave me has now become Thy double-edged sword at the gate of paradise. Oh, God, strike me blind again!

Luba. [*With a tantalizing laugh*] My poor Seer! If the sight of Luba did not strike you blind, nothing will. But then you may not have looked well at me. [*Whispering.*] Would you—would you try again? [*She places herself directly in his line of vision. With a few deft strokes, she adjusts her smock in such a fashion that the voluptuous lines of her young body strike his eye, while the discarded cap releases her wealth of amber-colored hair.*]

Itsikel. [*Makes a step towards her, his arms wildly groping for her body; gasping*] Let the wrath of God—I cannot leave you!

Luba. [*Throwing her arms around him*] You foolish, foolish Seer! No one runs away from Luba. Now, would you?

Itsikel. [*Whispering*] No, never. Help me chase that shadow back to the Manor House. [*Pleadingly.*] Wouldn't you help me, Luba? Wouldn't you? [*Attempts to reach her lips with his.*]

Luba. [*Suddenly growing immobile: distantly*] I don't know.

Itsikel. [*With an agonizing cry*] Oh, Luba, there! There! [*Tears himself loose.*] There it moves! And your shadow has joined him. Oh, God of Israel! There is a cross over your heads. [*Grabs her savagely and turns her face towards the wall where the shadowy figures and the cross above them are plainly visible.*] There! There!

Luba. [*Quietly*] When your lips came near mine, I could not help think of him and his kisses. Why were your lips so dry and parched and trembling with fear? His were like rose petals. [*Shrugging her shoulders.*] He was always so insistent and he will not be chased back. It will be better for you, Itsikel, if you will never look at Luba again.

Itsikel. [*Humbly*] No, I shall not. I am going now—going to my master in Lizensk. [*Turns towards door.*]

Luba. To Lizensk? Now? The blizzard is raging. [*Mockingly.*] Your ears will be frost-bitten again.

Itsikel. Neither blizzard nor prowling wolf will stop me. The Evil-One has made this house his abode. I am afraid—afraid—

Luba. [*Sarcastically*] Of shadows.

Itsikel. [*Transfixed*] "Into Thy hand I entrust my soul: Thou hast redeemed me. Oh, Lord God of Truth."

[*As he opens the door the howling of the wind fills the room with its ominous screech. He steps into the night.*]

CURTAIN

SCENE III

The house of the Zaddik of Lizensk. A room with two doors.

Zaddik. [*Seated at the head of the table, which is strewn with books. His head is slightly inclined and his eyes are half-closed, as he listens intently to the tale of Berke.*]

Berke. . . . But I first heard of it the following morning and, believe me, holy master, my heart died within me. To think that this delicate youth was walking from Krasnibrod to Lizensk in that terrible blizzard! So when she said to me, with that brazen smile she has: "Father, I am a deserted woman," I replied, with a terrible ache in my heart: "No, daughter, you are a widow."

Zaddik. The Lord of the World takes care of his own. He cannot afford to lose an Itsikel, when there are so few of them.

Berke. The Lord of the World has at least a few of them. I had only one to console me, to brighten my old age, to pray for my soul when I shall leave this world. Why must I lose him? Weeks and months have I waited for him to return. Three times a day I prayed for it. I hoped God would enlighten him and show him how bitterly he wronged me and mine. But last week when that messenger arrived, carrying the decree of divorce, the world came to an end. See, holy master. My hair turned white.

Zaddik. And did your daughter accept the decree in accordance with the law?

Berke. She was quite willing. But would I, her father, let her? I told that messenger that the old innkeeper of Krasnibrod will first be in his grave before he sees his only daughter divorced. And this is why I came to you, holy master. Itsikel is here with you. And is he not your disciple and bound to obey you? Oh, pity me! Help me!

Zaddik. My heart goes out to you, brother. But I am afraid I may not be able to do anything for you. Itsikel only hinted to me why he had left your house and your daughter. Mind you, he merely hinted. I am afraid that he will not go back. Still—

Berke. [*Elated*] Still there is hope. Isn't there, holy master?

Zaddik. [*Rising*] Lord of the World, how could I dismiss this poor brother of mine without making an effort to help him? [*Pacing the room silently for a moment.*] I cannot interfere with Itsikel much. His light is rising and will soon burst forth in divine glory. But even if I do not want to command him as master, may I not counsel him as brother? Yes, that much I shall permit myself. [*Opens door slightly.*] Be good enough to send Itsikel to me. [*Turning to* BERKE.] He will be here soon.

Berke. [*Animated*] May God recompense you, holy master. Now I shall see him again. He is still my son-in-law, my Itsikel!

Zaddik. [*Puts his arm around* BERKE's *shoulder*] It is the Torah that you love in Itsikel and how great that love burns in your heart! [*Raising his eyes heavenward.*] Thy bush is still burning, God of our Fathers—burning even in the heart of this humble innkeeper. May Thy reward come now, so that his light be not extinguished.

Itsikel. [*Entering quietly*] You have called me, master.

Zaddik. I regret to disturb your study, Itsikel. But here is one who has a great claim upon you and he must not be denied.

Itsikel. [*Raising his eyes and becoming aware of* BERKE] Ah! [*Pause; goes over to* BERKE *and takes his hand.*] Peace be with you.

Berke. With you be peace, son-in-law.

Itsikel. [*Shaking his head sadly*] No, no! I am no longer—

Zaddik. He still looks upon you as his son-in-law, since his daughter has not accepted the decree.

Itsikel. Hasn't she? [*Reflecting a moment.*] He may not know it, but she accepted it without his knowledge.

Berke. [*Bewildered*] Impossible! How? When?

Zaddik. Why don't you answer him, Itsikel?

Itsikel. Reb Berke was never aware of the ways of his daughter. He loved her too well.

Berke. [*Desperately*] Even so, even so! Still he can right the great wrong he has done to me and mine. Holy master, you are just and you are merciful and you know how deeply I have been hurt. Why is my daughter to be thrown away as if she were a leper? Why? Why?

Zaddik. Answer for yourself, Itsikel. I cannot help you.

Itsikel. Master, he asks the impossible. Even if I were willing to throw my life away, so that he may be spared this agony, I could no longer do it. None of us can reach her now. I am afraid that in the sight of God, she is not even his daughter any longer.

Berke. Woe to me! What is this he is saying?

Zaddik. What has happened, Itsikel? Speak, speak!

Itsikel. I would, if I could. But the master knows that I cannot. I am not permitted yet to give utterance to the things I see. Another messenger has been chosen for this. Oh, master, suffer me to go now.

Zaddik. No! You shall stay with us to the end. He is weak; I am old. And shall we face all this alone? You stay here, Itsikel.

Itsikel. [*Bowing his head*] Then I shall, master. [*Pause.*] I think someone is knocking at the door. [*Opens door.*]

Marriage Broker. [*Entering hastily*] I am looking for the innkeeper of Krasnibrod, one by the name of Berke. Forgive me, holy master. It is a matter— Oh! I cannot utter it.

Berke. [*Wild-eyed*] Don't torture me! Speak!

Marriage Broker. You should not have left your daughter for a moment. It's too late now.

Zaddik. What happened?

Marriage Broker. She ran away—to the Manor House. She is staying there now. They say she is going to marry the young squire. Yes—and worse than that. They say that she was— God! I cannot say it. I cannot! [*Weeps convulsively.*]

Zaddik. [*Shrieks*] Not baptized?

Berke. [*Petrified; mumbles automatically*] No, not baptized. No, no, no! [*Slinks into corner.*]

Itsikel. [*Shaking his head*] Yes—baptized. Oh, master, there was no one, either in heaven or on earth, that could have saved that strange and beautiful maiden. She simply went back to her source. She was never ours. [*Going over to* BERKE.] For some unknown reason, you were made the custodian of a strange gift. She was never yours; nor could I make her mine. The Lord of the World is my witness how much I wanted her. Nor was she unwilling to go through life at my side. But she could not. Her struggle and mine were of no avail.

Zaddik. A strange notion, Itsikel. It does not content me. I may not see as far as you, but the responsibility for the flock is still mine and not yours. I want to know more. When did it happen?

Itsikel. May I answer this, master? A few weeks ago I noticed that the cherry-tree near my window was covered with blossoms and I knew that the trees around the Manor House were in bloom. It was then that the beautiful Luba resumed her secret visits to the young squire. She was powerless; her destiny was calling her.

Zaddik. [*Indignantly*] But this cannot be final, Itsikel. Shall I permit this soul to be lost to us because you have pronounced judgment? You are taking too much upon yourself. I warn you!

Itsikel. [*Humbly*] If I have erred, let retribution fall on my head. But I have not erred. I once offered my life and my life's calling—ay, the very salvation of my soul—for the redemption of Luba. [*Agonizingly.*] I was refused, master. It was that night that I braved the blizzard and came running to you—bruised, weary of life, heartbroken. Am I guilty in your eyes, master? [*Raising his eyes heavenward.*] Am I guilty in Your eyes, God of Israel? [*Pause.*]

Zaddik. [*Wiping his eyes furtively*] But look at this poor brother of mine. He slunk away into a corner. There he sits muttering, muttering. What will you do for him, Itsikel? The eyes of the Seer pried out his shame. Will the hand of the Seer heal his wound?

Itsikel. The power of healing is not yet mine. But I shall offer him what pittance I have. [*Goes over to* BERKE.] Reb Berke, when the Creator, in His wisdom, shall demand of you to return to Him, I, Jacob Isaac, son of Maytel, shall offer the Kaddish three times a day for the salvation of your soul, as if I were your own son.

Berke. [*Stupefied*] Aye, aye, so you might. But then I shall not see her even there. No! I don't want your Kaddish. No, not from you— *Rising with a terrifying shriek*]—you scourge of God! May you— May you— [*The words choke in his throat.*]

Zaddik. [*Commandingly*] Silence! "Touch ye not my anointed!" *He and the* MARRIAGE BROKER *hustle the muttering* BERKE *out of the room. The* ZADDIK *returns soon. For a moment of ominous silence, he gazes at* ITSIKEL, *who is standing motionless.*]

Itsikel. Do not hesitate, master. The fire of his curse must be purged with fire more potent than his. This is a terrible disaster and I do not want to escape unscathed. [*Suppliantly.*] Master, I shall welcome your imprecation as if it were a blessing.

Zaddik. You are no more in my power, Seer, and I cannot touch you. If I were that girl's father, I would have taken the sight of your eyes from you—the sight of those eyes which pried out her shame. [*Pause.*] But I am old and bent. I am about to surrender to you my burden and my charges. I cannot reach you any longer.

Itsikel. Master, you must not refuse me. It is my last demand of the Zaddik of Lizensk.

Zaddik. [*In great pain*] The last demand. Well, then. I decree that the heavenly gift, bestowed upon you, shall die with you. Your sons and your sons' sons, until the tenth generation, shall not inherit the terrible

and ominous power which fell to your share. [*With rising inflection.*]
You shall be the first and the last of your line—the first and the last!

Itsikel. [*With bowed head*] The first and the last. Amen.

CURTAIN

THE SINNER

by SHOLEM ASCH

CHARACTERS

RABBI
FIRST DAYAN, *a judge in the synagogue*
SECOND DAYAN
GABBAI, *head of the synagogue*
ELDER GRAVEDIGGER
YOUNGER GRAVEDIGGER
FIRST IN THE CROWD
SECOND IN THE CROWD
THIRD IN THE CROWD
FOURTH IN THE CROWD
SHAMAS, *servant of the Rabbi*
A DEAF-AND-DUMB BEGGAR-HERMIT
JEWS, WOMEN AND BOYS

A Jewish graveyard in a small town, protected by a low fence, which
overgrown with lichen. Here and there are small, but thick
branched trees in whose shadows are hidden wooden and ston
tombstones that are half covered with wild grass. On the right si
there is a little, crooked hut with two small windows that face t
graveyard. Behind this is a wide, dark gate. In front of this are tu
black wooden pillars, on which are written prayers for the dead. B
fore the hut, among the half-destroyed graves, graze some goats th
are tied with a rope to a little post which is driven into the groun
Near the door of the hut, on an old, decrepit wagon, sits the loc
BEGGAR-HERMIT, wrapped in a tattered cloak, from under which pee
some underclothing that looks like white rags, and in some places

naked, sunburnt body. He sits motionless, his wide-opened eyes star-
ing fixedly.
Behind the fence can be seen the dark road, which twists and zig-zags
between two rows of tall, century-old elms.
On the distant horizon, against the background of a glowing evening sky
are seen outlines of the top of the steeple of the cloister, and the arms
of a windmill.
In the graveyard the two GRAVEDIGGERS *are digging.*
On the left side, fading into the gloom, are tombstones and trees.
The action begins with a sound that approaches from afar.
At times there is heard the whistle of the wind, and the ringing of a bell.
   The sunset fades. All grows dark.

Younger Gravedigger. His turn has come. He carried his pitcher of
water until—
Elder Gravedigger. We saw many like him. That one [*He points
with his finger.*] who lies near the fence with the man who hanged him-
self, was also a great *goy.*
Younger Gravedigger. They say he used to sit in the restaurant on
the Day of Atonement, eating chickens that were roasted in butter.
Elder Gravedigger. To feed the worms in the ground.
Younger Gravedigger. They couldn't even find a praying-shawl in
his house before his death.
Elder Gravedigger. They say that he was not married.
Younger Gravedigger. He lived with some woman, a Jewess or a
Christian. God knows whether she was his wife or his mistress.
Elder Gravedigger. I would not want to enjoy the fruit of his good
deeds.
Younger Gravedigger. She gave them perfumed soap to wash the
dead body.
Elder Gravedigger. A clean body helps nothing if the soul be un-
clean.
Younger Gravedigger. The burial society refused to bring his body
to the graveyard. She hired four carriers. [*He throws up a shovelful of
earth, out of which fall human bones.*]
Elder Gravedigger. Look, bones! [*Stops digging, comes nearer, and
looks at the bones. The other man stops with his spade in his hand, and
looks at the old man.*] The graveyard moves. Long ago, perhaps, this
place was the best one, nearest the gates, and now it is under the fence.
Now they bury hanged men and renegades here. The traces of the dead
disappear, and one can't even tell where the graves were. The living for-

get where the bones lie. The graves grew level with the earth, remained behind the fence, and were left for the Christian plough. I pity the unsown land.

[*It grows darker. A cold autumn wind blows, shaking the trees. Far on the horizon, gray clouds gather. On the dark road on the other side of the fence, the funeral procession comes nearer, four carriers bearing the dead man. Behind them walks a* WOMAN *in black. A little further, behind her, follow a few curious boys and young men, and the* GABBAI, *a small Jew with face thickly overgrown by black hair and a pair of heavy black eyebrows. All except the carriers and the* WOMAN *in black gather in a small group and whisper among themselves.*]

Younger Gravedigger. They bring the dead man.

Elder Gravedigger. We must wait for the Gabbai. [*The* GRAVEDIGGER *walk to the fence and beckon the* GABBAI *with their fingers.*] Gabbai. . .

Gabbai. [*Sticking his head through the fence*] What. . . . It isn' ready yet?

Elder Gravedigger. We found human bones in the hole. We put the earth back.

Gabbai. [*Retreating from the fence*] Where did the bones com from?

[*The black gates open. The carriers bear in the coffin with the corpse, se it down near the pillars, and remove the upper Board. From beneat the black coverlet protrude two feet and a head. The* WOMAN *i mourning stands silently at the head. The carriers make as if to tak up the coffin again. The voice of the* GABBAI *is heard from behind.*]

Gabbai. Stop! Stop!

[*The group crowds around, now looking at the* WOMAN, *now at th dead man, and whispering.*]

First in Crowd. The dead man waits for his grave, a bad sign.

Second in Crowd. Even Hell does not haste to receive him.

[*The* WOMAN *in black comes nearer to the dead man, and wants to r move the coverlet from his head. She wavers for an instant. Th people look at her with curiosity and fear. There is a pause.*]

Gabbai. [*Seeing the* WOMAN'*s movement, cries*] Don't let her. Sh mustn't do it.

Woman. [*In Polish*] Let me look but once at him. . . .

Gabbai. [*From behind the fence*] You mustn't.

[*The* WOMAN *silently steps back to her former place near the head the dead man.*]

First in Crowd. Who is she?

Second in Crowd. She came with him from beyond the frontier. No one knows whether she is his wife or mistress, a Jewess or a Christian. . . . She never comes to the synagogue, she never goes to the church.

Third in Crowd. She is going to pray for his soul.

Gabbai. [*To the* GRAVEDIGGERS, *pointing to a spot near the the fence*] Try to dig here.

Elder Gravedigger. [*Takes his spade in his hands*] Near the man who hanged himself?

Younger Gravedigger. A good enough neighborhood.

[*Both begin to dig.*]

First in Crowd. A fine grave for the dead man.

Second in Crowd. He deserved it.

Third in Crowd. He must not forget his name when the angel Domai [1] asks him how he is called.

Fourth in Crowd. He will talk with him in Polish.

Second in Crowd. He will offer him a Sabbath cigarette.

First in Crowd. With a chicken roasted in butter.

An Old Jew. Let him rest. He is dead.

Second in Crowd. They have found human bones.

[*The crowd becomes still. There is a pause.*]

Younger Gravedigger. My spade slides over something soft, as if there were no earth here.

Elder Gravedigger. I am afraid that—

Younger Gravedigger. I will dig no more.

Elder Gravedigger. Neither shall I.

Gabbai. [*From the distance*] What is the trouble now?

Younger Gravedigger. It seemed to me that my spade cut into human body.

[*There is a movement in the crowd. They surround the grave.*]

Gabbai. [*Putting on a pair of eyeglasses, which he takes out of his hip pocket*] What does this mean?

[*The crowd grows still. All look at each other silently. Suddenly a stream of water begins to gush out of the grave. All are excited. There is a long pause.*]

Gabbai. Water has appeared.

First in Crowd. The earth does not want to receive him.

[1] According to the old Jewish tradition, the asking for the name by angel Domai is the first test for admittance to heaven. The question must be answered with a passage from the Psalms and sinners forget the passage.

Second in Crowd. Even Hell closes its doors before him.

Third in Crowd. Lord of the world! How terrible his sins must be.

[*The crowd draws back from the dead man, leaving him with the* WOMAN *in black. She kneels before him, pressing her face to the folds of the cloth with which he is covered. The crowd no longer interferes, but draws away in amazement and fear, shaking their heads. There is a long pause. Gradually it grows darker. A murmuring is heard in the crowd.*]

Voices. What can we do? What will be?

Gabbai. Let someone call the Rabbi.

Gravediggers. Let them bring lanterns from the town.

[*One can hear the sound of dying footsteps.*]

First in Crowd. What can be done?

Gabbai. I advise you to dig a grave for the dead man near the grave of Rabbi Jehuda—

Elder Gravedigger. Beside Rabbi Jehuda? Beside him who was one of the thirty-six pillars of the earth?

Voices. Beside Rabbi Jehuda—a grave for *him?*

Gabbai. Yes, beside Rabbi Jehuda, beside the saint. The good deeds of Rabbi Jehuda will expiate the sins of the dead man, and the earth will receive the body. Beside him there will be no water. In order that the sinner may escape Hell, the saint must intercede for him.

First in Crowd. But what about the honor of Rabbi Jehuda?

Gabbai. Rabbi Jehuda never cared about honor during life, and it means less to him after death.

Elder Gravedigger. I cannot dig his grave near the grave of Rabbi Jehuda.

Younger Gravedigger. Nor I.

Gabbai. [*Stands above a low stone that is half-hidden beneath a tree, piously sways back and forth and begins to talk in a voice full of veneration*] It is known to Him, who said, "Let there be light," that it is not to offend thy worth that we want to bury this body near thee. But we know that the sinner shall find rest and quiet because of thy sanctity. Take him; let him find rest beside thee. [*He takes the spade and begins to dig.*]

First in Crowd. There is the stone on which Rabbi Jehuda lay for forty years and studied the Torah.

Second in Crowd. His thin neck left a deep mark on this stone, which served him as a pillow for forty years.

Third in Crowd. After the death of Rabbi Jehuda, they put this stone on his grave as a monument.

[*On the road behind the fence, against the dark background of the night, gleam the fires of nearing lanterns. Men in dark coats, women in shawls, boys carrying lights, enter the graveyard, deeply excited and frightened, and ask each other:*] "What happened? What happened?" [*Noticing the corpse and the* WOMAN *in black who is standing near it, the new arrivals draw away in fear and join the crowd, which surrounds the open grave.*]

Gabbai. [*Stops digging suddenly*] Listen, my people. My spade strikes against something very hard. My spade cannot go any farther. . . .

Voices. Heavenly Father. . . .

[*The people crowd about the grave with strained curiosity and expectation, without taking their eyes from the* GABBAI, *who silently tries to push his spade into the earth.*]

Fourth in Crowd. Stop digging. Stop!

First in Crowd. [*Comes near to the* GABBAI, *tears the spade from his hands, and throws it down.*] . . .

Second in Crowd. What will happen to the dead man?

Voices. Wait for the Rabbi.

Other Voices. Go for the Dayans.

Still Others. Woe. . . . Woe. . . .

Gabbai. Bring nearer the lanterns; let us see what is in the grave.

Fourth in Crowd. I wouldn't advise you to do that.

Gabbai. [*Ascends from the grave, takes a lantern, descends again, and digs in the earth*] A stone.

First in Crowd. The stone of Rabbi Jehuda lies across his grave, and does not let them bury the corpse beside him.

Second in Crowd. The earth does not want to receive him.

Voices. What must be done? What must be done?

Second in Crowd. Be still. The Rabbi is coming.

[*On the road behind the graveyard can be seen the lights of torches by which may be discerned the silhouettes of three old men with long beards. In the middle walks the oldest and tallest of them, one hand resting on a long staff, one on the shoulder of his* SHAMAS. *The men walk silently and slowly in the light of the lanterns. The gates open, and the* RABBI *with the* DAYANS *enter the graveyard. For a moment they stop near the corpse, throwing a horrified look at the kneeling* WOMAN *near it; however, they at once turn away their eyes, and, sur-*

*rounded by the crowd, approach the fresh grave. A mysterious whis-
pering is heard in the crowd.*]

Rabbi. [*Whispers with the* DAYANS, *and then turns to the people*]
My people, we have decided that in order that this dead man should be
received into a grave of Israel, each of us must grant him one of his good
deeds before the face of the Lord. I give him, forever and ever, twenty
pages of *Berachoth,* from the Talmud that I know by heart. Dayans,
each of you give him something.

First Dayan. I present to him the observance of one Sabbath.

Second Dayan. And I, the fasting of one Day of Atonement.

Fourth in Crowd. And I, a morning prayer on a week-day.

Second in Crowd. And I give him one book of the Psalms of David.

Rabbi. Enough. [*To the* GRAVEDIGGERS.] Go, dig the grave.

[*The* GRAVEDIGGERS *begin to dig. There is heard the sharp grating of a
spade against a rock.*]

Elder Gravedigger. The stone does not move from its place.

[*Silence reigns in the crowd. The* RABBI *and the* DAYANS *whisper among
themselves. One can hear the quiet, heart-broken sobbing of the*
WOMAN *in black.*]

First Dayan. Perhaps the dead man has offended the honor of the
saints, and the holy men who dwell in the glory of the light of God.
[*There is a pause.*]

Rabbi. [*Whispers with the* DAYANS, *then turns to the graves*] Ye who
dwell in the glory of the light of God, perhaps this dust has offended
your honor and your worth during its life. In his name, and in the name
of Israel, we beg forgiveness. And thou, Rabbi Jehuda, renowned for thy
humility, and for thy indifference to glory, allow this dust to rest by thy
side.

[*There is a gravelike silence. From afar comes the half-choked sobbing
of the* WOMAN *in black. There is a pause.*]

Gabbai. [*To the* GRAVEDIGGERS] Dig. [*They dig. Again there is heard
the ring of iron against stone.*]

Elder Gravedigger. The stone does not move from its place. [*The*
RABBI *again whispers with the* DAYANS. *The crowd is hushed and ex-
pectant.*]

First Dayan. Perhaps the dead man has offended the earth.

Rabbi. [*Turning to the earth*] Earth, mother of the living and of
the dead, out of whose womb all is born, and into which all returneth—
if this dead man has offended thee while alive, I ask thee in his name,
and in the name of Israel, to grant him forgiveness. Receive his body.
For out of dust cometh man, and to dust he returneth.

[*A long pause. The* GRAVEDIGGERS *begin to dig once more. Again one can hear the ringing of the spade.*]

Elder Gravedigger. The stone does not move from its place.

[*There is a silence. The voice of the* WOMAN *is heard as if from afar.*]

First Dayan. Perhaps the dead man blasphemed before God?

Second Dayan. Perhaps the body does not belong in this graveyard?

Rabbi. [*After a short pause*] Gabbai.

Gabbai. Yes, Rabbi.

Rabbi. Listen. Bring wood, make a fire in the graveyard, and lay seven bricks into it. [*To the crowd:*] If the bricks fall apart, it will mean that his soul cannot stay in that world in which it has grown up; that the dead man does not belong in this graveyard, and that the earth will not receive him.

[*Wood is brought, and a fire is started near the dead man. Seven bricks are thrown into it. The fire grows brighter and lights the surrounding crowd and the half-decayed, crooked tombstones; throws a bright glow on the corpse and the kneeling* WOMAN *near it. There is a long pause. Suddenly there is heard a cry:*] "A brick has cracked."]

Rabbi. So far there is only one.

[*There is a crack. Another falls apart.*]

Voices. It has fallen apart.

Rabbi. It is only the second.

[*There is another crack, and all the bricks fall to pieces, all except one, which still holds together. The crowd stands as if shocked by something tremendous. Some cry out in fear and amazement.*]

Voices. God Almighty! Heavenly Father!

First in Crowd. What could this man have done?

Rabbi. One brick still holds.

Voices. And that one is cracking, too.

Others. We hear it crack.

Voices. There! There!

Rabbi. It has not fallen apart yet.

First in Crowd. The halves of the brick hold together as if they were soldered with fire.

First Dayan. It is not so easy for a Jewish soul to tear itself away from the mother-stem.

Second Dayan. Surely he must have suffered much before he came to this.

Rabbi. [*Approaches and points with his hand*] Even as this brick is tortured in the fire, so his soul tortured itself in life. [*The fire begins to die. Only ashes and live coals remain. The* RABBI *and the* DAYANS *come near the dying fire, and look carefully at the bricks. Then the* RABBI *turns to the grave, and says in quiet, commanding tones:*] You must receive him, for he has remained a Jew, and belongs in this graveyard. [*To the other graves:*] And ye must receive him in your midst, whether ye will it or not.

Gabbai. [*To the* GRAVEDIGGERS] Dig. [*They dig.*]

Elder Gravedigger. The stone falls to pieces beneath my spade.

Younger Gravedigger. It crumbles like sand.

Rabbi. [*To the* SHAMAS] Go near to the dead man and tell him that he is not the husband of this woman, and that she is not his wife. [*He takes off a silken belt and gives it to the* SHAMAS.]

Shamas. [*Girding himself with the belt, comes near the dead man, and says*] You are not her husband. She is not your wife.

[*The* GABBAI *and another man approach the corpse and bear it to the grave. The* WOMAN *in black remains alone, still kneeling. The corpse is taken from the stretcher and lowered into the ground in a white winding sheet.*]

Gabbai. [*Breaks an earthen pot and lays the shards on the eyes and mouth of the dead man*] I close the eyes which have seen evil and the lips which have uttered it.

[*The grave is covered with earth. The crowd with lanterns file out one by one, leaving only the* WOMAN, *and the* ELDER GRAVEDIGGER. *The latter, by the light of his lantern and the dying fire, nails a board above the new grave. On the dark road which leads to the town are seen the retreating lights of many lanterns.*]

Elder Gravedigger. [*Stands still above the fresh grave for a while, then says*] May thy sinful soul have rest. [*Goes away with his lantern.*]

[*It grows dark. In the depths of the night still glow the last cinders of the fire. In their dim light one can see how the* WOMAN *in black rises, and slowly and quietly approaches the grave and throws her black covering over it. The black wings of the clouds beat about her very head. From the mist of these clouds the* WOMAN *emerges in a white dress, and slowly, noiselessly, she walks to the road that twists into the night beyond the graveyard. Far in front of her are still seen the glimmering lights of the disappearing lanterns. The curtain descends very slowly.*]

THAT SPECK

by s. n. behrman

Hugo. [*Not too seriously*] There's no such thing as absolute friendship. Like everything else, friendship is relative—a thermometer of expediency.

Lael. That's too cynical. Not bad as an epigram though. But you can't compress the truth about anything into a sentence. It's like pressing a drop of blood on a slide and saying: "This is the stuff that flows in your veins!" It isn't though. When it's in your veins it's something different.

Hugo. I'm glad you can believe in friendship. It must be a great comfort to you!

Lael. Don't you? Don't you really?

Hugo. I did once.

Lael. During the trouble at home—did no one stand by you?

Hugo. I was aware of one friend. He was an unknown playwright. I felt this man to be, though he was even then middle-aged, the freshest and the most living voice, since Ibsen, in Europe. In my first published book a large part was devoted to him. But the book brought me more success than it brought him—as a result of it I was invited to lecture in America. I took his plays with me. I translated them and lectured on them from New York to San Francisco. Now, you must understand that in all this, I was exalting myself; it was the most any critic can be, a disciple of greatness.

Lael. [*Knowing he has begun to be afraid she will think him conceited*] I understand, Hugo.

Hugo. And I had the greatest reward such discipleship can have. As a result of my enthusiasm a curious phenomenon took place; the fame I created for him in America reverberated to Germany—and we began to accept him at home!

Lael. You mean Lehrmann, I suppose?

Hugo. Yes, Lehrmann.

Lael. He's your Grand Old Man, isn't he?

Hugo. Something like that. He's over sixty. I've hero-worshipped him for thirty years. I came to see him, sure that in his mellow greeting, I would be in some sense—restored. Because I actually felt a wavering of sanity. I had sent him the manuscript of my pamphlet. I began to tell him how disturbed I was by the New Dispensation when I detected a new look in his eyes, a new manner. He had not smiled in greeting; he had not given me his hand. He refused point-blank to read my pamphlet; in a hard voice he advised me to tear it up. "This is a new day," he said to me. "There is no place in it for Oriental decadence!" Oriental! My family had lived in Germany for hundreds of years. I sat there staring at him. In his eyes, already glazed with mortality, I saw something impenetrable, incurably hostile, something that no appeal to the past could soften. That look did for me. I'd never had such a sense of helplessness. For in his youth this man had been the voice of the submerged—he had written the saga of the oppressed and the poor; he had been a living instrument of justice. There he sat, impersonal, hard, fanatical. He let me go without asking me to come to see him again, as you let go a servant who has cheated you and to whom you refuse to give a reference. . . . Friendship! [*A pause. He tries to gather himself together and speaks lightly.*] After all—it's none of your affair, is it?

Lael. [*Very quietly*] That's the unkindest thing, I think, that anyone's ever said to me.

Hugo. I'm sorry, but, really—I came here a complete stranger to you—you invite me to stay out of a fantastic goodness of heart. The least I can do in return is to be—jolly. As a matter of fact, I'm going away and that is partly why. It's too unfair to you.

Lael. You mustn't go until you've had a chance to get a perspective on yourself. Besides, where would you go?

Hugo. I was going to borrow from Sascha passage-money to America. They've started something there they call the University in Exile. Maybe I could get into that. I've cabled the director.

Lael. We'll see what can be done for you *here*.

Hugo. It won't be easy. To be at once an emigré and a critic—that is a double parasitism. Before I can be eloquent I need a masterpiece and before I can be witty I need something which fails to be a masterpiece.

Lael. [*Amused*] Have you heard yet from America?

Hugo. Not yet.

Lael. Well, I *do* wish you could feel welcome here, Hugo. Don't you like me?

Hugo. You've been very—gracious. It's that—! I feel—! [*He doesn't finish. She gives him a quick look. She realizes that she has a problem on her hands that will not yield to simple tact merely.*]

Lael. Hugo—

Hugo. Yes?

Lael. Do you mind if I speak to you—frankly. That is to say, critically?

Hugo. [*Smiles quizzically*] Do you think I'm thin-skinned?

Lael. I've avoided rather speaking to you about your—special experience. I've avoided it in a mistaken effort to keep your mind off it—but aren't you mistaking a mass antagonism for a personal one? Hugo, you don't want to develop a persecution mania.

Hugo. Is it a mania for the persecuted to believe in the reality of persecution?

Lael. No. The truth is there's a pest over all the world just now, an epidemic of hatred and intolerance that may engulf us all. That is perfectly possible. People have suffered too much during the last twenty years—they can't stand any more, that's all. In one way or another they're letting off steam—the form it's taken against you is peculiarly detestable. Everyone here abhors it. The whole world revolts against it. That is what you must remember. This is a different climate, Hugo; you are like a man who continues to shiver when he's left the Arctic—and moved into the tropics. There are other worlds, you must remember, than the one you've left. . . .

Hugo. Are there?

Lael. Oh, I know what you're saying to yourself: "It's easy enough for her to talk. She's at home, she's comfortable, she's secure." Am I though? There is no longer, in this curious moment of history, any security for anybody. What security should I have, as a liberal person, if the world goes Communist? Or Fascist? I think Hobart Eldridge and Lord Abercrombie might be—to say the least—unsympathetic to me. In any dictatorship, subleties of opinion and temperament are swept away; you're either black or white.

Hugo. [*Quizzically*] But you're not a luxury commodity!

Lael. I beg your pardon!

Hugo. Like the race of which I find myself suddenly an involuntary member!

Lael. But, Hugo, these days *every* hereditary aristocracy is a luxury commodity!

Hugo. [*He takes her hand and kisses it*] You're very sweet—but I'm afraid the analogy is not quite complete. They, I suppose I ought to say we, are like passengers on a vessel that lets them stay on board—and even enter the first-class salons occasionally—as long as the weather is fair—but ho! for the sharks the minute there's a storm. Our science and our art are tolerated and even praised while the economic level is high. Once the golden stream is dammed and constriction sets in we are the first to be squeezed. Of course the world has suffered, we among the rest, but, in its misery it singles us out to levy a secret and an ageless revenge.

Lael. [*After a moment*] Where is your legendary patience, your legendary capacity for endurance, your legendary—resignation?

Hugo. [*Almost gleefully*] I haven't it! That's my special dilemma. I am neither patient, nor resigned, nor enduring. You forget I am only a Jew by fraction! I suffer the disabilities without the hereditary armors. The Aryan seven-eighths of me wars against the Semitic eighth—wars and retreats—and I'm afraid nothing can be done for me.

Lael. That, Hugo, is a challenge to my resourcefulness! Promise me that you won't run away—if only because I like you and find you very sympathetic. [*Humorously.*] If you don't enjoy adapting yourself to Phoebe—adapt yourself to me.

Hugo. [*A slight pause, sincerely*] Shall I?

Lael. [*After a second—candidly*] No. Don't.

Hugo. The idea tempts me.

Lael. [*Resolutely*] It was automatically flirtatious. You deserve better than that of me—and so do I!

Hugo. [*Rather darting out at her*] You're in love with Rand!

Lael. [*After a moment*] One's an awful mixture, Hugo.

Hugo. [*Accepting it instantly as a fact*] Don't you feel a sense of—incongruity?

Lael. All the time. Yes. Keenly. It doesn't help though. [*A moment's pause. She walks about the room impatiently. He watches her.*] One gets so tired of one's own complexities. There's Rand, a symbol of simplicity, courage and directness. There, in a world of cruelty and chicanery, are honest purpose and generosity.

Hugo. So eloquent—and so unconvinced!

Lael. [*Looks at him quickly, then away*] You're shrewd, Hugo. You're diabolically shrewd.

Hugo. [*Watching her*] Am I?

Lael. Of course I'm unconvinced, but whether I'm convinced or not—there it is!

Hugo. [*Shrugging his shoulders*] Why attempt to rationalize the—elemental?

Lael. [*As if to herself*] Isn't it extraordinary how one can go on being agreeable and alert—so-called normal—and all the time nourish an obsession that has a life of its own, independent and arrogant—a fugue that seeks stubbornly its own resolution—at no matter what cost—to oneself? [*Rises and faces him.*] Hugo . . .

Hugo. [*Rises*] Yes?

Lael. [*Throwing away her pretences and appealing to him pitifully*] In you I feel—a special friend. Don't go. Please stay.

Hugo. [*Crosses to her*] All right. I'll stay. [*With great intensity.*] But not as a friend.

Lael. [*Almost whispers*] Hugo . . .

Hugo. Not even as a special friend.

Lael. On any terms.

Hugo. But because an obsession—may be destroyed.

Lael. [*Realizes the implication of what he has said and looks at him in surprise*] Hugo!

Hugo. [*Terrific determination*] Yes! It may be destroyed!

[*His hand closes on her arm. They stand near together, close and warm spiritually also. PHOEBE comes in. She is eaten with jealousy, blind with rage, behaves almost like a person paralyzed with drugs. Speaks and walks as if in automatism.*]

Phoebe. Do forgive me!

Lael. Hello, Phoebe. Won't you . . .

Phoebe. [*Without waiting to discover the invitation*] No, thank you very much. [*She stands at door leading to staircase and addresses* HUGO.] Liar! Liar! Liar!

[*She disappears.*]

Lael. Hugo! What does she mean? What did you tell her?

Hugo. [*Drily*] Well, she demanded to know whether there was anything between us, and I said there was not.

Lael. [*Mischievously*] Well, you really shouldn't have lied to her, Hugo.

Hugo. That was twenty minutes ago—and I didn't know. . . . [*She is amused and provoked and still a little disturbed by* PHOEBE's *plight. He stands looking at her, enchanted by her.*]

QUICK CURTAIN

RIPE POMEGRANATES

There is an unbroken poetic tradition in Jewish literature. It begins with the *Song of Deborah and Barak,* which was composed about 1100 B.C.E., and continues without interruption down to the present. Collections of great poetry like the *Book of Jashar* (from which we have several excerpts in the Bible) have been irrecoverably lost, but vast treasures out of medieval times and later have been rediscovered by modern scholars, from Leopold Zunz to Israel Davidson. The past fifty or more years have witnessed an efflorescence of Jewish poets and poetry.

The object of this section is to present the thread of poetic continuity which runs through and connects Jewish literature. Selections from the works of more than fifty poets—relatively few when one considers the scope of this section—offer some of the most precious creations of the Jewish spirit. Although religious poetry has been adequately represented, the attempt has been made to include a greater portion of secular, lyric poetry. Too, several long philosophical poems, like Ibn Gabriol's majestic *Keter Malkut,* had to be omitted for lack of space.

A cursory reading of this poetry indicates how misleading are the attempts to define and to isolate the spiritual tendencies in the stream of Jewish life. The great tribute to nature in the 104th Psalm, the profound religiousness of Ibn Gabriol and the tender lyricism of Lasker-Schueler have their counterpart in the expression of their times. To be sure, the landscape that permeates Jewish poetry was enriched by history and lore but it was always rooted in the general soil of humanity. What Zunz said of Jewish literature is certainly true of poetry: "Inasmuch as it shares the intellectual aspirations of past and present, their conflicts and reverses, it is supplementary to general literature. Its peculiar features, themselves falling under universal laws, are in turn helpful in the interpretation of general characteristics. If the aggregate results of mankind's intellectual activity can be likened unto a sea, Jewish literature is one of the tributaries that feed it. Jewish literature, like other literatures, reveals to the student the noble ideals the soul of man has cherished, and striven to realize, and discloses the varied achievements of the mind of man. . . . The ideals of the spirit consciously held by any portion of mankind lend freedom to thought, grace to feeling; and by sailing up this one stream we may reach the fountain-head whence all spiritual forces emanate, and about which, as a fixed pole, all currents eddy."

The Biblical selections are, with few exceptions, from the Authorized Versions. The translators of all other poetry are indicated in parentheses at the end of each poem. Where several translations of a poem exist, the editor has selected the one which in his opinion is the most beautiful.

THE SONG OF DEBORAH AND BARAK[1]

12th cent. B.C.

Praise ye the Lord for the avenging of Israel,
When the people willingly offered themselves.
Hear, O ye kings; give ear, O ye princes;
I, even I, will sing unto the Lord;
I will sing praise to the Lord God of Israel.

Lord, when thou wentest out of Seir,
When thou marchedst out of the field of Edom,
The earth trembled, and the heavens dropped,
The clouds also dropped water.
The mountains melted from before the Lord,
Even that Sinai from before the Lord God of Israel.

In the days of Shamgar the son of Anath,
In the days of Jael, the highways were unoccupied,
And the travellers walked through byways.
The inhabitants of the villages ceased, they ceased in Israel,
Until thou, Deborah, didst arise,
Till thou didst arise a mother in Israel.

They chose new gods;
Then was war in the gates:
Was there a shield or spear seen
Among forty thousand in Israel?
My heart is toward the governors of Israel,
That offered themselves willingly among the people.
Bless ye the Lord.
Speak, ye that ride on white asses,
Ye that sit in judgment, and walk by the way.
They that are delivered from the noise of archers
In the places of drawing water,
There shall they rehearse the righteous acts of the Lord,

---

[1] This ode, which is considered the oldest extant piece of Hebrew literature, is found in *Judges* 5: 2-31. It celebrates the first great victory of the tribes of Israel over the Canaanites in the late twelfth century, B.C.E. A prose account of the battle is preserved in the preceding chapter of the same book.

545

Even the righteous acts toward the inhabitants of his villages in Israel:
Then shall the people of the Lord go down to the gates.

Awake, awake, Deborah:
Awake, awake, utter a song:
Arise, Barak, and lead thy captivity captive, thou son of Abinoam.
Out of Ephraim was there a root of them against Amalek;
After thee, Benjamin, among thy people;
Out of Machir came down governors,
And out of Zebulun they that handle the pen of the writer.
And the princes of Issachar were with Deborah;
Even Issachar, and also Barak;
He was sent on foot into the valley.
For the divisions of Reuben
There were great thoughts of heart.
Why abodest thou among the sheepfolds,
To hear the bleatings of the flocks?
For the divisions of Reuben
There were great searchings of heart.
Gilead abode beyond Jordan:
And why did Dan remain in ships?
Asher continued on the sea shore,
And abode in his breaches.
Zebulun and Naphtali were a people that jeoparded their lives unto the death
In the high places of the field.

The kings came and fought,
Then fought the kings of Canaan
In Taanach by the waters of Megiddo;
They took no gain of money.
They fought from heaven;
The stars in their courses fought against Sisera.
The river of Kishon swept them away,
That ancient river, the river Kishon.
O my soul, thou hast trodden down strength.
Then were the horsehoofs broken
By the means of the prancings, the prancings of their mighty ones.

'Curse ye Meroz,' said the angel of the Lord,
'Curse ye bitterly the inhabitants thereof;
Because they came not to the help of the Lord,
To the help of the Lord against the mighty.'

Blessed above women shall Jael be,
The wife of Heber the Kenite,

Blessed shall she be above women in the tent.
He asked water, and she gave him milk;
She brought forth butter in a lordly dish
She put her hand to the nail,
And her right hand to the workmen's hammer;
And with the hammer she smote Sisera, she smote off his head.
When she had pierced and stricken through his temples.
At her feet he bowed, he fell, he lay down:
At her feet he bowed, he fell:
Where he bowed, there he fell down dead.

The mother of Sisera looked out at a window,
And cried through the lattice,
'Why is his chariot so long in coming?
Why tarry the wheels of his chariots?'
Her wise ladies answered her,
Yea, she returned answer to herself,
'Have they not sped? have they not divided the prey;
To every man a damsel or two;
To Sisera a prey of divers colours,
A prey of divers colours of needlework,
Of divers colours of needlework on both sides,
Meet for the necks of them that take the spoil?'

So let all thine enemies perish, O Lord:
But let them that love him be as the sun when he goeth forth in his might.

LAMENT [1]

by DAVID BEN JESSE

C. 1040 B.C.–970 B.C.

The beauty of Israel is slain upon thy high places:
How are the mighty fallen!
Tell it not in Gath,

[1] This moving dirge is probably the only surviving poem that actually was written by and not attributed to David. It was written on the occasion of the defeat of the Israelites by the Philistines in the Battle of Mt. Gilboa (c. 1010 B.C.E.) in which King Saul and Prince Jonathan were slain. The story is narrated in *I Samuel* 29-*II Samuel* 1. The poem originally appeared in the *Book of Jashar*, a collection of Hebrew poetry no longer extant.

Publish it not in the streets of Askelon;
Lest the daughters of the Philistines rejoice,
Lest the daughters of the uncircumcised triumph.

Ye mountains of Gilboa,
Let there be no dew, neither let there be rain, upon you, nor fields of offerings:
For there the shield of the mighty is vilely cast away,
The shield of Saul, as though he had not been anointed with oil.
From the blood of the slain, from the fat of the mighty,
The bow of Jonathan turned not back,
And the sword of Saul returned not empty.

Saul and Jonathan were lovely and pleasant in their lives,
And in their death they were not divided:
They were swifter than eagles,
They were stronger than lions.
Ye daughters of Israel, weep over Saul,
Who clothed you in scarlet, with other delights,
Who put ornaments of gold upon your apparel.
How are the mighty fallen in the midst of the battle!

O Jonathan, thou wast slain in thine high places.
I am distressed for thee, my brother Jonathan:
Very pleasant hast thou been unto me:
Thy love to me was wonderful,
Passing the love of women.
How are the mighty fallen,
And the weapons of war perished!

SPRING SONG[1]

9th cent. B.C.?

She: Hark! my beloved!
         Ah, here he comes,
         Leaping over the mountains,
         Skipping over the hills.
         My beloved is like a gazelle.

[1] One of the lyrics that comprise the *Song of Songs* (2: 8-17). Although some scholars believe that this book is the only surviving specimen of the Hebrew drama and the Synagogue and Church looked upon it as religious allegory, it is more probably a collection of folk poetry, of wedding songs. The book was ascribed to Solomon.

He appears as a young stag.
Ah! here he stands,
He is behind our wall,
Peering through the windows,
Looking through the lattices.
My beloved spoke, and called to me:

He: Rise up, my love,
My fair one, come away!
For, lo, the winter is past,
The rain is over and gone;
The flowers appear on the earth,
The birds' singing time is here,
And the call of the turtle-dove is heard in our land;
The fig tree ripens her winter fruit,
And blossoming vines give forth fragrance.
Rise up, my love,
My fair one, come away.

She: O my dove in the clefts of the rocks,
Who hides in the covert of the cliffs,
Let me see thy face,
Let me hear thy voice;
For sweet is thy voice,
And thy face comely.

He (sings): *"Catch for us the foxes, the little foxes,*
That despoil the vineyards,
For our vines are in blossom!"

She: My beloved is mine, and I am his:
He feedeth his flock among the lilies.
Until the evening breeze blows,
And the shadows disappear,
Turn away, my beloved!
Be thou as a young stag
Upon the cleft-riven hills!

LOVE [1]

9th cent. B.C.?

Set me as a seal upon thy heart,
As a seal upon thine arm;

[1] *Song of Songs* 8: 6-7. See note on page 548.

For love is strong as death,
Jealousy is cruel as the grave;
The flashes thereof are flashes of fire,
A very flame of God!
Many waters cannot quench love,
Neither can the floods drown it;
If a man would offer all his wealth for love,
He would be utterly despised.

TWO VISIONS [1]

by ISAIAH BEN AMOZ

c. 760–700 B.C.

I. THE HOUSE OF ISRAEL

Now will I sing to my wellbeloved
A song of my beloved touching his vineyard.

My wellbeloved hath a vineyard
In a very fruitful hill;
And he fenced it, and gathered out the stones thereof,
And planted it with the choicest vine,
And built a tower in the midst of it,
And also made a winepress therein;
And he looked that it should bring forth grapes,
And it brought forth wild grapes.

And now, O inhabitants of Jerusalem, and men of Judah,
Judge, I pray you, betwixt me and my vineyard.
What could have been done more to my vineyard,
That I have not done in it?
Wherefore, when I looked that it should bring forth grapes,
Brought it forth wild grapes?

And now go to; I will tell you
What I will do to my vineyard:

[1] These two examples of prophetic poetry are selected from the book of *Isaiah* (5: 1-7 and 2: 2-4). They were written toward the end of the eighth century B.C.E. The first poem indicates the use of the technique of a love poem to drive home the significance of the parable.

I will take away the hedge thereof, and it shall be eaten up;
And break down the wall thereof, and it shall be trodden down;
And I will lay it waste: it shall not be pruned, nor digged;
But there shall come up briers and thorns:
I will also command the clouds
That they rain no rain upon it.

For the vineyard of the Lord of hosts is the house of Israel,
And the men of Judah his pleasant plant;
And he looked for judgment, but behold oppression;
For righteousness, but behold a cry.

II. PEACE

And it shall come to pass in the last day,
That the mountain of the Lord's house
Shall be established in the top of the mountains,
And shall be exalted above the hills;
And all nations shall flow unto it.

And many people shall go and say,
"Come ye, and let us go up to the mountain of the Lord,
To the house of the God of Jacob;
And he will teach us of his way,
And we will walk in his paths.
For out of Zion shall go forth the law,
And the word of the Lord from Jerusalem."

And he shall judge among the nations,
And shall rebuke many people;
And they shall beat their swords into plowshares,
And their spears into pruning hooks.
Nation shall not lift up sword against nation,
Neither shall they learn war any more.

TRAVAIL [1]

by JEREMIAH BEN HILKIAH

c. 640 B.C.–585 B.C.

My bowels, my bowels!
I am pained at my very heart;
My heart maketh a noise in me,
I cannot hold my peace,
Because thou hast heard, O my soul,
The sound of the trumpet,
The alarm of war;
Destruction upon destruction is cried,
For the whole land is despoiled,
Suddenly my tents are spoiled,
And my curtains in a moment.
How long shall I see the standard,
And hear the sound of the trumpet?

When I would comfort myself against sorrow,
My heart is faint within me.
Behold the voice of the cry of the daughter of my people,
Because of them that dwell in a far country,
Is not the Lord in Zion?
Is not her King in her!
Why have they provoked me to anger
With their graven images, and with strange vanities?
The harvest is past,
The summer is ended,
And we are not saved.
For the hurt of the daughter of my people am I hurt;
I am black; astonishment hath taken hold on me.
Is there no balm in Gilead?
Is there no physician there?
Why then is not the health of the daughter of my people recovered?
Oh, that my head were waters,
And mine eyes a fountain of tears,

---

[1] In these poems Jeremiah expresses his profound sympathy with the sorrows of his people and his deep personal grief. They are selected from the book of *Jeremiah* (4: 19-21; 23-26; 8: 18-9: 1; 20: 7-12; 14-18).

That I might weep day and night
For the slain of the daughter of my people!

O Lord, thou hast deceived me,
And I was deceived;
Thou art stronger than I
And hast prevailed.
I am become a laughingstock all the day;
Every one mocketh me.
For as often as I speak I cry out,
I cry, "Violence and spoil."
Because the word of the Lord is made a reproach unto me,
And a derision all the day.
And if I say, I will not make mention of him
Nor speak any more in his name,
Then there is in mine heart as it were
A burning fire shut up in my bones,
And I am weary with forbearing
And I cannot contain myself.

Cursed be the day wherein I was born,
Let not the day wherein my mother bare me be blessed.
Cursed be the man who brought tidings to my father,
Saying, "A man child is born unto thee," making him glad.
Wherefore came I forth out of the womb to see labour and sorrow,
That my days should be consumed with shame?

HO, EVERY ONE THAT THIRSTETH [1]

c. 6th cent. B.C.

"Ho, every one that thirsteth, come ye to the waters,
And he that hath no money; come ye, buy, and eat;
Yea, come, buy wine and milk
Without money and without price.
Wherefore do ye spend money for that which is not bread?

[1] The anonymous author of this poem is generally referred to as the Second Isaiah because his prophetic visions were placed together with (chaps. 40-55) those of Isaiah. He lived in the sixth century B.C.E. during the time of Cyrus, but his country—either Babylon or Palestine—is still a matter of controversy. His poetry and his conception of man and history attain grandeur in the so-called 'Servant-Songs' (*Isaiah* 42: 1-4; 49: 1-6; 50: 4-9; 52: 13-53). The above selection is chapter 55.

And your labour for that which satisfieth not?
Hearken diligently unto me, and eat yet that which is good,
And let your soul delight itself in fatness.

Incline your ear, and come unto me;
Hear, and your soul shall live;
And I will make an everlasting covenant with you,
Even the sure mercies of David.
Behold, I have given him for a witness to the people,
A leader and commander to the people.
Behold, thou shalt call a nation that thou knowest not,
And nations that knew not thee shall run unto thee
Because of the Lord thy God,
And for the Holy One of Israel; for he hath glorified thee.

Seek ye the Lord while he may be found,
Call ye upon him while he is near:
Let the wicked forsake his way,
And the unrighteous man his thoughts:
And let him return unto the Lord,
And he will have mercy upon him;
And to our God,
For he will abundantly pardon.
For my thoughts are not your thoughts,
Neither are your ways my ways," saith the Lord.
"For as the heavens
Are higher than the earth,
So are my ways higher than your ways,
And my thoughts than your thoughts.
For as the rain cometh down, and the snow from heaven,
And returneth not thither, but watereth the earth,
And maketh it bring forth and bud,
That it may give seed to the sower, and bread to the eater:
So shall my word be that goeth forth out of my mouth:
It shall not return unto me void,
But it shall accomplish that which I please,
And it shall prosper in the thing whereto I sent it.

For ye shall go out with joy,
And be led forth with peace:
The mountains and the hills shall break forth before you into singing,
And all of the trees of the field shall clap their hands.
Instead of the thorn shall come up the fir tree,
And instead of the brier shall come up the myrtle tree:

And it shall be to the Lord for a name,
For an everlasting sign that shall not be cut off."

BEYOND KNOWLEDGE[1]
400 B.C.?

There be three things which are too wonderful for me,
Yea, four which I know not:
The way of an eagle in the air;
The way of a serpent upon a rock;
The way of a ship in the midst of the sea;
And the way of a man with a maid.

GO TO THE ANT, THOU SLUGGARD[2]
400 B.C.?

Go to the ant, thou sluggard;
Consider her ways, and be wise:
Which having no chief,
Overseer, or ruler,
Provideth her meat in the summer,
And gathereth her food in the harvest.

How long wilt thou sleep, O sluggard?
When wilt thou arise out of thy sleep?
Yet a little sleep, a little slumber,
A little folding of the hands to sleep:
So shall thy poverty come as a robber,
And thy want as an armed man.

[1] The proverb was a popular form of wisdom literature among all peoples in ancient times. The Hebrew name *mashal* suggests the allegorical character of these pithy sayings about the etiquette and morals of society. The selection is from *Proverbs* 30: 18-19.

[2] *Proverbs* 6: 6-11. See note on last poem.

DIVINE CHALLENGE [1]

c. 400 B.C.?

Who is this that darkeneth counsel by words without knowledge?
Gird up now thy loins like a man;
For I will demand of thee, and declare thou unto me.
Where wast thou when I laid the foundations of the earth?
Declare, if thou hast understanding.
Who determined the measures thereof, if thou knowest?
Or who stretched the line upon it?
Whereupon were the foundations thereof fastened?
Or who laid the corner stone thereof;
When the morning stars sang together,
And all the sons of God shouted for joy?
Or who shut up the sea with doors,
When it brake forth, as if it had issued out of the womb;
When I made the cloud the garment thereof,
And thick darkness a swaddlingband for it,
And prescribed for it my decree,
And set bars and doors,
And said, Hitherto shalt thou come, but no further;
And here shall thy proud waves be stayed?
Hast thou commanded the morning since thy days began,
And caused the dayspring to know its place;
That it might take hold of the ends of the earth,
And the wicked be shaken out of it?
It is changed as clay under the seal;
And all things stand forth as a garment:
And from the wicked their light is withholden,
And the high arm is broken.
Hast thou entered into the springs of the sea?
Or hast thou walked in the recesses of the deep?
Have the gates of death been revealed unto thee?
Or hast thou seen the gates of the shadow of death?
Hast thou comprehended the breadth of the earth?
Declare, if thou knowest it all.

[1] The book of *Job* is one of the masterpieces of world literature. It is a dramatic poem dealing with the problems of human suffering and human limitations. The material for the poem was derived from tradition. The above passage comprises chapters 38 and 39.

Where is the way to the dwelling of light,
And as for darkness, where is the place thereof;
That thou shouldest take it to the bound thereof,
And that thou shouldest discern the paths to the house thereof?
Doubtless, thou knowest, for thou wast then born,
And the number of thy days is great!
Hast thou entered the treasuries of the snow,
Or hast thou seen the treasuries of the hail,
Which I have reserved against the time of trouble,
Against the day of battle and war?
By what way is the light parted,
Or the east wind scattered upon the earth?
Who hath cleft a channel for the waterflood,
Or a way for the lightning of the thunder;
To cause it to rain on a land where no man is;
On the wilderness, wherein there is no man;
To satisfy the waste and desolate ground;
And to cause the tender grass to spring forth?
Hath the rain a father?
Or who hath begotten the drops of dew?
Out of whose womb came the ice?
And the hoary frost of heaven, who hath gendered it?
The waters are hidden as with stone
And the face of the deep is frozen.
Canst thou bind the cluster of the Pleiades,
Or loose the bands of Orion?
Canst thou lead forth the Mazzaroth in their season?
Or canst thou guide the Bear with her train?
Knowest thou the ordinances of the heavens?
Canst thou establish the dominion thereof in the earth?
Canst thou lift up thy voice to the clouds,
That abundance of waters may cover thee?
Canst thou send forth lightnings, that they may go,
And say unto thee, Here we are?
Who hath put wisdom in the inward parts?
Or who hath given understanding to the mind?
Who can number the clouds by wisdom?
Or who can pour out the bottles of heaven,
When the dust runneth into a mass,
And the clods cleave fast together?
Wilt thou hunt the prey for the lioness?
Or satisfy the appetite of the young lions,
When they couch in their dens,

And abide in the covert to lie in wait?
Who provideth for the raven his food,
When his young ones cry unto God,
And wander for lack of meat?

Knowest thou the time when the wild goats of the rock bring forth?
Or canst thou mark when the hinds do calve?
Canst thou number the months that they fulfil?
Or knowest thou the time when they bring forth?
They bow themselves, they bring forth their young,
They cast out their sorrows.
Their young ones are in good liking, they grow up in the open field;
They go forth, and return not again.
Who hath sent out the wild ass free?
Or who hath loosed the bands of the wild ass?
Whose house I have made the wilderness,
And the salt land his dwelling place.
He scorneth the tumult of the city,
Neither heareth he the shoutings of the driver.
The range of the mountains is his pasture,
And he searcheth after every green thing.
Will the wild-ox be content to serve thee?
Or will he abide by the crib?
Canst thou bind the wild-ox with his band in the furrow?
Or will he harrow the valleys after thee?
Wilt thou trust him, because his strength is great?
Or wilt thou leave to him thy labour?
Wilt thou confide in him, that he will bring home thy seed,
And gather the corn of thy threshing-floor?
The wing of the ostrich rejoiceth;
But are her pinions and feathers kindly?
For she leaveth her eggs on the earth,
And warmeth them in the dust,
And forgetteth that the foot may crush them,
Or that the wild beast may trample them.
She is hardened against her young ones, as if they were not hers;
Though her labour be in vain, she is without fear;
Because God hath deprived her of wisdom,
Neither hath he imparted to her understanding.
What time she lifteth up herself on high,
She scorneth the horse and his rider.

Hast thou given the horse his might?
Hast thou clothed his neck with the quivering mane?
Hast thou made him to leap as a locust?

The glory of his snorting is terrible.
He paweth in the valley, and rejoiceth in his strength:
He goeth out to meet the armed men.
He mocketh at fear, and is not dismayed;
Neither turneth he back from the sword.
The quiver rattleth against him.
The flashing spear and the javelin.
He swalloweth the ground with fierceness and rage;
Neither believeth he that it is the voice of the trumpet.
As oft as the trumpet soundeth he saith, Aha!
And he smelleth the battle afar off,
The thunder of the captains, and the shouting.
Doth the hawk soar by thy wisdom
And stretch her wings toward the south?
Doth the eagle mount up at thy command,
And make her nest on high?
She dwelleth on the rock, and hath her lodging there,
Upon the crag of the rock, and the strong hold.
From thence she spieth out the prey;
Her eyes behold it afar off.
Her young ones also suck up blood:
And where the slain are, there is she.

GOD IN NATURE [1]

c. 350 B.C.?

Bless the Lord, O my soul.
O Lord my God, thou art very great;
Thou art clothed with honour and majesty.
Who coverest thyself with light as with a garment;
Who stretchest out the heavens like a curtain;
Who layeth the beams of his chambers in the waters;
Who maketh the clouds his chariot;
Who walketh upon the wings of the wind;
Who maketh winds his messengers;
His ministers a flaming fire:
Who laid the foundations of the earth,
That it should not be moved for ever.

[1] This poem, selected from the book of *Psalms* (104), reveals a rare and delicate feeling for nature, but its exquisite imagery is characteristic of Hebrew poetry. It has been pointed out that the poem closely resembles the unique "sun hymn" of the Egyptian King Amenophis IV.

Thou coveredst it with the deep as with a vesture;
The waters stood above the mountains;
At thy rebuke they fled;
At the voice of thy thunder they hasted away;

They went up by the mountains, they went down by the valleys,
Unto the place which thou hadst founded for them.
Thou hast set a bound that they may not pass over;
That they turn not again to cover the earth.
He sendeth forth springs into the valleys;
They run among the mountains:
They give drink to every beast of the field;
The wild asses quench their thirst.
By them the fowl of the heaven have their habitation.
They sing among the branches.
He watereth the mountains from his chambers:
The earth is satisfied with the fruit of thy works.
He causeth the grass to grow for the battle,
And herb for the service of man;
That he may bring forth food out of the earth;
And wine that maketh glad the heart of man,
And oil to make his face to shine,
And bread that strengtheneth man's heart.
The trees of the Lord are satisfied;
The cedars of Lebanon, which he hath planted;
Where the birds make their nests:
As for the stork, the fir trees are her house.
The high mountains are for the wild goats;
The rocks are a refuge for the conies.
He appointed the moon for seasons:
The sun knoweth his going down.
Thou makest darkness, and it is night;
Wherein all the beasts of the forest do creep forth.
The young lions roar after their prey,
And seek their meat from God.
The sun ariseth, they get them away,
And lay them down in their dens.
Man goeth forth unto his work and to his labour until the evening.
O Lord, how manifold are thy works!
In wisdom hast thou made them all:
The earth is full of thy riches.

AS A SIGNET OF CARBUNCLE[1]

by SIMEON BEN SIRA
c. 3rd–2nd cent. B.C.

As a signet of carbuncle
In a setting of gold,
So is a concert of music in a banquet of wine.
As a signet of emerald
In a work of gold,
So is a strain of music with pleasant wine.

POEMS

by ELEAZAR BEN KALIR
8th–9th cent. C.E.

I. JEREMIAH AND ISRAEL

Full in her glory, she as Tirzah fair
Hath sinned and fallen; lo! the angels weep
There at the threshold of her sanctuary.
Forth from the Temple, over Zion's mount
Wandered Hilkiah's son, and chanced to meet
A woman, beauteous, but with grief distraught.
"Appalled I ask, in name of God and man!
Art thou dread phantom? Art thou human form?
For while thy beauty mouldeth woman fair,
Awe shadoweth spirit from the vast unknown!"

"I am no phantom nor vile clay of earth;
I shall be known when I return in rest.

[1] The apocryphal book *Ecclesiasticus* from which the above poem was selected (32: 5-6) has considerable literary as well as historical interest. Schechter has written a superb essay about it in his *Studies in Judaism*, Second Series, pp. 55-101. The above poem is one of the few drinking songs in ancient Hebrew literature. That there existed a good many of them is indicated in *Amos* 6: 5, *Isaiah* 22: 13, and *Wisdom of Solomon* 2: 7.

Lo! of the one am I! of three am I!
Lo! of six hundred thousand, and of twelve!
Yea, and behold me of the seventy-one!
O Prophet! know: the 'one' is Abraham;
'Three' be the fathers; verily in me
Behold the third, God's messenger of peace;
The 'twelve' I show thee be the tribes of God,
Six hundred thousand of redeemed men;
And their Sanhedrin wrought of seventy-one."

"List to my counsel: O return! repent!
Since thou art thus endowed, so proud in state,
'Tis fitting that thou shouldst exultant rise,
To glory in the good awaiting thee;
'Backsliding Daughter!' cast that brand of shame!"

"Can I rejoice, or lift my voice in song?
Behold my children given to the foe!
My prophets martyred, yea, their life-blood spilt!
My kings, my princes, and my holy priests
Borne into distant exile, fetter-bound.
Far from mine House the Sacred Presence fled,
Shunning the place of mine iniquity;
Yea, thence did my Belovèd flee away,
And left the beauty of my tent to wane
And set in darkness nevermore to rise.
How doth the city, once with heroes thronged,
Great 'mid the nations, now sit solitary!"
Pausing, she glided to the Prophet's side,
And with imploring utterance whispering spake:
"Plead to thy God for this my bitter wound;
Beseech Him for the tempest stricken soul;
Until He softened say: 'It is enough!'
And save my sons from exile and the sword."

With suppliant's plea he prayed before his Lord:
"O God of mercy! let compassion flow,
E'en as a father pitieth his son;"
And cried: "Doth not a father mourn his child
Carried away to harsh captivity?
And woe unto the son in exile chained,
When at his father's board his place is void!"

"Prophet! arise, depart!" the vision bade:
"Call now the sleeping fathers from their rest;

And Moses, yea, and Aaron shall arise;
O let the shepherds peal to Heaven a wail,
For lo! the wolves of night have torn the lamb!"

The Prophet's voice with mighty yearning swelled,
And shook with heaving sobs Machpelah's cave:
"O glorious sires! lift up your voice and weep:
Your sons have erred; behold them captives bound!
If they, weak mortals, have transgressed the bond,
Where, fathers! doth your merit slumber now,
That sanctified of old the covenant?"

"What crave ye, sons, from Me? The doom is fixed.
This is My judgment; this is My decree.
The shrine is desolate, bereft of men;
None cometh in upon the solemn day;
Beheld, the steps of My belovèd fall."—

"But Thou wilt yet restore them as of old,
O Thou Sustainer! Thou that givest strength!
And pity Zion; for the time is come."
(*Nina Salaman*)

II. PRAYER FOR DEW

Dew, precious dew, unto Thy land forlorn!
Pour out our blessings in Thy exultation,
To strengthen us with ample wine and corn
And give Thy chosen city safe foundation
         In dew.

Dew, precious dew, the good year's crown, we wait,
That earth in pride and glory may be fruited,
And that the city now so desolate
Into a gleaming crown may be transmuted
         By dew.

Dew, precious dew, let fall upon the land,
From heaven's treasury be this accorded,
So shall the darkness by a beam be spanned,
The faithful of Thy vineyard be rewarded
         With dew.

Dew, precious dew, to make the mountains sweet,
The savour of Thy excellence recalling!
Deliver us from exile, we entreat,

So we may sing Thy praises, softly falling
    As dew.

Dew, precious dew, our granaries to fill,
And us with youthful freshness to enharden!
Belovèd God, uplift us at Thy will
And make us as a richly-watered garden
    With dew.

Dew, precious dew, that we our harvest reap,
And guard our fatted flocks and herds from leanness!
Behold our people follows Thee like sheep,
And looks to Thee to give the earth her greenness
    With dew.

                              (*Israel Zangwill*)

POEMS

by SOLOMON IBN GABIROL

1021–1070

I. NIGHT

Night, and the heavens beam serene with peace,
Like a pure heart benignly smiles the moon.
Oh, guard thy blessed beauty from mischance,
This I beseech thee in all tender love.
See where the Storm his cloudy mantle spreads,
An ashy curtain covereth the moon.
As if the tempest thirsted for the rain,
The clouds he presses, till they burst in streams.
Heaven wears a dusky raiment, and the moon
Appeareth dead—her tomb is yonder cloud,
And weeping shades come after, like the people
Who mourn with tearful grief a noble queen.
But look! the thunder pierced night's close-linked mail,
His keen-tipped lance of lightning brandishing;
He hovers like a seraph-conqueror.—
Dazed by the flaming splendor of his wings,
In rapid flight as in a whirling dance,
The black cloud-ravens hurry scared away.

So, though the powers of darkness chain my soul,
My heart, a hero, chafes and breaks its bonds.

(*Emma Lazarus*)

II. NIGHT-THOUGHTS

Will night already spread her wings and weave
Her dusky robe about the day's bright form,
Boldly the sun's fair countenance displacing,
And swathe it with her shadow in broad day?
So a green wreath of mist enrings the moon,
Till envious clouds do quite encompass her.
No wind! and yet the slender stem is stirred,
With faint, slight motion as from inward tremor.
Mine eyes are full of grief—who sees me, asks,
"Oh, wherefore dost thou cling unto the ground?"
My friends discourse with sweet and soothing words;
They all are vain, they glide above my head.
I fain would check my tears; would fain enlarge
Unto infinity, my heart—in vain!
Grief presses hard my breast, therefore my tears
Have scarcely dried, ere they again spring forth.
For these are streams no furnace heat may quench,
Nebuchadnezzar's flames may dry them not.
What is the pleasure of the day for me,
If, in its crucible, I must renew
Incessantly the pangs of purifying?
Up, challenge, wrestle, and o'ercome! Be strong!
The late grapes cover all the vine with fruit.
I am not glad, though even the lion's pride
Content itself upon the field's poor grass.
My spirit sinks beneath the tide, soars not
With fluttering seamews on the moist, soft strand.
I follow Fortune not, where'er she lead.
Lord o'er myself, I banish her, compel,
And though her clouds should rain no blessed dew,
Though she withhold the crown, the heart's desire,
Though all deceive, though honey change to gall,
Still am I lord, and will in freedom strive.

(*Emma Lazarus*)

III. MEDITATIONS

Forget thine anguish,
    Vexed heart, again.
Why shouldst thou languish,
    With earthly pain?
The husk shall slumber,
    Bedded in clay
Silent and sombre,
    Oblivion's prey!
But, Spirit immortal,
Thou at Death's portal,
    Tremblest with fear.
    If he caress thee,
    Curse thee or bless thee,
    Thou must draw near,
From him the worth of thy works to hear.

    Why full of terror,
    Compassed with error,
    Trouble thy heart,
    For thy mortal part?
    The soul flies home—
    The corpse is dumb.
    Of all thou didst have,
Follows naught to the grave,
    Thou fliest thy nest,
Swift as a bird to thy place of rest.

    What avail grief and fasting,
    Where nothing is lasting?
    Pomp, domination,
    Become tribulation.
    In a health-giving draught,
    A death-dealing shaft.
    Wealth—an illusion,
    Power—a lie,
    Over all, dissolution
    Creeps silent and sly.
    Unto others remain
    The goods thou didst gain
    With infinite pain.

Life is a vine-branch;
    A vintager, Death.

He threatens and lowers
  More near with each breath.
Then hasten, arise!
  Seek God, O my soul!
For time quickly flies,
  Still far is the goal.
Vain heart praying dumbly,
  Learn to prize humbly,
  The meanest of fare.
Forget all thy sorrow,
  Behold, Death is there!

Dove-like lamenting,
  Be full of repenting,
Lift vision supernal
To raptures eternal.
  On ev'ry occasion
  Seek lasting salvation.
Pour thy heart out in weeping,
While others are sleeping.
  Pray to Him when all's still,
  Performing his will.
And so shall the angel of peace be thy warden,
And guide thee at last to the heavenly garden.

              (*Emma Lazarus*)

IV. HYMN

ALMIGHTY! what is man?
  But flesh and blood.
Like shadows flee his days,
He marks not how they vanish from his gaze,
  Suddenly, he must die—
He droppeth, stunned, into nonentity.

Almighty! what is man?
A body frail and weak,
  Full of deceit and lies,
  Of vile hypocrisies.
Now like a flower blowing,
Now scorched by sunbeams glowing.
And wilt thou of his trespasses inquire?
  How may he ever bear
Thine anger just, thy vengeance dire?

Punish him not, but spare,
For he is void of power and strength!

Almighty! what is man?
　By filthy lust possessed,
Whirled in a round of lies,
　Fond frenzy swells his breast.
The pure man sinks in mire and slime,
The noble shrinketh not from crime,
Wilt thou resent on him the charms of sin?
　Like fading grass,
　So shall he pass.
　Like chaff that blows
　Where the wind goes.
Then spare him, be thou merciful, O King,
Upon the dreaded day of reckoning!

Almighty! what is man?
　The haughty son of time
Drinks deep of sin,
　And feeds on crime
Seething like waves that roll,
Hot as a glowing coal.
And wilt thou punish him for sins inborn?
　Lost and forlorn,
Then like the weakling he must fall,
Who some great hero strives withal.
Oh, spare him, therefore! let him win
　Grace for his sin!

Almighty! what is man?
　Spotted in guilty wise,
A stranger unto faith,
　Whose tongue is stained with lies,
And shalt thou count his sins—so is he lost,
　Uprooted by thy breath.
Like to a stream by tempest tossed,
His life falls from him like a cloak,
　He passes into nothingness, like smoke.
　Then spare him, punish not, be kind, I pray,
To him who dwelleth in the dust, an image wrought in clay!

Almighty! what is man?
　A withered bough!
When he is awe-struck by approaching doom,

Like a dried blade of grass, so weak, so low
The pleasure of his life is changed to gloom.
He crumbles like a garment spoiled with moth;
According to his sins wilt thou be wroth?
He melts like wax before the candle's breath,
Yea, like thin water, so he vanisheth,
Oh, spare him therefore, for thy gracious name,
And be not too severe upon his shame!

    Almighty! what is man?
      A faded leaf!
If thou dost weigh him in the balance—lo!
He disappears—a breath that thou dost blow.
  His heart is ever filled
  With lust of lies unstilled.
  Wilt thou bear in mind his crime
  Unto all time?
He fades away like clouds sun-kissed,
  Dissolves like mist.
Then spare him! let him love and mercy win,
According to thy grace, and not according to his sin!
                (*Emma Lazarus*)

V. TO A DETRACTOR

The Autumn promised, and he keeps
His word unto the meadow-rose.
The pure, bright lightnings herald Spring,
Serene and glad the fresh earth shows.
The rain has quenched her children's thirst,
Her cheeks, but now so cold and dry,
Are soft and fair, a laughing face;
With clouds of purple shines the sky,
Though filled with light, yet veiled with haze.
Hark! hark! the turtle's mocking note
Outsings the valley-pigeon's lays.
Her wings are gemmed, and from her throat,
When the clear sun gleams back again,
It seems to me as though she wore
About her neck a jewelled chain.
Say, wilt thou darken such a light,
Wilt drag the clouds from heaven's height?
Although thy heart with anger swell,
Yet firm as marble mine doth dwell.

Therein no fear thy wrath begets.
It is not shaken by thy threats.
Yea, hurl thy darts, thy weapons wield,
The strength of youth is still my shield.
My winged steed toward the heights doth bound,
The dust whirls upward from the ground;
My song is scanty, dost thou deem
Thine eloquence a mighty stream?
Only the blameless offering.
Not the profusion man may bring,
Prevaileth with our Lord and King.
The long days out of minutes grow,
And out of months the years arise,
Wilt thou be master of the wise,
Then learn the hidden stream to know,
That from the inmost heart doth flow.

(Emma Lazarus)

VI. STANZAS

"With tears thy grief thou dost bemoan,
Tears that would melt the hardest stone,
Oh, wherefore sing'st thou not the vine?
Why chant'st thou not the praise of wine?
It chases pain with cunning art,
The craven slinks from out thy heart."

But I: Poor fools the wine may cheat,
Lull them with lying visions sweet.
Upon the wings of storms may bear
The heavy burden of their care.
The father's heart may harden so,
He feeleth not his own child's woe.

No ocean is the cup, no sea,
To drown my broad, deep misery.
It grows so rank, you cut it all,
The aftermath springs just as tall.
My heart and flesh are worn away,
Mine eyes are darkened from the day.

The lovely morning-red behold
Wave to the breeze her flag of gold.
The hosts of stars above the world,
Like banners vanishing are furled.

The dew shines bright; I bide forlorn,
And shudder with the chill of morn.

(*Emma Lazarus*)

VII. WINE AND GRIEF

With heavy groans did I approach my friends,
Heavy as though the mountains I would move.
The flagon they were murdering; they poured
Into the cup, wild-eyed, the grape's red blood.
No, they killed not, they breathed new life therein.
Then, too, in fiery rapture, burned my veins,
But soon the fumes had fled. In vain, in vain!
Ye cannot fill the breach of the rent heart.
Ye crave a sensuous joy; ye strive in vain
To cheat with flames of passion, my despair.
So when the sinking sun draws near to night,
The sky's bright cheeks fade 'neath those tresses black.
Ye laugh—but silently the soul weeps on;
Ye cannot stifle her sincere lament.

(*Emma Lazarus*)

VIII. DEFIANCE

"Conquer the gloomy night of thy sorrow, for the morning greets thee with
laughter.
Rise and clothe thyself with noble pride,
Break loose from the tyranny of grief.
Thou standest alone among men,
Thy song is like a pearl in beauty."

So spake my friend. 'T is well!
The billows of the stormy sea which overwhelmed my soul,—
These I subdue; I quake not
Before the bow and arrow of destiny.
I endured with patience when he deceitfully lied to me
With his treacherous smile.

Yea, boldly I defy Fate,
I cringe not to envious Fortune.
I mock the towering floods.
My brave heart does not shrink—
This heart of mine, that, albeit young in years,
Is none the less rich in deep, keen-eyed experience.

(*Emma Lazarus*)

IX. A DEGENERATE AGE

Where is the man who has been tried and found strong and sound?
Where is the friend of reason and of knowledge?
I see only sceptics and weaklings.
I see only prisoners in the durance of the senses.
And every fool and every spendthrift
Thinks himself as great a master as Aristotle.
Think'st thou that they have written poems?
Call'st thou that a Song?
I call it the cackling of ravens.
The zeal of the prophet must free poesy
From the embrace of wanton youths.
My song I have inscribed on the forehead of Time,
They know and hate it—for it is lofty.

(*Emma Lazarus*)

POEMS

by MOSES IBN EZRA
c. 1070-1139

I. SONGS

I

The shadow of the houses leave behind,
In the cool boscage of the grove reclined,
The wine of friendship from love's goblet drink,
And entertain with cheerful speech the mind.

Drink, friend! behold, the dreary winter's gone,
The mantle of old age has time withdrawn.
The sunbeam glitters in the morning dew,
O'er hill and vale youth's bloom is surging on.

Cup-bearer! quench with snow the goblet's fire,
Even as the wise man cools and stills his ire.
Look, when the jar is drained, upon the brim
The light foam melteth with the heart's desire.

Cup-bearer! bring anear the silver bowl,
And with the glowing gold fulfil the whole,

Unto the weak new vigor it imparts,
And without lance subdues the hero's soul.

My love sways, dancing, like the myrtle-tree,
The masses of her curls disheveled, see!
She kills me with her darts, intoxicates
My burning blood, and will not set me free.

Within the aromatic garden come,
And slowly in its shadows let us roam,
The foliage be the turban for our brows,
And the green branches o'er our heads a dome.

All pain thou with the goblet shalt assuage,
The wine-cup heals the sharpest pangs that rage,
Let others crave inheritance of wealth,
Joy be our portion and our heritage.

Drink in the garden, friend, anigh the rose,
Richer than spice's breath the soft air blows.
If it should cease a little traitor then,
A zephyr light its secret would disclose.

II

Thou who art clothed in silk, who drawest on
Proudly thy raiment of fine linen spun,
Bethink thee of the day when thou alone
Shalt dwell at last beneath the marble stone.

Anigh the nests of adders thine abode,
With the earth-crawling serpent and the toad.
Trust in the Lord, He will sustain thee there,
And without fear thy soul shall rest with God.

If the world flatter thee with soft-voiced art,
Know 'tis a cunning witch who charms thy heart,
Whose habit is to wed man's soul with grief,
And those who are close-bound in love to part.

He who bestows his wealth upon the poor,
Has only lent it to the Lord, be sure—
Of what avail to clasp it with clenched hand?
It goes not with us to the grave obscure.

The voice of those who dwell within the tomb,
Who in corruption's house have made their home;
"O ye who wander o'er us still today,
When will ye come to share with us the gloom?"

How can'st thou ever of the world complain,
And murmuring, burden it with all thy pain?
Silence! thou art a traveller at an inn,
A guest, who may but over night remain.

Be thou not wroth against the proud, but show
How he who yesterday great joy did know,
Today is begging for his very bread,
And painfully upon a crutch must go.

How foolish they whose faith is fixed upon
The treasures of their worldly wealth alone,
Far wiser were it to obey the Lord,
And only say, "The will of God be done!"

Has Fortune smiled on thee? Oh, do not trust
Her reckless joy, she still deceives and must.
Perpetual snares she spreads about thy feet,
Thou shalt not rest till thou art mixed with dust.

Man is a weaver on the earth, 'tis said,
Who weaves and weaves—his own days are the thread,
And when the length allotted he hath spun,
All life is over, and all hope is dead.

(Emma Lazarus)

II. IN THE NIGHT

Unto the house of prayer my spirit yearns,
Unto the sources of her being turns,
To where the sacred light of heaven burns,
She struggles thitherward by day and night.

The splendor of God's glory blinds her eyes,
Up without wings she soareth to the skies,
With silent aspiration seeks to rise,
In dusky evening and in darksome night.

To her the wonders of God's works appear,
She longs with fervor Him to draw anear,

The tidings of His glory reach her ear,
From morn to even, and from night to night.

The banner of thy grace did o'er me rest,
Yet was thy worship banished from my breast.
Almighty, thou didst seek me out and test
To try and to instruct me in the night.

Infatuate I trifled youth away,
In nothingness dreamed through my manhood's day.
Therefore my streaming tears I may not stay,
They are my meat and drink by day and night.

In flesh imprisoned is the son of light,
This life is but a bridge when seen aright.
Rise in the silent hour and pray with might,
Awake and call upon the God by night!

Hasten to cleanse thyself of sin, arise!
Follow Truth's path that leads unto the skies,
As swift as yesterday existence flies,
Brief even as a watch within the night.

Men enters life for trouble; all he has,
And all that he beholds, is pain, alas!
Like to a flower does he bloom and pass,
He fadeth like a vision of the night.

The surging floods of life around him roar,
Death feeds upon him, pity is no more,
To others all his riches he gives o'er,
And dieth in the middle hour of night.

Crushed by the burden of my sins I pray,
Oh, wherefore shunned I not the evil way?
Deep are my sighs, I weep the livelong day,
And wet my couch with tears night after night.

My spirit stirs, my streaming tears still run,
Like to the wild birds' notes my sorrows' tone,
In the hushed silence loud resounds my groan,
My soul arises moaning in the night.

Within her narrow soul oppressed with dread,
Bare of adornment and with grief-bowed head

Lamenting, many a tear her sad eyes shed,
She weeps with anguish in the gloomy night.

For tears my burden seem to lighten best,
Could I but weep my heart's blood, I might rest.
My spirit bows with mighty grief oppressed,
I utter forth my prayer within the night.

Youth's charm has like a fleeting shadow gone,
With eagle wings the hours of life have flown.
Alas! the time when pleasure I have known,
I may not now recall by day or night.

'The haughty scorn pursues me of my foe,
Evil his thought, yet soft his speech and low.
Forget it not, but bear his purpose so
Forever in thy mind by day and night.

Observe a pious fast, be whole again,
Hasten to purge thy heart of every stain.
No more from prayer and penitence refrain,
But turn unto thy God by day and night.

He speaks: "My son, yea, I will send thee aid,
Bend thou thy steps to me, be not afraid.
No nearer friend than I am, hast thou made,
Possess thy soul in patience one more night."

(Emma Lazarus)

III. ELEGY

My thoughts impelled me to the resting-place
Where sleep my parents, many a friend and brother.
I asked them (no one heard and none replied):
"Do ye forsake me, too, oh father, mother?"
Then from the grave, without a tongue, these cried,
And showed my own place waiting by their side.

(Emma Lazarus)

POEMS

by JUDAH HALEVI
c. 1085–1140

I. A LETTER TO HIS FRIEND ISAAC

But yesterday the earth drank like a child
  With eager thirst the autumn rain.
Or like a wistful bride who waits the hour
  Of love's mysterious bliss and pain.
And now the Spring is here with yearning eyes;
  Midst shimmering golden flower-beds,
On meadows carpeted with varied hues,
  In richest raiment clad, she treads.
She weaves a tapestry of bloom o'er all,
  And myriad eyed young plants upspring,
White, green, or red like lips that to the mouth
  Of the beloved one sweetly cling.
Whence come these radiant tints, these blended beams?
  Here's such a dazzle, such a blaze,
As though earth stole the splendor of the stars,
  Fain to eclipse them with her rays.
Come! go we to the garden with our wine,
  Which scatters sparks of hot desire,
Within our hand 't is cold, but in our veins
  It flashes clear, it glows like fire.
It bubbles sunnily in earthen jugs.
  We catch it in the crystal glass,
    Then wander through cool, shadowy lanes and breathe
  The spicy freshness of the grass.
Whilst we with happy hearts our circuit keep,
  The gladness of the Earth is shown.
She smileth, though the trickling rain-drops weep
  Silently o'er her, one by one.
She loves to feel the tears upon her cheek,
  Like a rich veil, with pearls inwove.
Joyous she listens when the swallows chirp,
  And warbles to her mate, the dove.
Blithe as a maiden midst the young green leaves,
  A wreath she'll wind, a fragrant treasure;

All living things in graceful motion leap,
    As dancing to some merry measure.
The morning breezes rustle cordially,
    Love's thirst is sated with the balm they send.
Sweet breathes the myrtle in the frolic wind,
    As though remembering a distant friend.
The myrtle branch now proudly lifted high,
    Now whispering to itself drops low again.
The topmost palm-leaves rapturously stir,
    For all at once they hear the birds' soft strain.
So stirs, so yearns all nature, gayly decked,
    To honor *Isaac* with her best array.
Hear'st thou the word? She cries—I beam with joy,
Because with Isaac I am wed today.

(Emma Lazarus)

II. ADMONITION

Long in the lap of childhood didst thou sleep,
Think how thy youth like chaff did disappear;
Shall life's sweet Spring forever last? Look up,
Old age approaches ominously near.
Oh, shake thou off the world, even as the bird
Shakes off the midnight dew that clogged his wings.
Soar upward, seek redemption from thy guilt
And from the earthly dross that round thee clings.
Draw near to God, His holy angels know,
For whom His bounteous streams of mercy flow.

(Emma Lazarus)

III. LOVE SONGS

"See'st thou o'er my shoulders falling,
    Snake-like ringlets waving free?
Have no fear, for they are twisted
    To allure thee unto me."

Thus she spake, the gentle dove,
    Listen to thy plighted love:—
"Ah, how long I wait, until
    Sweetheart cometh back (she said)
Laying his caressing hand
    Underneath my burning head."

(Emma Lazarus)

By the life of our troth, my love,
By thy life and the life
Of love which hath shot an arrow at me,
Verily have I become a slave to Love, that hath pierced
Mine ear, that hath cloven my heart in twain.

(Nina Salaman)

Ophra washeth her garments in the waters
Of my tears, and spreadeth them out in the sunshine of her radiance.
She demandeth no water of the fountains, having my two eyes;
And no other sunshine than her beauty.

(Nina Salaman)

IV. SEPARATION

And so we twain must part! Oh, linger yet,
    Let me still feed my glance upon thine eyes.
Forget not, love, the days of our delight,
    And I our nights of bliss shall ever prize.
In dreams thy shadowy image I shall see,
    Oh, even in my dream be kind to me!

Though I were dead, I none the less would hear
    Thy step, thy garment rustling on the sand.
And if thou waft me greetings from the grave,
    I shall drink deep the breath of that cold land.
Take thou my days, command this life of mine,
    If it can lengthen out the space of thine.

No voice I hear from lips death-pale and chill,
    Yet deep within my heart it echoes still.
My frame remains—my soul to thee yearns forth.
    A shadow I must tarry still on earth.
Back to the body dwelling here in pain,
    Return, my soul, make haste and come again!

(Emma Lazarus)

V. LONGING FOR JERUSALEM

O city of the world, with sacred splendor blest,
My spirit yearns to thee from out the far-off West,
A stream of love wells forth when I recall thy day,
Now is thy temple waste, thy glory passed away.
Had I an eagle's wings, straight would I fly to thee,
Moisten thy holy dust with wet cheeks streaming free.

Oh, how I long for thee! albeit thy King has gone,
Albeit where balm once flowed, the serpent dwells alone.
Could I but kiss thy dust, so would I fain expire,
As sweet as honey then, my passion, my desire!

(*Emma Lazarus*)

VI. ON THE VOYAGE TO JERUSALEM

I

My two-score years and ten are over,
  Never again shall youth be mine.
The years are ready-winged for flying,
  What crav'st thou still of feast and wine?
Wilt thou still court man's acclamation,
  Forgetting what the Lord hath said?
And forfeiting thy weal eternal,
  By thine own guilty heart misled?
Shalt thou have never done with folly,
  Still fresh and new must it arise?
Oh, heed it not, heed not the senses,
  But follow God, be meek and wise;
Yea, profit by thy days remaining,
  They hurry swiftly to the goal.
Be zealous in the Lord's high service,
  And banish falsehood from thy soul.
Use all thy strength, use all thy fervor,
  Defy thine own desires, awaken!
Be not afraid when seas are foaming,
  And earth to her foundations shaken.
Benumbed the hand then of the sailor,
  The captain's skill and power are lamed.
Gayly they sailed with colors flying,
  And now turn home again ashamed.
The ocean is our only refuge,
  The sandbank is our only goal,
The masts are swaying as with terror,
  And quivering does the vessel roll.
The mad wind frolics with the billows,
  Now smooths them low, now lashes high.
Now they are storming up like lions,
  And now like serpents sleek they lie;
And wave on wave is ever pressing,
  They hiss, they whisper, soft of tone.
Alack! was that the vessel splitting?

Are sail and mast and rudder gone?
Here, screams of fright, there, silent weeping,
  The bravest feels his courage fail.
What stead our prudence or our wisdom?
  The soul itself can naught avail.
And each one to his God is crying,
  Soar up, my soul, to Him aspire,
Who wrought a miracle for Jordan,
  Extol Him, oh angelic choir!
Remember Him who stays the tempest,
  The stormy billows doth control,
Who quickeneth the lifeless body,
  And fills the empty frame with soul.
Behold! once more appears a wonder,
  The angry waves erst raging wild,
Like quiet flocks of sheep reposing,
  So soft, so still, so gently mild.
The sun descends, and high in heaven,
  The golden-circled moon doth stand.
Within the sea the stars are straying,
  Like wanderers in an unknown land.
The lights celestial in the waters
  Are flaming clearly as above,
As though the very heavens descended,
  To seal a covenant of love.
Perchance both sea and sky, twin oceans,
  From the same source of grace are sprung.
'Twixt these my heart, a third sea, surges,
  With songs resounding, clearly sung.

II

A watery waste the sinful world has grown,
With no dry spot whereon the eye can rest,
No man, no beast, no bird to gaze upon,
Can all be dead, with silent sleep possessed?
Oh, how I long the hills and vales to see,
To find myself on barren steppes were bliss.
I peer about, but nothing greeteth me,
Naught save the ship, the clouds, the waves' abyss,
The crocodile which rushes from the deeps;
The flood foams gray; the whirling waters reel,
Now like its prey whereon at last it sweeps,
The ocean swallows up the vessel's keel.

The billows rage—exult, oh soul of mine,
Soon shalt thou enter the Lord's sacred shrine!

III. TO THE WEST WIND

O West, how fragrant breathes thy gentle air,
Spikenard and aloes on thy pinions glide.
Thou blow'st from spicy chambers, not from there
Where angry winds and tempests fierce abide.
As on a bird's wings thou dost waft me home,
Sweet as a bundle of rich myrrh to me.
And after thee yearn all the throngs that roam
And furrow with light keel the rolling sea.
Desert her not—our ship—bide with her oft,
When the day sinks and in the morning light.
Smooth thou the deeps and make the billows soft,
Nor rest save at our goal, the sacred height.
Chide thou the East that chafes the raging flood,
And swells the towering surges wild and rude.
What can I do, the elements' poor slave?
Now do they hold me fast, now leave me free;
Cling to the Lord, my soul, for He will save,
Who caused the mountains and the winds to be.

(*Emma Lazarus*)

POEMS

by ABRAHAM IBN EZRA

1092-1167

I. THE LAW

My help, my hope, my strength shall be,
Thou perfect law of God, in thee!

My faith shall be my rock of might,
Its law my portion and my right,
Its testimonies my delight,
And day by day, my voice I raise
In song and hymn to chant their praise.

How did the angelic host lament
When from their midst, by God's intent,

The holy law to earth was sent.
"Woe that the pure and sanctified
Should now on sinful lips abide."

The people trembled when they saw
Approaching them the heavenly law—
Their voices rose in joy and awe:
"Thy covenant, O Lord, fulfil,
Declare it, we will do Thy will."

Great wonders He on Sinai wrought,
When unto us His law He taught,
Wherefore to praise His name I sought;
But what am I and what my words
Before the Almighty Lord of lords?

Hear Thou Thy people's prayer, O King,
When like the heavenly host they sing
Thrice Holy, Holy—uttering
Sweet hymns and songs of pleasantness
With joy and awe Thy name to bless.

(*Alice Lucas*)

II. THE SONG OF CHESS

I will sing a song of battle
Planned in days long passed and over.
Men of skill and science set it
On a plain of eight divisions,
And designed in squares all chequered.
Two camps face each one the other,
And the kings stand by for battle,
And twixt these two is the fighting.
Bent on war the face of each is,
Ever moving or encamping,
Yet no swords are drawn in warfare,
For a war of thoughts their war is.
They are known by signs and tokens
Sealed and written on their bodies;
And a man who sees them, thinketh,
Edomites and Ethiopians
Are these two that fight together.
And the Ethiopian forces
Overspread the field of battle,
And the Edomites pursue them.

First in battle the foot-soldier [1]
Comes to fight upon the highway,
Ever marching straight before him,
But to capture moving sideways,
Straying not from off his pathway,
Neither do his steps go backwards;
He may leap at the beginning
Anywhere within three chequers.
Should he take his steps in battle
Far away unto the eighth row,
Then a Queen to all appearance
He becomes and fights as she does.
And the Queen directs her moving
As she will to any quarter.
Backs the Elephant [2] or advances,
Stands aside as 'twere an ambush;
As the Queen's way, so is his way,
But o'er him she hath advantage,
He stands only in the third rank.
Swift the Horse [3] is in the battle,
Moving on a crooked pathway;
Ways of his are ever crooked;
Mid the Squares, three form his limit.

Straight the Wind moves o'er the war-path
In the field across or lengthwise;
Ways of crookedness he seeks not,
But straight paths without perverseness.
Turning every way the King goes,
Giving aid unto his subjects;
In his actions he is cautious,
Whether fighting or encamping.
If his foe come to dismay him,
From his place he flees in terror,
Or the Wind [4] can give him refuge.
Sometimes he must flee before him;
Multitudes at times support him;
And all slaughter each the other,
Wasting with great wrath each other.

[1] The pawn.
[2] The Bishop.

[3] The Knight.
[4] The Rook.

Mighty men of both the sovereigns
Slaughtered fall, with yet no bloodshed.
Ethiopia sometimes triumphs,
Edom flees away before her;
Now victorious is Edom:
Ethiopia and her sovereign
Are defeated in the battle.

Should a King in the destruction
Fall within the foeman's power,
He is never granted mercy,
Neither refuge nor deliv'rance,
Nor a flight to refuge-city.
Judged by foes, and lacking rescue,
Though not slain he is checkmated.
Hosts about him all are slaughtered,
Giving life for his deliverance.
Quenched and vanished is their glory,
For they see their lord is smitten;
Yet they fight again this battle,
For in death is resurrection.

(*Nina Salaman*)

LOVE SONG

by JUDAH ALHARIZI

died c. 1230

The long-closed door, oh open it again, send me back once more my fawn
that had fled.
On the day of our reunion, thou shalt rest by my side, there wilt thou shed
over me the streams of thy delicious perfume.
Oh, beautiful bride, what is the form of thy friend, that thou say to me,
Release him, send him away?
He is the beautiful-eyed one of ruddy glorious aspect—that is my friend, him
do thou detain.

Hail to thee, Son of my friend, the ruddy, the bright-colored one! Hail to thee
whose temples are like a pomegranate.

Hasten to the refuge of thy sister, and protect the son of Isaiah against the troops of the Ammonites.

What art thou, O Beauty, that thou shouldst inspire love? that thy voice should ring like the voices of the bells upon the priestly garments?

The hour wherein thou desireth my love, I shall hasten to meet thee. Softly will I drop beside thee like the dew upon Hermon.

(Emma Lazarus)

THE BURNING OF THE LAW [1]

by MEIR OF ROTHENBURG
1220–1293

Ask, is it well, O thou consumed of fire,
  With those that mourn for thee,
That yearn to tread thy courts, that sore desire
  Thy sanctuary;

That, panting for thy land's sweet dust, are grieved,
  And sorrow in their souls,
And by the flames of wasting fire bereaved,
  Mourn for thy scrolls;

That grope in shadow of unbroken night,
  Waiting the day to see
Which o'er them yet shall cast a radiance bright,
  And over thee?

Ask of the welfare of the man of woe,
  With breaking heart, in vain
Lamenting ever for thine overthrow,
  And for thy pain;

Of him that crieth as the jackals cry,
  As owls their moaning make,
Proclaiming bitter wailing far and nigh;
  Yea, for thy sake.

[1] This dirge was written on the occasion of the burning of twenty-four wagons of Hebrew books on a Sabbath eve in June, 1244. The author was an eye-witness of the event; his poem was incorporated into the liturgy and is chanted on the ninth of Ab when the destruction of the Temple in Jerusalem is commemorated.

And thou revealed amid a heavenly fire,
  By earthly fire consumed,
Say how the foe unscorched escaped the pyre
  Thy flames illumed!

How long shalt thou that art at ease abide
  In peace, unknown to woe,
While o'er my flowers, humbled from their pride,
  Thy nettles grow?

Thou sittest high exalted, lofty foe!
  To judge the sons of God;
And with thy judgments stern dost bring them low
  Beneath thy rod.

Yea, more, to burn the Law thou durst decree—
  God's word to banish hence:
Then blest be he who shall award to thee
  Thy recompense!

Was it for this, thou Law, my Rock of old
  Gave thee with flames begirt,
That in thine after-days should fire seize hold
  Upon thy skirt?

O Sinai! was it then for this God chose
  Thy mount of modest height,
Rejecting statelier, while on thee arose
  His glorious light?

Wast thou an omen that from noble state
  The Law should lowly be?
And lo! a parable will I relate
  Befitting thee.

'Tis of a king I tell, who sat before
  The banquet of his son
And wept: for 'mid the mirth he death foresaw;
  So thou hast done.

Cast off thy robe; in sackcloth folds of night,
  O Sinai! cover thee;
Don widow's garb, discard thy raiment bright
  Of royalty.

Lo, I will weep for thee until my tears
  Swell as a stream and flow

Unto the graves where thy two princely seers
  Sleep calm below:

Moses; and Aaron in the Mountain Hor;
  I will of them inquire:
Is there another to replace this Law
  Devoured of fire?

O thou third month most sacred! woe is me
  For treason of the fourth,
Which dimmed the sacred light that shone from thee
  And kindled wrath;

And brake the tablets, yea, and still did rage:
  And lo! the Law is burnt!
Ye sinful! is not this the twofold wage
  Which ye have earnt?

Dismay hath seized upon my soul; how, then,
  Can food be sweet to me,
When, O thou Law, I have beheld base men
  Destroying thee?

They cast thee out as one despised, and burn
  The wealth of God Most High;
They whom from thine assembly thou wouldst spurn
  From drawing nigh.

I cannot pass along the highway more,
  Nor seek thy ways forlorn;
How do thy paths their loneliness deplore!
  Lo! how they mourn!

The mingled cup shall taste as honey sweet
  Where tears o'erbrim the wine;
Yea, and thy chains upon my shackled feet
  Are joy divine.

Sweet would it be unto mine eyes alway
  A rain of tears to pour,
To sob and drench thy sacred robes, till they
  Could hold no more.

But lo! my tears are dried, when, fast outpoured,
  They down my cheeks are shed;
Scorched by the fire within: because thy Lord
  Hath turned and fled.

Taking His holy treasure, He hath made
  His journey far away;
And with Him hath not thy protecting shade
  Vanished for aye?

And I am desolate and sore bereft,
  Lo! a forsaken one:
Like a sole beacon on a mountain left,
  A tower alone.

I hear the voice of singers now no more,
  Silence their song hath bound;
The strings are broken which on harps of yore
  Breathed forth sweet sound.

In sackcloth I will clothe and sable band,
  For well-beloved by me
Were they whose lives were many as the sand—
  The slain of thee.

I am astonished that the day's fair light
  Yet shineth brilliantly
On all things:—it is ever dark as night
  To me and thee.

Send with a bitter cry to God above
  Thine anguish, nor withhold:
Ah! that He would remember yet His love,
  His troth of old!

Gird on the sackcloth of thy misery
  For that devouring fire,
Which burst forth ravenous on thine and thee
  With wasting dire.

E'en as thy Rock hath sore afflicted thee,
  He will assuage thy woe,
Will turn again the tribes' captivity,
  And raise the low.

Yet shalt thou wear thy scarlet raiment choice,
  And sound the timbrels high,
And yet amid the dancers shalt rejoice
  With gladdened cry.

My heart shall be uplifted on the day
  Thy Rock shall be thy light,

When He shall make thy gloom to pass away,
Thy darkness bright.

(Nina Salaman)

SPRING SONG

by NAHUM

c. 1300

I

Now the dreary winter's over,
    Fled with him are grief and pain,
When the trees their bloom recover,
    Then the soul is born again.
Spikenard blossoms shaking,
    Perfume all the air,
And in bud and flower breaking,
    Stands my garden fair.
While with swelling gladness blest,
Heaves my friend's rejoicing breast.
Oh, come home, lost friend of mine,
Scared from out my tent and land.
    Drink from me the spicy wine,
    Milk and must from out my hand.

Cares which hovered round my brow,
Vanish, while the garden now
Girds itself with myrtle hedges,
    Bright-hued edges
    Round it lie.
        Suddenly
All my sorrows die.
See the breathing myrrh-trees blow,
    Aromatic airs enfold me.
While the splendor and the glow
    Of the walnut-branches hold me.
And a balsam-breath is flowing,
    Through the leafy shadows green,
On the left the cassia's growing,
    On the right the aloe's seen.
Lo, the clear cup crystalline,

In itself a gem of art,
Ruby-red foams up with wine,
Sparkling rich with froth and bubble.
I forget the want and trouble,
    Buried deep within my heart.

    Where is he who lingered here,
    But a little while agone?
    From my homestead he has flown,
    From the city sped alone,
    Dwelling in the forest drear.
Oh, come again, to those who wait thee long,
And who will greet thee with a choral song!
    Beloved, kindle bright
    Once more thine everlasting light.
Through thee, oh cherub with protecting wings,
My glory out of darkness springs.

II

Crocus and spikenard blossom on my lawn,
The brier fades, the thistle is withdrawn.
Behold, where glass-clear brooks are flowing,
The splendor of the myrtle blowing!
The garden-tree has doffed her widow's veil,
And shines in festal garb, in verdure pale.
    The turtle-dove is cooing, hark!
    Is that the warble of the lark!
Unto their perches they return again.
Oh, brothers, carol forth your joyous strain,
Pour out full-throated ecstasy of mirth,
Proclaiming the Lord's glory to the earth.
    One with a low, sweet song,
    One echoing loud and long,
Chanting the music of a spirit strong.

In varied tints the landscape glows.
In rich array appears the rose.
While the pomegranate's wreath of green,
The gauzy red and snow-white blossoms screen.
Who loves it, now rejoices for its sake,
And those are glad who sleep, and those who wake.
When cool-breathed evening visited the world,
In flower and leaf the beaded dew is pearled,

Reviving all that droops at length,
And to the languid giving strength.

Now in the east the shining light behold!
The sun has oped a lustrous path of gold.
Within my narrow garden's greenery,
Shot forth a branch, sprang to a splendid tree,
Then in mine ear the joyous words did ring,
"From Jess's root a verdant branch shall spring."
My Friend has cast His eyes upon my grief,
According to His mercy, sends relief.
Hark! the redemption hour's resounding stroke,
For him who bore with patient heart the yoke!

(*Emma Lazarus*)

COME, MY BELOVÈD

by SOLOMON HALEVI ALKABEZ

c. 1550

Come, my belovèd, to meet the Bride;
Now welcome we the Sabbath-tide.

"Keep and remember," said the Lord,
The only God, in a single word.
The Lord is One, and one His Name;
This is His glory and praise and fame.

Come, my belovèd, to meet the Bride;
Now welcome we the Sabbath-tide.

To meet the Sabbath let us go;
She is the fount whence blessings flow,
In earliest beginnings wrought—
Last to be made, but first in thought.

Come, my belovèd, to meet the Bride;
Now welcome we the Sabbath-tide.

O sacred city, royal shrine,
Arise from out these ruins thine!
Too long hast sat in the vale of tears,
For He that is full of pity hears.

Come, my belovèd, to meet the Bride;
Now welcome we the Sabbath-tide.

So shake thee from the dust; arise,
Bedeck thy form in glorious guise;
Because of David, Jesse's son,
Be now my soul's redemption won.

Come, my belovèd, to meet the Bride;
Now welcome we the Sabbath-tide.

O wake thee, wake thee, people mine!
Thy light is come—arise and shine!
Awake and sing, for all can see
The glory of the Lord on thee.

Come, my belovèd, to meet the Bride;
Now welcome we the Sabbath-tide.

Be not ashamed, be not dismayed;
Why art cast down and why afraid?—
(In Thee my suffering people trust
To raise their city from the dust.)

Come, my belovèd, to meet the Bride;
Now welcome we the Sabbath-tide.

And they that spoil shall be despoiled,
They that would swallow thee be foiled,
Thy God rejoicing at thy side
Like groom rejoicing o'er his bride.

Come, my belovèd, to meet the Bride;
Now welcome we the Sabbath-tide.

To right and left hand thou shalt spread,
And serve the Lord with love and dread;
And through the stock which Perez [1] bore
Shall we be glad for evermore.

Come, my belovèd, to meet the Bride;
Now welcome we the Sabbath-tide.

Crown of thy husband, come in peace,
O come with joy and glad release!

[1] A son of Judah and ancestor of David and of the Messiah indicated in this
erse.

Amid the faithful now abide—
Amid the chosen—Come, O Bride!

Come, my belovèd, to meet the Bride;
Now welcome we the Sabbath-tide.
                    (*Nina Salaman*)

LOVED OF MY SOUL

by ISRAEL NAJARA

c. 1550–1600

Loved of my soul! Father of grace!
    Lead on Thy servant to thy favoring sight;
He, fleetly as the hart, shall speed his pace
    To bow him low before thy glorious might.
Sweet is Thy love to him beyond compare,
Sweeter than honey, fairer than things fair.

Splendor of worlds! honored, adored!
    My soul is sick with pining love of Thee;
My God! I pray Thee, heal her: be implored;
    And o'er her let Thy holy sweetness be
A soothing strength to stay her yearning sore,
And joy shall be for her for evermore.

Source of all good! pity Thou me!
    And be Thou moved for thy beloved son.
Ah! would that I could rise aloft and see
    The beauty of Thy strength, Thou mighty one!
These things my soul desireth: Lord, I pray,
Grant me Thy mercy; turn Thee not away.

Be Thou revealed, Dearest of mine!
    And spread o'er me Thy canopy of peace;
Lo! with Thy glory all the earth shall shine,
    And we shall know a joy that shall not cease.
Hasten, Beloved, for the time is nigh,
And have compassion as in days gone by.
                    (*Nina Salaman*)

SONG

by RACHEL MORPURGO
1790–1871

Ah, vale of woe, of gloom and darkness moulded,
   How long wilt hold me bound in double chain?
Better to die—to rest in shadows folded,
   Than thus to grope amid the depths in vain!

I watch the eternal hills, the far, far lying,
   With glorious flowers ever over-run;
I take me eagles' wings, with vision flying
   And brow upraised to look upon the sun.

Ye skies, how fair the paths about your spaces!
   There freedom shines for ever like a star;
The winds are blowing through your lofty places,
   And who, ah, who can say how sweet they are?
                  (*Nina Salaman*)

DONNA CLARA

by HEINRICH HEINE
1797–1856

In the evening through her garden
Wanders the Alcalde's daughter;
Festal sounds of drum and trumpet
Ring out hither from the castle.

"I am weary of the dances,
Honeyed words of adulation
From the knights who still compare me
To the sun,—with dainty phrases.

"Yes, of all things I am weary,
Since I first beheld by moonlight,

Him my cavalier, whose zither
Nightly draws me to my casement.

"As he stands, so slim and daring,
With his flaming eyes that sparkle
From his nobly-pallid features,
Truly he St. George resembles."

Thus went Donna Clara dreaming,
On the ground her eyes were fastened,
When she raised them, lo! before her
Stood the handsome, knightly stranger.

Pressing hands and whispering passion,
These twain wander in the moonlight.
Gently doth the breeze caress them,
The enchanted roses greet them.

The enchanted roses greet them,
And they glow like love's own heralds;
"Tell me, tell me, my belovèd,
Wherefore, all at once thou blushest?"

"Gnats were stinging me, my darling,
And I hate these gnats in summer,
E'en as though they were a rabble
Of vile Jews with long, hooked noses."

"Heed not gnats nor Jews, belovèd,"
Spake the knight with fond endearments.
From the almond-tree dropped downward
Myriad snowy flakes of blossoms.

Myriad snowy flakes of blossoms
Shed around them fragrant odors.
"Tell me, tell me, my belovèd,
Looks thy heart on me with favor?"

"Yes, I love thee, oh my darling,
And I swear it by our Savior,
Whom the accursèd Jews did murder
Long ago with wicked malice."

"Heed thou neither Jews nor Savior,"
Spake the knight with fond endearments;
Far-off waved as in a vision
Gleaming lilies bathed in moonlight.

Gleaming lilies bathed in moonlight
Seemed to watch the stars above them.
"Tell me, tell me, my belovèd,
Didst thou not erewhile swear falsely?"

"Naught is false in me, my darling,
E'en as in my bosom floweth
Not a drop of blood that's Moorish,
Neither of foul Jewish current."

"Heed not Moors nor Jews, belovèd,"
Spake the knight with fond endearments.
Then towards a grove of myrtles
Leads the Alcalde's daughter.

And with love's slight, subtle meshes,
He hath trapped her and entangled;
Brief their words, but long their kisses,
For their hearts are overflowing.

What a melting bridal carol,
Sings the nightingale, the pure one!
How the fire-flies in the grasses
Trip their sparkling, torch-light dances!

In the grove the silence deepens;
Naught is heard save furtive rustling
Of the swaying myrtle branches,
And the breathing of the flowers.

But the sound of drum and trumpet
Burst forth sudden from the castle.
Rudely they awaken Clara,
Pillowed on her lover's bosom.

"Hark, they summon me, my darling,
But before I go, oh tell me,
Tell me what thy precious name is,
Which so closely thou hast hidden."

And the knight, with gentle laughter,
Kissed the fingers of his donna,
Kissed her lips and kissed her forehead,
And at last these words he uttered:

"I, Señora, your belovèd,
Am the son of the respected

Worthy, erudite Grand Rabbi,
Israel of Saragossa!"
(*Emma Lazarus*)

WINE

by MICAH JOSEPH LEBENSOHN

"And wine maketh glad the life. . . ." Ecclesiastes 10: 19.

1828–1852

Like an arrow shot
To Death from Birth:
Such is your lot,
Your day upon earth.

Each moment is
A graveyard board
For moments that
Come afterward.

Now Death and Life
Like brethren act:
Beneath the sky
They made their pact.

So Void and Vita
Destroy, create;
Now swallow up,
Regurgitate.

The past is past;
The future lies
Still overcast;
The present flies.

Who shall rejoice
Us, scatter woe,
Make sweet our life
And bring Death low!

My hearties, wine!
Wine scatters woe,

Makes glad the life,
And brings Death low!
(*Abraham M. Klein*)

HORSE AND RIDER

by J. L. GORDON
1830–1892

On a wild horse, scattering rage and terror,
The rider passed through the streets of the city.
Like storm and the breath of the tempest
Galloped the horse: and like the spray on the surf
Was the foam of its gasping on its nostrils.
Its hooves were harder than the fabulous shamir-stone,
And the rain of sparks flew upward from the road.
And a boy passed with those that went along the road:
"How goodly, how beautiful is that horse,
How well that he crushes not under his hooves
Those that come in at the gate."
And the rider on the horse of terror answered:
"Seest thou not, foolish boy,
The ring and the bridle which hold him back and guide him?
Know that without them he would scatter death
And in the flash of an eye the passers-by would be slain."
How many wilt thou not find on earth,
Wild as the untrained steed, wild as the breath of the tempest,
Whose wickedness would carry the world to destruction,
If it were not for the ring and the bridle of the faith.

(*Maurice Samuel*)

VENUS OF THE LOUVRE

by EMMA LAZARUS
1849–1887

Down the long hall she glistens like a star,
The foam-born mother of Love, transfixed to stone,
Yet none the less immortal, breathing on.

Time's brutal hand hath maimed but could not mar.
When first the enthralled enchantress from afar
  Dazzled mine eyes, I saw not her alone,
  Serenely poised on her world-worshipped throne
As when she guided once her dove-drawn car,—
But at her feet a pale, death-stricken Jew,
  Her life-adorer, sobbed farewell to love.
Here Heine wept! Here still he weeps anew,
  Nor ever shall his shadow lift or move,
While mourns one ardent heart, one poet brain,
For vanished Hellas and Hebraic pain.

THE MESSIAH

by DAVID FRISHMAN
1860–1916

In the dead of night I heard a sound of storm,
A storm of shaken chains,
The clash of link on link—
The heavens were opened.
And a great golden glory beat upon me suddenly,
A splendour of beams was poured like a bursting tempest around me
On all: confusion of crimson and blue.
And I fell to the earth and bowed myself and kneeled.

Behold, the Lord, the Lord God of Hosts, the Lord God Sabaoth,
In the midst of amber and chrysolite, in the midst of crimson clouds,
Clouds ascending and clouds descending—
There above the flame that flickers like the whiteness of sapphire
Is the lofty and exalted Throne,
The Moon is His footstool and the Sun the pillow of His head,
And the folds of Him are spilled through the seven heavens.
Thus in glory sits the Lord God of Hosts. . . .
But who is this that is chained to the Throne on high,
Who is this that is chained with chains of gold,
With chains that will not break?
It is our Lord, the King Messiah. . . .

Lo, by thy signs, Messiah, I knew thee:
By the fire that burns in thine eyes,
(This is the sacred fire

That glows in the eyes of all that are singers,
Of all that are seers, redeemers and prophets),
By the spirit which is poured out upon thy brow,
By the signal of pity in thy fallen cheeks,
By the fierce sparks that play about thy lips:
But, more than these,
By the chains which are laid upon thine arms
(Chains like these I saw once before,
And they were laid upon the limbs of Prometheus
Because he had brought down fire to the sons of man).
By all these signs wert thou known to me, Messiah.
Art thou not he, our Lord, the King Messiah?

And a thousand years these chains,
These chains of gold that will not break,
Have bound thee to the throne of the Lord God Sabaoth,
Have bound thee that thou stir not.
And from above thine eyes look down
Upon all the furies and terrors of life
That seize upon thy brothers,

And thy hand is powerless to help.
And daily, hourly, momently,
As thine eyes see the new evils,
And thine ears hear the crying of new blood
Calling to thee from the earth,
Thy soul, too, grows impotent within thee,
And rage consumes thee like fire, and thy veins are convulsed,
And thou art filled with longing and desire,
And thou girdest thyself with all thy strength
To burst thy chains and break a way to freedom,
That thou mightest descend swiftly to earth,
To redeem and deliver
The oppressed from the oppressor, and the poor from those that rob them.
And a voice is heard in the clashing of the links of thy chains,
As often as thou strainest to burst them,
As often as thou callest: "Now I can bear no more!
Now I will descend, now I will come, now I will save!
In a little while I will deliver them!"
And behold thy straining is in vain,
And thou fallest backward again,
And all things become again as they were.
And see, it is a thousand years that this voice is heard in the night,

The sound of the straining at thy chains—
And in the dead of night I too have heard.

In the dead of night I have heard: "Lord God, Lord God, how long?
I wither, I wither!
Wherefore hast Thou breathed this soul into me?
And wherefore hast Thou planted this heart in me?
To feel all pain, all suffering, all evil,
To bear the burden of all oppression,
All unhappiness and all misfortune—
And hast bound mine hands that I may not save?
Wherefore hast Thou given me an eye that sees,
And ears that listen,
That I may see the generations and their tears,
That I may hear the generations and their sighing,
My heart wounded with the wounds of all men,
And hast bound mine hands that I may not save?
Wherefore hast Thou created this sea of wretchedness,
And all the evil and all the oppression,
Which mine eyes have looked upon from of old,
And which mine eyes will look upon for the eternity to come,
And hast breathed a spirit into me,
To curse all evil and to blast it—
But hast set a seal upon my lips that I may not curse?
Wherefore these countless multitudes of the unhappy
Which are yet to be until the end of the generations,
With the countless multitudes of their tears
Which will yet be poured into the nether waters,
And wherefore hast Thou made me to hear
The great noise of their weeping which splitteth the rocks,
And hast bound mine hands that I may not save?
Wherefore hast Thou given me the strength
To save and to redeem, to help and to rescue,
To comfort those that mourn,
To heal hearts that are broken,
To bind up all sorrows—
And hast laid chains upon mine arm?
Lord God, wherefore hast Thou made me a Redeemer,
And hast forbidden me to redeem?"

And in the dead of night there is heard a sound of storm,
The storm of golden chains,
A storm of links that clash upon each other,
As often as the Messiah strains to burst his bonds,

And tears with the strength of his arm
At the Throne of Glory and the pillars thereof,
And at the heavens, and the heaven of heavens—
And an echo is heard against it, in the dead of night,
The sound of a storm of chains of iron
On the face of the earth below,
From end to end of the face of earth below.
And it chances that from amidst the crimson clouds,
From amidst the chrysolite and amber,
From amidst the whiteness of white sapphire,
A Voice is heard answering: "Until a new generation arise,
A generation that will understand redemption,
A generation that will desire to be redeemed,
Whose soul will be prepared to be redeemed!
Then wilt thou too achieve thy destiny and be redeemed:
Then wilt thou too achieve thy destiny and redeem!"

(*Maurice Samuel*)

THE GOLDEN KEY

by S. FRUG

1860–1916

Once, upon a time far distant,
Lived, they say, an ancient monarch.
Wonderful beyond all telling
Were the riches he possessed.

There were mounds of gold and silver,
Heaps of diamonds and pearls.
Guarded had they lain for ages,
Hid within the mighty palace.

And the palace door was closed,
Fastened, with a lock tremendous;
But the key that turned the lock
Was a little, tiny key!

Of the finest gold, the purest,
Fashioned only was the little,
Little key, and very easy,
See you, had it been to lose it.

So the king, to make his riches
Safer yet, he took the key,
And securely he attached it
To a great and heavy chain.
Lo, the key art thou, my people,
To the old king's palace door!

.   .   .   .   .   .

And the key to all those wondrous,
All those dear and priceless treasures:
Torah, charity and faith!—
Only, so that never, never,

Thee in all this world, my people,
Should he lose, has thy Creator
Fastened thee beyond escaping
To a great and heavy chain.

To a heavy chain of sorrows
God has made thee fast, and said:
Go, my people! Tho' the storm wind
And the tempest rage around thee,
Thou endurest—thou endurest!

(*Helena Frank*)

THE JEWISH MAY

by MORRIS ROSENFELD

1862–1924

May has come from out the showers,
Sun and splendour in her train;
All the grasses and the flowers
Waken up to life again.
Once again the leaves do show,
And the meadow-blossoms blow;
Once again thro' hills and dales
Ring the songs of nightingales.

Wheresoe'er on field or hill-side
With her paint-brush Spring is seen,
In the valley, by the rill-side,
All the earth is decked with green.

Once again the sun beguiles,
Moves the drowsy world to smiles.
See! the sun, with mother-kiss,
Wakes her child to joy and bliss.

Now each human feeling presses,
Flow'r-like, upward to the light,
Softly, thro' the heart's recesses,
Steal sweet fancies, pure and bright.
Golden dreams, their wings out-shaking,
Now are making
Realms celestial,
All of Azure,
New life waking,
Bringing treasure
Out of measure
For the soul's delight and pleasure.

Who then, tell me, old and sad,
Nears us, with a heavy tread,
On the sward in verdure clad?
See, he looks, and shakes his head.
Lonely is the strange newcomer,
Wearily he walks and slow—
His sweet spring-time and his summer
Faded long and long ago!

Say, who is it yonder walks
Past the hedgerows decked anew,
While a fearsome spectre stalks
By his side, the woodland thro'?
'Tis our ancient friend the Jew!
No sweet fancies hover round him,
Nought but terror and distress,
While, revealed
In wounds unhealed,
Wither corpses—old affections,
Ghosts of former recollections,
Buried youth and happiness.

Briar and blossom bow to meet him
In derision round his path;
Gloomily the hemlocks greet him,
And the crow screams out in wrath.
Strange the birds, and strange the flowers,

Strange the sunshine seems and dim,
Folk on earth and heav'nly powers—
Lo, the May is strange to him!

Little flowers, it were meeter
If ye made not quite so bold.
Sweet are ye, but oh, far sweeter
Knew he in the days of old!
Oranges by thousands glowing
Gilled the groves on either hand,
All the plants were God's own sowing
In his happy, far-off land!

Ask the cedars on the mountain!
Ask them, for they knew him well!
Myrtles green by Sharon's fountain,
In whose shade he loved to dwell!
Ask the Mount of Olives beauteous,
Ev'ry tree by ev'ry stream!
One and all will answer duteous
For the fair and ancient dream. . . .
O'er the desert and the pleasance
Breeze of Eden softly blew,
And the Lord his loving Presence
Evermore declared anew.

And the children at their leisure
Played in thousands round his tent,
Countless thoughts of joy and pleasure
God to his beloved sent.
There, in bygone days and olden,
From a wondrous harp and golden
Charmed he sings of beauty rare,
Holy, chaste beyond compare.
Never with the ancient sweetness,
Never in their old completeness,
Shall they sound: our dream is ended,
On a willow-bough suspended. . . .

Gone that dream so fair and fleeting!
Yet, behold: thou dream'st anew!
Hark! a *new* May gives thee greeting
From afar. Dost hear it, Jew?
Weep no more, altho' with sorrows
Wearied e'en to death, I see

Happier years and brighter morrows
Dawning, oh my Jew, for thee!
Hear'st thou not the promise ring
Where, like doves on silver wing,
Thronging cherubs sweetly sing
New-made songs of what shall be?

Hark! your olives shall be shaken,
And your citrons and your limes
Filled with fragrance; God shall waken,
Lead you, as in olden times.
In the pastures by the river
Ye once more your flocks shall tend,
Ye shall live, and live for ever,
Happy lives that know no end.
No more wand'ring, no more sadness;

Peace shall be your lot, and still
Hero-hearts shall throb with gladness
'Neath Moriah's silent hill.
Nevermore of dread afflictions
Or oppressions need ye tell;
Filled with joy and benedictions
In the old home shall ye dwell.
To the fatherland returning,
Following the homeward path,
Ye shall find the embers burning,
Still, upon the ruined hearth!

(*Helena Frank*)

HEAR, O ISRAEL!

by ANDRÉ SPIRE

1868–

HEAR, O Israel!
Will you never tire of repeating in your prayers:
"Praised be the Eternal, who avengeth my injuries,
Who protecteth my rights, who supporteth me in need,
Who crusheth my foes, who killeth my oppressors,
Praised be the Eternal, who girdeth my loins for battle!"

Hear, O Israel!
Have you seen your enemies blush, felled before you?
Have your eyes lowered to mock them in their ruin?
Did your God splinter the bones of their jaws?
And did He break the teeth of the wicked?
Did your ears hear in gladness the loss
Of those who joined themselves against you?
And has the Eternal made your old age resplendent
As that of an olive-tree in blossom?

Hear, O Israel!
You have engraved His Law on your heart:
You unroll it from your left arm morning and evening;
You bind it as a frontlet between your eyes;
You set it upon the doorposts of your gates
—And you! You are the contempt of all nations,
They spit on you as on an impure woman!

Hear, O Israel!
Will you put your hope forever in your strong God?
Will you never dare one day to scratch at His image?
Just look at His hand trailing beneath the clouds:
Is it a hand for action?
Is it a worker's hand?
Is it a hand for justice?
Without blisters, wrinkles, calluses, or bruises?

Hear, O Israel!
Torrents still are rolling down small rounded pebbles
For the slings of the Davids to come!
Quarries are full of fine rock to make grindstones
For resharpening the points of your old swords;
And you will find furnaces, sledges, and anvils
For reforging the shares of your wornout ploughs
Into elegant, sure-firing guns . . .

Hear, O Israel:
To arms!

(*Stanley Burnshaw*)

POEMS

by YEHOASH
1870–1926

I. AN OLD SONG

In the blossom-land Japan
Somewhere thus an old song ran

Said a warrior to a smith
"Hammer me a sword forthwith.
Make the blade
Light as wind on water laid.
Make it long
As the wheat at harvest song.
Supple, swift
As a snake, without rift,
Full of lightnings, thousand-eyed!
Smooth as silken cloth and thin
As the web that spiders spin.
And merciless as pain, and cold."

"On the hilt what shall be told?"

"On the sword's hilt, my good man,"
Said the warrior of Japan,
"Trace for me
A running lake, a flock of sheep
And one who sings her child to sleep."
                              (*Marie Syrkin*)

II. JEPHTHAH'S DAUGHTER

"**And it** became a custom in Israel that the daughters of Israel went from year
to year to lament for the daughter of Jephthah, the Gileadide, four days in the
year."—*Judges*.

There is a lonely mountain-top,
    A curse upon it lies;
No blade of grass upon it grows,
    No flowers greet the eyes.

But cold, bare cliffs of granite stand,
　　Like sentinels of stone,
Year after year, through wind and snow,
　　Around a craggy throne.

And on the topmost, coldest peak
　　There is a spot of woe—
A little tomb, an old gray tomb,
　　Raised centuries ago.

For there within her grave she lies
　　Plucked in an evil hour—
The martyred daughter of her race,
　　Israel's fairest flower!

There Jephthah's maid forever sleeps—
　　The victim that he vowed—
But, four days in the dreary year,
　　The loneliness is loud.

And Gilead's mourning daughters
　　Up from the valley throng—
The mountain glens reverberate
　　With sorrow and with song!

Oh, loud and long and wild they wail
　　The light, untimely spent,
And dance upon the mountain-top
　　A choral of lament.

And as they dance they seem to see
　　Another dancer, too,
And hear, amidst the measure rise,
　　The voice of her they rue!

　　　　　　　　　　(*Alter Brody*)

POEMS

by HAYYIM NAHMAN BIALIK
1873–1934

I. NIGHT

I know that this my crying, like the crying
Of owls on ruins in a wilderness,
Wakes neither consolation nor despair.
I know that these my tears are as a cloud
Of barren waters in a desert land,
That my lament, grown old with many years,
Is strengthless in the stony hearts of men. . . .
Still the unhappy heart in vain laments
And seeks in vain to weep itself to rest.

From my pent prison I put forth my head
And call upon the storm and question it,
And search the clouds and with the gloom confer—
When will the darkness and the tempest pass?
When will the whirlwind die and the clouds scatter
And moon and stars break forth again in light?
I search from heaven to earth, from earth to heaven:
No sign, or answer—only storm and night.

Within the womb God consecrated me
To sickness and to poverty and said:
Go forth and find thy vanished destiny.
And among the ways of life buy air to breathe
And steal with craft a beggar's dole of light,
Carry from door to door thy beggar's pack;
Before the wealthy crook the knees for bread. . . .
But I am weary now with wandering:
Ah, God, my God, how long is yet the road?

From the dark womb, like an uncleanliness,
On a heap of gathered foulness I was cast,
Unwashed from filth, with rags for swaddling-clothes,
My mother stretched to me a withered breast
And stilled me with the bitter milk of madness.
And in my heart a viper made its nest

And sucks my blood to render it in poison.
Where can I hide me from its burning fangs?
God! answer me with either life or death.

In the broad sky the light clouds are unraveled
And stars among them are like single pearls.
The wind moves dreamlike in the tranquil darkness
And in the wind still broods the peace of God.
And a faint whisper, like a secret kiss,
Laden with revelation, stirs the grass,
And sleep that heals and comforts falls on earth—
But not on me, the outcast,—not on me.

In the dead night-time I begin my song,
When two alone awake, my pain and I.
Beneath my skin my bones are turned to dust,
My weak eyes fall, for they have wept too long.
Now my song wakens like a bird at dawn,
Her dewy wings beat rain into my heart
And melt the tear-drops on my frozen eyes. . . .
In vain, in vain, for tears alone I know.

Bring me not rain-drops, but a fount of tears,
Tears that will shake the hearts of men with storm;
Then by the ancient mounds of desolation,
By the ruined Temple, by my fathers' graves,
Where the road passes I will take my stand,
And travelers on the road will pity me,
And charity will waken with their pity.
There let men hear thee, O my song, until
Thy tears are ended and my pain is stilled.

(*Maurice Samuel*)

II. THE MATHMID

There are abandoned corners of our Exile,
Remote, forgotten cities of Dispersion,
Where still in secret burns our ancient light,
Where God has saved a remnant from disaster.
There, brands that glimmer in a ruin of ashes,
Pent and unhappy souls maintain the vigil—
Spirits grown old beyond the count of time,
Grown old beyond the reckoning of days.
And when thou goest forth alone, at nightfall,
Wandering in one of these, the sacred cities,

When heaven above is quick with breaking stars,
And earth beneath with whispering spirit-winds—
Thine ear will catch the murmur of a voice,
Thine eye will catch the twinkle of a light
Set in a window, and a human form—
A shadow, like the shadow of death—beyond,
A shadow trembling, swaying back and forth,
A voice, an agony, that lifts and falls,
And comes toward thee upon the waves of silence.
Mark well the swaying shadow and the voice:
It is a *Mathmid* in his prison-house,
A prisoner, self-guarded, self-condemned,
Self-sacrificed to study of the Law. . . .

Within these walls, within this prison-house,
Six years have passed above his swaying form:
Within these walls the child became the youth,
The youth became the man, fore-ripened, swift,
And swift as these went, swifter yet were gone
The cheek's bloom and the luster of his eyes.
Six years have passed since first he set his face
To the dark corner of the inner walls;
Six years since he has seen, for joyous sunlight,
Gray limestone, lizards and the webs of spiders;
Six years of hunger, years of sleeplessness,
Six years of wasting flesh and falling cheeks—
And all, to him, as if it had not been.
He knows that Jews have studied thus of old,
He knows the fame and glory they have won.

             .   .   .

Since that dark corner has become his own,
No man, no living thing, has seen his coming,
No man, no living thing, has seen his going.
Not even the rising and the setting suns
Have witnessed his arrival, his return;
The morning-star, black midnight and the moon
Alone knew when he slept and when he rose:
Daylight has never looked upon his ways,
The mid-day sun has never burned his skin.
In the dimmest dawn, "before thou canst distinguish
A white thread from an azure, wolf from dog"—
(Thereby the Jew shall know, the Rabbis say,
The hour for morning-prayer is not yet come)—
In the dimmest dawn, while through the lifeless dark

Ten thousand times ten thousand stars yet shine,
Before the crowing of the cock disturbs
The burghers of the city, sleep-enfolded,
Yea, even before the most elect of faith
Rise to do honor to Creation's Lord:
In that hour, when the world in silence trembles
Before the new awakening of life,
Trembles as if she dreamed the last of dreams,
As if a wandering and secret thought
Made a light stirring in her folded wings—
In that hour from his stolen sleep he starts,
Dresses in darkness and to his corner runs.
Light are his footsteps on the garden path,
Only the winds have heard them passing by,
Only the stars have seen them running swift.

But there are moments when a playful wind
Out of the blue deep like the Tempter comes,
And with a loving hand his earlock fondles,
And whispers to him with dissolving sweetness.
And the boy's eyelids cling to one another,
As if they pleaded with him: *"Brother, brother,*
Have pity on the dark eyes under us;
And we are weary, for with thee we suffer;
A full day we have toiled, a summer day,
And half a summer night: it is enough.
Brother, return and sleep, and we with thee,
Too short thy sleep was to restore our strength. . . ."
But sudden starts the boy, draws his lean hand
Across his eyes, as if temptation sat
Upon his leaden lid: and clear and swift
His footsteps echo from the empty streets.

And then the wind that blows about the garden
Takes up the theme, and gentle is its voice:
"Green is my cradle, child of happiness,
Joy in my blossom, ere thine own be withered. . . ."
And left and right of him the flowers and grasses
Speak to him from their dreams, *"We too are sleeping."*
Even the stars above him take on voices,
And wink: *"We sleep, although our eyes are open."*
The drunken odors of a thousand flowers
Mount to his nostrils in resistless waves:
They break upon his eyes, his lips, his throat.

He bares his breast then to receive the wind,
And lifts his strengthless hands as if in prayer:
"O dear wind, take me, carry me from here,
And find a place for me where I may rest;
For here is only weariness and pain. . . ."
His raised hands bruise against the garden fence,
And tell him he has wandered from the path:
Swift he recalls his vows, recalls his corner,
And turns from the Tempter's voice, and flees.

In the Yeshivah reigns a sacred silence
Which he, the sacred youth, is first to break;
For there, in the dark corner, wait for him—
Faithful companions since the day he came—
Three friends: his stand, his candle and his Talmud.
As if the moments could not move too swiftly
That lie between him and his trusted friends,
He hastens to his place and takes his stand,
And like a pillar stands from morn till night.
Still standing he will eat his midday crust,
Still standing he will half outwatch the night.
Granite is yielding clay compared with him—
A Jewish boy unto the Torah vowed.

"Oi, omar Rabba, tonu rabonon,
Thus Rabba speaks, and thus our teachers taught,"
(Backward and forward swaying he repeats,
With ceaseless singsong the undying words);
The dawn, the garden, the enchanted fields,
Are gone, are vanished like a driven cloud,
And earth and all her fullness are forgotten. . . .

(Maurice Samuel)

III. TWO STEPS FROM MY GARDEN RAIL

Two steps from my garden rail
Sleeps my well beneath its pail:
    Every sabbath comes my love
    And I let him drink there.

All the world is sleeping now
Like the fruit beneath the bough.
    Father, mother, both are gone
    And my heart wakes here alone.

And the pail awakes with me,
Dripping, dripping, drowsily:
    Drops of gold and crystal clear . . .
    And my love is drawing near.

Hist! I think that something stirred;
Was it he, or but a bird?
    Dearest friend, my lover dear,
    There is no one with me here.

By the trough we sit and speak,
Hand in hand and cheek to cheek;
    Hear this riddle: Can you tell
    Why the pitcher seeks the well?

That you cannot answer, nor
What the pail is weeping for?
    Morn to even, drop by drop,
    Fall its tears and cannot stop.

This then tell me, why my breast
Daylong, nightlong is oppressed.
    Spoke my mother truth in saying
    That your heart from me was straying?

And my lover answered: See,
Enemies have slandered me.
    Ere another year be gone,
    We shall marry, foolish one.

On that golden day of days
Shall the summer be ablaze.
    Fruited branches overhead
    Shall in benediction spread.

Friend and kinsman, young and old
Shall be gathered to behold,
    And with music and with mirth
    They shall come to lead us forth.

And the bridal canopy
In this place shall lifted be.
    I shall slip a ring of gold
    On this finger that I hold.

And pronounce the blessing: "Thee
God makes consecrate to me."

And my enemies shall there
Burst with envy and despair.
(*Maurice Samuel*)

IV. QUEEN SABBATH

The sun o'er the treetops is no longer seen;
Come, let us go forth to greet Sabbath the Queen!
Behold her descending, the holy and blest,
And with her the angels of peace and of rest.
　　Welcome, O Queen, welcome!
　　Enter thou, enter, O bride!
Unto you be there peace, ye angels of Peace.

The Sabbath is greeted with song and with praise,
We go slowly homewards, our hearts full of grace.
The table is spread there, the candles give light,
Every nook in the house is shining and bright.
　　Sabbath is peace and rest.
　　Sabbath is peaceful and blest.
Enter in peace, ye angels of Peace.

O pure one, be with us and light with Thy ray
The night and the day, then go on Thy way,
And we do Thee honour with garments most fine,
With songs and with psalms and with three feasts with wine.
　　And by sweetest peace,
　　And by perfect peace.
Bless us in peace, ye angels of Peace!

The sun in the treetops is no longer seen,
Come forth; we will speed our Sabbath the Queen,
Go thou in peace, our holy and pure one!
Know that for six days we wait you, our sure one!
　　Thus for the coming Sabbath,
　　Thus for the coming Sabbath!
Pass forth in peace, ye angels of Peace!

(*I. M. Lask*)

THE END OF SORROW

by EDMOND FLEG
1874–

The Jews:
Will the wolves lie down with the lambs and feed them?

The Dreamer:
Sighs in the distance, and who shall heed them?

The Jews:
And the lion-cub lie down with the sheep?

The Dreamer:
I know you, voices, and I hear you weep.

The Jews:
When will the blade of the sword be rusted,
and beaten into the plough-share—when?

The Dreamer:
I dreamed. And thou dost call me dream-invested,
O world forgotten, to wake again.

The Jews:
When from the rim of the world will you gather,
children of men, in the house of your father,
builded of gold, and the break of day.

The Dreamer (waking):
Where is this sunlight sorrow dips in grey?

The Jews:
When, being part of one another,
will you raise your voices, brother by brother
when the horn—

The Wandering Jew (awake):
                    The voice of men who mourn.

He saw the Tribes by the wall of granite,
    and the centuries with them,

shared the high sorrow, murmuring in it:
　"O lost Jerusalem."

The Jews:
We of our sorrows build in the days to come
for the soul of man that tall and ultimate home.
But you that pass tomorrow, as you pass today,
build you as true as we, and go your way.

And then the sleeper, rising, cried on God:
　"Again the torture, and again the road."
And stepping out into the dawn of all
he heard the Jews still weeping by the Wall.

　"Dark are thy ways! O who can find them?
　O Lord of distance, and yet we see
　the dayspring a wisp of Thy glory behind them,
　the nightfall a step on the path to Thee."
                                   (*Humbert Wolfe*)

POEMS

by SAUL TCHERNIHOWSKY
1875–

I. BEFORE THE STATUE OF APOLLO

To thee I come, O long-abandoned god
Of early moons and unremembered days,
To thee whose reign was in a greener world
Among a race of men divine with youth,
Strong generations of the sons of earth:
To thee, whose right arm broke the bound of heaven
To set on thrones therein thy strongest sons,
Whose proud brows with victorious bays were crowned.
Amongst the gods of old thou wert a god,
Bringing for increase to the mighty earth
A race of demi-gods, instinct with life,
Strange to the children of the house of pain.
A boy-god, passionate and beautiful,
Whose mastery was over the bright sun

And over the dark mysteries of life,
The golden shadow-treasuries of song,
The music of innumerable seas—
A god of joyousness and fresh delight,
Of vigor and the ecstasy of life.

I am the Jew. Dost thou remember me?
Between us there is enmity forever!
Not all the multitudes of ocean's waters,
Storm-linking continent with continent,
Could fill the dark abyss between us yawning.
The heavens and the boundless wilderness
Were short to bridge the wideness set between
My fathers' children and thy worshippers.
And yet behold me! I have wandered far,
By crooked ways, from those that were before me,
And others after me shall know this path.
But amongst those that will return to thee
I was the first to free my soul that groaned
Beneath the agony of generations;
For a day came I would endure no more,
And on that day my spirit burst its chains
And turned again towards the living earth.

The people and its God have aged together!
Passions which strengthlessness had laid to sleep
Start into sudden life again, and break
Their prison of a hundred generations.
The light of God, the light of God is mine!
My blood is clamorous with desire of life.
My limbs, my nerves, my veins, triumphant shout
For life and sunlight.
                              And I come to thee,
And here before thy pedestal I kneel
Because thy symbol is the burning sun.
I kneel to thee, the noble and the true,
Whose strength is in the fullness of the earth,
Whose will is in the fullness of creation,
Whose throne is on the secret founts of being.
I kneel to life, to beauty and to strength,
I kneel to all the passionate desires
Which they, the dead-in-life, the bloodless ones,
The sick, have stifled in the living God,

The God of wonders of the wilderness,
The God of gods, Who took Canaan with storm
Before they bound Him in phylacteries.

(Maurice Samuel)

II. BARUCH OF MAYENCE

Here are the graves. And here is thy grave too.
Three days ago their bloody sacrifices
Were brought here to be thrust into the earth.
Thou too art buried here, my dearest one!
Not even a Star of Zion marks the spot.
Yet I have found thee. . . . Secretly I came,
And not one living eye has seen my coming.
I came to tell thee all that chanced to me
Since the dread day whereon I met my death. . . .
For I am dead! And I who speak to thee—
I am no longer I. . . . I am another. . . .

Dost thou remember yet the desolate day,
The day of wrath, when God abandoned me?
On that day all the bells throughout the land
Woke storm and tumult with their evil tidings.
And wild one bell unto the other called,
"Woe to the daughter of the House of Jacob"
And in the streets the thronging multitudes
Peasant and soldier, artisan and priest,
Gathered like famished wolves about their prey—
Deaf to the weeping of the children, deaf
To the moaning of the mothers, blind and deaf
To age and sickness. And about the victims,
Spattered with foulness, driven torn and bleeding,
They howled like wolves for blood, for blood, for slaughter!
And suddenly a poignard flashed before me,
A band was gathered round me, and one voice
Above the others howled the question at me.
I saw their wild-beast faces. And I saw
The hand outstretched, the poignard at my throat.
And I made answer in a stifled voice,
And what I answered I remember not.
But I remember now their house of prayer,
The pealing of the organ, candle-lights . . .
A multitude of voices like a sea,

The priests, the cowls, the singing of the monks—
And in me the bewilderment of death.

．　　　　．　　　　．　　　　．　　　　．

And then I cursed my people and my God.
I cursed the breasts that once had suckled me.
And all that had been sacred to my fathers,
I spat upon! pronounced anathema
Against the hopes and longings that had been
Until that day the dearest of my life.
Yea, I denied my people and my God,
The God of holiness.
                              Then suddenly
My childhood rose to life before my eyes.
And I was young again. I was a boy
Awaiting my Bar-mitzvah, and again
For the first time I bound upon my arm
The Tephilin; and I saw my father's face
Shining with happiness. And through my flesh
There ran a thrill of joy and holy pride.
For I was now a man, and on my shoulders
Rested the sacred burden of the Law,
The Torah of my Maker and Redeemer.
What strength was in my soul! In all the world
That day, there was no happiness like mine.
And as I bound the Tephilin on my arm
I counted: One, two, three . . . and seven times
I wound them on my flesh, and drew them tight
Until the skin beneath was flecked with blood.
"Behold I bind thee unto Me forever!"
And I had shamed the bond God made with me.
"I bind thee unto me in faithfulness!"
And I was faithless in the day of trial.

．　　　　．　　　　．　　　　．　　　　．

Listen, dear heart; listen, my dearest one,
For now thou wakest. I have brought with me
Tidings of horror. Listen, dearest one,
And I will whisper to thee. Dost thou know?
Our children, our two daughters, now are free. . . .
My hand gave back the freedom to their souls.
Miriam rebelled at first, and Zipporah
Clung to her sister and looked long at me
As if imploring mercy. . . . She was first.
I could not bear the pleading in her eyes. . . .

My daughters, O my daughters, turn from me!
Mine eyes are seared. One vision like a flame
Burns up my brain, and withers with its fury
My heart, my blood, my strength.

> I am the man, the father, who
> With his own hand his daughters slew.
> The knife was firm and trembled not
> Until the hilt with blood was hot.
> The lives which God to gladness gave
> I have imprisoned in the grave:
> I could not, dared not let them live,
> Their young and stainless spirits give
> A prey to those whose hands were red
> With bloody guilt of human dead. . . .
> O well for thee, in darkness set!
> Rememberest thou thy daughters yet? . . .
>   O my daughter, my daughters, my daughters!

Accursed be thou for ever, cruel race!
Accursed for ever be thy evil name!
The wrath of God shall dwell with thee for ever.
The blood that thou hast sacrificed, the tears,
The moaning of thy victims, shall arise
In one wild flood against thee, and the sound
Shall be a horror in the stormy night.

> Ha! How fearful is the night!
>   Here in the dark I feel
> The cold that cuts into my heart
>   Like driven steel.
> But through the town are crimson flames
>   As from a furnace blown.
> And the hand that lit the furnace there
>   Was mine alone.
> Look! The dull-glowing clouds of smoke
>   Roll further, higher.
> The monastery burns and wraps
>   The town in fire.
> When I had lit the funeral pile
>   I lingered there
> And joy was in my heart to watch
>   Their fierce despair!

How good, how good, to mark the bitter tears
  The holy fathers shed!
To hear the wailing and the wild lamenting
  For the dead!
I laughed to see one man wrapped up
  In flames as in a mesh,
Screaming he ran, and as he ran
  The fire devoured his flesh.
Oh, long I laughed remembering
  The horrible eyes,
The terror and the flight, the prayers,
  The dying cries.

And when the altar was prepared
  Then did I bring
Two daughters for a sacrifice—
  A burnt offering.
Then from the town I came to thee.
Arise, dear heart, return with me.
The flames I lit are burning bright,
Arise, and we will walk in light.
And where the flames the fiercest burn,
Thy daughters wait for thy return. . . .

(Maurice Samuel)

III. CREDO

Laugh at all my dreams, my dearest;
  Laugh, and I repeat anew
That I still believe in man—
  As I still believe in you.

For my soul is not yet unsold
  To the golden calf of scorn
And I still believe in man
  And the spirit in him born.

By the passion of his spirit
  Shall his ancient bonds be shed.
Let the soul be given freedom,
  Let the body have its bread!

Laugh, for I believe in friendship,
  And in one I still believe,

One whose heart shall beat with my heart
  And with mine rejoice and grieve.

Let the time be dark with hatred,
  I believe in years beyond
Love at last shall bind the peoples
  In an everlasting bond.

In that day shall my own people
  Rooted in its soil arise,
Shake the yoke from off its shoulders
  And the darkness from its eyes.

Life and love and strength and action
  In their heart and blood shall beat,
And their hopes shall be both heaven
  And the earth beneath their feet.

Then a new song shall be lifted
  To the young, the free, the brave,
And the wreath to crown the singer
  Shall be gathered from my grave.
                (*Maurice Samuel*)

MY PEOPLE

by ELSE LASKER-SCHÜLER
1876–

That rock is crumbling
Whence I spring,
That rock whereto my hymns I sing . . .
Abruptly I sheer from the path,
And privily
I purl, far, far, across the mourning stones,
Toward the sea.

I have streamed off
From the fermenting must
Of my own blood.
And still, and still, ever the echo thrills

In me,
When shudderingly against the east
That crumbling rockrib,
My people,
Cries to God.

(*Babette Deutsch*)

SONGS

by ABRAHAM RAISEN
1876–

I. FOR SUNDOWN

The sweetest melody
Your heart can sing,
Keep for your autumn hour,
Not for the spring.

Glad is the blossom time
With its own tune and chime;
Ah, but the sunset day—
Sing it away.

(*Marie Syrkin*)

II. HEALING

Sweetheart, kiss the gray
From my hair.
Maybe they'll grow black
Again there.

Sweetheart, kiss the gloom
From my eyes.
Maybe they'll turn good
Again—wise!

Kiss the gall from off my mouth
And my tongue.
Maybe I'll turn foolish
And young.

(*Marie Syrkin*)

III. NOSTALGIA

On with another new love,
Off with the past love's pain;
Yet ever the old love, the old love
Steals to the heart again.

On with another new love,
Burning and bright and keen,
Yet terribly dear in the distance
Shines the love that has been.

On with another new love,
Kisses and hands that meet—
Yet, oh to be close to the old love
And beg for content at her feet!

(Marie Syrkin)

IV. PEARLS

I gave them the gold of my spirit,
    My heart-hidden treasures I poured,
My joys and my loves and my longings—
    They gave me back stones in reward.

But mark ye, I know how to handle
    The stones of the ignorant throng;
And, lo, when they enter my spirit
    They turn into pearls of song!

(Alter Brody)

POEMS

by JACOB KAHAN

1877–

I. YOU MUST NOT CRY

Girl, you must not cry: I tell you, you must not cry,
For even your tears are empty of meaning.
Oh, I know, I know, they come from the heart—

And in your heart—let be there what will—
Only love is not there.

I ask you now: What is it you want?
Are you thirsty for kisses? You have had kisses enough.
More, have you given me more kisses,
That you ask more kisses of me?

For I cannot bear any longer your shallowness, your poutings,
I cannot bear the falseness in you.
What! You are offended? No, no, you must not be offended.
I know, I know, you are honest, you are truthful—
Only all this is false, false.

What are you crying for? No, no, you must not cry.
I cannot bear to see a girl crying. . . .
The tears fall like burning coals on my heart,
They burn, they tear my heart.

. . . Once there was a woman—
That was long ago, long ago—and she loved me.
Her love was strong with the strength of God,
And infinite, like the infinite universe. . . .
That woman was my mother. She is dead.

Among the terrible crags I have chosen a path—
Alone.
Has a care ever been yours how I fare on my way?
Has a single Godspeed of yours ever gone out with me?

And why are you still crying? Ah, no, no, no, you must not cry,
You must not, or I will be crying too.
And yet . . .
Perhaps, perhaps . . .
Perhaps, after all, a spark of my mother's soul has awakened in you.

And you rise, you throw your arms round me.
So, so . . . kiss me, kiss me.
By heaven, I am not wicked, I am not wicked.
Only do not cry, girl, do not cry.

II. FOR THE BEAUTY WHICH DECAYETH

Give me free space! For my imprisoned sighs
Give me free space, and for my burning eyes.
I fail, as into crushing armour thrust.

I cannot weep, the heavy clouds of dust
Come up and blind me. And I cannot cry
For I am stifled.

        Like the fires that lie
Pent in the iron bosom of the earth,
And eat her heart, and cannot issue forth,
So fires of fury in my heart are pent,
And wither up my blood, and find no vent.

Give me free space! For my imprisoned sighs
Give me free space, and for my burning eyes,
And for the life that sickens,
And for the bloom that falls before it quickens,
In the evil of the generation.
I have seen spirits gentle as the day
On dark and dissolute waters borne away,
In the evil of the generation.
I have seen sons of God deny their birth,
And soil their heritage with lusts of earth,
In the evil of the generation.
And for a vain illusion youth is sold,
And hearts that wake are stilled again with cold
In the evil of the generation.

Where is the trumpet of Messiah
Whose blast of fire
Shall rouse the blood of men and fill
Their hearts with an exalted will
That they may rescue from eternal shame
The works God wrought to glorify His name?
Where is the whip whose burning thongs shall brand
The noble of our land,
Who hide themselves from sight
In marble halls and gardens of delight,
And there grow weary of their empty rest,
And void of strength are unto death opprest;
And tremble not before the wonder,
The vision and the voice of thunder,
Though they have seen and heard the signs that send
Their warning through the land, from end to end.

Blessed the great of heart who shall withstand
The stubborn days and the oppressor's hand,

Whose tears shall fall like quickening rain
And living dew upon the withered plain,
Whose breath shall be to men a wind of grace
In an abandoned and decaying place;
And when the sun shall issue in his might,
The dens of darkness shall be filled with light,
And the smitten blossoms shall rejoice and know
The sun, and raise their heads, brought low
In the evil of the generation.

(Maurice Samuel)

III. DO YOU KNOW WHAT THE MOUNTAINS ARE?

Do you know what the mountains are?
The mountains are cries,
Cries of freedom, a wild shouting, vehement voices.
Which broke forth in tempestuous power
From the heart girdled with strength, thirsting for might and drunk with it,
The heart of life—
Broke forth, sprang out against the skies—
And were frozen.
And the frozen cries stand
Like memorials in the wastes of the world,
From eternity to eternity.
And the wind will not bear them away,
Never shall the wind bear them away.
The silent snow rests on them,
And the sun shines on them, and the moon shines on them,
And about them life pours onwards, a rushing of bubbles—
And they stand there, frozen,
From eternity unto eternity.

(Maurice Samuel)

ROAST LEVIATHAN

by LOUIS UNTERMEYER

1885–

"Old Jews!" Well, David, aren't we?
What news is that to make you see so red,
To swear and almost tear your beard in half?

Jeered at? Well, let them laugh.
You can laugh longer when you're dead.

What? Are you still too blind to see?
Have you forgot your Midrash? . . . They were right,
The little *goyim,* with their angry stones.
You should be buried in the desert out of sight
And not a dog should howl miscarried moans
Over your foul bones. . . .

Have you forgotten what is promised us,
Because of stinking days and rotting nights?
Eternal feasting, drinking, blazing lights.
With endless leisure, periods of play!
Supernal pleasures, myriads of gay
Discussions, great debates with prophet-kings!
And rings of riddling scholars all surrounding
God who sits in the very middle, expounding
The Torah. . . . *Now* your dull eyes glisten!
Listen:
It is the final Day.
A blast of Gabriel's horn has torn away
The last haze from our eyes, and we can see
Past the three hundred skies and gaze upon
The Ineffable Name engraved deep in the sun.
Now one by one, the pious and the just
Are seated by us, radiantly risen
From their dull prison in the dust.
And then the festival begins!
A sudden music spins great webs of sound
Spanning the ground, the stars and their companions;
While from the cliffs and cañons of blue air,
Prayers of all colors, cries of exultation
Rise into choruses of singing gold.
And at the height of this bright consecration,
The whole Creation's rolled before us.
The seven burning heavens unfold. . . .
We see the first (the only one we knew)
Dispersed and, shining through,
The other six declining: Those that hold
The stars and moons, together with all those
Containing rain and fire and sullen weather;
Cellars of dew-fall higher than the brim;
Huge arsenals with centuries of snows;
Infinite rows of storms and swarms of seraphim. . . .

Divided now are winds and waters. Sea and land,
Tohu and Bohu, light and darkness, stand
Upright on either hand.
And down this terrible aisle,
While heaven's ranges roar aghast,
Pours a vast file of strange and hidden things;
Forbidden monsters, crocodiles with wings
And perfumed flesh that sings and glows
With more fresh colors than the rainbow knows. . . .
The *reëm,* those great beasts with eighteen horns,
Who mate but once in seventy years and die
In their own tears which flow ten stadia high.
The *shamir,* made by God on the sixth morn,
No longer than a grain of barley corn
But stronger than the bull of Bashan and so hard
It cuts through diamonds. Meshed and starred
With precious stones, there struts the shattering *ziz*
Whose groans are wrinkled thunder. . . .
For thrice three hundred years the full parade
Files past, a cavalcade of fear and wonder.
And then the vast aisle clears.

Now comes our constantly increased reward.
The Lord commands that monstrous beast,
Leviathan, to be our feast.
What cheers ascend from horde on ravenous horde!
One hears the towering creature rend the seas,
Frustrated, cowering, and his pleas ignored.
In vain his great, belated tears are poured—
For this he was created, kept and nursed.
Cries burst from all the millions that attend:
"Ascend, Leviathan, it is the end!
We hunger and we thirst! Ascend!" . . .

Observe him first, my friend.

> *God's deathless plaything rolls an eye*
> *Five hundred thousand cubits high.*
> *The smallest scale upon his tail*
> *Could hide six dolphins and a whale.*
> *His nostrils breathe—and on the spot*
> *The churning waves turn seething hot.*
> *If he be hungry, one huge fin*
> *Drives seven thousand fishes in;*

And when he drinks what he may need,
The rivers of the earth recede.
Yet he is more than huge and strong—
Twelve brilliant colors play along
His sides until, compared to him,
The naked, burning sun seems dim.
New scintillating rays extend
Through endless singing space and rise
Into an ecstasy that cries:
"Ascend, Leviathan, ascend!"

God now commands the multi-colored bands
Of angels to intrude and slay the beast
That His good sons may have a feast of food.
But as they come, Leviathan sneezes twice . . .
And, numb with sudden pangs, each arm hangs slack.
Black terror seizes them; blood freezes into ice
And every angel flees from the attack!
God, with a look that spells eternal law,
Compels them back.
But though they fight and smite him tail and jaw,
Nothing avails; upon his scales their swords
Break like frayed cords and—worse than blades of straw—
Bend towards the hilt, wilting like faded grass.
Defeat and fresh retreat. . . . But once again
God's murmurs pass among them and they mass
With firmer steps upon the crowded plain.
Vast clouds of spears and stones rise from the ground.
But every dart flies past and rocks rebound
To the disheartened angels falling around.

A pause.
The angel host withdraws
With empty boasts throughout its sullen files.
Suddenly God smiles.
On the walls of heaven a tumble of light is caught.
Low thunder rumbles like an afterthought;
And God's slow laughter calls:
"Behemot!"

Behemot, sweating blood,
Uses for his daily food
All the fodder, flesh and juice
That twelve tall mountains can produce.

Jordan, flooded to the brim,
Is a single gulp to him;
Two great streams from Paradise
Cool his lips and scarce suffice.

When he shifts from side to side
Earthquakes gape and open wide;
When a nightmare makes him snore,
All the dead volcanoes roar.

In the space between each toe,
Kingdoms rise and saviours go;
Epochs fall and causes die
In the lifting of his eye.

Wars and justice, love and death,
These are but his wasted breath;
Chews a planet for his cud—
Behemot sweating blood.

Roused from his unconcern,
Behemot burns with anger.
Dripping sleep and languor from his heavy haunches,
He turns from deep disdain and launches
A mountain on the thickening air,
And with weird cries of sickening despair,
Flies at Leviathan.
None can surmise the struggle that ensues—
The eyes lose sight of it and words refuse
To tell the story in its gory might.
Night passes after night,
And still the fight continues, still the sparks
Fly from the iron sinews . . . till the marks
Of fire and belching thunder fill the dark
And, almost torn asunder, one falls stark,
Hammering upon the other! . . .
What clamor now is born, what crashings rise!
Hot lightnings lash the skies and frightening cries
Clash with the hymns of saint and seraphim.
The bloody limbs thrash through a ruddy dusk,
Till one great tusk of Behemot has gored
Leviathan, restored to his full strength,
Who, dealing fiercer blows in those last throes,
Closes on reeling Behemot at length—
Piercing him with steel-pointed claws,

Straight through the jaws to his disjointed head.
And both lie dead.

Then come the angels!
With hoists and levers, joists and poles,
With knives and cleavers, ropes and saws,
Down the long slopes to the gaping maws,
The angels hasten; hacking and carving,
So nought will be lacking for the starving
Chosen of God, who in frozen wonderment
Realize now what the terrible thunder meant.
How their mouths water while they are looking
At miles of slaughter and sniffing the cooking!
Whiffs of delectable fragrance swim by;
Spice-laden vagrants that float and entice,
Tickling the throat and brimming the eye.
Ah! What rejoicing and crackling and roasting!
Ah! How the boys sing as, cackling and boasting,
The angels' old wives and their nervous assistants
Run in to serve us. . . .
                              And while we are toasting
The Fairest of All, they call from the distance—
The rare ones of Time, they share our enjoyment;
Their only employment to bear jars of wine
And shine like the stars in a circle of glory.
Here sways Rebekah accompanied by Zilpah;
Miriam plays to the singing of Bilhah;
Hagar has tales for us, Judith her story;
Esther exhales bright romances and musk.
There, in the dusky light, Sàlome dances.
Sara and Rachel and Leah and Ruth,
Fairer than ever and all in their youth,
Come at our call and go by our leave.
While, from her bower of beauty, Eve smiles
As, with the voice of a flower, she sings
Of Eden, young earth and the birth of all things. . . .

Peace without end.
Peace will descend on us, discord will cease;
And we, now so wretched, will lie stretched out
Free of old doubt, on our cushions of ease.
And, like a gold canopy over our bed,
The skin of Leviathan, tail-tip to head,
Soon will be spread till it covers the skies.
Light will still rise from it; millions of bright

Facets of brilliance, shaming the white
Glass of the moon, inflaming the night.

So Time shall pass and rest and pass again,
Burn with an endless zest and then return,
Walk at our side and tide us to new joys;
God's voice to guide us, beauty as our staff.
Thus shall Life be when Death has disappeared. . . .

Jeered at? Well, let them laugh.

TWILIGHT

by MANE LAYB
1884–

Blue and very quiet hour of evening,
Silently my dream on night reposes;
Now, more burningly and brightly glimmer
The dark wounds that are my crimson roses.
Now, the street's loud murmur fades and passes.
Steps and speech sound quietly and lightly.
Eyes that long for eyes flame paler, gentler.
Hands close-locked now do not press so tightly
Now, my longing turns to gold enkindled.
Eye and heart a tenser warmth discloses.
Now, now, glow more burningly and brightly
The dark wounds that are my crimson roses.

(*Marie Syrkin*)

POEMS

by ZALMAN SCHNAIUR
1887–

I. YOU WILL LIFT UP YOUR EYES TO THE HEAVENS

You will lift up your eyes to the heavens and know them not,
Their blue laughter will be hidden under a mask of clouds,

You will break through with your gaze to the light of day,
You will think in your pride:
"I am the fount of the world's great artifice. I—man.
From me go forth twin streams of light which guild the secret mountains.
From me the self-same streams of light which touch with silver the mountains
    of the deep.
Mighty Gods are nourished by my visions,
Out of my lowliness they grew to greatness, and in my greatness they will
    fall low."

And in that mournful hour you will suddenly know:
Not unto you belongs, and not of the flesh was born,
The mighty Idea which fills universal space.
But He is the father of all, and in the play of chance
You too were born unto Him, you, the artist.
And with hand, and foot, and tooth you cling to Him.
As the insect clings to the flower.
And with Him, together with Him, you are onward borne.
And can you say whither He bears you?

II. AND THERE ARE TIMES . . .

And there are times when dreams are vanities.
Shadows of beauty, altars unto love,
And, in the heart, the longings that arise—
All, all are beautiful—and all are lies.

For wind is not a comfort unto hunger,
Nor gold a snare to immortality.
I cry then: "For the bitter truth I long,
Though grim like iron, yet like iron strong!"

I cry then: "Weary is my soul of dreams,
False prophecies, and golden visions false;
For, blinded with their vacant light, I gave
My strength to beauty, an eternal slave."

Though all are trapped, must I with them be trapped?
I shall be first to tear the treacherous net,
And thunder, as the golden strands I sever,
"Down, down with gold: Let iron live for ever!"

III. BENEATH THE HAMMER

Thud! thud! the hammer in the hands of time
Beats on my heart beneath its thunderous rhyme.
Hoary and dumb is he, but on his arm,
With lift and swing, the rolling muscles swarm.
His beard upon his bosom trembling lies,
And strength has veiled its secret in his eyes.

The days with all their sorrows pass like ghosts,
And with the hammer beats the march of hosts.
So changed beneath the tireless fall and rise,
'Tis not my heart that on the anvil lies—
So vacant and so wan, so void of dreams,
And once resplendent with a thousand gleams.

'Tis not my heart, my heart of passions vain,
The plaything of the daughters of disdain,
The slave of every wandering ray of grace,
Bribed with the laughter in a girlish face.
'Tis not my heart since I have made my vow:
To you, blind smith, it is abandoned now.

Smite hard, old smith, smite hard and do not spare,
My heart has paid with weeping and despair.
Smite on the weaknesses that still remain,
Smite hard until the heart is mute to pain—
A heart of dreams and weakness is not meet
In days of greed, of softness and deceit . . .

And you, my pretty ones, the days are gone
When, flesh and blood for you to feed upon,
My heart was with eternal want accursed—
And yours be now the hunger and the thirst.
Bite on my heart now as you did of yore,
And break your teeth upon the iron core.

(Maurice Samuel)

THESE ARE THE CHOSEN PEOPLE

by ROBERT NATHAN
1894–

These are the chosen people. He has set
Upon their brow the diadem of thorn,
The one imperishable coronet,
The crown of pain, the briar branch of scorn.
Around their shoulders He has hung His scrolls,
Dark as the desert, yellow as the light;
His is the voice of ages in their souls,
The burning bush, the pillar in the night.
These are the chosen; He has named them all.
None can escape the poison of His grace,
Or ever ease the everlasting smart.
It is for them, the honey and the gall,
To be the wakeful, the abiding race,
And guard the wells of pity of the heart.

PSALM: 1933

by BABETTE DEUTSCH
1895–

By the rivers of Babylon
We sat down, we wept . . .

And the sun goes down, and the waters are dark. Whitely,
Like the fist of a dead man, or a fragment of bone,—
Curving over the river, against the windows,
Now the moon, like a stone carelessly thrown.

We sat down, we wept
When we remembered Zion . . .

We have bad memories. We read the papers,
Sitting on Riverside Drive, or anywhere,
Behind drawn blinds, under the lamps, frowning,
Turning the page again with a dry-eyed stare.

Upon the willows in the midst thereof
We hanged up our harps.

When Tara's walls were down, a broken harping
Sounded until the minstrel fell. Tune in on
Götterdämmerung tonight. There's static
Only when there is storm. But this is none.

For they that led us captive required of us songs,
And they that wasted us required of us mirth:
Sing us one of the songs of Zion.

The words are lost. Shall we sing "Go down, Moses"?
We always liked that one. Or "Weep no more,
My lady, for your old Kentucky home"?
There are good tunes in any Sullivan score.

How shall we sing the Lord's song
In a strange land?

And the sun goes down, and the waters are dark. Whitely,
Murmurous with her millions, a quivering gem,
Over the river, the city: New York, Paris, Berlin,
Puts out Jerusalem.

If I forget thee,
Let my right hand forget its cunning;
Let my tongue cleave to the roof of my mouth
If I prefer not Jerusalem above my chief joy.

Is she down, is she gone and forgotten?
So they trample a grave that is swept
Of even a stone for remembrance?
By the rivers of Babylon we sat down, we wept . . .

FOR ALL THAT EVER HAS BEEN OURS . . .

by SICHA LANDAU

1889–

For our sore-shattered Jewish life
I kneel, and pray to Thee for grace;

I weep for our old mother Vilna,
For Brod; for yet another place;

I weep for Warsaw, Kovno, Lemberg,
For every large and little town
On which the foe of yore has fallen,
On which the foe will fall upon.

For every dirty Jewish alley,
For every shop—I weep and wail;
For every pawn-shop, tavern, ale-house;
For our false measure, weight, and scale.

For every merry Jewish brothel,
That stood upon a Gentile street,
For all that ever has been ours . . .
(Marie Syrkin)

THE JEW

by ISAAC ROSENBERG
1890–1918

Moses, from whose loins I sprung,
Lit by a lamp in his blood
Ten immutable rules, a moon
For mutable lampless men.

The blonde, the bronze, the ruddy,
With the same heaving blood,
Keep tide to the moon of Moses.
Then why do they sneer at me?

FROM A ZIONIST IN THE TRENCHES

by MARTIN FEINSTEIN
1892–1926

Out of the murk of wild and sinister day,
Out of the mist,

Sun-radiant City of Peace, though the death-whip flays,
I keep my tryst.

You will be fair as of old, and on your hills
There will be spring,
Bright with myrtle and arbutus, and the rills
All murmuring.

There will be sound of cymbals and horns blowing,
And high-borne voices,
Soft and loud with the play of the wind; and knowing,
My heart rejoices.

Though here in the striding storm and dusk-thunder,
Here in the mist,
Death and darkness break my dream asunder,—
I keep my trust.

POEMS

by URI ZWI GREENBERG
1894–

I. KINGS OF THE EMEK

What is the crown of kings, and what the glory
That troubadours have sung in seventy tongues
To royalty ensconced in palaces?
What is the marvel of blue blood in kings?

The time has come for men to stand erect,
Though shoeless, in a tattered gaberdine,
And know the benison of fingers ten,
The worth of native soil to simple men:

By heart let young men con this Hebrew epic;
The splendour of the barefoot pilgrimage
Of this most modern age;

For we have seen the red of Hebrew blood
Streaming through fields and making soft the glebe
Gentiles who sowed in joy, in gladness reaped . . .

Now do we know fertility of a desert,
Now do we know why monarchs of the Emek
Are not arrayed in purple. . . .

(Abraham M. Klein)

II. UPON GOD'S ANVIL

As a woman who holds me within her spell
    God taunts. "If thou but canst—flee hence, flee!"
But I cannot flee.

    I fled from Him in wrath and despair,
An oath on my lips like a coal aflare,
"I look on Him no more."

    I come back again
And knock at His door
Like a chastened swain.
    —As though he had sent me word of his love.

(I. M. Lask)

POEMS

by ABRAHAM SHLONSKY

1900–

I. BEHOLD

Behold my country—the carcass of a savage,
Its hide is parchment—parchment for a Torah
Upon which the eternal quill
Has writ the word of God.
Where is the aborigine who may read
This scroll of Genesis?
Where is he, worthy to don tallis
In answer to the summoning of the Torah?

Perhaps these are the camels
That wandered in the wilderness
Out of the paths, well-trodden of the Lord . . .
That now do scratch their humps
Against the feet of the Heavenly throne . . .
Behold the camels of Gilboa lying down!

Strike well, O sun of Tammuz, upon my scaly land!
We will draw from the udders of the night
The milk of dew.

(*Abraham M. Klein*)

II. GRAPE-GATHERING

The clusters in Thy vineyard turn to gold,
  O God—
  Yet none do pluck the vine.
Milk-brimming is each udder; brooks glow full;
  Each grape o'erflows with wine.

The whole is ripe—bubbles towards Thy sun,
  O God,
  Which pours her rays from high,
And I—a vineshoot bearing clusters rich,
  A branch turned to the sky.

And of Thy vineyard's weighty yield of grapes,
  O God,
  Press down my head to earth.
O Lord! When in Thy winepress I am cast
  Shall I e'er find rebirth?

(*I. M. Lask*)

LYRICS

by RACHEL
1890–1931

I. NOW SUCH AM I . . .

Now such am I; as quiet
  As waters in a pool, as calm;
Loving unfestive peace, the eyes of little children,
  And the poems of Francis Jammes.

Once long ago, my soul arrayed in purple,
  I stood on mountain peaks,
And was as one with the great winds
  And with the eagle's shrieks!

Once long ago—ah, that was long ago!
  Times change; times pass away.
And now—
  Behold me, me today!

II. RACHEL

Her blood flows in my blood;
  Her voice in mine is heard,
Rachel, great ancestress,
  Keeper of Laban's herd.

My house is small for me,
  The city strange, since her
Wide robes were fluttered in
  The desert air.

Wherefore I shall keep fast
  Unto my chosen ways,
Knowing my very limbs
  Hold memories of those days!

III. KINNERETH

It may be these things never did occur.
Perhaps, somehow,
I never did arise at break of day
To do my labour in the garden
With the sweat of my brow;

Did never, in the long and fiery days
Of harvest time,
High on the waggon, laden with its sheaves,
Lift up my voice in rhyme;

Did never bathe within the blue
And quiet of thy stream,
O my Kinnereth, O Kinnereth mine!
Were you, indeed? Or did I dream a dream?

IV. DAWN

A jug of water in the hand, and on
My shoulder—basket, spade, and rake.
To distant fields,—to toil—my path I make.

Upon my right, the great hills fling
Protecting arms; before me—the wide fields!
And in my heart, my twenty Aprils sing . . .

Be this my lot, until I be undone:
Dust of thy road, my land, and thy
Grain waving golden in the sun!

V. THE CHILDLESS ONE

Would that I had a little boy,
    A wise lad, and with raven locks,
To take him by the hand, and walk
    Slowly upon the garden-walks.

And "Uri" would I call my son,
    A delicate name, and full of joy,
A name that is a sunbeam—such
    The name of my small winsome boy.

Yet shall I grow bitter, like Mother Rachel . . .
Yet shall I pray, like Hannah in Shiloh . . .
Yet shall I wait
For him.

(Abraham M. Klein)

JOY OF KNOWLEDGE

by ISIDOR SCHNEIDER

1896–

With such a throb does blood
within the marrying flesh
cry out that all's attained.
The pulses of the mind
measure such ecstasies.

For knowledge, like the earth,
a tireless copesmate is.
To love her is to be
sweet wearied and relaxed
upon infinity;
to have the mind become
an actual seed of time;

to be so much empowered
its wish may be its hand,
pull petals from the sun,
and atoms pick apart.

SÜSSKIND OF TRIMBERG

by HARRY ALAN POTAMKIN

1900–1933

Süsskind of Trimberg clad his soul in byssus,
Into the Minneburg in soft sandals walked.
To Walther and Wolfram and Wolfgang, sons of Jesus,
Love is a virgin, but Süsskind's way is chalked. . . .

He must wear the yellow funnel for dunce and Jew alike,
Must only wonder at far things and sing of distances,
And when the eager heart shall call, his will shall be the dyke,
To hold the lash of wave remote from God and verities. . . .

But still the anxious call is heard persistent and elusive,
His song is not a madrigal, he cannot sing desire.
"Let's hear the Jew! Let's hear the Jew!" the Christian mob abusive
Hurls down its hate, "Let's hear the Jew! Let's hear the Crucifier!"

A gentle lay, symbolic love, allusions kabbalistic
Chant at the harp, the strings grow taut,
The lover is the mystic . . .

*"I sing the glory of the scented river
That guides the fragrant barque of death . . ."*

"Give us," they cry, "a Christian fever
For Mary the Mother or have of our wrath!
Give us of woman, sing passion, O Jew;
Walther the bird has chanted of her!"

But his heart goes in where it needs are few,
Deep in the pasture where dark things stir;
And his song is a query that knows no reply,
A mist of the earth where his soul must bore,
A mist of the earth that veils his eye,
A mist of the earth that is core of his core.

He sings of the planets, the wonders of space,
God that is glory and God that is gleam:
*"Oh, I have looked once on a woman's face
And found it a moment out of a dream.
What is the meaning? And what meaneth glory?
And shall then the heavens devour their own?"*

"Give us, O Jew, a battle-story,
Sound us the war-cry and stifle the groan!
Give us the soldier, the madman, the killer!"

The singers compete, each offers his slaughter. . . .
Süsskind is silent, thinks: "God is the miller,
Are these the grindings of windmill and water?"

EXILE CONSUMED

by I. M. LASK

1905–

How do I love you? I never seek to know
When just your eyes suffice to make me glow
As though the Sabbath candles had been lit
Within my weekday soul;

               as though the pit
Of nothingness that waits below my feet
Were one huge diamond flashing down the street
Of long long years with you;

               as though the flame
Of ancient beacons on Judaean heights
Still clamoured to my exile, while I came
Like all our fathers groping through the nights
Of my own blindness till my sudden sight
Rose to the height of Zion from the plain
Where I stood parched and withered suffering the bane
Of Lot's wife turned to salt.

               And then it seemed
The way grew short below me and redeemed
I stood within the Temple at the hour
They poured the water.

All around me teemed
The multitudes of Israel.

In that hour
I, of the priesthood's blossoms, rose and poured
The oil of those anointed of the Lord
Within the lamps, kindling a diadem
Of flame illumining Jerusalem,
Leaving no hidden corner where might stir
The darkness of my exile.

For you were
Before me with your eyes where I might nest,
Being welcome and an ever-loved guest.

HAGGADAH

by ABRAHAM M. KLEIN

1909–

ETCHING

The sky is dotted like th' unleavened bread,
The moon a golden platter in the sky,
Old midget Jews, with meditated tread,
Hands clasped behind, and body stooped ahead,
Creep from the synagogue and stare on high
Upon a golden platter in a dotted sky . . .

ONCE IN A YEAR

Once in a year this comes to pass:
My father is a king in a black skull cap,
My mother is a queen in a brown perruque,
A princess my sister, a lovely lass,
My brother a prince, and I a duke . . .

Silver and plate, and fine cut-glass
Brought from the cupboards that hid them till now
Banquet King David's true lineage here.
Once in a year this comes to pass,
Once in a long unroyal year . . .

BLACK DECALOGUE

Compute the plagues; your little finger dip
In spittle of the grape, and at each pest
Shake off the drop with the vindictive zest:
Thus first: The Nile—a gash; then frogs that skip
Upon the princess' coverlet; the rip
Made by dark nails that seek the itching guest;
The plague of murrained carcasses; the pest;
Full boils that stud the Ethiop, leg to lip . . .
The visitation of hot hail, the fists of God;
The swarm of locusts nibbling Egypt clean;
Thick darkness oozing from out Moses' rod;
And first-born slain, the mighty and the mean;
Compute these plagues that fell on Egypt's sod,—
Then add: In Goshen these were never seen . . .

THE BITTER DISH

This is the bread of our affliction, this
The symbol of the clay that built Rameses,
And that horseradish-root of bitterness,
And you, my brethren, yea,
You are the afflicted, the embittered, and the clay . . .

SONG

Fill the silver goblet
Make open the door-way,
Let there be no sob; let
Elijah come our way . . .
And let him come singing,
Announcing as nigh a
Redemption, and drinking
The health of Messiah! . . .

HAD GADYA

This is a curious plot
Devised for eager riddling:
My father had a kidling
For two good zuzim bought.

Graymalkin ate it; and
A dog munched sleek Graymalkin
Whereat a Rod did stalk in
Beating his reprimand

Upon the Dog's spine. Came
Red Fire, and did sputter
His wrath on Rod; came Water
And, sizzling, quenched the flame.

And down a bovine throat
Went Water, which throat, tickled
By pious Shochet, trickled
Red blood upon his coat.

The Angel of Death flew
And smote the Shochet; whereat
The Lord gave him his merit—
The Lord the Angel slew.

In that strange portal whence
All things come, they re-enter;
Of all things God is centre,
God is circumference . . .

This is a curious plot
Devised for eager riddling:
My father had a kidling
For two good zuzim bought.

THE STILL SMALL VOICE

The candles splutter; and the kettle hums;
The heirloomed clock enumerates the tribes;
Upon the wine-stained table-cloth lie crumbs
Of matzoh whose wide scattering describes
Jews driven in far lands upon this earth.
The kettle hums; the candles splutter; and
Winds whispering from shutters tell re-birth
Of beauty rising in an eastern land,
Of paschal sheep driven in cloudy droves;
Of almond-blossoms colouring the breeze;
Of vineyards upon verdant terraces;
Of golden globes in orient orange-groves . . .
And those assembled at the table dream
Of small schemes that an April wind doth scheme,
And cry from out the sleep assailing them:
Jerusalem, next year! Next year, Jerusalem!

HE WELL OF WISDOM

For the person who has a taste for the pursuit of ideas and a curiosity about the intellectual concerns of the Jewish people, the following thirty selections will be highly illuminating. They are not intended to show the full development of Jewish thought or to illustrate cultural movements and trends in Jewish history. Nor do they constitute the biography of any single idea or intellectual pattern which may be characteristic of Jewish thinkers throughout the ages. They present, rather, a general introduction to what some representative spokesmen of the Jewish people have thought about their people in relation to themselves and the world and about the significance of Judaism.

In choosing the opening statement from a work which belongs to the seventh century B.C.E., we do not imply that Jews were not concerned with such problems in preceding centuries. They were. But the book of *Deuteronomy* is an expression of an epoch-making synthesis of the prophetic and priestly viewpoints. It constituted, until modern times, the basic philosophy of the *galuth,* giving Judaism an international and universal mold. Other varying conceptions of life and destiny are mirrored in the ancient literature that has been included in preceding sections. The gentle but convincing skepticism of *Ecclesiastes,* the apotheosis of wisdom in the *Wisdom of Solomon* and the philosophic allegorizing of Philo indicate that Jewish minds in the ancient world thought in as many different patterns as they do today.

More space has been given to thinkers of the 19th and 20th centuries inasmuch as they deal with the problems that agitate the contemporary Jew. Mendelssohn's discussion of the implications of minority rights is not unrelated to a clause of the Versailles Treaty, dealing with that question. Marx's vitriolic but astute analysis of the Jewish problem still echoes in the lively debates in contemporary periodicals and books. Here, too, it must be pointed out that it has been impossible to include many keen thinkers: the Hegelian Krochmal, prophetic Salvador, Spinozistic Brunner, Neo-Kantian Cohen, Marxist-Zionist Borochov, Yiddishist Zhitlowsky. . . .

The dismemberment and chaos of the contemporary world and their enormous effect upon Jewish life are apparent in these writings. The secularization of life has resulted in greater concern for Jews than for Judaism. Social and economic adjustments overshadow religious and philosophic aspirations. There is lacking a secular as well as a religious bond of unity in a world which looks upon the Jews and deals with them as though they were a unified minority. Apparently, the perennial Jewish problem not only continues to exist and challenge society but it has also changed its form and essence. What the actual character of these changes are and what this implies constitutes the central problem of our intellectual guides.

DIVINE MANIFESTO [1]

A ND it shall come to pass when all these things are come upon thee, the blessing and the curse, which I have set before thee, and thou shalt call them to mind among all the nations, whither the Lord thy God hath driven thee, and shalt return unto the Lord thy God, and shalt obey his voice according to all that I command thee this day, thou and thy children, with all thine heart, and with all thy soul; that then the Lord thy God will turn thy captivity, and have compassion upon thee, and will return and gather thee from all the peoples, whither the Lord thy God hath scattered thee. If any of thine outcasts be in the uttermost parts of heaven, from thence will the Lord thy God gather thee, and from thence will he fetch thee: and the Lord thy God will bring thee into the land which thy fathers possessed, and thou shalt possess it; and he will do thee good, and multiply thee above thy fathers. And the Lord thy God will circumcise thine heart, and the heart of thy seed, to love the Lord thy God with all thine heart, and with all thy soul, that thou mayest live. And the Lord thy God will put all these curses upon thine enemies, and on them that hate thee, which persecuted thee. And thou shalt return and obey the voice of the Lord, and do all his commandments which I command thee this day. And the Lord thy God will make thee plenteous in all the work of thine hand, in the fruit of thy body, and in the fruit of thy cattle, and in the fruit of thy ground, for good: for the Lord will again rejoice over thee for good, as he rejoiced over thy fathers: if thou shalt obey the voice of the Lord thy God, to keep his commandments and his statutes which are written in this book of the law; if thou turn unto the Lord thy God with all thine heart, and with all thy soul.

For this commandment which I command thee this day, it is not

[1] The book of *Deuteronomy* from which the above selection is taken (chapter 30) is considered by modern scholars to be a product of the 7th century B.C. It is probably the book discovered in the temple in Jerusalem in 621 B.C. during the reign of Josiah. The work is written in the form of an oration by Moses, and it is unquestionably one of the finest expressions of prophetic teaching. Its stress upon monotheism and social justice, and its emphasis of love as the spring of human action left a deep impression on later thought and literature.

too hard for thee, neither is it far off. It is not in heaven, that thou shouldest say, Who shall go up for us to heaven, and bring it unto us, and make us to hear it, that we may do it? But the word is very nigh unto thee, in thy mouth, and in thy heart, that thou mayest do it.

See, I have set before thee this day life and good, and death and evil; in that I command thee this day to love the Lord thy God, to walk in his ways, and to keep his commandments and his statutes and his judgments, that thou mayest live and multiply, and that the Lord thy God may bless thee in the land whither thou goest in to possess it. But if thine heart turn away, and thou wilt not hear, but shalt be drawn away, and worship other gods, and serve them; I denounce unto you this day, that ye shall surely perish; ye shall not prolong your days upon the land, whither thou passest over Jordan to go in to possess it. I call heaven and earth to witness against you this day, that I have set before thee life and death, the blessing and the curse: therefore choose life, that thou mayest live, thou and thy seed: to love the Lord thy God, to obey his voice, and to cleave unto him: for he is thy life, and the length of thy days: that thou mayest dwell in the land which the Lord sware unto thy fathers, to Abraham, to Isaac, and to Jacob, to give them.

(c. 621 b.c.)

OF WISDOM AND LOVE[1]

AND all such things as are either secret or manifest, them I know. For wisdom, which is the worker of all things, taught me; for in her is an understanding spirit, holy, one only, manifold, subtil, lively, clear, undefiled, plain, not subject to hurt, loving the thing that is good, quick, which cannot be letted, ready to do good. Kind to man, stedfast, sure, free from care, having all power, overseeing all things and going through all understanding, pure, and most subtil, spirits. For wisdom is more moving than any motion: she passeth and goeth through all things by reason of her pureness. For she is the breath of the power of God, and

[1] The above selection is out of *The Wisdom of Solomon*. It was probably written by an Alexandrian Jew about the first century b.c. Composed in Greek, it is addressed to Jews who came under the influence of Greek culture. The above passages (7: 22-28; 9: 1-4; 11: 21-26) indicate the author's conception of wisdom and of God's love.

a pure influence flowing from the glory of the Almighty: therefore can no defiled thing fall into her. For she is the brightness of the everlasting light, the unspotted mirror of the power of God, and the image of his goodness. And being but one, she can do all things: and remaining in herself, she maketh all things new: and in all ages entering into holy souls, she maketh them friends of God, and prophets. For God loveth none but him that dwelleth with wisdom. For she is more beautiful than the sun, and above all the order of stars: being compared with the light, she is found before it. For after this cometh night: but vice shall not prevail against wisdom. Wisdom reacheth from one end to another mightily: and sweetly doth she order all things.

O God of my fathers, and Lord of mercy, who hast made all things with thy word, and ordained man through thy wisdom, that he should have dominion over the creatures which thou hast made, and order the world according to equity and righteousness, and execute judgment with an upright heart: give me wisdom, that sitteth by thy throne; and reject me not from among thy children. . . . For thou canst shew thy great strength at all times when thou wilt; and who may withstand the power of thine arm? For the whole world before thee is as a little grain of the balance, yea as a drop of the morning dew that falleth down upon the earth. But thou hast mercy upon all; for thou canst do all things, and winkest at the sins of men, because they should amend. For thou lovest all the things that are, and abhorrest nothing which thou hast made: for never wouldst thou have made any thing, if thou hadst hated it. And how could any thing have endured, if it had not been thy will? or been preserved, if not called by thee? But thou sparest all: for they are thine, O Lord, thou lover of souls. . . . But by such works hast thou taught thy people that the just man should be merciful, and has made thy children to be of a good hope.

(c. 100 B.C.?)

MEDITATIONS OF A SCEPTIC [1]

VANITY of vanities, saith the preacher; vanity of vanities, all is vanity. What profit hath man of all his labour wherein he laboureth under the sun? One generation goeth, and another generation cometh; and the earth abideth for ever. The sun also ariseth, and the sun goeth down, and hasteth to his place where he ariseth. The wind goeth toward the south, and turneth about unto the north; it turneth about continually in its course, and the wind returneth again to its circuits. All the rivers run into the sea, yet the sea is not full; unto the place whither the rivers go, thither they go again. All things are full of weariness; man cannot utter it: the eye is not satisfied with seeing, nor the ear filled with hearing. That which hath been is that which shall be; and that which hath been done is that which shall be done; and there is no new thing under the sun. Is there a thing whereof men say, See, this is new? it hath been already, in the ages which were before us. There is no remembrance of the former generations; neither shall there be any remembrance of the latter generations that are to come, among those that shall come after.

I the preacher was king over Israel in Jerusalem. And I applied my heart to seek and to search out by wisdom concerning all that is done under heaven: it is a sore travail that God hath given to the sons of men to be exercised therewith. I have seen all the works that are done under the sun; and, behold, all is vanity and a striving after wind. That which is crooked cannot be made straight: and that which is wanting cannot be numbered. I communed with mine own heart, saying, Lo, I have gotten me great wisdom above all that were before me in Jerusalem: yea, my heart hath had great experience of wisdom and knowledge. And I applied my heart to know wisdom, and to know madness and folly: I perceived that this also was a striving after wind. For in much wisdom is much grief: and he that increaseth knowledge increaseth sorrow.

I said in mine heart, Go to now, I will prove thee with mirth; therefore enjoy pleasure: and, behold, this also was vanity. I said of laughter

[1] This selection is an abridgement of the book of *Ecclesiastes* which is the most unique of the reflective writings in the Old Testament. The authorship is ascribed to King Solomon who as a man of wide experience and of great wisdom would naturally strengthen the thesis that man's fate is predestined and he is helpless to change it. For a thoughtful discussion and modern translation of the book see Jastrow's *A Gentle Cynic* (1919) and Duncan B. Macdonald's *The Hebraic Philosophical Genius* (1936).

It is mad: and of mirth, What doeth it? I searched in mine heart how to cheer my flesh with wine, mine heart yet guiding me with wisdom, and how to lay hold on folly, till I might see what it was good for the sons of men that they should do under the heaven all the days of their life. I made me great works; I builded me houses; I planted me vineyards; I made me gardens and parks, and I planted trees in them of all kinds of fruit: I made me pools of water, to water therefrom the forest where trees were reared: I bought men-servants and maidens, and had servants born in my house; also I had great possessions of herds and flocks, above all that were before me in Jerusalem: I gathered me also silver and gold, and the peculiar treasure of kings and of the provinces: I got me men singers and women singers, and the delights of the sons of men, concubines very many. So I was great, and increased more than all that were before me in Jerusalem: also my wisdom remained with me. And whatsoever mine eyes desired I kept not from them: I withheld not my heart from any joy, for my heart rejoiced because of my labour; and this was my portion from all my labour. Then I looked on all the works that my hands had wrought, and all the labour that I had laboured to do: and, behold, all was vanity and a striving after wind, and there was no profit under the sun.

And I turned myself to behold wisdom, and madness and folly: for what can the man do that cometh after the king? even that which hath been already done. Then I saw that wisdom excelleth folly, as far as light excelleth darkness. The wise man's eyes are in his head, and the fool walketh in darkness: and yet I perceived that one event happeneth to them all. Then said I in my heart, As it happeneth to the fool, so will it happen even to me; and why was I then more wise? Then I said in my heart, that this also was vanity. For of the wise man, even as of the fool, there is no remembrance for ever; seeing that in the days to come all will have been already forgotten. And how doth the wise man die even as the fool! So I hated life; because the work that is wrought under the sun was grievous unto me; for all is vanity and a striving after wind.

And I hated all my labour wherein I laboured under the sun: seeing that I must leave it unto the man that shall be after me. And who knoweth whether he shall be a wise man or a fool? yet shall he have rule over all my labour wherein I have laboured, and wherein I have shewed wisdom under the sun. This also is vanity. Therefore I turned about to cause my heart to despair concerning all the labour wherein I had laboured under the sun. For there is a man whose labour is with wisdom, and with knowledge, and with skilfulness; yet to a man that hath not laboured therein shall he leave it for his portion. This also is vanity and a great evil. For what hath a man of all his labour, and of the striving of his heart, wherein he laboureth under the sun? For all his days are but sorrows, and his travail is grief; yea, even in the night his heart taketh no rest. This also is vanity.

There is nothing better for a man than that he should eat and drink, and make his soul enjoy good in his labour. This also I saw, that it is from the hand of God. For who can eat, or who can have enjoyment, more than I? For to the man that pleaseth him God giveth wisdom, and knowledge, and joy: but to the sinner he giveth travail, to gather and to heap up, that he may give to him that pleaseth God. This also is vanity and a striving after wind.

To every thing there is a season, and a time to every purpose under the heaven: a time to be born, and a time to die; a time to plant, and a time to pluck up that which is planted; a time to kill, and a time to heal; a time to break down, and a time to build up; a time to weep, and a time to laugh; a time to mourn, and a time to dance; a time to cast away stones, and a time to gather stones together; a time to embrace, and a time to refrain from embracing; a time to seek, and a time to lose; a time to keep; and a time to cast away; a time to rend, and a time to sew; a time to keep silence, and a time to speak; a time to love, and a time to hate; a time for war, and a time for peace. What profit hath he that worketh in that wherein he laboureth? I have seen the travail which God hath given to the sons of men to be exercised therewith. He hath made every thing beautiful in its time; also he hath set the world in their heart, yet so that man cannot find out the work that God hath done from the beginning even to the end. I know that there is nothing better for them, than to rejoice, and to do good so long as they live. And also that every man should eat and drink, and enjoy good in all his labour, is the gift of God. I know that, whatsoever God doeth, it shall be for ever: nothing can be put to it, nor any thing taken from it: and God hath done it, that men should fear before him. That which is hath already been: and God seeketh again that which is passed away.

And moreover I saw under the sun, in the place of judgment, that wickedness was there. I said in mine heart, God shall judge the righteous and the wicked: for there is a time there for every purpose and for every work. I said in mine heart, It is because of the sons of men, that God may prove them, and that they may see that they themselves are but as beasts. For that which befalleth the sons of men befalleth beasts; even one thing befalleth them: as the one dieth, so dieth the other; yea, they have all one breath; and man hath no preeminence above the beasts: for all is vanity. All go unto one place; all are of the dust, and all turn to dust again. Who knoweth the spirit of man whether it goeth upward, and the spirit of the beast whether it goeth downward to the earth? Wherefore I saw that there is nothing better, than that a man should rejoice in his works; for that is his portion: for who shall bring him back to see what shall be after him?

Then I returned and saw all the oppressions that are done under the sun: and behold, the tears of such as were oppressed, and they had no comforter; and on the side of their oppressors there was power, but they had no comforter. Wherefore I praised the dead which are already dead more than the living which are yet alive; yea, better than them both did I esteem him which hath not yet been, who hath not yet seen the evil work that is done under the sun.

Then I saw all labour and every skilful work, that for this a man is envied of his neighbour. This also is vanity and a striving after wind. The fool foldeth his hands together, and eateth his own flesh. Better is an handful with quietness, than two handfuls with labour and striving after wind.

Then I returned and saw vanity under the sun. There is one that is alone, and he hath not a second; yea, he hath neither son nor brother; yet is there no end of all his labour, neither are his eyes satisfied with riches. For whom then, saith he, do I labour, and deprive my soul of good? This also is vanity, yea, it is a sore travail. Two are better than one; because they have a good reward for their labour. For if they fall, the one will lift up his fellow: but woe to him that is alone when he falleth, and hath not another to lift him up. Again, if two lie together, then they have warmth: but how can one be warm alone? And if a man prevail against him that is alone, two shall withstand him; and a three-fold cord is not quickly broken.

Better is a poor and wise youth than an old and foolish king, who knoweth not how to receive admonition any more. For out of prison he came forth to be king; yes even in his kingdom he was born poor. I saw all the living which walk under the sun, that they were with the youth, the second, that stood up in his stead. There was no end of all the people, even of all them over whom he was: yet they that come after shall not rejoice in him. Surely this also is vanity and a striving after wind.

For all this I laid to my heart, even to explore all this; that the righteous, and the wise, and their works, are in the hand of God: whether it be love or hatred, man knoweth it not; all is before them. All things come alike to all: there is one event to the righteous and to the wicked; to the good and to the clean and to the unclean; to him that sacrifieth and to him that sacrifieth not: as is the good, so is the sinner; and he that sweareth, as he that feareth an oath. This is an evil in all that is done under the sun, that there is one event unto all: yea also, the heart of the sons of men is full of evil, and madness is in their heart while they live, and after that they go to the dead.

For to him that is joined with all the living there is hope: for a living dog is better than a dead lion. For the living know that they shall die: but the dead know not any thing, neither have they any more a reward; for the memory of them is forgotten. As well their love, as their hatred and their envy, is now perished; neither have they any more a portion forever in any thing that is done under the sun.

Go thy way, eat thy bread with joy, and drink thy wine with a merry heart; for God hath already accepted thy works. Let thy garments be always white; and let not thy head lack ointment. Live joyfully with the wife whom thou lovest all the days of the life of thy vanity, which he hath given thee under the sun, all the days of thy vanity: for that is thy portion in life, and in thy labour wherein thou labourest under the sun. Whatsoever thy hand findeth to do, do it with thy might; for there is no work, nor device, nor knowledge, nor wisdom, in the grave, whither thou goest.

I returned, and saw under the sun, that the race is not to the swift, nor the battle to the strong, neither yet bread to the wise, nor yet riches to men of understanding, nor yet favour to men of skill; but time and chance happeneth to them all. For man also knoweth not his time: as the fishes that are taken in an evil net, and as the birds that are caught in the snare, even so are the sons of men snared in an evil time, when it falleth suddenly upon them.

I have also seen wisdom under the sun on this wise, and it seemed great unto me: there was a little city, and few men within it; and there came a great king against it, and built great bulwarks against it: now there was found in it a poor wise man, and he by his wisdom delivered the city; yet no man remembered that same poor man. Then said I, Wisdom is better than strength: nevertheless the poor man's wisdom is despised, and his words are not heard.

Cast thy bread upon the waters: for thou shalt find it after many days. Give a portion to seven, yea, even unto eight; for thou knowest not what evil shall be upon the earth. If the clouds be full of rain, they empty themselves upon the earth: and if a tree fall toward the south or toward the north, in the place where the tree falleth, there shall it be. He that observeth the wind shall not sow; and he that regardeth the clouds shall not reap. As thou knowest not what is the way of the wind, nor how the bones do grow in the womb of her that is with child; even so thou knowest not the work of God who doeth all. In the morning sow thy seed, and in the evening withhold not thine hand; for thou knowest not which shall prosper, whether this or that, or whether they both shall be alike good. Truly the light is sweet, and a pleasant thing it is for the eyes to behold the sun. Yea, if a man live many years, let him rejoice in them all; but let him remember the days of darkness, for they shall be many. All that cometh is vanity.

Rejoice, O young man, in thy youth; and let thy heart cheer thee in the days of thy youth, and walk in the ways of thine heart, and in the sight of thine eyes: but know thou, that for all these things God will bring thee into judgement. Therefore remove sorrow from thy heart, and put away evil from thy flesh: for youth and the prime of life are vanity. Remember also thy Creator in the days of thy youth, or ever the evil days come, and the years draw nigh, when thou shalt say, I have no pleasure in them; or ever the sun, and the light, and the moon, and the stars, be darkened, and the clouds return after the rain: in the day when the keepers of the house shall tremble, and the strong men shall bow themselves, and the grinders cease because they are few, and those that look out of the windows be darkened, and the doors shall be shut in the street; when the sound of the grinding is low, and one shall rise up at the voice of a bird, and all the daughters of music shall be brought low; yea, they shall be afraid of that which is high, and terrors shall be in the way; and the almond tree shall blossom, and the grasshopper shall be a burden, and the caper-berry shall fail: because man goeth to his long home, and the mourners go about the streets: or ever the silver cord be loosed, or the golden bowl be broken, or the pitcher be broken at the fountain, or the wheel broken at the cistern; and the dust return to the earth as it was, and the spirit return unto God who gave it. Vanity of vanities, saith the Preacher; all is vanity.

And further, because the Preacher was wise, he still taught the people knowledge; yea, he pondered, and sought out, and set in order many proverbs. The Preacher sought to find out acceptable words, and that which was written uprightly, even words of truth.

The words of the wise are as goads, and as nails well fastened are the words of the masters of assemblies, which are given from one shepherd. And furthermore, my son, be admonished: of making many books there is no end; and much study is a weariness of the flesh.

This is the end of the matter; all hath been heard: fear God, and keep his commandments; for this is the whole duty of man. For God shall bring every work into judgement, with every hidden thing, whether it be good or whether it be evil.

(c. 300 B.C.?)

OF GOD AND MAN

by PHILO OF ALEXANDRIA

IT is a tenet of the lawgiver also that the perfect man seeks for quietude. For the words addressed to the Sage with God as the speaker, "stand thou here with Me" (*Deut.* 5: 31), shew most plainly how unbending, unwavering and broad-based is his will. Wonderful indeed is the soul of the Sage, how he sets it, like a lyre, to harmony not with a scale of notes low and high, but with the knowledge of moral opposites, and the practice of such of them as are better; how he does not strain it to excessive heights, nor yet relax it and weaken the concord of virtues and things naturally beautiful, but keeps it ever at an equal tension and plays it with hand or bow in melody. Such a soul is the most perfect instrument fashioned by nature, the pattern of those which are the work of our hands. And if it be well adjusted, it will produce a symphony the most beautiful in the world, one which has its consummation not in the cadences and tones of melodious sound, but in the consistencies of our life's actions. Oh! if the soul of man, when it feels the soft breeze of wisdom and knowledge, can dismiss the stormy surge which the fierce burst of the gale of wickedness has suddenly stirred, and levelling the billowy swell can rest in unruffled calm under a bright clear sky, can you doubt that He, the Imperishable Blessed One, who has taken as His own the sovereignty of the virtues, of perfection itself and beatitude, knows no change of will, but ever holds fast to what He purposed from the first without any alteration?

With men then it must needs be that they are ready to change, through instability whether it be in themselves or outside them. So for example often when we have chosen our friends and been familiar with them for a short time, we turn from them, though we have no charge to bring against them, and count them amongst our enemies, or at best as strangers. Such action proves the facile levity of ourselves, how little capacity we have for stoutly holding to our original judgements. But God has no such fickleness. Or again, sometimes we are minded to hold to the standards we have taken but we find ourselves with others who have not remained constant, and thus our judgements perforce change with theirs. For a mere man cannot foresee the course of future events, or the judgements of others, but to God as in pure sunlight all things are manifest. For already He has pierced into the recesses of our soul, and what is invisible to others is clear as daylight to His eyes. He employs the forethought and foreknowledge which are virtues peculiarly His own, and suffers nothing to escape His control or pass outside His comprehension. For not even about the future can uncertainty be found with Him, since nothing is uncertain or future to God. No one doubts that the parent must have knowledge of his offspring, the craftsman of his handiwork, the steward of things entrusted to his stewardship. But God is in very truth the father and craftsman and steward of the heaven and the universe and all that is therein. Future events lie shrouded in the darkness of the time that is yet to be at different distances, some near, some far.

But God is the maker of time also, for He is the father of time's father, that is of the universe, and has caused the movements of the one to be the source of the generation of the other. Thus time stands to God in the relation of a grandson. For this universe, since we perceive it by our senses, is the younger son of God. To the elder son, I mean the intelligible universe, He assigned the place of firstborn, and purposed that it should remain in His own keeping. So this younger son, the world of our senses, when set in motion, brought that entity we call time to the brightness of its rising. And thus with God there is no future, since He has made the boundaries of the ages subject to Himself. For God's life is not a time, but eternity, which is the archetype and pattern of time; and in eternity there is no past nor future, but only present existence.

Let us flee, then, without a backward glance from the unions which are unions for sin, but hold fast to our alliance with the comrades of good sense and knowledge. And therefore when I hear those who say, "We are all sons of one man, we are peaceful (*Gen.* 43:11), I am filled with admiration for the harmonious concert which their words reveal. "Ah! my friends," I would say, "how should you not hate war and love peace—you who have enrolled yourselves as children of one and the same Father, who is not mortal but immortal—God's Man, who being the Word of the Eternal must needs himself be imperishable?" Those whose system includes many origins for the family of the soul, who affiliate themselves to that evil thing called polytheism, who take in hand to render homage some to this deity, some to that, are the authors of tumult and strife at home and abroad, and fill the whole of life from birth to death with internecine wars.

But those who rejoice in the oneness of their blood and honour one father, right reason, reverence that concert of virtues, which is full of harmony and melody, and live a life of calmness and fair weather. And yet that life is not, as some suppose, an idle and ignoble life, but one of high courage, and the edge of its spirit is exceeding sharp to fight against those who attempt to break treaties and ever practise the violation of the vows they have sworn. For it is the nature of men of peace that they prove to be men of war, when they take the field and resist those who would subvert the stability of the soul.

The truth of my words is attested first by the consciousness of every virtue-lover, which feels what I have described, and secondly by a chorister of the prophetic company, who possessed by divine inspiration spoke thus: "O my mother, how great didst thou bear me, a man of combat and a man of displeasure in all the earth! I did not owe, nor did they owe to me, nor did my strength fail from their curses" (*Jer.* 15: 10). Yes, is not every wise man the mortal foe of every fool, a foe who is equipped not with triremes or engines, or body-armour or soldiers for his defence, but with reasonings only?

For who, when he sees that war, which amid the fullest peace is waged among all men continuously, phase ever succeeding phase, in private and public life, a war in which the combatants are not just nations and countries, or cities and villages, but also house against house and each particular man against himself, who, I say, does not exhort, reproach, admonish, correct by day and night alike, since his soul cannot rest, because its nature is to hate evil? For all the deeds of war are done in peace. Men plunder, rob, kidnap, spoil, sack, outrage, maltreat, violate, dishonour and commit murder sometimes by treachery, or if they be stronger without disguise. Every man sets before him money or reputation as his aim, and at this he directs all the actions of his life like arrows against a target. He takes no heed of equality, but pursues inequality. He eschews thoughts of fellowship, and his eager desire is that the wealth of all should be gathered in his single purse. He hates others, whether his hate be returned or not. His benevolence is hypocrisy. He is hand and glove with canting flattery, at open war with genuine friendship; an enemy to truth, a defender of falsehood, slow to help, quick to harm, ever forward to slander, backward to champion the accused, skilful to cozen, false to his oath, faithless to his promise, a slave to anger, a thrall to pleasure, protector of the bad, corrupter of the good.

These and the like are the much-coveted treasures of the peace which men admire and praise so loudly—treasures enshrined in the mind of every fool with wonder and veneration. But to every wise man they are, as they should be, a source of pain, and often will he say to his mother and nurse, wisdom, "O mother, how great didst thou bear me!" Great, not in power of body, but in strength to hate evil, a man of displeasure and combat, by nature a man of peace, but for this very cause also a man of war against those who dishonour the much-prized loveliness of peace. "I did not owe nor did they owe to me," for neither did they use the good I had to give, nor I their evil, but, as Moses wrote, "I received from none of them what they desired" (*Num.* 16: 15). For all that comes under the head of their desire they kept as treasure to themselves, believing that to be the greatest blessing which was the supreme mischief. "Nor did my strength fail from the curses which they laid upon me," but with all my might and main I clung to the divine truths; I did not bend under their ill-treatment, but used my strength to reproach those who refused to effect their own purification. For "God has set us up for a contradiction to our neighbours," as is said in a verse of the Psalms; us, that is all who desire right judgement. Yes, surely they are by nature men of contradiction, all who have ever been zealous for knowledge and virtue, who contend jealously with the "neighbors" of the soul; who test the pleasures which share our home, the desires which live at our side, our fears and faintings of heart, and put to shame the tribe of passions and vices. Further, they test also every sense, the eyes on what they see, the ears on what they hear, the sense of smell on its perfumes, the taste on its flavours, the touch on the characteristics which mark the qualities of substances as they come in contact with it. And lastly they test the utterance on the statements which it has been led to make.

For what our senses perceive, or our speech expresses, or our emotion causes us to feel, and how or why each result is attained, are matters which we should scrutinize carefully and expose every error that we find. He who contradicts none of these, but assents to all as they come before him, is unconsciously deceiving himself and raising up a stronghold of dangerous neighbours to menace the soul, neighbours who should be dealt with as subjects, not as rulers. For if they have the mastery, since folly is their king, the mischief they work will be great and manifold; but as subjects they will render due service and obey the rein, and chafe no more against the yoke.

And, when these have thus learnt the lesson of obedience, and those have assumed the command which not only knowledge but power has given them, all the thoughts that attend and guard the soul will be one in purpose and approaching Him that ranks highest among them will speak thus: "Thy servants have taken the sum of the men of war who were with us, and there is no discordant voice" (*Num.* 31:49). "We," they will continue, "like instruments of music where all the notes are in perfect tune, echo with our voices all the lessons we have received. We speak no word and do no deed that is harsh or grating, and thus we have made a laughing-stock of all that other dead and voiceless choir, the choir of those who know not the muse, the choir which hymns Midian, the nurse of things bodily, and her offspring, the heavy leathern weight whose name is Baal-Peor. For we are the 'race of the Chosen ones of that Israel' who sees God, 'and there is none amongst us of discordant voice'" (*Ex.* 24:11), that so the whole world, which is the instrument of the All, may be filled with the sweet melody of its undiscording harmonies.

And therefore too Moses tells us how peace was assigned as the prize of that most warlike reason, called Phinehas (*Num.* 25:12). Because, inspired with zeal for virtue and waging war against vice, he ripped open all created being; how in their turn that prize is given to those who, after diligent and careful scrutiny, following the more certain testimony of sight, rather than hearing, have the will to accept the faith that mortality is full of unfaith and clings only to the seeming.

Wonderful then indeed is the symphony of voices here described, but most wonderful of all, exceeding every harmony, is that united universal symphony in which we find the whole people declaring with one heart, "All that God hath said we will do and hear" (*Ex.* 19:8). Here the precentor whom they follow is no longer the Word, but God the Sovereign of all, for whose sake they become quicker to meet the call to action than the call of words. For other men act after they have heard, but these under the divine inspiration say—strange inversion—that they will act first and hear afterwards, that so they may be seen to go forward to deeds of excellence, not led by teaching or instruction, but through the self-acting, self-dictated instinct of their own hearts. And when they have *done,* then, as they say, they will *hear,* that so they may judge their actions, whether they chime with the divine words and the sacred admonitions.

(C. 30 C.E.)

THE SCIENCES AND THE AIM OF LIFE

by ABRAHAM IBN DAUD

T HE sciences are many, ranging one above the other, and the aim of all of them is the knowledge of God. Body is to many only a beast of burden, a stepladder, as it were, by which he may ascend to God. But there are some whose sole ambition is to stuff the beast with plenty of fodder—these are the people whose object in life is eating and drinking. There are others whose desire is to adorn the beast with an ornamental saddle, bridle and blanket—these are the people whose only object in life is to parade in gaudy clothes. Still others waste their entire life in trying to find out what kinds of sickness may befall the beast, how its health may be preserved and how its malady cured, and the nature of herbs and food that are beneficial or hurtful—these are the physicians. I do not mean to say that their art is altogether worthless. Quite the contrary, theirs is an honorable profession, which may do a lot of good in this world now, for through it the worldly life of man may be prolonged so that he may attain perfection and life of a higher kind. This art may also stand its owner in good stead in the world to come, inasmuch as the competent physician may be able to save the lives of God's servants from death and destruction. But I contend that whosoever makes this art the chief aim in life and wastes upon it his entire time does violence to his soul.

There are some who waste their time on something still more worthless, as those who make their chief occupation the art of grammar and of rhetoric, learning it first themselves and then teaching it to others to the end of their days.

Others waste their time in the art of numbers, trying to unravel strange, hypothetical puzzles . . . the like of which will never happen, and think that thereby they may be accounted as distinguished arithmeticians. Similarly others waste themselves on the subtleties of geometry. Of these sciences only that part is truly necessary which leads to a knowledge of astronomy.

Like the wasting of too much time on the preparations for the journey is one's excessive devotion to the arts which are mostly of use to the material world, as medicine and law. By this I mean to refer only to a person who wastes his time in the practice of medicine for the sake of picking up fees rather than for the sake of rendering merciful service, or to a person who similarly wastes his time in the practice of law in order to gain a reputation or to amass a fortune or to display his wit. Both of these sciences have something good in common, for both may be useful in alleviating certain evils. Law may do away with some of the unpleasantness that springs up in the mutual relations of men and may establish friendly intercourse among them. By medicine, too, many of the ills resulting from the discordant rheums and from the inclement seasons of the year may be remedied. There is, however, a difference between these two professions. If all men were honest and did no wrong to each other, there would hardly be any need for the legal profession. But without medicine it would never be possible for mankind to get along. . . .

Like the one who prolongs the journey by making too many unnecessary stops and by pacing slowly with lingering steps is the one who is given too much to the purification of the soul in an effort to cleanse it from the cardinal vices and the offshoot thereof.

Like the arrival at the journey's end is one's attainment of perfection in the knowledge of God.

(c. 1170.)

THE UNITY OF GOD

by BAHYA IBN PAKUDA

WITH regard to the various modes in which the Creator's Unity is conceived, I would say that the word "Unity," is necessarily current with monotheists. They have used it so frequently and so familiarly in their ordinary conversation that it has become for them a term to express surprise at the happening of good or ill-fortune. Shocked at a grave disaster, they employ it to indicate the stupendous and extraordinary character of the event. In their ignorance and indolence, they do not pause to consider the precise meaning of what their tongues utter. They imagine that just as they have the term intact, so they have also an intact understanding of the Unity of God. They do not comprehend that their hearts are void of the truth and their minds empty of its meaning. For they declare God's Unity only with their tongues. But in their hearts they conceive Him as more than one. They represent Him in their thoughts as being like other unities; they ascribe to Him attributes that cannot belong to the absolute Unity; because the concepts of the true and conventional Unity are, even among the monotheists, only understood by the select few who have thought deeply and apprehended the relations between Creator and creature as well as their differences, the marks which belong to absolute Unity and the respects in which it is unique. The philosopher spoke the truth when he said: "Only the prophet, by reason of his natural endowment, or the distinguished philosopher, through the wisdom he has acquired, is able to worship the First Cause. But all the rest worship someone else, since they cannot conceive of any being that is not composite."

Consequently, the acceptance of the Unity of God falls into four divisions, according to the differences between human beings in knowledge and intellectual capacity. The first of these is the acknowledgment of the Unity of God in words alone. This degree is attained by the child or the simple person who has no conception of the meaning of religion and in whose heart its truth is not fixed. The second is the profession of the Unity of God with the mind as well as in speech—but attained through tradition only; the believer having faith in those from whom he has received the tradition, without however knowing the truth by the exercise of his own intellect and understanding. Such a person is like a blind man led by one that can see. It is also possible that he is receiving the tradition from one who himself has only learnt it traditionally. This suggests comparison with a company of blind men, each of whom has his hand on the shoulder of the one in front of him; and so on till the file reaches a person, endowed with sight, who is at their head and acts as their guide. Should this seeing person fail in his duty, and neglect to watch over his company, or should any of them stumble or meet with any other mishap, the misfortune would affect them all. They would all miss their way, fall into a pit or ditch, or encounter an obstacle that would prevent their further progress. So, too, if a man accepts the doctrine of Unity on the ground of tradition only, he can never be sure that he will not come to associate the worship of the One God with the worship of another being. If he hears the statements and arguments of the Dualists, his views may possibly change and he may unawares fall into error. Hence our sages warned us, "Be sedulous in the study of the Torah, and know what answer to make to the unbeliever."

The third category is the acknowledgment of the Creator's Unity with mind and in speech after one is able to maintain the doctrine with proofs of the reality of His existence, according to the method of rational investigation, without the knowledge, however, of what is implied by true

Unity as distinguished from conventional Unity. A person who has attained this degree resembles a seeing man who is travelling to a distant country. At a certain point of the journey the road branches off into several paths, the directions of which are doubtful. The traveller does not know and cannot recognize the particular route that leads to the city which he wishes to reach. And so, though he knows the general direction and situation of his destination he, in spite of all his efforts, fails to reach it. And thus Scripture saith, "The labour of fools wearieth every one of them, for he knoweth not how to go to the city."

The fourth division is the acknowledgment of the Unity of God with mind and in speech after one knows how to adduce proofs of His existence and has arrived at a knowledge of the truth of His Unity by the method of rational investigation and by arguments that are right and reasonable. This is the fullest and worthiest category of belief. And this degree of faith, the prophet exhorts us to attain in the words "Know this day, and lay it to thy heart that the Lord, He is God."

(11th century)

OF THE FIRST AND THE LAST THINGS

From the *Zohar* [1]

"IN the Beginning God created . . ." contains the first precept of all, to wit, the fear of the Lord, as it is written: "The fear of the Lord is the beginning of wisdom," as well as: "The fear of the Lord is the beginning of knowledge." It is the beginning and the gateway of faith, and on this precept the whole world is established. There are three types of fear: two have no proper root, while the third is the real fear. There is the man who fears the Holy One, blessed be He, in order that his children may live and not die, or lest he be punished in his body or his possessions; and so he is in constant fear. Evidently this is not the genuine fear of God. Another man fears the Holy One, blessed be He, because he is afraid of punishment in the other world and the tortures of Gehinnom.

[1] The *Zohar* ("Illumination") is the Bible of Jewish mysticism. This Kabbalistic work was compiled by Moses de Leon (1250-1305) and arranged in the form of an exposition of the Pentateuch. A complete translation from which the above passages are reprinted (vol. I, pp. 47-50; vol. IV, pp. 173-176) was translated by Harry Sperling and Maurice Simon and issued by the Soncino Press (London, 1931-34).

This is a second type which is not genuine fear. The genuine type is that which makes a man fear his Master because He is the mighty ruler, the rock and foundation of all worlds, before whom all existing things are as nought, as it has been said: "and all the inhabitants of the earth are as nought," and place his goal in that spot which is called *yir'ah* (fear). Rabbi Simeon here wept and said: 'Woe to me if I tell and woe to me if I do not tell! If I tell, then the wicked will know how to worship their Master; and if I do not tell, then the companions will be left in ignorance of this discovery. Corresponding to the "holy fear" there is an "evil fear" below which scourges and accuses, and which is a lash for punishing the wicked. Now he whose fear is of punishment and accusation is not endowed with that fear of God which leads to life. The fear which rests upon him is that evil fear of the lash, but not the fear of the Lord. For this reason the spot which is called "the fear of the Lord" is also called "the beginning of knowledge." Hence this precept is laid down here, as it is the principle and root of all the other precepts of the Torah. He who cherishes fear observes the whole Torah, and he who does not cherish fear does not observe the other precepts of the Torah, since it is the gate of all. Therefore it is written: *Bereshith,* through a beginning, that is, fear, God created heaven and earth. For he who transgresses this transgresses all the precepts of the Torah; and his punishment is to be scourged by the evil lash. This is implied in the words: "And the earth was chaos and confusion (*tohu wabohu*), and darkness was upon the face of the abyss." This is an allusion to the four kinds of punishment which are meted out to the wicked: *tohu* (chaos) alludes to strangulation, as it is written: "a line of (*tohu*) chaos," meaning a measuring cord. *Bohu* (confusion) alludes to stoning ("stones of confusion") by the stones which are sunk in the great abyss for the punishment of the wicked; "Darkness" is burning, as it is written: "And it came to pass, when ye heard the voice out of the midst of the darkness, while the mountain did burn with fire," also: "and the mountain burned with fire into the heart of heaven and darkness, etc.": this is the fire that rests on the heads of the wicked to consume them. The "wind" alludes to beheading by the sword, which whirls around the wicked like a tempest, as it is said: "and the flaming sword which is turned every way." These punishments are meted out to those who transgress the precepts of the Torah, and the words which allude to them follow immediately after the word "beginning," which symbolises the fear of God, which is the summary of all the precepts. Then follow all the other precepts of the Torah.

'The second precept is the one which is indissolubly bound up with the precept of fear, namely, love: that a man should love his Master with a perfect love, that which is called "great love." This is implied in the command: "walk before me, and be thou wholehearted," to wit, in love. This is implied also in the verse: And God said, Let there be light, which alludes to the perfect love, called great love. Herein, then, is the precept for man to love his Master truly,' said Rabbi Eleazar, 'Father, I have heard a definition of perfect love.' His father said to him, 'Expound it, my son, whilst Rabbi Phineas is present, for he truly practises it.' Rabbi Eleazar then explained thus: "Great love" is the the love which is complete through the union of two phases, without which it is not genuine love; and this is signified by the dictum that the love of the Holy One, blessed be He, has two aspects. There is, for instance, the man who loves Him because he has riches, length of life, children, power over his enemies, success in all his undertakings—all these form the motive of his love. Should the Holy One, blessed be He, turn the wheel of fortune against him and bring suffering upon him, he will change and his love will be no more. This kind of love has no root. Perfect love is the kind which remains steadfast in both phases, whether of affliction or prosperity. The right way of loving one's Master is expressed in the traditional teaching which says: "even if he deprive thee of thy life." This is, then, perfect love, embracing two phases. It was for this reason that the light of creation which first emerged was afterwards withdrawn. When it was withdrawn suffering emerged, in order that there might be this perfect love.' Rabbi Simeon embraced his son and kissed him; Rabbi Phineas also came and kissed him and blessed him, saying: 'Of a surety, the Holy One, blessed be He, sent me hither, and this is the meaning of the "tiny light" which I was told was somewhere in my household and would illumine the whole world.' Said Rabbi Eleazar: 'Assuredly, fear must not be forgotten in any of the precepts, least of all in this precept of love, which requires the association of fear. How is this to be achieved? In this way. Love, as has been said, may in one phase be inspired by favours, such as riches, length of life, children, plenty, and affluence. In such cases a man should be ever haunted by the fear lest sin may cause a reversal. Of such a one it is written: "Happy is the man that feareth alway," since he combines fear and love. The "adverse influence" (sitra ahra) which brings suffering and chastisement is therefore necessary in the world, since it rouses in man fear: for through chastisement a man becomes filled with the true fear of God, and does not harden his heart; for if he does, then "he that hardeneth his heart shall fall into evil," to wit, into the hands of that "adverse influence" which is called "evil." Thus we have a love which is complete in both phases, and from this results a true and perfect love.

"The third precept is to acknowledge that there is a God, all-powerful and ruler of the universe, and to make due proclamation of His unity every day, as extending in the six supernal directions, and to unify them all through the six words contained in the *Shema Israel,* and in reciting these to devote oneself wholly to God. The word *Ehad* therefore must be dwelt on to the length of six words. This is implied in the passage, Let the waters under the heaven be gathered together unto one place: that is, let the grades beneath the heaven be unified in it so as to form one whole, perfect in all the six directions. With God's unity one must further associate fear, for which reason one must dwell on the *daleth,* the last letter of *Ehad,* the *daleth* being for that reason written larger than the other letters. And this is implied in the words "and let the dry land be seen," that is, let the *daleth,* which is a "dry land," be associated with that unity. After forming this union on high it is necessary to repeat the process for the lower world through all its multiplicity in the six lower directions. This is expressed in the verse we recite after the *Shema,* viz., "Blessed-be the-name-of-the-glory-of-His-Kingdom for-ever and-ever," which contains another six words expressive of the unity. In this way, what was dry land becomes fertile soil to produce fruits and flowers and trees. This is implied in the passage: "And God called the dry land earth," that is, by the manifestation of God's unity here below the earth was duly perfected. It is for this reason that in the account of the third day the expression "that it was good" appears twice, once for the manifestation of the unity above and once for the manifestation of the unity below. As soon as that unity was made manifest at both ends, the text says, "Let the earth put forth grass," that is, the earth was then fitted to produce fruits and flowers according to its capacity.

Rabbi Abba then discoursed on the text: "And the Lord (had) said unto the fish, and it vomited out Jonah upon the dry land." 'Where and when did God speak to the fish?' he asked. 'It was,' he replied, 'at the time of Creation, when the Holy One, blessed be He, created the world; to wit, on the fifth day, when He created the fishes of the sea. Then He ordained and appointed a certain fish to swallow up Jonah and retain him in its body three days and three nights and then eject him. And not only in this case, but with all that He created did God make certain stipulations. Thus, on the first day, when He created the heavens, He stipulated with them that they should take up Elijah into heaven by a whirlwind, and so it was as it is written, "and Elijah went up by a whirl-wind into heaven." On the same day He created the light and stipulated with it that the sun should become darkened in Egypt three days, as it is written, "and there was a thick darkness in all the land of Egypt three days." On the second day He created the firmament to divide the waters from the waters, and in doing so He stipulated that they should separate between defilement and purity on behalf of Israel and be to them a means of cleansing, and so it was. On the third day He made the dry land emerge from the waters and caused the waters to be gathered together into one place, forming from them the sea, and He stipulated with it that it should allow the Israelites to pass through it on dry land and then overwhelm the Egyptians. And so it happened, as it is written, "and the sea returned to its strength when the morning appeared," where the term *l'ethano* (to its strength), by a transposition of letters, can be read *litnao* (to its stipulation). In addition, God stipulated with the earth that it should open its mouth on the occasion of the rebellion of Korah and swallow him up with all his company. And so it happened. On the fourth day He created the sun and the moon, and He stipulated with the sun that he should stand still in the midst of heaven, in the days of Joshua; He also stipulated with the stars that they should wage war against Sisera. On the fifth day He created the fishes of the sea and the birds of heaven. With the birds he stipulated that they should feed Elijah when he restrained the heaven from rain, as it is written: "and I have commanded the ravens to feed thee there"; and He stipulated with the fishes of the sea to appoint one fish that should swallow up Jonah and then eject him. On the sixth day he created Adam and stipulated with him that a woman should descend from him who should sustain Elijah, as it is written, "Behold, I have commanded a widow there to sustain thee." Similarly, in regard to every unique phenomenon that has happened in the world, the Holy One, blessed be He, had predestined it from the time when the world was created. And so here the meaning of, "And the Lord said to the fish" is that He had commanded it at the creation of the world.

'In the story of Jonah we have a representation of the whole of a man's career in this world. Jonah descending into the ship is symbolic of man's soul that descends into this world to enter into his body. Why is she called Jonah (lit. aggrieved)? Because as soon as she becomes partner with the body in this world she finds herself full of vexation. Man, then, is in this world as in a ship that is traversing the great ocean and is like to be broken, as it says, "so that the ship was like to be broken." Furthermore, man in this world commits sins, imagining that he can flee from the presence of his Master, who takes no notice of this world. The Almighty then rouses a furious tempest; to wit, man's doom, which constantly stands before the Holy One, blessed be He, and demands his punishment. It is this which assails the ship and calls to mind man's sins that it may seize him; and the man is thus caught by the tempest and is struck down by illness, just as Jonah "went down into the innermost part of the ship; and he lay, and was fast asleep." Although the man is thus prostrated, his soul does not exert itself to return to his Master in order to make good his omissions. So "the shipmaster came to him," to wit, the good prompter, who is the general steersman, "and said unto him: What meanest thou that thou sleepest? Arise, call upon thy God," etc.; it is not a time to sleep, as they are about to take thee up to be tried for all that thou hast done in this world. Repent of thy sins. Reflect on these things and return to thy Master. "What is thine occupation," wherein thou wast occupied in this world; and make confession concerning it before the Master; "and whence comest thou"; to wit, from a fetid drop, and so be not thou arrogant before Him. "What is thy country"—reflect that from earth thou wast created and to earth thou wilt return; "and of what people art thou"; that is, reflect whether thou canst rely on merits of thy forbears to protect thee. When they bring him to judgment before the Heavenly Tribunal, that tempest, that is none other than the judgment doom which raged against him, demands from the King the punishment of all the King's prisoners, and then all the King's counsellors appear before Him one by one, and the Tribunal is set up. Some plead in defence of the accused, others against him. Should the man be found guilty, as in the case of Jonah, then "the men rowed hard to bring it to the land, but they could not"; so those who plead on his behalf find points in his favour and strive to restore him to this world, but they cannot; "for the sea grew more and more tempestuous against them;" the prosecution storms and rages against him, and, convicting him of his sins, prevails against his defenders. Then three appointed messengers descend upon the man; one of them makes a record of all the good deeds and the misdeeds that he has performed in this world; one casts up the reckoning of his days; and the third is the one who has accompanied the man from the time when he was in his mother's womb. As already said, the doom summons is not appeased until "they took up Jonah," until they take him from the house to the place of burial. Then proclamation is made concerning him. If he was a righteous man, it runs, Render honour to the King's image! "He entereth into peace, they rest in their beds, each one that walketh in his uprightness." But when a wicked man dies, the proclamation runs: Woe to that man, it would have been better for him had he never been born! Regarding such a man it is written, "and they cast him forth into the sea, and the sea ceased from its raging," that is, only after they have placed him in the grave, which is the place of judgment, does the judgment summons cease from its raging. For the fish that swallowed him is, in fact, the grave; and so "Jonah was in the belly of the fish," which is identified with "the belly of the underworld" (*sheol*), as is proved by the passage, "Out of the belly of the underworld (*sheol*) cried I." "Three days and three nights": these are the three days that a man lies in his grave before his belly splits open. After three days it ejects the putrid matter on his face, saying: "Take back what thou gavest me; thou didst eat and drink all day and never didst thou give anything to the poor; all thy days were like feasts and holidays, whilst the poor remained hungry without partaking of any of thy food. Take back what thou gavest me." In regard to this it is written: "and I will spread dung upon your faces," etc. Again, after the lapse of three days, the man receives chastisement in each organ—in his eyes, his hands, and his feet. This continues for thirty days, during which time the soul and body are chastised together. The soul therefore remains all that time on earth below, not ascending to her place, like a woman remaining apart all the days of her impurity. After that the soul ascends whilst the body is being decomposed in the earth, where it will lie until the time when the Holy One, blessed be He, will awaken the dead. A voice will then resound through the graves, proclaiming: "Awake and sing, ye that dwell in the dust, for thy dew is as the dew of light, and the earth shall cast forth the dead (*rephaim*)." That will come to pass when the Angel of Death will depart from the world, as it is written: "He will destroy death for ever, and the Lord God will wipe away tears from off all faces; and the reproach of his people will he take away from off all the earth." It is of that occasion that it is written: "And the Lord spoke unto the fish, and it vomited out Jonah upon the dry land"; for as soon as that voice will resound among the graves they will all cast out the dead bodies that they contain. The term *rephaim* (the dead) being akin to the root, *rapha* (healing), indicates that the dead will be restored to their former physical condition. But, you may say, is it not written elsewhere, "the *rephaim* will not rise"? The truth is that all the dead will be restored to their former state whilst in the graves, but some of them will rise and others will not. Happy is the portion of Israel, of whom it is written, "My dead bodies shall arise." Thus in the narrative of that fish we find words of healing for the whole world. As soon as it swallowed Jonah it died, but after three days was restored to life and vomited him forth. In a similar way the Land of Israel will in the future first be stirred to new life, and afterwards "the earth will cast forth the dead."

(c. 1300)

ISRAEL AND THE WORLD [1]

by JUDAH HALEVI

The Rabbi: The root of all knowledge was deposited in the Ark which took the place of the heart, viz., the Ten Commandments, and its branch is the Torah on its side, as it is said: "Put it in the side of the ark of the covenant of the Lord your God." From there went forth a twofold knowledge, first, the scriptural knowledge, whose bearers were the priests; secondly, the prophetic knowledge which was in the hands of the prophets. Both classes were, so to speak, the people's watchful advisers, who compiled the chronicles. They, therefore, represent the head of the people.

Al Khazari: So you are today a body without either head or heart.

The Rabbi: Thou sayest rightly, but we are not even a body, only scattered limbs, like the "dry bones" which Ezekiel saw in his vision. These bones, however, O king of the Khazars, which have retained a trace of vital power, having once been the seat of a heart, brain, breath, soul, and intellect, are better than certain bodies formed of marble and plaster, endowed with heads, eyes, ears, and all limbs, in which never dwelt the spirit of life, nor can dwell in them, since they are but imitations of man, not man in reality.

Al Khazari: It is as thou sayest.

The Rabbi: The "dead" nations which desire to be held equal to the "living" people can obtain nothing more than an external resemblance. They built houses for hermits and ascetics in order to secure inspiration, but it came not. They, then, deteriorated, became disobedient, and wicked; yet no fire fell down from heaven upon them, nor rapid pestilence, as a manifest punishment from God for their disobedience. Their heart, I

[1] The book *Kuzari* from which this selection is taken was written in the form of a dialogue between a rabbi and the King of the Khazars who decided to embrace Judaism. The actual event took place in the eighth century.

mean the house in which they used to meet, was destroyed, but otherwise their status was not affected. This could only take place in accordance with the largeness or smallness of their number, with their strength or weakness, disunion or unity, following upon natural or accidental causes. We, however, since our heart, I mean the Holy House, was destroyed, were lost with it. If it be restored, we, too, will be restored, be we few or many, or in whichever way this may happen. For our master is the living God, our King, who keeps us in this our present condition in despersion and exile.

Al Khazari: Certainly. A similar dispersion is not imaginable in any other people, unless it became absorbed by another, especially after so long a period. Many nations which arose after you have perished without leaving a memory, as Edom, Moab, Ammon, Aram, the Philistines, Chaldeans, Medians, Persians, Brahmans, Sabaeans and many others.

The Rabbi: Do not believe that I, though agreeing with thee, admit that we are dead. We still hold connexion with that Divine Influence through the laws which He has placed as a link between us and Him. There is circumcision of which it is said: "My covenant shall be in your flesh for an everlasting covenant." There is further the Sabbath, "It is a sign between me and you throughout your generations." Besides this there is "the covenant of the Fathers," and the covenant of the law, first granted on Horeb, and then in the plains of Moab in connexion with the promises and warnings laid down in the section: "When thou shalt beget children and grandchildren." Compare further the antithesis: "If any of thine be driven out into the utmost parts of heaven." "Thou shall return unto the Lord thy God." We are not like the dead, but rather like an ailing and attenuated person who has been given up by the physicians, and yet hopes for a miracle or an extraordinary recovery, as it is said: "Can these bones live?" Compare also the simile in the words: "Behold my servant shall prosper"; "He has no form nor comeliness," "Like one from whom men hid their faces," which means that, on account of his deformity and repulsive visage, he is compared to an unclean thing, which man only beholds with disgust, and turns away from; "despised and rejected of men," "A man of pains and acquainted with disease."

Al Khazari: How can this serve as a comparison for Israel, as it is said: "Surely he has borne our disease"? That which has befallen Israel has come to pass on account of his sins.

The Rabbi: Israel amidst the nations is like the heart amidst the organs of the body; it is at one and the same time the most ailing and the most healthy of them.

Al Khazari: Make this a little clearer.

The Rabbi: The heart is exposed to all sorts of diseases, and frequently visited by them, such as sadness, anxiety, wrath, envy, enmity, love, hate, and fear. Its temperament changes continually, undulating between excess and deficiency, and it is moreover influenced by inferior nourishment, by movement, exertion, sleep, or wakefulness. They all affect the heart whilst the limbs rest.

Al Khazari: Now I understand how it can be the most ailing and most healthy of all organs simultaneously.

The Rabbi: Is it possible that it could suffer from swelling, or a cancer, or boils, swound, weakness, and asthma, as is possible in other organs?

Al Khazari: Impossible. For the smallest trace of these would bring on death. Its extreme sensibility, caused by the purity of its blood, and its great intelligence causes it to feel the slightest symptom, and expels it as long as it is able to do so. The other organs lack this fine sensibility, and it is therefore possible that they can be affected by some strange matter which produces illness.

The Rabbi: Thus its sensibility and feeling expose it to many ills, but they are at the same time the cause of their own expulsion at the very beginning, and before they have time to take root.

Al Khazari: Quite so.

The Rabbi: Our relation to the divine influence is the same as that of the soul to the heart. For this reason it is said: "You only have I known of all the families of the earth, therefore I will punish you for all your iniquities." These are the illnesses. As regards its health, it is alluded to in the words of the sages: He forgives the sins of his people, causing the first of them to vanish first. He does not allow our sins to become overwhelming, or they would destroy us completely by their multitude. Thus he says: "For the iniquity of the Amorites is not yet full." He left them alone till the ailment of their sins had become fatal. Just as the heart is pure in substance and matter, and of even temperament, in order to be accessible to the intellectual soul, so also is Israel in its component parts. In the same way as the heart may be affected by disease of the other organs, viz., the lusts of the liver, stomach and genitals, caused through contact with malignant elements; thus also is Israel exposed to ills originating in its inclinings towards the Gentile. As it is said: "They were mingled among the heathens and learned their words." Do not consider it strange if it is said in the same sense: "Surely, he has borne our griefs and carried our sorrows." Now we are burdened by them, whilst the whole world enjoys rest and prosperity. The trials which meet us are meant to prove our faith, to cleanse us completely, and to remove all taint from us. If we are good, the divine influence is with us in this world. Thou knowest that the elements gradually evolved metals, plants, animals, man, finally the pure essence of man. The whole evolution took place for the sake of this essence, in order that the divine influence should inhabit it. That essence, however, came into existence for the sake of the highest essence, viz., the prophets and the pious. A similar gradation can be observed in the prayer: "Give thy fear, O Lord our God, over all Thy works." Then: "Give glory to Thy people"; finally: "The pious shall see and rejoice, because they are the purest essence."

Al Khazari: Thy interesting comparison has completely riveted my attention. But I should expect to see more hermits and ascetics among you than among other people.

The Rabbi: I regret that thou hast forgotten those fundamental principles in which thou didst concur. Did we not agree that man cannot approach God except by means of deeds commanded by him? Dost thou think that this can be gained by meekness, humility, etc., alone?

Al Khazari: Certainly, and rightly so. I think I read in your books as follows: "What doth the Lord thy God require of thee, but to fear the Lord thy God?" and many similar passages.

The Rabbi: These are the rational laws, being the basis and preamble of the divine law, preceding it in character and time, and indispensable in the administration of every human society. Even a gang of robbers must have a kind of justice among them if their confederacy is to last. When Israel's disloyalty had come to such a pass that they disregarded rational and social principles (which are as absolutely necessary for a society as are the natural functions of eating, drinking, exercise, rest, sleeping, and waking for the individual), but held fast to sacrificial worship and other divine laws, He was satisfied with even less. It was told to them: "Haply you might observe those laws which rule the smallest and meanest community, such as refer to justice, good actions, and recognition of God's bounty." For the divine law cannot become complete till the social and rational laws are perfected. The rational law demands justice and recognition of God's bounty. What has he, who fails in this respect, to do with offerings, Sabbath, circumcision, etc., which reason neither demands, nor forbids? These are, however, the ordinations especially given to Israel as a corollary to the rational laws. Through this they received the advantage of the divine influence, without knowing how it came to pass that the "Glory of God" descended upon them, and that "the fire of God" consumed their offerings; how they heard the allocution of the Lord; and how their history developed. These are matters which reason would refuse to believe if they were not guaranteed by irrefutable evidence. In a similar sense it was said to them: "What doth the Lord thy God require of thee?" and "Add your burnt offerings." Can it be imagined that the Israelites observe "the doing of justice and the love of mercy," but neglect circumcision, Sabbath, and the other laws, and felt happy withal?

Al Khazari: After what thou hast said I should not think so. In the opinion of philosophers, however, he becomes a pious man who does not mind in which way he approaches God, whether as a Jew or a Christian, or anything else he chooses. Now that we have returned to reasoning, speculating and dialectics, everyone might try to belong to a creed dictated by his own speculation, a thing which would be absurd.

The Rabbi: The divine law imposes no asceticism on us. It rather desires that we should keep the equipoise, and grant every mental and physical faculty its due, as much as it can bear, without overburdening one faculty at the expense of another. If a person gives way to licentiousness he blunts his mental faculty; he who is inclined to violence injures some other faculty. Prolonged fasting is no act of piety for a weak person who, having succeeded in checking his desires, is not greedy. For him feasting is a burden and self-denial. Neither is diminution of wealth an act of piety, if it is gained in a lawful way, and if its acquisition does not interfere with study and good works, especially for him who has a household and children. He may spend part of it in almsgiving, which would not be displeasing to God; but to increase it is better for himself. Our law, as a whole, is divided between *fear, love,* and *joy,* by each of which one can approach God. Thy contrition on a fast day does nothing to bring thee nearer to God than thy joy on the Sabbath and holy days, if it is the outcome of a devout heart. Just as prayers demand devotion, so also is a pious mind necessary to find pleasure in God's command and law; that thou shouldst be pleased with the law itself from love of the Lawgiver. Thou seest how much He has distinguished thee, as if thou hadst been His guest invited to His festive board. Thou thankest Him in mind and word, and if thy joy lead thee so far as to sing and dance, it becomes worship and a bond of union between thee and the divine influence. Our law did not consider these matters optional, but laid down decisive injunctions concerning them, since it is not in the power of mortal man to apportion to each faculty of the soul and body its right measure, or to decide what amount of rest and exertion is good, or to determine how long the ground should be cultivated till it finds rest in the years of release and jubilee, or the amount of tithe to be given, etc. God commanded cessation of work on Sabbath and holy days, as well as in the culture of the soil, all this "as a remembrance of the exodus from Egypt," and "remembrance of the work of creation." These two things belong together, because they are the outcome of the absolute divine will, and not the result of accident or natural phenomena. It is said: "For ask now of the days that are past—Did ever a people hear the voice of God—Or hath God assayed?" etc. The observance of the Sabbath is itself an acknowledgement of His omnipotence, and at the same time a recognition of the creation by the divine word. He who observes the Sabbath because the work of creation was finished on that day acknowledges the creation itself. He who believes in the creation believes in the Creator. He, however, who does not believe in it falls a prey to doubts of God's eternity and to doubts of the existence of the world's Creator. Therefore, the observance of the Sabbath is nearer to God than monastic retirement and asceticism. Behold how the divine influence attached itself to Abraham, then to all those who shared his excellence, and to the Holy Land. This influence followed him everywhere, and guarded his posterity, preventing the detachment of any of them, it brought them to the most sheltered and best place, and caused them to multiply in a miraculous manner, and finally raised them to a degree worthy of such excellence. He is, therefore, called: "God of Abraham," "God of the land," "Dwelling between the Cherubim," "Dwelling in Zion," "Abiding in Jerusalem," these places being compared to heaven. As it is said: "Dwelling in heaven" His light shines in these places as in heaven, although through mediums which are fit to receive this light. He sheds it upon them, and this it is that is called *love*. It has been taught us, and we have been enjoined to believe in it, as well as to praise and thank Him in the prayer: "With eternal love Thou lovest us"; so that we should bear in mind that it originally came from Him, but not from us. To give an instance, we do not say that an animal created itself, but that God formed and fashioned it, having selected the proper matter for it. In the same manner it was He who initiated our delivery from Egypt to be His people and to acknowledge Him as king, as He said: "I am the Lord your God who led you out of the land of Egypt to be unto you a God." He also says: "O Israel, in whom I will be glorified."

Al Khazari: This sentence seems to go too far, and is overbold in assuming that the Creator is glorified through mortal man.

The Rabbi: Wouldst thou find this less strange in the creation of the sun?

Al Khazari: Certainly, on account of its great power. Next to God it is the cause of being. By its means night and day and the seasons of the year are determined; minerals, metals, plants, and animals were developed through its instrumentality. Its light produced sight and colors. Wherefore should not the action of such a thing be an object of glory among men?

The Rabbi: Are not the intellectual faculties much finer than the light that is seen? Or were not the inhabitants of the earth prior to the Israelites in blindness and error excepting those few whom I mentioned? Some people have said that there was no Creator; that no part of the world was more worthy of being created than being creator, the universe being eternal. Others say that the spheres are eternal and creative. They consequently adore them. Others again assert that the fire is the essence of light and all the miraculous products of its power; it must, therefore, be worshipped. "The soul also is fire" they say. Others worship different things, viz., sun, moon, stars, and animal forms, which are in connexion with special phenomena. Other people adore their kings and sages. All, however, agree that there is nothing in the world which is contrary to nature, nor is there any Providence. Even philosophers who, with their refined intuition and clear view, acknowledge a Prime Cause different from earthly things and unparalleled, are inclined to think that this Prime Cause exercises no influence on the world, and certainly not on individuals, as He is too exalted to know them, much less to make them the basis of a new entity. The community was at last considered sufficiently pure for the light to dwell on it, to be worthy of seeing miracles which changed the course of nature, and to understand that the world had a King who watched and guarded it, who knew both great and small, rewarded the good and the wicked, and directed the hearts. All who came after these philosophers could not detach themselves from their principles, so that today the whole civilised world acknowledges that God is eternal, and that the world was created. They look upon the Israelites and all that befell them as a proof of this.

(c. 1130)

OF PROPHECY

by MOSES BEN MAIMON

THERE are as many opinions concerning prophecy as concerning the eternity or non-eternity of the universe. For we have shown that those who assume the existence of God as proved may be divided into three classes, according to the view they take of the question, whether the universe is eternal or not. Similarly there are three different opinions on prophecy. I will omit from consideration the views of the atheist; he does not believe in the existence of God, much less in prophecy. I will content myself with discussing the various opinions on prophecy held by those who believe in God.

Among those who believe in prophecy, and even among our co-religionists, there are some ignorant people who think as follows: God selects any person He pleases, inspires him with the spirit of prophecy, and entrusts him with a mission. It makes no difference whether that person be wise or stupid, old or young, provided he be, to some extent, morally good. These persons have not yet gone so far as to maintain that God might also inspire a wicked person with His spirit. They admit that this is impossible, unless God has previously caused him to improve his ways.

The philosophers hold that prophecy is a certain faculty of man in a state of perfection, which can only be obtained by study. Although the faculty is common to the whole race, yet it is not fully developed in each individual, either on account of the individual's defective constitution, or on account of some external cause. This is the case with every faculty common to a class. It is only brought to a state of perfection in some individuals, and not in all; but it is impossible that it should not be perfect in some individual of the class; and if the perfection is of such a nature that it can only be produced by an agent, such an agent must exist. Accordingly, it is impossible that an ignorant person should be a prophet; or that a person who is no prophet in the evening, should, unexpectedly on the following morning, find himself become a prophet in the manner which will be described; for prophecy is a natural faculty of man. It is impossible that a man who has the capacity for prophecy should prepare himself for it without attaining it, just as it is impossible that a person with a healthy constitution should be fed well, and yet not properly assimilate his food.

The third view is that which is taught in Scripture, and which forms one of the principles of our religion. It coincides with the opinion of the philosophers in all points except one. For we believe that even if one has the capacity for prophecy, and has duly prepared himself, it may yet happen that he does not actually prophesy. It is in such a case the will of God that withholds from him the use of the faculty. According to my opinion, this fact is as exceptional as any other miracle, and acts in the same way. For the laws of Nature demand that everyone should be a prophet, who has a proper physical constitution, and has been duly prepared as regards education and training. If such a person is not a prophet, he is in the same position as a person who, like Jeroboam, is deprived of the use of his hand, or of his eyes, as was the case with the army of Syria, in the history of Elisha. As for the principle which I laid down, that preparation and perfection of moral and rational faculties are the *sine qua non,* our Sages say exactly the same: "The spirit of prophecy only rests upon persons who are wise, strong, and rich."

Prophecy is, in truth and reality, an emanation sent forth by the Divine Being through the medium of the Active Intellect, in the first instance to man's rational faculty, and then to his imaginative faculty; it is the highest degree and greatest perfection man can attain; it consists in the most perfect development of the imaginative faculty. Prophecy is a faculty that cannot in any way be found in a person, or acquired by man, through a culture of his mental and moral faculties; for even if these faculties were as good and perfect as possible, they would be of no avail, unless they were combined with the highest moral excellence of the imaginative faculty. You know that the full development of any faculty of the body, such as the imagination, depends upon the condition of the organ by means of which the faculty acts. This must be the best possible in the matter of temperament and breadth, of equal excellence in the purity of its substance. Any defect in this respect cannot in any way be supplied or remedied by training. For when any organ is defective in its temperament, proper training can at best restore a healthy condition to some extent, but cannot make such an organ perfect. But if the organ is defective in breadth, position, or in the substance and matter of which the organ is formed, there is no remedy. You know all this; I need not explain it to you at length.

Part of the functions of the imaginative faculty is, as you well know, to retain impressions by the senses, to combine them, and chiefly to form images. The principal and highest function is performed when the senses are arrested and inactive; for then it receives divine inspiration in the measure as it is predisposed to this influence. This is the nature of those dreams which prove true, and also of prophecy, the difference being one of quantity, not of quality. Thus our Sages say, that dream is the sixtieth part of prophecy; and no such comparison could be made between two things of different kinds, for we cannot say the perfection of man is so many times the perfection of a horse. In *Bereshit Rabba* the following saying of our Sages occurs, "Dream is the *nobelet* (the unripe fruit) of prophecy." This is an excellent comparison, for the unripe fruit (*nobelet*) is really the fruit in a limited degree; only it has fallen from the tree before attaining to ripeness. In a similar manner the action of the imaginative faculty during sleep is the same as when it receives a prophecy; only in the first instance it is not fully developed, and has not yet reached its highest measure of excellence. But why quote the words of our Sages, when I can refer you to the following passage of Scripture: "If there be among you a prophet, I, the Lord, will make myself known unto him in a vision, in a dream will I speak to him." Here the Lord tells us what the real essence of a prophecy is, that it is a perfection acquired in a dream or in a vision (the original *mareh* is a noun derived from the verb *raah*); the imaginative faculty acquired such an efficiency in its processes that it sees the thing as it came from without, and perceives it as if through the medium of bodily senses. These two modes of prophecy, vision and dream, include all its different degrees. It is a well known fact that the thing which earnestly engages man's attention whilst he is awake and in the full possession of his senses forms during his sleep the object of the processes of his imaginative faculty. Imagination is then only influenced by the intellect in so far as it is predisposed for such influence. It would be quite useless to illustrate this by a simile, or to explain it more fully, as it is self-evident. It is like the processes of the senses, the existence of which no person with common sense would ever deny.

After these introductory remarks it becomes clear that a person must satisfy the following conditions before he can become a prophet: The substance of the brain must from the very beginning be in the most perfect condition as regards purity of matter, composition of its different parts, breadth and position; no part of his body must suffer from ill health; he must, in addition, have studied and acquired wisdom, so that his rational faculty passes from a state of potentiality to that of actuality; his intellect must be as developed and perfect as human intellect can be; his passions pure and equally balanced; all his desires must aim at obtaining a knowledge of the hidden laws and causes which are in force in the universe; his thoughts must be engaged in lofty matters; his attention directed to the knowledge of God, to the consideration of His works, and to that which he must believe concerning these things. There must be an absence of the lower desires and appetites, of the seeking after pleasure in eating, drinking, and cohabitation; and, in short, every pleasure connected with the sense of touch. Aristotle correctly says that this sense is a disgrace to us, since we possess it only in virtue of being animals; it does not include any specifically human element, whilst enjoyments connected with other senses, as smell, hearing and sight, though likewise of a material nature, may sometimes induce intellectual pleasure, appealing to man as man. This observation, although forming no part of our subject, is not superfluous, for the thoughts of the most renowned wise men are in large measure affected by the pleasures of this sense, and filled with a desire for them. Yet people are surprised that these scholars do not prophesy, if prophesying be nothing but a certain degree in the natural development of man. It is further necessary to suppress every thought or desire for unreal power and dominion; that is to say, for victory, for increase of followers, for acquisition of honour, and for service from the people without any ulterior object. On the contrary, the multitude must be considered according to their true worth; some of them are undoubtedly like domesticated cattle, and others like wild beasts, and these only engage the mind of the perfect and distinguished man in so far as he desires to guard himself from injury, in case of contact with them, and to derive some benefit from them when necessary. A man who satisfies these conditions, whilst his fully developed imagination is in action, influenced by the Active Intellect according to his mental training,—such a person will undoubtedly perceive nothing but things very extraordinary and divine, and see nothing but God and His angels. His knowledge will include only that which is real knowledge, and his thought will be directed only to such general principles as would tend to improve the social relations between man and woman.

We have thus described three kinds of perfection: mental perfection acquired by training, perfection of the natural constitution of the imaginative faculty, and moral perfection produced by the suppression of every thought of bodily pleasures, and of every kind of foolish or evil ambition. These qualities are, as is well known, possessed by the wise men in different degrees, and the degrees of prophetic faculty vary in accordance with this difference. Faculties of the body are, at one time weak, wearied, and corrupted, at others in a healthy state. Imagination is certainly one of the faculties of the body. Therefore you find that prophets are deprived of the faculty of prophesying when they mourn, are angry, or are similarly affected. Our Sages say, inspiration does not come upon a prophet when he is sad or languid. This is why Jacob did not receive any revelation during the period of his mourning, when his imagination was engaged with the loss of Joseph. The same was the case with Moses, when he was in a state of depression through the multitude of his troubles, which lasted from the murmurings of the Israelites in consequence of the evil report of the spies, till the death of the warriors of that generation. He received no message of God, as he used to do, even though he did not receive prophetic inspiration through the medium of the inspirative faculty, but directly through the intellect. More than once we have said that Moses, unlike other prophets, did not speak in similes. There were also persons who prophesied for a certain time and then left off altogether, something occurring to cause them to discontinue prophesying. The same circumstance, prevalence of sadness and dulness, was undoubtedly the direct cause of the interruption of prophecy during the exile. For can there be any greater misfortune for man than this: to be a slave bought for money in the service of ignorant and voluptuous masters, and powerless against them as they unite in themselves the absence of true knowledge and the force of all animal desires? Such an evil state has been prophesied to us in the words, "They shall run to and fro to seek the word of God, but shall not find it"; "Her king and her princes are among the nations, the law is no more, her prophets also find no vision from the Lord." This is a real fact, and the cause is evident; the prerequisites of prophecy have been lost. In the messianic period—may it soon commence—prophecy will therefore again be in our midst, as has been promised by God.

(c. 1200)

IN DEFENSE OF REPUBLICS

by ISAAC ABRAVANEL

BEHOLD, it behooves us to know whether a monarch is a fundamental necessity that a people cannot do without, or if it can dispense with him. Philosophers agree on the people's need of him. They see in the service rendered by the king in the political organization a service not dissimilar to the relation of the heart to the body in animals possessing a heart, or to the relation of the First Cause to the entire universe. Now if students of government opine that a kingdom must be based on three things (firstly, unity and absence of partnership; secondly, continuity and absence of change; thirdly, absolute power), then their conclusion as to the necessity of a monarch is indeed fallacious. For it is not impracticable that a people should have many leaders, united, agreeing, and concurring in one counsel, which should render judgment in administrative and judicial matters. This militates against the first principle. Then, why should not their administration be for one year, or for three years, like the years of a hireling, and even less than that? When the turn of other judges and officers comes, they will arise in their stead, and investigate whether the first ones have not failed in their trust, and he whom they condemn shall make good the wrong he committed. This militates against the second principle. Then again, why should not their power be limited and regulated according to the laws and statutes? A common-sense principle tells us that when one man disagrees with the majority, it is the majority that has the deciding voice on a law. It is more likely that one man should trespass, through his folly, or strong temptations or anger (as it is written: 'the wrath of a king is as messengers of death,') than that many men taking counsel should transgress. For if one of them turns aside from the right path, the others will rise up against him. Moreover, since their administration is temporary, and they must render account after a short while, the fear of man will be upon them. But what need is there of producing abstract arguments, since experience is more forceful than logic? Behold and see the countries where the administration is in the hands of kings, and you will observe their abominations and corruptions; everyone of them does that which is right in his own eyes; for the earth is filled with wickedness through them. On the other hand, we see at this day many countries where the administration is in the hands of judges; temporary rulers are elected there, and over them is a chief against whom no protest may avail; they choose that which is right by definite regulations; they rule over the people, and decide concerning matters appertaining to war; none can withstand them, whether it be for the rod or for the land. Dost thou not know? hast thou not heard that there was a great country that had dominion over all the world? She devoured the whole earth, trod it down, shattered it into pieces, while her administration was in the hands of numerous consuls, who were faithful, numerous, and held temporary offices. But when an emperor was given rule over it, it became tributary. Even today Venice rules as mistress, great among nations, princess among states, and the state of Florence is the glory of all lands. There are likewise other states, great and small, which have no king, and are governed by leaders elected for a fixed period. Now in elected governments, in which there is nothing crooked or perverse, no man lifts his hand or his foot to commit any manner of trespass. They conquer countries with wisdom, understanding, and knowledge. All this proves that the existence of a monarch is not necessary; nay, it is harmful, and is a great danger. In a similar manner the author of the *Guide to the Perplexed* warned against the great dangers incurred in travelling on the seas and in serving kings, on account of the similarity that exists between the two in what they offer in the way of potential danger, both being alike, the stormy wind upon the sea and the perverse spirit of the ruler. It is surprising that the adherents of such an erroneous opinion should have compared the unity of a king elected by the authority and will of men to the unity of the First Cause, which is blessed, the necessarily eternal. Indeed, wise men have written concerning the body of an animal that there are three vital members which control it. Even if according to the opinion of the chief of the philosophers the heart is the only vital member, this merely refers to the production of the spirit; but he does not deny the control of the body by other faculties: by the psychical, which are from the brain, and the physical which are from the liver. To conclude, things of nature are inevitably arrayed in this manner, but those which result from the action of the will belong to the category of the contingent. The one cannot be compared to the other.

No objection can be raised from the saying: 'For the transgression of a land many are the princes thereof': for that verse speaks of the princes, not of the leaders and judges. How can we ignore self-evident facts? For if the leaders are good, it is better that they should be many and not one; if they are bad, one left free to his lusts is more dangerous than many.

I therefore think that kings were at first set up to rule not by the people's elections, but by force: the one that was stronger prevailed; as it is written: 'Let us go up against Judah, and vex it, and set up a king in the midst of it.' Even these were only appointed as a matter of trust, to serve the people; but they made themselves masters, as if God, who is blessed, gave them the earth and the fulness thereof, and they leave it as an inheritance to their children after them and to their children's children for ever, as if it were a plot of land which one acquires for money. This cursed plague has spread so much that sometimes a man arises, and rules alone, and governs according to his fancy. This, however, is not alike in all kingdoms; for in some of them the king does not have so much power in the administration. But the better of the two is the one that does not yet exist.   (c. 1500)

IN DEFENSE OF THE TORAH

by JOSEPH ALBO

IN a discussion I had with a Christian scholar he said to me: A thing must be tested by reference to its causes, the material, the formal, the efficient and the final. If we test the Torah of Moses in this way, we find that it is defective in all four respects. It is defective in respect to its matter, for it contains stories and other matters which are not Torah, i.e., teaching and guidance; whereas the teaching of Jesus has nothing but instruction. It is defective in respect to the efficient cause, because it expresses the divine mysteries alluding to the Trinity in a very obscure manner, so that it is not possible to understand from it the perfection of the Maker and His attributes; while it is very clear in the teaching of Jesus the Nazarene that God is father, son and holy ghost, and that they are all one. It is defective in respect to the final cause, for it says nothing about spiritual happiness, which is the purpose of man, but speakes only of material happiness. The teaching of Jesus, on the other hand, promises spiritual happiness and not material prosperity. It is defective in respect to the formal cause, for a law should embrace three things: 1. The relations between man and God, i.e., commandments relating to divine worship, called *ceremoniales* in their language, "cere" in Greek meaning God. 2. Relations between man and man; these are judgments, called *judiciales,* i.e., rules and principles having their origin in the business transactions of a man with his fellow. These are necessary for the maintenance of the social group. 3. Relations between a man and himself, called *morales.* These are precepts which a man follows in order to acquire a good character, such as virtuous living, humility, and so on, which develop character.

Now his opinion was that if we examine the Law of Moses in respect to these three kinds of precepts, we find that it is defective in all of them. It is defective in the duties of man to God, i.e., in the ceremonial part, which prescribes the manner of divine worship. For it commands the slaughter of animals, the burning of the flesh and the fat, the sprinkling of the blood, all of which are unclean forms of worship; whereas the manner of worship prescribed in the law of Jesus is clean, consisting of bread and wine. It is defective also in the social and judicial precepts, which concern human relations, for it permits interest, saying: "Unto a foreigner thou mayest lend upon interest"; whereas interest is destructive of social life. Also it prescribes that an unintentional homicide should live in exile until the death of the high priest. But this is an unequal punishment, for sometimes the period is long and sometimes it is short. Moreover, an unintentional homicide is not deserving of death, and yet the law of Moses exposes his life to the avenger of the blood, who may kill him with impunity; the result is that the intentional homicide goes free, while the unintentional loses his life. This is not so in the law of Jesus, where all depends upon the opinion of the judges. It is defective in the matter of a man's duty to himself, for the law of Moses commands only right action, and says nothing about purity of heart; whereas the law of Jesus commands purity of heart, and thus saves man from the judgment of gehenna. This is the gist of the views of the Christian scholar.

My answer was as follows: All these statements are untrue, and are due to a lack of understanding or insight or knowledge of the ideas of the Torah. Before answering his arguments, however, I will make an introductory statement which no man of intelligence can doubt, namely, that anything that is the subject of belief must be conceivable by the mind, though it may be impossible so far as nature is concerned, as was explained in the twenty-second chapter of the First Book. Such natural impossibilities as the dividing of the Red Sea, the turning of the rod into a serpent, and the other miracles mentioned in the Torah or in the Prophets can be conceived by the mind, hence we can believe that God has power to produce them. But a thing which the mind can not conceive, for example, that a thing should be and not be at the same time, or that a body should be in two places at the same time, or that one and the same number should be both odd and even, and so on, can not be the subject of belief, and God can not be conceived as being able to do it, as God can not be conceived able to create another like Him in every respect, or to make a square whose diagonal is equal to its side, or to make now what has happened not to have happened. For since the mind can not conceive it, God can not do it, as it is inherently impossible. Therefore it can not be the subject of belief, for belief in impossible things does not give perfection to the soul, else reason would have been given to man to no purpose, and man would have no superiority to animals, since the mind does not affect belief.

Having made this preface, I will say that the opponent's statement that the law of Moses is defective in respect of its matter shows his ignorance of the law of Moses. For there is not a word and not a narrative in the law of Moses which is not essential either to inculcate an idea or moral, or to explain one of the commandments. Even the verse, "And Timna was concubine to Eliphaz, Esau's son," serves a necessary purpose, namely, to differentiate between Amalek, whose destruction is commanded in the Torah, and the other sons of Esau, concerning whom it is said: "Thou shalt not abhor an Edomite, for he is thy brother." So are all other narratives understood by the initiated, and the commentators of our Torah have explained them at length.

As for the law of Jesus, we do not find that Jesus gave a law. He commanded his followers to keep the law of Moses. The Gospels are not a law, but an account of the life of Jesus; and the miracles which they say he performed are similar to those which we find were performed by the prophets, who did not give any law. The moral instruction in the Gospels and the teaching of right conduct are expressed altogether in the form of parables and dark sayings, which is not appropriate for a law. For it is hard to get at the meaning of anything expressed in the form of parable and metaphor. Hence the Torah says plainly in reference to the prophecy of Moses that it was not in the form of dark sayings. For since the Torah was given through him, it was not proper that he should speak in dark sayings, like the prophets of an inferior grade. A statement expressed in the form of a parable or allegory, like the prophecies of Zechariah, has not the perfection it ought to have, for it needs explanation, and may bear many different meanings. This is why Ezekiel complained because his prophetic messages took the form of parables: "Ah, Lord God! they say of me: Is he not a maker of parables"; indicating that this was a defect. And God then spoke to him in plain words. Now it is clear that a law must represent the very highest degree of prophetic message, and for this reason the Bible praises the prophecy of Moses: "With him do I speak mouth to mouth, even manifestly, and not in dark speeches." From this it is clear that any legislative matter expressed in obscure language is defective in respect to its matter, and we come to an opposite conclusion from that of the Christian.

He also said that the Torah is defective in respect of the efficient cause, because it does not describe the attributes of God. But the very opposite is the case. The Torah expressly emphasizes the dogma of the unity and incorporeality, and makes clear that God cannot be apprehended, "For man shall not see Me and live." It also declares that the conception we have of God comes from the qualities shown in His government of His creatures, as He explained to Moses. Moses said to God, "Show me now Thy ways, that I may know Thee, to the end that I may find grace in Thy sight." And God replied that the thirteen attributes with which He governs His creatures are His ways, which man may know more or less, depending upon the ability of the person, but His essential attributes can not be known.

The law of Moses says nothing about trinity because it is not true from the point of view of reason, and the Torah does not inculcate an idea which is not true, such as that one is three and three are one, while remaining separate and distinct, as they say. The statement of the philosophers that God is intellect, intelligent and intelligible, and at the same time one, is a different thing. For they do not believe that there are in Him three different things self-existing, Heaven forbid! They merely say that the one Being may be called by those three names from three different aspects. God Himself is a simple intellect without any composition. But since He is intellect, He must necessarily comprehend, therefore He is intelligent. But He comprehends nothing except Himself, for His perfection can not depend upon another, so that the other should cause Him to pass from potentiality to actuality. Hence, from this point of view, He is always intelligible, and yet His unity is not in any way changed to plurality. But that there should be in Him three distinct things, each one existing by itself, *distintos en personas* as they say, and that they should nevertheless be one, this is impossible, unless two contradictories can be true at the same time, which is opposed to the primary axioms and inconceivable by the mind. For the same reason the Torah rejects corporeality and admonishes us not to believe in it: "Take ye therefore good heed unto yourselves—for ye saw no manner of form . . . lest ye deal corruptly and make you a graven image, even the form of any figure. . . ."

As for his statement that the Torah is defective in respect of its purpose because it does not speak of spiritual happiness, it is not true. There is an allusion which the wise understand, as we shall explain in the Fourth Book with the help of God. The reason this point is not clearly stated and at length is because the Torah was not given to the wise and intelligent only, but to all people, great and small, wise and foolish. It must therefore contain such things as are understandable of all and calculated to inspire belief.

Now those things which can be perceived by everyone with his senses, inspire strong belief, whereas those things which are apprehended by the intellect and cannot be perceived by the senses, being understood by the wise only, do not inspire belief at all. The people say that that which can not be perceived by the senses is improbable and untrue. For this reason the Torah of Moses promised explicitly corporeal rewards, which everyone can see and perceive with his senses, whereas intellectual things, which the intelligent alone understand, are contained by way of illusion. The purpose is that everyone may understand, according to his ability, that through the Torah is obtained all corporeal and spiritual happiness, so long as sin does not prevent. Nay, the corporeal rewards which can not be obtained in the ordinary way of nature are evidence of spiritual rewards.

Balaam also, who was a great sage and a prophet, though not a member of the Israelitish nation, testifies to this. He said: "Let me die the death of the righteous, and let mine end be like his." It seems that through his wisdom or prophetic inspiration he understood that Israel had an end and a hope after death, hence he expressed the desire to have after his death such an end and hope as Israel had. He understood that providence in this world proves happiness in the world to come. And especially when extraordinary miracles take place constantly in the life of a nation, it is proof of their spiritual happiness in the next world. During the whole period of the first temple prophecy existed in Israel continually, and even in the time of the second temple, when there was no prophecy, the people often had their questions answered by a voice from heaven, and there were other miracles taking place constantly, for example, every sixth year the land produced enough for three years, as we read: "I will command My blessing upon you in the sixth year, and it shall bring forth produce for the three years." Also, in accordance with the verse, "Assemble the people, the men, and the women, and the little ones, and thy stranger that is within thy gates . . . ," all Israel went up during the feast of tabernacles of the sabbatical year to Jerusalem to hear the Torah, and the Bible says: "Neither shall any man covet thy land, when thou goest up to appear. . . ." And there were many other miracles constantly in the temple, such as are enumerated in the treatise Abot. In Yoma we are told that a thread of red wool turned white every year on the day of atonement. And there are other miracles told there which took place continually. The Christians have no continuous miracle to prove the truth of their belief.

(c. 1425)

OF RACE SUPERIORITY

by BARUCH SPINOZA

EVERY man's true happiness and blessedness consist solely in the enjoyment of what is good, not in the pride that he alone is enjoying it, to the exclusion of others. He who thinks himself the more blessed because he is enjoying benefits which others are not, or because he is more blessed or more fortunate than his fellows, is ignorant of true happiness and blessedness, and the joy which he feels is either childish or envious and malicious. For instance, a man's true happiness consists only in wisdom, and the knowledge of the truth, not at all in the fact that he is wiser than others, or that others lack such knowledge: such considerations do not increase his wisdom or true happiness.

Whoever, therefore, rejoices for such reasons, rejoices in another's misfortune, and is, so far, malicious and bad, knowing neither true happiness nor the peace of the true life.

When Scripture, therefore, in exhorting the Hebrews to obey the law, says that the Lord has chosen them for Himself before other nations (*Deut.* 10:15); that He is near them, but not near others (*Deut.* 4:7); that to them alone He has given just laws (*Deut.* 4:8); and, lastly, that He has marked them out before others (*Deut.* 4:32); it speaks only according to the understanding of its hearers, who, as we have shown in the last chapter, and as Moses also testified (*Deut.* 4:6, 7), knew not true blessedness. For in good sooth they would have been no less blessed if God had called all men equally to salvation, nor would God have been less present to them for being equally present to others; their laws would have been no less just if they had been ordained for all, and they themselves would have been no less wise. The miracles would have shown God's power no less by being wrought for other nations also; lastly, the Hebrews would have been just as much bound to worship God if He had bestowed all these gifts equally on all men.

When God tells Solomon (*I Kings* 3:12) that no one shall be as wise as he in time to come, it seems to be only a manner of expressing surpassing wisdom; it is little to be believed that God would have promised Solomon, for his greater happiness, that He would never endow anyone with so much wisdom in time to come; this would in no wise have increased Solomon's intellect, and the wise king would have given equal thanks to the Lord if everyone had been gifted with the same faculties.

Still, though we assert that Moses, in the passages of the Pentateuch just cited, spoke only according to the understanding of the Hebrews, we have no wish to deny that God ordained the Mosaic law for them alone, nor that He spoke to them alone, nor that they witnessed marvels beyond those which happened to any other nation; but we wish to emphasize that Moses desired to admonish the Hebrews in such a manner and with such reasonings as would appeal most forcibly to their childish under-standing and constrain them to worship the Deity. Further, we wished to show that the Hebrews did not surpass other nations in knowledge, or in piety, but evidently in some attribute different from these; or (to speak like the Scriptures, according to their understanding), that the Hebrews were not chosen by God before others for the sake of the true life and sublime ideas, though they were often thereto admonished, but with some other object. What that object was I will duly show.

But before I begin, I wish in a few words to explain what I mean by the guidance of God, by the help of God, external and inward, and lastly, what I understand by fortune.

By the help of God, I mean the fixed and unchangeable order of nature or the chain of natural events: for I have said before and shown elsewhere that the universal laws of nature, according to which all things exist and are determined, are only another name for the eternal decrees of God, which always involve eternal truth and necessity.

So that to say that everything happens according to natural laws, and to say that everything is ordained by the decree and ordinance of God, is the same thing. Now since the power in Nature is identical with the power of God, by which alone all things happen and are determined, it follows that whatsoever man, as a part of Nature, provides himself with to aid and preserve his existence, or whatsoever Nature affords him with-out his help, is given to him solely by the Divine power, acting either through human nature or through external circumstance. So whatever human nature can furnish itself with by its own efforts to preserve its existence, may be fitly called the inward aid of God, whereas whatever else accrues to man's profit from outward causes may be called the ex-ternal aid of God.

We can now easily understand what is meant by the election of God. For since no one can do anything save by the predetermined order of Nature, that is by God's eternal ordinance and decree, it follows that no one can choose a plan of life for himself, or accomplish any work save by God's vocation choosing him for the work or the plan of life in question, rather than any other. Lastly, by fortune, I mean the ordinance of God in so far as it directs human life through external and unexpected means. With these preliminaries I return to my purpose of discovering the reason why the Hebrews were said to be elected by God before other nations, and with the demonstration I thus proceed.

All objects of legitimate desire fall, generally speaking, under one of these three categories:

1. The knowledge of things through their primary causes.

2. The government of the passions, or the acquirement of the habit of virtue.

3. Secure and healthy life.

The means which most directly conduce towards the first two of these ends, and which may be considered their proximate and efficient causes are contained in human nature itself, so that their acquisition hinges only on our own power, and on the laws of human nature. It may be concluded that these gifts are not peculiar to any nation, but have always been shared by the whole human race, unless, indeed, we would indulge the dream that Nature formerly created men of different kinds. But the means which conduce to security and health are chiefly in external circumstance, and are called the gifts of fortune because they depend chiefly on objective causes of which we are ignorant; for a fool may be almost as liable to happiness or unhappiness as a wise man. Nevertheless, human management and watchfulness can greatly assist towards living in security and warding off the injuries of our fellow men, and even of beasts. Reason and experience show no more certain means of attaining this object than the formation of a society with fixed laws, the occupation of a strip of territory, and the concentration of all forces, as it were, into one body, that is the social body. Now for forming and preserving a society, no ordinary ability and care is required: that society will be most secure, most stable, and least liable to reverses, which is founded and directed by far-seeing and careful men; while, on the other hand, a society constituted by men without trained skill, depends in a great measure on fortune, and is less constant. If, in spite of all, such a society lasts a long time, it is owing to some other directing influence than its own; if it overcomes great perils and its affairs prosper, it will perforce marvel at and adore the guiding Spirit of God (in so far, that is, as God works through hidden means, and not through the nature and mind of man), for everything happens to it unexpectedly and contrary to anticipation, it may even be said and thought to be by miracle. Nations, then, are distinguished from one another in respect to the social organization and the laws under which they live and are governed; the Hebrew nation was not chosen by

God in respect to its wisdom nor its tranquillity of mind, but in respect to its social organization and the good fortune with which it obtained supremacy and kept it so many years. This is abundantly clear from Scripture. Even a cursory perusal will show us that the only respects in which the Hebrews surpassed other nations, are in their successful conduct of matters relating to government, and in their surmounting great perils solely by God's external aid; in other ways they were on a par with their fellows, and God was equally gracious to all. For in respect to intellect (as we have shown in the last chapter) they held very ordinary ideas about God and Nature, so that they cannot have been God's chosen in this respect; nor were they so chosen in respect of virtue and the true life, for here again they, with the exception of a very few elect, were on an equality with other nations: therefore their choice and vocation consisted only in the temporal happiness and advantages of independent rule. In fact, we do not see that God promised anything beyond this to the patriarchs or their successors; in the law no other reward is offered for obedience than the continual happiness of an independent commonwealth and other goods of this life; while, on the other hand, against contumacy and the breaking of the covenant is threatened the downfall of the commonwealth and great hardships. Nor is this to be wondered at; for the ends of every social organization and commonwealth are (as appears from what we have said, and as we will explain more at length hereafter) security and comfort; a commonwealth can only exist by the laws being binding on all. If all the members of a state wish to disregard the law, by that very fact they dissolve the state and destroy the commonwealth. Thus, the only reward which could be promised to the Hebrews for continued obedience to the law was security and its attendant advantages, while no surer punishment could be threatened for disobedience, than the ruin of the state and the evils which generally follow therefrom, in addition to such further consequences as might accrue to the Jews in particular from the ruin of their especial state. But there is no need here to go into this point at more length. I will only add that the laws of the Old Testament were revealed and ordained to the Jews only, for as God chose them in respect to the special constitution of their society and government, they must, of course, have had special laws. Whether God ordained special laws for other nations also, and revealed Himself to their lawgivers prophetically, that is, under the attributes by which the latter were accustomed to imagine Him, I cannot sufficiently determine. It is evident from Scripture itself that other nations acquired supremacy and particular laws by the external aid of God.

If anyone wishes to maintain that the Jews . . . have been chosen by God for ever, I will not gainsay him if he will admit that this choice, whether temporary or eternal, has no regard, in so far as it is peculiar to the Jews, to aught but dominion and physical advantages (for by such alone can one nation be distinguished from another), whereas in regard to intellect and true virtue, every nation is on a par with the rest, and God has not in these respects chosen one people rather than another.

(1670)

ATTICISM AND JUDAISM

by SAMUEL DAVID LUZZATTO

THE civilization of the world today is a product of two dissimilar elements: Atticism and Judaism. To Athens we owe philosophy, the arts, the sciences, the development of the intellect, order, love of beauty and grandeur, intellectual and studied morality. To Judaism we owe religion, the morality which springs from the heart and from selflessness, and love of good. Atticism is progressive, for the intellect is capable of continuous development and of new discoveries. Judaism is stationary, its teachings are immutable. The heart is capable of corruption, but not of further perfection. goodness is inborn, wickedness acquired. Judaism may rid itself of some addition alien to it; it may restore itself to its primordial condition; but it cannot be perfected. Atticism, being progressive, takes on constantly new forms, through which it pleases, charms and attracts. Judaism, immutable, appears older and uglier every day; consequently, it bores, displeases, repels. Hence the apparent dominance and triumph of the former over the latter.

Yet there is in human nature an inextinguishable need for the good. Beauty and grandeur cannot take the place of good. Society needs emotion; but intellect and Atticism, far from inspiring emotion, weaken it and snuff it out. This is why human nature reacts—and always will react—in favor of the heart, of good, of Judaism.

If ever Atticism should suffer defeat, human nature would likewise rally to its defense, for intellectual development is included among its needs. Then Atticism may conquer anew; but never shall it enjoy a lasting preponderance unclouded by opposition and reaction.

As a result, the course of civilization is necessarily periodic, and not steadily progressive. There is no point at which it may halt. A state of repose is inconceivable without a perfect conciliation of the two elements; and this could not take place without great sacrifice on the part of the progressive element, which would have to subject its onward march to very considerable and useless restraint. The stationary element is, by virtue of its essential immutability, incapable of sacrifice.

It might, of course, shake off those of its components which are distinct from morality. That is to say, it might renounce its quality as supernatural revelation and dispense with all its theological and historical portions; or it might, while preserving its divinity, divest itself of all or of some of the ceremonies unconnected with morality. But in either case it would lose if not all, at least a large part of its influence, over the human heart—an influence which it owes entirely to faith in its divine origin and its changelessness. Moreover, all such sacrifices notwithstanding, the conflict between Judaism and Atticism would never cease, because of the essentially progressive nature of the second as opposed to the anti-progressive character of the first.

(c. 1850)

CIVIL AND RELIGIOUS AUTONOMY [1]

by MOSES MENDELSSOHN

Autonomy, granted to a minority, pertains either to civil or ecclesiastical affairs. The former concerns merely the social relations amongst the members of the minority. There everything depends on agreements. The rights to property, and whatsoever is connected therewith, are alienable rights, which may be yielded and assigned to others by voluntary determination and agreement. When this is done on the required conditions, they instantly become the property of him to whom they have been yielded and he cannot dispose of them without injustice. There, everything may be left to the agreements and covenants of the group. If they think it preferable to have the litigations of their mem-

---

[1] In a book entitled *On the Civil Emancipation of the Jews*, Christian Wilhelm Dohm (a friend of Mendelssohn's), proposed complete emancipation and minority rights or autonomy for the Jews. Mendelssohn dealt with the proposal in a preface to a German edition of Menasseh ben Israel's *The Plea for the Jews*, from which the above passage is selected.

bers decided by their own laws, according to their own forms, the State evidently may indulge them in it, without any prejudice to itself. Now, as Mr. Dohm very justly observes, "Since the Jews consider as divine commandments also those written laws of Moses which bear no reference to Judea or to the ancient juridical and ritual system, as well as the deductions from, and elucidations and interpretations of, the same, either received by oral tradition, or got at by logical growth, they may be allowed to bind their members amongst themselves by a voluntary covenant, to have their disputes judged and decided by their own laws."

"Are those decisions to be given by Jewish or by Christian judges?" My reply is: "By the civil judges, whether they follow the Jewish or any other religion." When the members of the State, whatever their opinions may be on theological questions, equally enjoy the rights of man, that difference cannot form the least consideration. The judge is to be a conscientious man, and to understand fully the laws by which he administers justice to his fellowmen, let him think of theological subjects according to what doctrine he pleases. If the government deem him fit for the judicial office, and appoint him to it, his legal decisions must stand. Do we not place our health, our life, in the hands of a physician, without any regard to difference of religion? Why then not equally our property in those of a judge? A conscientious physician who values his profession will treat today, after all its rules, the very malefactor who is to be executed tomorrow, and seek to cure him of his complaint. So will a judge, if he have the feelings of a man, bestow justice on all parties in respect to the interests of this life, whether, according to his own principles, they will be saved or damned in the next. A Göttingen reviewer, indeed, thinks that the Jews would have no confidence in a Christian judge's knowledge of their laws. Mr. Dohm, however, is justified by, and can produce the evidence of, learned Christians, who not only suppose the contrary, but declare themselves to have frequently experienced it. And if any distrust of that sort had really prevailed, would it not have been natural since hitherto the learned amongst the Christians so little concerned themselves about our jurisprudence?

But how is it to be in ecclesiastical matters, in things which relate to the religion of the minority? What is the extent of the jurisdiction of every minority in religious matters, and that of the Jewish in particular, over its members? What authority may it exert, what degree of force may it use, to compel its members to preserve purity of doctrine and life? How far may it stretch forth its ecclesiastical arm, to correct or expel the refractory, and put the stray and deviating again into the right track?

"Ecclesiastical jurisdiction," "ecclesiastical authority and power!" I must confess that these phrases are unintelligible to me. I know of no rights over either persons or things, which can possibly have any connection with, or dependence on doctrines, or no rights which men acquire when they concur in certain propositions relative to immutable truths, or forfeit when they cannot or will not concur in them; and still less do I know of any right and power over opinions that are supposed to be conferred by religion and to belong to the church. True divine religion arrogates no dominion over thought and opinion; it neither gives nor takes away any claim to earthly goods, any right to fruits, domain, or property; it knows of no other force than that of winning by argument, or convincing and rendering blessed by conviction. True divine religion needs neither arms nor fingers for its use; it is all spirit and heart.

By "right" is meant the quality of doing or forbearing, the moral faculty of acting; namely, a voluntary act is just and moral when it is consistent with the rules of wisdom and goodness, and that by which this consistency is acknowledged to exist, is called a right. Now let me turn this idea whichever side I will, I cannot discover in it any reference to dogmas and opinions that relate to immutable truths. How can my assenting, or not assenting to general propositions extend or restrict that quality, give me, or deprive me of, a moral dominion over persons and things, over their use and fruits? In which way does a *modus acquirendi* (another quality to appropriate to ourselves certain things, as means of our happiness, and use them at our will and pleasure) arise out of an opinion, or yet out of the system of all opinions together? What common characteristic have those two disparities, right and opinion, that they can ever come together, and be brought in connection, in any proposition? But if the laws of nature and of reason admit a right, founded on the receiving or rejecting of an opinion, inevitably there must be a way of uniting those two ideas in a proposition, and of clearly showing, from the approbation which I give or refuse to a doctrine, why this or that indication of my industry is or is not due to me; why, according to the immutable laws of wisdom and goodness, a certain use and enjoyment of the goods of this world are or are not granted me. I must confess, I do not see the possibility of the union.

But mankind may, perhaps, render such a union possible by positive laws and covenants, or they may, by expressed or tacit agreement, mutually assume rights supposed to be founded on doctrine and opinion. And although such a thing be unknown in the state of nature, may not the state of society, the social compact, introduce such a regulation, or actually, have introduced it? Have not covenants wrought so many changes in human nature, and in the system of its offices and rights? Why might they not also originate rights, which were not to be found in nature?

By no means, I think. As little as cultivation is able to develop a fruit of which nature has not furnished the germ; as little as art, by practice and perseverance, can bring forth a spontaneous motion, where nature has not placed a muscle; just as little can all the covenants and agreements of mankind create a right, of which the foundation is not to be met with in nature. By covenants merely imperfect rights may be changed to perfect, indeterminate duties to determinate ones. What I am bound to perform to the human race at large may, by a covenant, be limited to a certain person, and thereby the indeterminate internal duty to mankind be transformed into a determinate external duty to that person. This same person, who had before only an imperfect right to expect of the human race, or of nature generally, a certain contribution towards his happiness, acquires by the covenant, a perfect external right to demand that contribution of me, or of my substance, and to enforce it. But as, in a state of nature, all positive duties of man to each other, all obligations to act or perform, are mere imperfect duties and obligations, many of them may, and must be determined, further limited, and transformed into perfect ones, in society. But where, without a covenant, neither duties nor rights can be imagined, all the covenants between men, all their understandings, are empty sounds and nothing else, words spent in the air without force or consequence. Therefore I do not see how the quality of attaching prerogatives to opinions, a quality utterly alien to nature, can belong to human society.

And, moreover, a jurisdiction over opinions, over our fellow-men's views of immutable and necessary truths! What man, what society of men dare to arrogate it? As those opinions do not immediately depend on our will, the only right that belongs to us ourselves, is the right of examining them, or putting them to the rigid test of reason, and suspending our judgment until it has decided, and so on.

But that right is inseparable from the person, and, from its nature, can as little be alienated, parted with or made over to others, as the right of appeasing our hunger or the liberty of breathing. Covenants about it are absurd, contrary to the nature and essence of actions, and therefore without any consequence or effect. We may bind ourselves by covenants not to let certain voluntary acts depend upon our own judgment and determination, but to submit them to another's man's opinion and thereby renounce in our own judgment, as far as it may pass into an act, and be attended with consequences. But our judgment itself is an inseparable, immovable, and accordingly, an inalienable property. That distinction, however nice it may seem, is of the utmost importance here, if we would not confound ideas, and involve ourselves in absurd conclusions and discrepancies. Foregoing one's opinion so as not to act thereon, is one thing; giving up one's opinion, another. Acting rests immediately with our will and pleasure; opinion does not. Thus the mother nation itself is not qualified to attach the enjoyment of any worldly good or privilege to a doctrine particularly pleasing to it, or to reward or punish the adopting or rejecting thereof. How can it concede to a minority that which is not in its own power?

I can scarcely conceive how a writer of Mr. Dohm's great judgment could say: "As all other religious societies have a right of expelling members, either for a limited time or for ever, the Jewish religion should have it too; and, in case of resistance of the rabbi's sentence, it should be supported by the civil authorities." All societies have a right of expelling members; only religious ones have not. For it runs diametrically contrary to their principle and object, which is joint edification and participation in the outpouring of the heart, by which we evince our thankfulness to God for the many bounties he bestows on us, and our filial trust in his sovereign goodness and mercy. Then, with what conscience can we deny entrance to dissenters, separatists, misbelievers or sectarians, and deprive them of the benefit of that edification? For rioters and disturbers there is the law and the police. Disorders of that kind may, nay must, be restrained by the secular arm. But a quiet and inoffensive attendance at the meeting may not be forbidden even to an offender, unless we purposely want to bar to him every road to reformation. The doors of the house or rational devotion require neither bars nor bolts. There is nothing locked up within, and, therefore, no occasion to be particular in admitting from without. Whoever chooses to be a tranquil spectator, or even to join in the worship, has the right of every pious man, at the hour of his own devotions.

I do not find that the wisest of our forefathers ever did pretend to any such right as excluding individuals from religious exercises.

When King Solomon had finished the building of the temple, he included in his sublime dedication prayer even strangers, a class in his days synonymous with idolators. He spread forth his hands towards heaven, saying: "Moreover concerning a stranger that is not of thy people Israel, but cometh out of a far country for thy name's sake (for they shall hear of thy strong hand, and of thy stretched-out arm), when he shall come and pray toward this house; hear thou in heaven thy dwelling-place, and do according to all that the stranger calleth to thee for: that all people of the earth may know thy name, as do thy people Israel; and that they may know that this house which I have builded, is called by Thy name." In the same manner our rabbis directed the voluntary gifts, and votive offerings of idolators to be accepted in the temple, and not to turn away the sacrifice of even an offender belonging to the nation itself, as long as he had not positively abjured his religion, in order, they said, that he may have an opportunity and inducement to amend. So they thought at a period when they had a little more power and authority to be exclusive in religious matters. Yet shall we presume to shut out dissenters from our barely tolerated religious meetings?

I shall forbear speaking of the danger there is in entrusting anyone with the power of excommunication, with the abuse inseparable from the right of anathema, as indeed with every other form of church discipline or ecclesiastical power. Alas! it will require ages yet, before the human race shall have recovered from the blows which those monsters inflicted on it. I can imagine no possibility of bridling false religious zeal as long as it sees that road open before it; for a spur will never be wanting. Mr. Dohm fancies he is offering us an ample guarantee from all the like abuses by taking for granted that the right of anathema, entrusted to the minority, "will never reach beyond religious society, and have no effect at all on the civil; and this, because an expelled member of any church whatsoever may be a very valuable and estimable citizen notwithstanding: a principle in universal ecclesiastical law," he continues, "which should be no longer questioned in our days."

But if universal ecclesiastical law, as it is called, at last acknowledges the important principle, in which I concur with all my heart, "that an expelled member of any and every church, may be a very useful and respected citizen notwithstanding," the evil is far from being remedied by that weak reservation. For, in the first place, this very estimable and useful citizen, who, perhaps, is also internally a very religious man, may not like to be debarred from all meetings for worship, from all religious solemnities, and may not like to be entirely without the formalities of religion. Now, if he have the misfortune to be thought a dissenter by the congregation he belongs to, and his conscience forbids him to join any other religious group established or tolerated in the state, must not this very useful and estimable citizen be exceedingly unhappy when his own congregation is allowed to exclude him, and he finds the doors of their religious assemblies shut against him? And it is possible, that he may find them so everywhere; for every religious community would perhaps turn him away by the same right. But how can the state allow any one of its useful and estimable citizens to be made unhappy by the laws? Secondly, what church excommunication, what anathema is entirely without secular consequences, without any influence whatever on, at least, the civil respectability, on the fair reputation of the excommunicated, on the confidence of his fellow-citizens, without which no one can exercise his calling and be useful to the state? As the boundary laws of this nice distinction between the civil and the ecclesiastical are barely perceptible to the keenest eye, it becomes truly impossible to draw them so firmly and precisely, in any state, as to make them obvious to every citizen, and cause them to have the desired effect in common civil life. They will ever remain dubious and undefined, and very frequently expose innocence itself to the sting of persecution and blind religious zeal.

To introduce church discipline and yet not impair civil happiness, seems to me a problem, which yet remains for politics to solve. It is the answer of the Most High Judge to Satan: "He is in thine hand but save his life," or, as the commentators add: "Demolish the cask, but let not the wine run out."

I shall not enquire how the complaints, of late publicly made, about abuses of that kind, which a certain eminent rabbi thought proper to commit, are or are not founded. The statement being *ex parte,* I am willing to believe that many circumstances have been exaggerated; that, on the one hand, the guilt of the accused has been softened down, the same as, on the other hand, the harshness of the proceedings was studiously overrated. The case, it is reported, has been laid before the regular authorities, who will investigate it, and do the parties justice. However, let the affair terminate as it may, I wish the particulars, as they figure in the protocols, may be published, to make either the over-hasty rabbi or his open accusers ashamed of their conduct.

But be this as it may, brotherly love has not yet made that progress amongst men, that we may disregard all fear and apprehension of this kind from the introduction of church discipline. As yet there is not a clergy sufficiently enlightened, that such a right (if it exist at all) may be entrusted to them without any harm. Nay, the more enlightened they are, the less they will trust themselves in this; the more reluctant they will be, to take in their hands an avenging sword, which madness only thinks it can manage surely. I have that confidence in the more enlightened amongst the rabbis and elders of my nation, that they will be glad to relinquish so pernicious a prerogative, that they will cheerfully do away with all church and synagogue discipline, and let their flock enjoy, at their hands, even that kindness and forbearance, which they themselves have been so long panting for. Ah, my brethren, you have hitherto felt too hard the yoke of intolerance, and perhaps thought it a sort of satisfaction, if the power of bending those under you to such another yoke were allowed to you. Revenge will be seeking an object; and if it cannot wreak itself on strangers, it even tortures its own flesh and blood. Perhaps, too, you let yourselves be seduced by the general example. All the nations of the earth, hitherto, appear to have been infatuated by the error, that religion can be maintained by iron force, doctrines of blessedness inculcated by unblest persecution, and true notions of God, who, as we all acknowledge, is love itself, communicated by the workings of hatred and ill-will only. You, perhaps, let yourselves be persuaded to adopt the very same system; and the power of persecuting was to you the most important prerogative which your own persecutors could bestow upon you. Thank the God of your forefathers, thank the God who is all love and mercy, that that error appears to be gradually vanishing. The nations are now tolerating and bearing with one another, while to you also they are showing kindness and forbearance, which, with the help of Him who disposes the hearts of men, may grow to true brotherly love. Oh, my brethren, follow the example of love, the same as you have hitherto followed that of hatred. Imitate the virtues of the nations whose vices you hitherto thought you must imitate. If you would be protected, tolerated and indulged, protect, tolerate and indulge one another. Love and ye will be beloved.

(1783)

EMANCIPATION AND JUDAISM

by SAMSON RAPHAEL HIRSCH

Is emancipation in harmony with the spirit of Judaism?

When Israel began its great wandering through the ages and nations, Jeremiah proclaimed the following as its duty: "Build houses and dwell therein; plant gardens and eat the fruit thereof; take wives unto yourselves, and beget sons and daughters, and take wives for your sons and give your daughters in marriage that they bear sons and daughters, and that you multiply there and diminish not. And seek the peace of the city whither I have exiled you, and pray for it to the Lord, for in its peace there will be unto you peace."

To be trodden upon and restricted is, therefore, not an essential condition of the *galuth,* Israel's exiled state among the nations; on the contrary, it is our duty to join ourselves as closely as possibly to the state which receives us into its midst, to promote its welfare and not to consider our well-being as in any way separate from that of the state of which we are citizens. This close connection with all states is in nowise in contradiction to the spirit of Judaism. The former independent state of Israel was not even then the essence or purpose of our national existence. It was only a means of fulfilling our spiritual mission.

Land and soil were never Israel's bond of union, but only the common task of the Torah. Therefore it still forms a united body, though separated from a national soil; nor does this unity lose its reality, though Israel accept everywhere the citizenship of the nations amongst which it is dispersed. This coherence of sympathy, this spiritual union, which may be designated by the Hebrew terms *am* and *goy* but not by the expression "nation" (unless one can separate from the term the concept of common territory and political power), is the only communal bond we possess, or ever expect to possess, until the great day shall arrive when the Almighty shall see fit, in His inscrutable wisdom, to unite again His scattered servants in one land, and the Torah shall be the guiding principle of a state, an exemplar of the meaning of divine revelation and the mission of humanity.

For this future, which is promised us in the glorious predictions of the inspired prophets, whom God raised up for our ancestors, we hope and pray; but actively to accelerate its coming were sin, and is prohibited to us. The entire purpose of the messianic age is that we may, in prosperity, exhibit to mankind a better example of "Israel" than did our ancestors the first time; hand in hand with us, the entire race will be joined in universal brotherhood through the recognition of God, the All-One.

Because of the spiritual nature of the national character of Israel it is capable of the complete identification with states, with this difference: while others seek in the state only the material benefits which it secures, considering possession and enjoyment as the highest good, Israel can only regard it as a means of fulfilling the mission of humanity.

Summon up, I pray you, the picture of such an Israel, dwelling in freedom in the midst of the nations, and striving to attain unto its ideal, every son of Israel a respected and influential exemplar priest of righteousness and love, disseminating among the nations not specific Judaism, for proselytism is interdicted, but pure humanity. What a mighty impulse to progress, what a luminary and staff in the gloomy days of the Middle Ages, had not Israel's sin and the insanity of the nations rendered such a *galuth* impossible! How impressive, how sublime it would have been, if, in the midst of a race that adored only power, possessions, and enjoyment, and that was oft blinded by superstitious imaginings, there had lived quietly and publicly human beings of a different sort, who beheld in material possessions only the means of practising justice and love towards all; whose minds, pervaded with the wisdom and truth of the law, maintained simple, straightforward views, and emphasized them for themselves and others in expressive, vivid deed-symbols. But it would seem as though Israel was to be prepared by the endurance of harsh and cruel exile for the proper appreciation and utilization of its milder and gentler form.

When the *galuth* will be comprehended and accepted as it should be, when in suffering, the service of God and His Torah will be understood as the only task of life, when even in misery God will be served, and external abundance regarded as only a means of this service, then, perhaps, Israel will be ready for the greater temptations of prosperity and happiness in dispersion. Just as it is our duty to endeavor to obtain those material possessions which are the fundamental condition of life, so also is it the duty of everyone to take advantage of every alleviation and improvement of his condition open to him in a righteous way. For th, more means, the more opportunity is given to him to fulfill his mission in its broadest sense; and no less than of the individual is it the duty of the community to obtain for all its members the opportunities and privileges of citizenship and liberty. Do I consider it desirable? I bless emancipation, when I see how the excess of oppression drove Israel away from human intercourse, prevented the cultivation of the mind, limited the free development of the noble elements of character, and compelled many individuals to enter, for the sake of self-support, upon paths which men, filled with the true spirit of Judaism, would have shunned even in the extremest necessity, but the temptation to enter upon which they were too weak to withstand.

I bless emancipation when I notice that no spiritual principle, even such as are born of superstitious self-deception, stands in its way, but only those passions degrading to humanity, lust for gain and narrow selfishness. I rejoice when I perceive in emancipation regard for the inalienable right of men to live as equals among equals, and the principle that whosoever bears the seal of a child of God, unto whom belongs the earth, shall be willingly acknowledged without force or compulsion, but purely through the power of their inner truth. I welcome this as the dawn of reviving humanity in mankind, as a preliminary step to the universal recognition of God as the only Lord and Father, of all human beings as the children of the All-One, and consequently brethren, and of the earth as soil common to all, and bestowed upon them by God to be administered in accordance with His will. But for Israel I only bless it if at the same time there awakens in Israel the true spirit, which, independent of emancipation or nonemancipation, strives to fulfill the Israel-mission; to elevate and ennoble ourselves, to implant the spirit of Judaism in our souls, in order that it may produce a life in which that spirit shall be reflected and realized. I bless it, if Israel does not regard emancipation as the goal of its task, but only as a new condition of its mission, and as a new trial, much severer than the trial of oppression; but I should grieve if Israel understood itself so little, and has so little comprehension of its own spirit that it would welcome emancipation as the end of the *galuth,* and the highest goal of its historic mission. If Israel regards this glorious concession merely as a means of securing a greater degree of comfort in life and greater opportunities for the acquisition of wealth and enjoyments, it would indicate that Israel had not comprehended the spirit of its own Law, nor learnt aught from the *galuth.* But sorrowfully, indeed, would I mourn, if Israel should so far forget itself as to regard emancipation as larger opportunity for the acquisition of profit and pleasure through freedom from unjust oppression, and as not too dearly purchased through capricious curtailment of the Torah, capricious abandonment of the chief element of our vitality. We must become Jews, Jews in the true sense of the word, permitting the spirit of the Law to pervade our entire being, accepting it as the fountain of spiritual and ethical life. Then will Judaism gladly welcome emancipation as affording a greater opportunity for the fulfillment of its task, the realization of a noble and ideal life.

(1836)

THE EMANCIPATION OF THE JEW

by KARL MARX

WE will try to dispose of the theological conception of the Jewish question. The question of the capacity of the Jews for emancipation is from our standpoint transformed into the question, what particular social element has to be overcome in order to abolish Judaism? For the capacity for emancipation of the modern Jew is the relation of Judaism to the emancipation of the modern world. This relation is necessarily disclosed by the special position of Judaism in the modern subjugated world.

Let us consider the real worldly Jews, not the Sabbath Jews, as Bauer does, but the every-day Jews.

We will not look for the secret of the Jew in his religion, but we will look for the secret of religion in the real Jew.

What is the secular basis of Judaism? Practical needs, egoism.

What is the secular cult of the Jew? Huckstering. What is his secular God? Money.

Very well. Emancipation from huckstering and from money, and therefore from practical, real Judaism would be the self-emancipation of our epoch.

An organization of society, which would abolish the fundamental conditions of huckstering, and therefore the possibility of huckstering, would render the Jew impossible. His religious consciousness would dissolve like a mist in the real vital air of society. On the other hand: if the Jew recognizes as valueless this his practical essence, and labours for its abolition, he would work himself free of his previous development, and labour for human emancipation generally, turning against the supreme practical expression of human self-alienation.

We therefore perceive in Judaism a general pervading anti-social element, which has been carried to its highest point by the historical development, in which Jews in this bad relation have zealously co-operated, a point at which it must necessarily dissolve itself.

The emancipation of the Jews in its last significance is the emancipation of mankind from Judaism.

The Jew has already emancipated himself in Jewish fashion. "The Jew who in Vienna, for example, is only tolerated, determines by his financial power the fate of the whole Empire. The Jew who may be deprived of rights in the smallest German State, determines the fate of Europe."

"While the corporations and guilds excluded the Jew, the enterprise of industry laughs at the obstinacy of the medieval institution." (Bauer, "The Jewish Question," p. 14.)

This is no isolated fact. The Jew has emancipated himself in Jewish fashion, not only by taking to himself financial power, but by virtue of the fact that with and without his co-operation, money has become a world power, and the practical Jewish spirit has become the practical spirit of Christian nations. The Jews have emancipated themselves in so far as Christians have become Jews.

"The pious and politically free inhabitant of New England," relates Colonel Hamilton, "is a kind of Laokoon, who does not make even the slightest effort to free himself from the serpents which are throttling him. Mammon is his god, he prays to him, not merely with his lips, but with all the force of his body and mind.

"In his eyes, the world is nothing more than a Stock Exchange, and he is convinced that here below he has no other destiny than to become richer than his neighbours. When he travels, he carries his shop or his counter on his back, so to speak, and talks of nothing but interest and profit."

The practical domination of Judaism over the Christian world has reached such a point in North America that the preaching of the Gospel itself, the Christian ministry, has become an article of commerce, and the bankrupt merchant takes to the Gospel, while the minister grown rich goes into business.

"He whom you see at the head of a respectable congregation began as a merchant; his business failing, he became a minister. The other started his career in the ministry, but as soon as he had saved a sum of money, he abandoned the pulpit for the counter. In the eyes of a large number, the ministry is a commercial career." (Beaumont.)

According to Bauer, to withhold political rights from the Jew in theory, while in practice he wields enormous power, exercising wholesale the influence he is forbidden to distribute in retail, is an anomaly.

The contradiction between the practical, political power of the Jew and his political rights is the contradiction between politics and financial power generally. While the former is raised ideally above the latter, it has in reality become its bond slave.

Judaism has persisted alongside of Christianity not only as religious criticism of Christianity, not only as the embodiment of doubt in the religious parentage of Christianity, but equally because Judaism has maintained itself, and even received its supreme development, in Christian society. The Jew who exists as a peculiar member of bourgeois society, is only the particular expression of the Judaism of bourgeois society.

Judaism has survived not in spite of, but by virtue of history.

Out of its own entrails, bourgeois society continually creates Jews.

What was the foundation of the Jewish religion? Practical needs, egoism. Consequently the monotheism of the Jew is in reality the polytheism of many needs. Practical needs or egoism are the principle of bourgeois society, and they appear openly as such so soon as bourgeois society gives birth to the political state. The God of practical needs and egoism is money.

Money is the jealous God of Israel, by the side of which no other god may exist. Money degrades all the gods of man and converts them into commodities. Money is the general and self-constituted value of all things. Consequently it has robbed the whole world—the world of mankind as well as Nature—of its peculiar value. Money is the being of man's work and existence alienated from himself, and this alien being rules him and he prays to it.

The God of the Jews has secularized himself and become the universal God. Exchange is the Jew's real God.

The conception of Nature which prevails under the rule of private property and of money is the practical degradation of Nature, which indeed exists in the Jewish religion, but only in imagination.

In this sense Thomas Münzer declared it to be intolerable "that all creatures have been turned into property, the fishes in the water, the birds in the air, the growths of the soil."

What remains as the abstract part of the Jewish religion, contempt for theory, for art, for history, for man as an end in himself, is the real conscious standpoint and virtue of the monied man. The generic relation itself—the relation of man to woman, etc., becomes an object of commerce. Woman is bartered.

The chimerical nationality of the Jew is the nationality of the merchant, of the monied man generally.

The baseless law of the Jew is only the religious caricature of the baseless morality and of right generally, of the merely formal ceremonies which pervade the world of egoism.

Here also the highest relation of man is the legal relation—the relation to laws which do not govern him because they are the laws of his own will and being, but because they are imposed on him from without. Any infraction thereof is punished.

Jewish Jesuitism, the same practical Jesuitism that Bauer infers from the Talmud, is the relation of the world of egoism to the laws which dominate it, and the cunning circumvention of which is the supreme art of this world.

The movement of this work within its laws is necessarily a continual abrogation of the law.

Judaism cannot develop any further as a religion, that is theoretically, because the philosophy of practical needs is limited by its nature and is exhausted in a few moves.

Judaism could create no new world; it could only draw the new world creations and world relations within the orbit of its activity, because the practical need whose rationale is egoism remains a passive state, which does not extend itself by spontaneous act, but only expands with the development of social conditions.

Judaism reaches its acme with the completion of bourgeois society, but bourgeois society first completes itself in the Christian world. Only under the reign of Christianity, which turns all national, natural, moral and theoretical relations into relations external to man, can bourgeois society separate itself entirely from the political life, dissever all the generic ties, and dissolve the human world into a world of atomized, mutually hostile individuals.

Christianity sprang out of Judaism. It has again withdrawn into Judaism.

The Christian from the outset was the theorizing Jew; the Jew is therefore the practical Christian, and the practical Christian has again become a Jew.

Christianity had only appeared to overcome Judaism. It was too noble, too spiritual to abolish the crudeness of practical needs except by elevation into the blue sky.

Christianity is the sublime idea of Judaism. Judaism is the common application of Christianity, but this application could only become general after Christianity had completed the alienation of man from himself, and theoretically from Nature. Not until then could Judaism attain to general domination and turn the alienated individual and alienated Nature into alienable and saleable objects.

Just as the individual while he remained in the toils of religion could only objectivize his being by turning it into a fantastic and alien being, so under the domination of egoistic needs he can only manifest himself in a practical way and only create practical objects by placing both his products and his activity under the domination of an alien being, and investing them with the significance of an alien being—of money.

The Christian selfishness of bliss is necessarily transmuted in its completed practice into the material selfishness of the Jew, heavenly needs become earthly needs, and subjectivity becomes egoism. We do not explain the Jew's tenacity from his religion, but rather from the human basis of his religion, that is, practical needs, egoism.

Because the real essence of the Jew has been generally realized and secularized in bourgeois society, the latter could not convince the Jew of the unreality of his religious essence, which is merely the ideal reflexion of his practical needs.

Consequently, it is not only in the Pentateuch or the Talmud, but also in present-day society that we find the essence of the modern Jew, not as an abstract, but as an extremely empirical being, not merely in the form of the Jew's limitations, but in that of the Jewish limitations of society.

As soon as society succeeds in abolishing the empirical essence of Judaism, the huckster, and the conditions which produce him, the Jew will become impossible, because his consciousness will no longer have a corresponding object, because the subjective basis of Judaism, viz.: practical needs, will have been humanized, because the conflict of the individual sensual existence with the generic existence of the individual will have been abolished.

The social emancipation of the Jew is the emancipation of society from Judaism.

(1844)

JUDAISM AND NATIONALITY

by MOSES HESS

AMONG the nations believed to be dead and which, when they become conscious of their historic mission, will struggle for their national rights, is also Israel. For two thousand years it has defied the storms of time, and in spite of having been tossed by the currents of history to every part of the globe, has always cast yearning glances toward Jerusalem and is still directing its gaze thither. Fortified by its racial instinct and by its cultural and historical mission to unite all humanity in the name of the Eternal Creator, this people has conserved its nationality, in the form of its religion and united both inseparably with the memories of its ancestral land. No modern people, struggling for its own fatherland, can deny the right of the Jewish people to its former land, without at the same time undermining the justice of its own strivings. . . . The voices that are heard from various parts of the world, demanding the national regeneration of Israel, find justification, first of all, in the Jewish religion, in the national character of Judaism, and, even more, in the general process of development of humanity and its obvious results, and finally, in the present situation of human life.

We are on the eve of the Sabbath of history and should prepare for our last mission through a thorough understanding of our historical religion.

We cannot understand a single word of the Holy Scriptures as long as we do not possess the point of view of the genius of the Jewish nation which produced these writings. Nothing is more foreign to the spirit of Judaism than the idea of the salvation of the individual which, according to the modern conception, is the corner-stone of religion. Judaism has never drawn any line of separation between the individual and the family, the family and the nation, the nation and humanity as a whole, humanity and the cosmos, creation and the Creator. Judaism has no other dogma but the teaching of the Unity. But this dogma is for Judaism not a mere fossilized and therefore barren belief, but a living, continually recreating principle of knowledge. Judaism is rooted in the love of the family; patriotism and nationalism are the flowers of its spirit, and the coming regenerated state of human society will be its ripe fruit. Judaism might have shared the fate of other religions which were fossilized through their dogmas, and which will finally disappear through the conflict with science, had it not been for the fact that its religious teachings are the product of life. Judaism is not a passive religion, but an active life factor, which has coalesced with the national consciousness into one organic whole. It is primarily the expression of a nationality whose history, for thousands of years, coincides with the history of the development of humanity; and the Jews are a nation which, having once acted as the leaven of the social world, is destined to be resurrected with the rest of civilized nations.

In Eastern and Central Europe there live millions of our brethren who earnestly believe in the restoration of the Jewish kingdom and pray for it fervently in their daily services. These Jews have preserved, by their belief in Jewish nationality, the very kernel of Judaism in a more faithful manner than have our Occidental Jews. The latter have endeavored to revive much of our religion, but not the great hope which created our faith and preserved it through all storms of time, namely, the hope of the restoration of Jewish nationality. To those millions of my brethren I turn and exclaim, "Carry thy standard high, oh my people!" The Jewish nation still preserves the fruitful seed of life, which, like the grains of corn found in the graves of Egyptian mummies, though buried for thousands of years, have never lost their power of productivity. The moment the rigid form in which it is enclosed is shattered, the seed, placed in the fertile soil of the present environment and given air and light, will strike root and prosper.

The rigid forms of orthodoxy, the existence of which was justified before the century of rebirth, will naturally, through the productive power of the national idea and the historical cult, relax and become fertile. It is only with the national rebirth that the religious genius of the Jews, like the giant of legend touching mother earth, will be endowed with new strength and again be reinspired with the prophetic spirit. No aspirant for enlightenment, not even a Mendelssohn, has so far succeeded in crushing the hard shell with which Rabbinism has encrusted Judaism without, at the same time, destroying the national ideal in its innermost essence.

The Greeks had sanctified and worshiped nature in their religious cult only in its finished and harmonious form, but not in its creative and becoming aspect. Man also had been deified in the Grecian world only as a complete organization, as a being who stands at the height of organic life, but not as the representative of a new life sphere; not as a moral and social being, who is to be looked upon as in the midst of becoming and developing, as is the case with Christianity, the descendant of the historical religion of Judaism. The Jews, on the other hand, had turned the tables, deifying *the becoming;* worshiping the God whose very name expresses past, present and future. Even the cosmic and organic life spheres, which are already completed in this universal epoch, are not considered by the Bible as eternal and unchangeable, but viewed from the creative standpoint. The Bible begins with the creation of the world and the declaration of the natural Sabbath, but the prophets have gone further and completed the process, embracing as they did the entire history of human development and foreseeing the final historical Sabbath. The tendency to view God in history, not only in the history of humanity, but also in the history of the cosmic and organic world, is an essential expression of the Jewish spirit. This striving after the recognition of God is developed in historical studies, through observation of historical facts; but in nature-study, it posits a certain mental direction as a starting-point, one that is wholly unknown to modern scientists. Goethe and Humboldt were utterly opposed to the tendency of spiritualizing nature, which is so closely united with the Jewish God-idea.

The Greeks sanctified the wholeness of nature, including man as a complete product; the Jews sanctified the wholeness of history, including that of the organic and cosmic life; and the Christian deified and sanctified the individual. Individuality had thus found its complete expression through Christian apotheosis. Such a view does man both justice and injustice; for in order to delineate the rights of the individual, man must be conceived abstractly and not as he really exists, united with nature and history, family and country. The fall of the ancient world and the entry of the Germanic race upon the arena of history have brought about both the strengthening of individuality and its one-sidedness, which today is undermining individuality, but true personality will rise again when individualism will be united with other higher tendencies. The realization of this higher unity can be made possible only by viewing the Jewish historical religion in a scientific manner. The religion which will be raised to a science is none other than the Bible religion, which preaches the genesis and the unity of cosmic, organic and social life, and to the development and dissemination of which the genius of the Jews after their regeneration as an independent nation will be devoted.

The laws of universal history, I mean the history of the universe, namely, those of the cosmic, organic and social life, are as yet little known. We have particular sciences, but not a science of the universe; we still do not know the unity of all life. One thing, however, is certain, that a fusion of cults, an ideal to which so many aspire, and which was realized, at least in part, for thousands of years by Catholic Rome, will as little establish a lasting peace in human society as the philanthropic but unscientific belief in the absolute equality of men. In their attempt to base the granting of equal rights to all men on the primitive uniformity of all races and types, the humanitarians confound the organization of social life on the basis of solidarity, which is the result of a long and painful process of historical development, with a ready-made, inorganic equality and uniformity, which becomes rarer and rarer the farther back we go in history. The reconciliation of races follows its own natural laws, which we can neither arbitrarily create nor change. As to the fusion of cults, it is really a past stage in the development of social life. It was the watchword of that religion which owes its existence to the death of the nations of antiquity, i.e., Christianity. Today the real problem is how to free the various oppressed races and folk-types and allow them to develop in their own way. The dangerous possibility that the various nationalities will separate themselves entirely from each other or ignore each other, is to be feared as little as the danger that they will fight among themselves and enslave one another.

The present-day national movement not only does not exclude humanitarianism, but strongly asserts it; for this movement is a wholesome reaction, not against humanism, but against the things that would encroach upon it and cause its degeneration, against the leveling tendencies of modern industry and civilization which threaten to deaden every original organic life-force, by introducing a uniform inorganic mechanism. As long as these tendencies were directed against the antiquated institutions of a long-passed historical period their existence was justified. Nor can this nationalistic reaction object to them, insofar as they endeavor to establish closer relations between the various nations of the world. But, unfortunately, people have gone so far in life, as well as in science, as to deny the typical and the creative; and as a result the vapor of idealism, on the one hand, and the dust of atomism on the other, rest like mildew on the red corn, and stifle the germinating life in the bud. It is against these encroachments on the most sacred principles of creative life that the national tendencies of our time react, and it is against these destructive forces that I appeal to the original national power of Judaism.

(1863)

THE INTERPRETATION OF JUDAISM

by ABRAHAM GEIGER

THE Greeks were not all Phidias' or Praxiteles', but the Greek nation was alone capable of producing such great masters. The same was the case with Judaism. It is certain that not all Jews were prophets. The exclamation, "Would that all the people were prophets!" was a pious wish; the other, "I shall pour my spirit upon all flesh," is a promise which has never been realized. Nevertheless, Israel is the people of revelation, the favored organs of which came from that people; it is as though the rays of light had been dispersed, and were concentrated into a flame by those gifted with higher endowments. A thornbush produces no vine, a neglected people produces no prophets such as the people of Judah gave to the world. It is true that the historical books of the Bible inveigh against the morals and the depravity of the people during the time of the kings. They intend to prepare us for the devastation that came upon them as a punishment for their sinfulness. Yet, that people must have possessed noble powers in great abundance; it must have had a native endowment, considering that it could produce such men. Judaism was not merely a preacher in the wilderness, and though it did not prevail altogether, it was nevertheless a power which existed, it is true, in many men in a small degree, yet in such a measure that it could produce such heroes of the spirit.

Nor does Judaism claim to be the work of single individuals, but of the whole people. It does not speak of the God of Moses, or of the God of the Prophets, but of the God of Abraham, Isaac and Jacob, of the God of the whole race, of the patriarchs who were equally gifted with prophetic vision. It is revelation which lay dormant in the whole people, and was concentrated in individuals. The fact that the greatest prophet left his work unfinished contains a profound truth: He must not be regarded as the Atlas who bears the whole world upon his shoulders, who completes a work without the cooperation of others, who gives the impulse thereto and, at the same time, finishes it. It is not known where he is buried, and our ancient teachers remark: "His grave should not serve for a place of pilgrimage whither men go to do honor to one, and thus raise him above the level of man." Moses did his share of the work according to his great capacity as one of the whole people.

Yes, Judaism has grown from the people of revelation. Why, then, should we not employ the term where we touch the fundamental source? I refer to the illumination which proceeds from the higher spirit, which cannot be explained, which is not a composition created by a process of development, but which suddenly presents itself as a whole, like every new creation proceeding from the original spirit. We will not narrow down the term within definite limits in the manner of dogmatic theory. It may be understood in different ways, but its essence is ever the same. It indicates the point of contact between human reason with the fundamental source of all things. The ancient teachers of Judaism never denied that this sublime phenomenon was connected with some human quality. "The spirit of God," they say, "rests only upon a wise man, upon a man possessed of moral power, who is independent because he is contented, having conquered all ambition, all desire." A man who feels the divine in him, alone is capable of receiving the divine. He is not a mere trumpet through which words uttered pass without his being conscious thereof, but a man in the true meaning of the term, touching the divine and therefore susceptible of it. A man of the Middle Ages, a profound thinker and true poet, Jehuda Halevi, emphatically maintains that revelation animated the whole people. "Israel," he says, "is the heart of mankind, which in its unity ever preserved its higher susceptibility, and the several distinguished men were the hearts of that heart." Maimonides speaks of revelation as "a lightning-like illumination; to some, this illumination was granted only for a short time; for others, it was repeated; but with the majority, it was a lasting one which lightens the darknesses, affording man an insight into all that is hidden, that discloses to him what remains concealed for others." Judaism is a religion of truth, because its view of the nature of things is infallible, discovering as it does the unchangeable and everlasting. This is its eternal essence.

It is folly to assert that Judaism teaches the doctrine of a national God, belonging exclusively to the Jews. Such an assertion in the very face of oft-repeated proclamations, prognosticating a future when God will be one and His name one, is truly childish. Now and then an expression is found apparently attributing some importance to idols, such as, "Greater is our Lord than all gods," and others like it, but how does the prophet so often characterize them? "One breath and there is nothing good in them." And with what irony does he show how the gods are made, how the workmen labor with their hammers and assist each other, and how one portion of the materials is used to prepare food with it, while the other is employed to fashion a god from it! How can one speak of a national God in Judaism? Yes, a God is spoken of who was first acknowledged by that nation and by that nation alone. But who then is the God of the whole world, the God who fills all time and space, the God who shall be acknowledged by all nations? We perceive here a struggle in which many expressions that do not correspond with its spiritual sublimity are used, but crystal clarity gradually gains the ascendency. We behold the ancient Jacob as he must struggle surrounded by mighty darkness. The hollow of his thigh gets out of joint, but nevertheless, he prevails both physically and spiritually, and becomes a blessing for all mankind.

But Judaism was destined not alone to introduce a new idea concerning God into the world, but also to dignify and ennoble all human relations. The men who taught in ancient times, "The true foundation and nerve of the Law is this: whatever displeases thee do not unto others. All the rest is commentary," and "Thou shalt love thy neighbor as thyself. This is the cardinal principle of the Law"—taught us to be men, and to recognize all men as our peers under all circumstances. The Hillels, Akibas, Ben Somas, who taught such lessons, are the great props and pillars of Judaism, and we must take to heart their words. Judaism, I repeat, did not enter into this world to present a new idea of God, but to purify all human relations as well as the knowledge and appreciation of man. But even with regard to the relation between man and man, the idea must now and then contract itself, as it were, must accommodate itself to the various conditions, if it would succeed. An individual, also, however distinguished he may be, will labor without effect, as long as he keeps himself aloof from his fellows, as long as he does not participate in their aspirations. His fellowmen may look up to him with reverence, but they will not be influenced by him. If a man desires to see his work crowned with success, he must accept existing conditions—there must be mutual accommodation. There is no compromise with the God-Idea for there can be no mediation between the pure spirit and corporeality. In this respect Judaism cannot be indulgent, and all opposition must be contended against with unswerving determination. It is otherwise with regard to the relations among men. Here the Idea must perform its work of purification and sanctification by a gradual process, until the hard shell goes to pieces and falls off by itself.

Tradition is the developing power, continuing in Judaism as an invisibly creative agent which will never obtain its full expression, but will ever work and create. Tradition is the life-giving soul of Judaism; it is the daughter or revelation, enjoying the same rights with her mother. Tradition never did and never will vanish from Judaism. It is the fountain that ever fertilizes the times and, whenever it comes into contact with the outer world, creates new formations, according to the everchanging wants and necessities of life. If ever a time should come—but it will never come—when the stream of tradition shall be dried up; when Judaism may be regarded as something completely concluded; when with a retrospective glance, men will contemplate the creations of former times and desire blindly to preserve them; when others will not willingly bow to the past, but yet look with romantic reverence, with a nostalgic affection, upon Judaism as upon ruins; or others again will pass by those ruins with aristocratic indifference, and no living power will be manifest anywhere:—whenever such a time should come, then, indeed, you may prepare a grave for Judaism. Then it will be dead and its spirit will have vanished altogether. It will be like a walking skeleton that may continue for some time, but will surely advance towards dissolution. Judaism has a continuously creative tradition. Yes, let us honor this word! Tradition is, like revelation, a spiritual power, that ever continues to work: a higher power that does not proceed from man, but is an emanation from the divine spirit; a power which works among all, chooses its own ministers, manifests itself by its ever purer and maturer fruits, and thus preserves vitality and existence itself.

(1864)

THE LAW IN JUDAISM

by SOLOMON SCHECHTER

JEWISH tradition indeed attributes the composition of the daily public prayers, as well as of others for private worship, to the very men whom modern biblical criticism holds responsible for the introduction of the Priestly Code. Now this fact may perhaps be disputed, but there is little doubt that the age in which these prayers were composed was one of flourishing legalism. Nor is there any proof that the synagogues and their ritual were in opposition to the temple. From the few documents belonging to this period, it is clear that there was no opposition to the legalistic spirit by which the Priestly Code was actuated. This would prove that legalism meant something more than tithes and sacrifices for the benefit of the priests.

Nor is it true that the legal tendency aimed at narrowing the mind of the nation, turning all its thoughts into the one direction of the law. Apart from the fact that the Torah contained other elements besides its legalism, the prophets were not forgotten, but were read and interpreted from a very early age. It was under the predominance of the Law that the Wisdom literature was composed, which is by no means narrow or one-sided, but is even supposed by some critics to contain many foreign elements. In the book of Job, the great problems of man's existence are treated with a depth and grandeur never equalled before or since. This book alone ought partly to compensate the modern school for the disappearance of prophecy, which is usually brought as a charge against the Law. Then, too, the Psalms, placed by the same school in the post-exilic period, are nothing but another aspect of prophecy, with this difference, perhaps, that in the Prophets God speaks to man, while in the Psalms it is man who establishes the same communion by speaking to God. There is no reason why the critical school, with its broad conception of inspiration, and with its insistence that prophecy does *not* mean prediction, should so strongly emphasise this difference. If "it is no longer as in the days of Amos, when the Lord Yahveh did nothing without revealing his counsel to his servants the prophets," there is in the days of the Psalmist nothing in man's heart, no element in his longings and meditations and aspirations, which was not revealed to God. Nay, it would seem that at times the Psalmist hardly ever desires the revelation of God's secrets. Let future events be what they may, he is content, for he is with God. After all his trials, he exclaims, "And yet I am continually with thee; thou hast taken hold of my right hand. According to thy purpose wilt thou lead me, and afterwards receive me with glory. Whom have I (to care for) in heaven? and possessing thee, I have pleasure in nothing upon earth. Though my flesh and my heart should have wasted away, God would for ever be the rock of my heart and my portion" (*Ps.* lxxiii 23-26). How an age producing a literature containing passages like these—of which Welhausen in his *Abriss* (p. 95) justly remarks, that we are not worthy even to repeat them—can be considered by the modern school as wanting in intimate relation to God and inferior to that of the prophets is indeed a puzzle.

Now a few words as to the actual life under the Law. Here, again, there is a fresh puzzle. On the one side, we hear the opinions of so many learned professors, proclaiming *ex cathedrâ,* that the Law was a most terrible burden, and the life under it the most unbearable slavery, deadening body and soul. On the other side we have the testimony of a literature extending over about twenty-five centuries, and including all sorts and conditions of men, scholars, poets, mystics, lawyers, casuists, schoolmen, tradesmen, workmen, women, simpletons, who all, from the author of the 119th Psalm to the last pre-Mendelssohnian writer—with a small exception which does not even deserve the name of a vanishing minority —give unanimous evidence in favour of this Law, and of the bliss and happiness of living and dying under it,—and this, the testimony of people who were actually living under the Law, not merely theorising upon it, and who experienced it in all its difficulties and inconveniences. The Sabbath will give a fair example. The law of the Sabbath is one of those institutions the strict observance of which was already the object of attack in early New Testament times. Nevertheless, the doctrine proclaimed in one of the Gospels—that the son of man is Lord also of the Sabbath—was also current among the Rabbis. They, too, taught that the Sabbath had been delivered into the hand of man (to break, if necessary), and not man delivered over to the Sabbath. And they even laid down the axiom that a scholar who lived in a town, where among the Jewish population there could be the least possibility of doubt as to whether the Sabbath might be broken for the benefit of a dangerously sick person, was to be despised as a man neglecting his duty; for, as Maimonides points out, the laws of the Torah are not meant as an infliction upon mankind, "but as mercy, loving-kindness, and peace."

The attacks upon the Jewish Sabbath have not abated with the lapse of time. The day is still described by almost every Christian writer on the subject in the most gloomy colours, and long lists are given of minute and easily transgressed observances connected with it, which, instead of a day of rest, would make it to be a day of sorrow and anxiety, almost worse than the Scotch Sunday as depicted by continental writers. But it so happens that we have the prayer of Rabbi Zadok, a younger contemporary of the Apostles, which runs thus: "Through the love with which Thou, O Lord our God, lovest Thy people Israel, and the mercy which Thou hast shown to the children of Thy covenant, Thou hast given to us in love this great and holy Seventh Day." And another Rabbi, who probably flourished in the first half of the second century, expresses himself (with allusion to *Exod.* xxxi. 13: Verily my Sabbaths ye shall keep . . . that ye may know that I am the Lord that doth sanctify you)—"The Holy One, blessed be He, said unto Moses, I have a good gift in my treasures, and Sabbath is its name, which I wish to present to Israel. Go and bring to them the good tidings." The form again of the Blessing over the Sanctification-cup—a ceremony known long before the destruction of the Second Temple—runs: "Blessed art Thou, O Lord our God, who hast sanctified us by Thy commandments, and hast taken pleasure in us, and in love and grace hast given us Thy holy Sabbath as an inheritance." All these Rabbis evidently regarded the Sabbath as a gift from heaven, an expression of the infinite mercy and grace of God which He manifested to His beloved children.

Such was the Sabbath of the old Rabbis and the same spirit continued through all ages. The Sabbath was and is still celebrated by the people who did and do observe it, in hundreds of hymns, which would fill volumes, as a day of rest and joy, of pleasure and delight, a day in which man enjoys some foretaste of the pure bliss and happiness which are stored up for the righteous in the world to come. Somebody, either the learned professors, or the millions of the Jewish people, must be under an illusion. Which it is I leave to the reader to decide.

It is also an illusion to speak of the burden which a scrupulous care to observe six hundred and thirteen commandments must have laid upon the Jew. Even a superficial analysis will discover that in the time of Christ many of these commandments were already obsolete (as for instance those relating to the tabernacle and to the conquest of Palestine), while others concerned only certain classes, as the priests, the judges, the soldiers, the Nazirites, or the representatives of the community, or even only one or two individuals among the whole population, as the King and the High-Priest. Others, again, provided for contingencies which could occur only to a few, as for instance the laws concerning divorce or levirate marriages, whilst many—such as those concerning idolatry, and incest, and the sacrifice of children to Moloch—could scarcely have been considered as a practical prohibition by the pre-Christian Jew; just as little as we can speak of Englishmen as lying under the burden of a law preventing them from burning widows or marrying their grandmothers, though such acts would certainly be considered as crimes. Thus it will be found by a careful enumeration that barely a hundred laws remain which really concerned the life of the bulk of the people. If we remember that even this includes such laws as belief in the unity of God, the necessity of loving and fearing Him, and of sanctifying His name, of loving one's neighbour and the stranger, of providing for the poor, exhorting the sinner, honouring one's parents and many more of a similar character, it will hardly be said that the ceremonial side of the people's religion was not well balanced by a fair amount of spiritual and social elements. Besides, it would seem that the line between the ceremonial and the spiritual is too often only arbitrarily drawn. With many commandments it is rather a matter of opinion whether they should be relegated to the one category or the other.

The legalistic attitude may be summarily described as an attempt to live in accordance with the will of God, caring less for what God is than for what He wants us to be. But, nevertheless, on the whole this life never degenerated into religious formalism. Apart from the fact that during the second temple there grew up laws, and even beliefs, which show a decided tendency towards progress and development, there were also ceremonies which were popular with the masses, and others which were neglected. Men were not, therefore, the mere soulless slaves of the Law; personal sympathies and dislikes also played a part in their religion. Nor were all the laws actually put upon the same level. With a happy inconsistency men always spoke of heavier and slighter sins, and by the latter—excepting, perhaps, the profanation of the Sabbath—they mostly understood ceremonial transgressions. The statement made by Professor Toy (p. 243), on the authority of James (ii. 10), that "the principle was established that he who offended in one point was guilty of all," is hardly correct; for the passage seems rather to be laying down a principle, or arguing that logically the law ought to be looked upon as a whole, than stating a fact. The fact was that people did not consider the whole law as of equal importance, but made a difference between laws and laws, and even spoke of certain commandments, such as those of charity and kindness, as outweighing all the rest of the Torah. It was in conformity with this spirit that in times of great persecution the leaders of the people had no compunction in reducing the whole Law to the three prohibitions of idolatry, of incest, and of bloodshed. Only these three were considered of sufficient importance that men should rather become martyrs than transgress them.

These, then, are some of the illusions and misrepresentations which exist with regard to the Law.

(1890)

SOME COMFORT

by AHAD HAAM

IN all this fresh outbreak of calamities that has come upon us of late, there is nothing so distressing to every Jew as the recrudescence of the "blood-accusation." This abominable charge, old though it is, strikes us, and will always strike us, as something new; and since the Middle Ages it has always profoundly agitated the spirit of the Jewish people, not only in the actual place where the cry has been raised, but even in distant countries where the incident has been merely reported.

If I say that this blood-accusation has profoundly agitated the spirit of the Jewish people, it is because the roots of this phenomenon lie, to my mind, not in any external cause, but in the innermost spirit of the Jew. If in medieval instances of the blood-accusation we find that the whole people used to regard itself as standing at the judgment bar together with the wretches whom fortune made the immediate victims of the scourge, we may explain this fact as a result of the physical danger to the whole people, which was involved in every local incident of this kind. Again, if, fifty years ago, the Damascus blood-accusation so cruelly disturbed the halcyon calm of European Jewry, one might attribute this to just the opposite cause, to the extreme jealousy of the emancipated Jews for their newly-won dignity and privileges. But at the present day neither explanation is open. On the one hand, the physical danger is no longer serious, especially in the case of distant communities; on the other hand, we have grown used to listening with equanimity to those who revile us, and we are no longer consumed with a jealous regard for our dignity. Yet even today the blood-accusation comes as a rude and violent shock, which rouses the whole of Jewry to a passionate repudiation of this outrageous charge. Clearly, then, it is not a question of mere regard for personal safety or dignity: the spirit of the people is stung to consciousness and activity by the sense of its shame. In all else it might be said of us, in the words of the wise prince of old time, that "the dead flesh feels not the knife;" but here the knife cuts not only the flesh—it touches the soul.

Yet "there is no evil without good," that is, without a good moral. The great evil with which we are concerned here is not without its useful lesson, which it were well that we should learn. We are not masters of our fate: good and evil we accept from without, as perforce we must; so that it is fitting that we should always look for the useful lesson hidden in the evil that comes upon us, and find thus at least some consolation.

Convention is one of the most important factors in social life. There was a time when even philosophers thought that the universal acceptance of an idea was a certain proof of its truth, and used this as an argument in their demonstration of the existence of God. That is no longer so. Philosophers know now that there is no lie, no piece of folly, which cannot gain universal acceptance under suitable conditions. But this knowledge is confined to philosophers; for the mass of men there is still no greater authority than this conventional acceptance. If "everybody" believes that this or that is so, of course it *is* so; if I do not understand it, others do; if I see what appears to contradict it, why, "everybody" sees the same thing, and yet believes, and am I wiser than the whole world? Such is roughly the reasoning, conscious or vaguely conscious, of the plain man; and, having reasoned thus, he too accepts the idea, and helps to make it an accepted convention.

It is a powerful force, this of convention, so powerful, that, generally speaking, a man cannot escape its influence even when he is himself its object. If "everybody" says of such an one that he is a profound thinker or a sincere believer, that he has this or that good or bad quality, he ends by accepting this idea himself, even though at first he may not have discovered in himself that superiority or defect which others ascribe to him. Nay, more: this acceptance of an idea by its object moulds him little by little, until he approximates, or at least tends to approximate, to the state of mind in which "everybody" assumes him to be. For this reason educationalists rightly warn us against directing the attention of children, at the beginning of their development, to their moral shortcomings, and still more against attributing to them imaginary shortcomings: because by such means we may accentuate the real faults, and create a tendency towards the imaginary ones.

But of course "everybody" means something different for each man. For each of us "the world" is that society of which he considers himself a member, and with the other members of which he finds a certain point of contact. No man is affected by the conventional beliefs of groups which are entirely strange to him in spirit, with which he feels no connection in thought. Take for instance the "orthodox" and the "enlightened" Jews. Each school has its own conventional ideas; neither pays any attention to those of the other, even in matters which do not affect religion; and their mutual scorn and ridicule have not the least effect, because each regards the other as non-existent. But when conditions arise which force the members of the two schools into constant intercourse, and they get used to meeting on a broad basis of common humanity, then "the world" becomes a bigger world, and the views of all are affected in many ways by the conventional beliefs of "the world" in its new and wider sense.

This will explain why in the old days, when our ancestors believed in a literal sense that they were "the chosen people" the purity of their souls was not sullied by the shame which the world imputed to them. Conscious of their own worth, they were not in the least affected by the conventional ideas of the outside world, which was to them a society of alien beings, fundamentally different from and unrelated to themselves. In those days the Jew could listen unmoved to the tale of moral defects and sins of conduct which the world told and believed of him, without feeling any inner sense of shame or humiliation. What mattered the ideas of these aliens about him and his work? All that he asked of them was to let him live in peace. But in modern times it is different. Our "world" has expanded: what Europe believes, affects every side of our lives in the most vital way. And since we no longer treat the outside world as a thing apart, we are influenced, despite ourselves, by the fact that the outside world treats *us* as a thing apart. It was recently asked by a Russian writer, in all simplicity: Since everybody hates the Jews, can we think that everybody is wrong, and the Jews are right? There are many among us Jews on whom a similar question half-consciously forces itself. Can we think, they ask, that all the vicious characteristics and evil practices which the whole world ascribes to the Jews are sheer imagination?

This doubt, once aroused, is easily strengthened by those false inferences from particular to universal which are so common among ordinary men. There is a well-known story about a traveller who, happening on an inn where the Hostler stammered, wrote in his diary, "The hostlers in X. are stammerers." This story is a comic illustration of the kind of logic on which most plain man's general propositions are based. He generalizes from the particular instance to the whole class with the name of which that instance is normally labelled. He does not see that one particular may belong to several classes, that is, may have affinities with one class of things by virtue of one of its qualities, and with another class by virtue of a second, whereas its name only indicates its connection with one of these classes through a single aspect, not through all its aspects. It is in propositions of this kind that the universally accepted ideas about the Jews can and do find their support. "A and B are Jews by name and dishonest by character: *ergo,* the Jews are dishonest." True logic will reply, of course, that even if all the Jews of modern times were really dishonest, that would still not prove the general proposition, that "the Jews are dishonest," that is, that the quality of dishonesty, which belongs to every Jew, belongs to him by virtue of his inclusion of the class of Jews, and not by virtue of his inclusion in some other class—for instance, that of a tradesman—which embraces the individual Jew together with other individuals who have no connection with the class of Jews. In order to decide this question, we must first of all examine the other individuals who are included, together with the Jews, in other classes. If this examination shows that the quality of dishonesty does not belong to any class which embraces both Jews and non-Jews, then, but not till them, have we the right to lay down the judgment that Judaism is the source of dishonesty. But, as I have said, men are not usually very logical, and we cannot demand strict logic even of the ordinary run of Jews. They hear the universally accepted judgment; they see that it is actually true of a good many Jews; and this is sufficient to make them begin to subscribe to the judgment themselves. Thus "Jewish characteristics" pass from hand to hand like an honest coin, which, having become current in the outside world, gains currency also among the Jews. But there is this difference. The outside world recounts our bad qualities one by one, with a mocking and triumphant exultation, while we repeat the lesson after them word for word, in the still small voice of puling self-extenuation. For them (to borrow a simile from Talmudic law) we are the earthenware vessel which cannot be cleansed, but must be broken; for ourselves we are the vessel of metal, which may be cleansed by water and fire.

But this state of things, if it continues, may do us a great moral harm. There is nothing more dangerous for a nation or for an individual than to plead guilty to imaginary sins. Where the sin is real, there is opportunity for repentance; by honest endeavor the sinner may purify himself. But when a man has been persuaded to suspect himself unjustly, how can he get rid of his consciousness of guilt? "Remove the beam from your eye" they tell him; and he would fain obey, but cannot, because the beam is not really there. He is in the position of the nomomaniac who, for some reason, has come to believe that a heavy weight is hanging from his nose and cannot be removed. But the evil goes further than this. Sometimes the conviction of sin actually produces in the individual that failing with which he believes the whole people to be infected, although, as an individual, he is entirely free from any predisposition towards it. For instance: a people which has produced men like Maimonides must number in its ranks even today sytematic, orderly, and methodical persons, who might be able to permeate the work of the community in which they take part with their own habits, and to influence their fellow-workers in the same direction. But it is an accepted idea that objection to order and method is a Jewish quality; and we ourselves have accepted this idea, though it is by no means clear whether this characteristic, which is, in fact, common among a large section of Jews, belongs to the Jews as such, or is due, as appears more probable, to the Hedder training. Hence those of us who have a love of order come to believe that there is no going against the national character, and are therefore powerless to reform. Indeed, if they are patriotic, they actually set about to conquer their own "anti-Jewish" love of order and teach themselves to behave in true "Jewish" fashion.

What we need, then, is some means of emancipating ourselves from the influence of conventional prejudices as to the characteristics and moral worth of the Jews. We must get rid of this self-contempt, this idea that we are really worse than all the world. Otherwise we may in course of time become in reality what we now imagine ourselves to be.

This necessary means of escape the world itself, with its accepted beliefs, affords us—through the blood-accusation. This accusation is the solitary case in which the general acceptance of an idea about ourselves does not make us doubt whether all the world can be wrong, and we right, because it is based on an absolute lie, and is not even supported by any false inference from particular to universal. Every Jew who has been brought up among Jews knows as an indisputable fact that throughout the length and breadth of Jewry there is not a single individual who drinks human blood for religious purposes. We ought, therefore, always to remember that in this instance the general belief, which is brought to our notice ever and anon by the revival of the blood-accusation, is absolutely wrong; because this will make it easier for us to get rid of the tendency to bow to the authority of "everybody" in other matters. Let the world say what it will about our moral inferiority: we know that its ideas rest on popular logic, and have no real scientific basis. Who has ever penetrated into the very heart of the Jew, and discovered his essential nature? Who has ever weighed the Jew against the non-Jew of the same class—Jewish tradesman against non-Jewish tradesman, persecuted Jew against persecuted non-Jew, starved Jew against starved non-Jew, and so on—who has carried out this test, scientifically and impartially, and found the balance inclined to this side or to that?

"But"—you ask—"is it possible that everybody can be wrong, and the Jews right?"

Yes, it is possible: the blood-accusation proves it possible. Here, you see, the Jews are right and perfectly innocent. A Jew and blood—could there be a more complete contradiction? And yet . . .

(1892)

THE JEWISH QUESTION

by THEODOR HERZL

No one can deny the gravity of the Jewish situation. Wherever they live in perceptible numbers, Jews are more or less persecuted. Their equality before the law, granted by statute, has become practically a dead letter. They are debarred from filling even moderately high positions, either in the army, or in any public or private capacity. And attempts are made to crowd them out of business also. "No dealing with Jews!"

Attacks in Parliaments, in assemblies, in the press, in the pulpit, in the streets, on journeys—for example, their exclusion from certain hotels —even in places of recreation, become daily more numerous, the forms of persecution varying according to the countries in which they occur. In Russia, impositions are levied on Jewish villages; in Roumania, a few human beings are put to death; in Germany, they get a good beating when the occasion serves; in Austria, antisemites exercise terrorism over all public life; in Paris, they are shut out of the so-called best social circles and excluded from clubs. Shades of anti-Jewish feeling are innumerable. But this is not to be an attempt to make out a doleful category of Jewish hardships; it is futile to linger over details, however painful they may be.

I do not intend to awaken sympathetic emotions on our behalf. That would be a foolish, futile, and undignified proceeding. I shall content myself with putting the following questions to the Jews: Is it true that, in countries where we live in perceptible numbers, the position of Jewish lawyers, doctors, men of science, teachers, and officials of all descriptions, becomes daily more intolerable? True, that the Jewish middle classes are seriously threatened? True, that the passions of the mob are incited against our wealthy representatives? True, that our poor endure greater sufferings than any other proletariat?

I think that this external pressure makes itself felt everywhere. In our upper classes it causes unpleasantness, in our middle classes continual and grave anxieties, in our lower classes absolute despair.

Everything tends, in fact, to one and the same conclusion, which is clearly enunciated in that classic Berlin phrase: "Juden raus!" (Out with the Jews!)

I shall now put the Jewish Question in the curtest possible form: Are we to "get out" now? And if so, to what place?

Or, may we yet remain? And if so, how long?

Let us first settle the point of staying where we are. Can we hope for better days, can we possess our souls in patience, can we wait in pious resignation till the princes and peoples of this earth are more mercifully disposed towards us? I say that we cannot hope for a change in the current of feeling. And why not? Were we as near to the hearts of princes as are their other subjects, even so they could not protect us. They would only feed popular hatred of Jews by showing us too much favor. By "too much," I really mean less than is claimed as a right by every ordinary citizen, and by every tribe.

Every nation in whose midst Jews live is, either covertly or openly, antisemitic.

The common people have not, and indeed cannot have, any historic comprehension. They do not know that the sins of the Middle Ages are now being visited on the nations of Europe. We are what the Ghetto made us. We have doubtless attained preeminence in finance, because mediaeval conditions drove us to it. The same process is now being repeated. Modern conditions force us again into finance, now the stock-exchange, by keeping us out of all other branches of industry. Being on the stock-exchange, we are therefore again considered contemptible. At the same time we continue to produce an abundance of mediocre intellects which finds no outlet, and this endangers our social position as much as does our increasing wealth. Educated Jews without means are now fast becoming Socialists. Hence we are certain to suffer very severely in the struggle between classes, because we stand in the most exposed position in the camps of both Socialists and capitalists.

The artificial means heretofore employed to overcome the troubles of Jews have been either too petty—such as attempts at colonization, or mistaken in principle—such as attempts to convert the Jews into peasants in their present homes.

What is the result of transporting a few thousand Jews to another country? Either they come to grief at once, or prosper, and then their prosperity creates antisemitism. We have already discussed these attempts to divert poor Jews to fresh districts. This diversion is clearly inadequate and futile, if it does not actually defeat its own ends; for it merely protracts and postpones a solution, and perhaps even aggravates difficulties.

Whoever were to attempt a conversion of the Jews into a husbandman would be making an extraordinary mistake. For a peasant is a historical category, as is proved by his costume, which in some countries he has worn for centuries; and by his tools, which are identical with those used by his earliest forefathers. His plough is unchanged; he carries the seed in his apron; mows with the historical scythe, and threshes with the time-honored flail. But we know that all this can be done by machinery. The agrarian question is only a question of machinery. America must conquer Europe, in the same way as large landed possessions absorb small ones.

The peasant is consequently a type which is in course of extinction. Whenever he is artificially preserved, it is done on account of the political interests which he is intended to serve. It is absurd, and indeed impossible, to make modern peasants on the old pattern. No one is wealthy or powerful enough to make civilization take a single retrograde step. The mere preservation of obsolete institutions is a task severe enough

to require the enforcement of all the despotic measures of an autocrati-
cally governed State.

Are we therefore to credit Jews, who are intelligent, with a desire
to become peasants of the old type? One might just as well say to them:
"Here is a cross-bow; now go to war." What? with a cross-bow, while
the others have rifles and Maxim guns? Under these circumstances the
Jews are perfectly justified in refusing to stir when people try to agrari-
anize them. A cross-bow is a beautiful weapon, it inspires me with
mournful feelings when I have time to give way. But it belongs rightly
in a museum.

Now, there certainly are districts where desperate Jews go out, or at
any rate are willing to go out, and till the soil. And a little observation
shows that these districts—such as portions of Hessen in Germany, and
some provinces in Russia—these very districts are the principal seats of
antisemitism.

For the world's reformers, who send the Jews to the plough, forget
a very important person, who has a decided objection to seeing them
there. This person is the agriculturist. And the agriculturist is also perfectly justified in his objections. For the tax on land, the risks attached
to crops, the pressure of large proprietors who cheapen labor, and American competition in particular, combine to make his life hard enough.
The duties on corn cannot go on increasing indefinitely. Nor can the
manufacturer be allowed to starve; his political influence is, in fact, in
the ascendant, and he must therefore be treated with additional consideration.

All these difficulties are well known, therefore I only referred to
them cursorily. I merely wanted to indicate clearly how futile had been
past attempts—most of them well intentioned—to solve the Jewish Question. Neither a diversion of the stream, nor an artificial depression of
the intellectual level of our proletariat, will overcome the difficulty. The
supposed infallible expedient of assimilation has already been dealt with.

We cannot get the better of antisemitism by any of these methods.
It cannot die out so long as its causes are not removed. Are they re-
movable?

We shall not again touch on those causes which are a result of
temperament, prejudice and limited views, but shall here restrict ourselves to political and economic causes alone. Modern antisemitism is not
to be confounded with the religious persecution of the Jews of former
times. It does occasionally take a somewhat religious bias, but the main
current of the aggressive movement has now changed. In the principal

countries where antisemitism prevails, it does so as a result of the emancipation of the Jews. When civilized nations awoke to the inhumanity of exclusive legislation and enfranchised us, our enfranchisement came too late. It was no longer possible legally to remove our disabilities in our old homes. For we had, curiously enough, developed while in the Ghetto into a bourgeois people, and we stepped out of it only to enter into fierce competition with the middle classes. Hence, our emancipation set us suddenly within this middle-class circle, where we have a double pressure to sustain, from within and from without. The Christian bourgeoisie would not be unwilling to cast us as a sacrifice to socialism, though that would not greatly improve matters. At the same time, the equal rights of Jews before the law cannot be withdrawn where they have once been conceded. Not only because their withdrawal would be opposed to the spirit of our age, but also because it would immediately drive all Jews, rich and poor alike, into the ranks of the revolutionary army.

Nothing effectual can really be done to our injury. In old days our jewels were seized. How is our movable property to be got hold of now? It is comprised in printed papers which are scattered over the world, locked up maybe in the coffers of Christians. It is of course possible to get at shares and debentures in railways, banks and industrial concerns of all descriptions, by taxation, and where the progressive income-tax is in force, all our realized property can eventually be laid hold of. But all these efforts cannot be directed against Jews alone, and where they have nevertheless been made, severe economic crises with far-reaching effects have been their immediate consequence. The very impossibility of getting at the Jews nourishes and embitters hatred of them. Antisemitism increases day by day and hour by hour among the nations; indeed, it is bound to increase, because the causes of its growth continue to exist, and cannot be removed. Its remote cause is our loss of the power of assimilation during the Middle Ages; its immediate cause is our excessive production of mediocre intellects, who cannot find an outlet downwards or upwards—that is to say, no wholesome outlet in either direction. When we sink, we become a revolutionary proletariat, the subordinate officers of the revolutionary party; when we rise, there rises also our terrible power of the purse.

The oppression we endure does not improve us, for we are not a whit better than ordinary people. It is true that we do not love our enemies; but he alone who can conquer himself dare reproach us with that fault. Oppression naturally creates hostility against oppressors, and our hostility aggravates the pressure. It is impossible to escape from this eternal round.

"No!" some soft-hearted visionaries will say; "no, it is possible! Possible by means of the ultimate perfection of humanity."

Is it worth while pointing out the sentimental folly of this view? He who would found his hope for improved conditions on the ultimate perfection of humanity, would indeed be painting a Utopia!

I referred previously to our "assimilation"; I do not for a moment wish to imply that I desire such an end. Our national character is too historically famous, and, spite of every degradation, too fine, to make its annihilation desirable. We might perhaps be able to merge ourselves entirely into surrounding races, if these were to leave us in peace for a space of two generations. But they will not leave us in peace. For a little period they manage to tolerate us, and then their hostility breaks out again and again. The world is provoked by our prosperity, because it has for many centuries been accustomed to consider us as the most contemptible among the poverty-stricken. It forgets, in its ignorance and narrowness of heart, that prosperity weakens our Judaism and extinguishes our peculiarities. It is only pressure that forces us back to the parent stem; it is only hatred encompassing us that makes us strangers once more.

Thus, whether we like it or not, we are now, and shall henceforth remain, a historic group with unmistakable characteristics common to us all.

We are one people—our enemies have made us one in our despite, as repeatedly happens in history. Distress binds us together, and, thus united, we suddenly discover our strength. Yes, we are strong enough to form a State, and a model State. We possess all human and material resources necessary for the purpose.

This is the strictly appropriate place for an account of what has been somewhat rudely termed our human material. But it would not be appreciated till the broad lines of the plan, on which everything depends, had first been marked out.

The whole plan is in its essence perfectly simple, as it must necessarily be if it is to come within the comprehension of all.

Let the sovereignty be granted us over a portion of the globe large enough to satisfy the reasonable requirements of a nation; the rest we shall manage for ourselves.

The creation of a new State is neither ridiculous nor impossible. We have in our day witnessed the process in connection with nations which were not in the bulk of the middle class, but poorer, less educated, and consequently weaker than ourselves. The Governments of all countries scourged by antisemitism will serve their own interests in assisting us to obtain the sovereignty we want.

(1896)

SOCIALISM AND ZIONISM

by NAHMAN SYRKIN

ANTISEMITISM originates in physical superiority and is fed by the ever-increasing class struggle. The Jew derives from antisemitism a spiritual force, an impetus for his rejuvenation and renaissance. Whereas the Jew previously found solace in passively ignoring and detesting the enemy, his attitude has changed to a conscious and active protest. This process of moral purification is yet in its beginning, because the Jewish people is too much subjugated by the spirit of assimilation. The Jewish people, however, possesses forces which will guide it in the right direction.

A classless society and autonomous national power are the only means of solving the Jewish problem completely. The social revolution and cessation of the class struggle will assist in removing the abnormal condition of Jewry. Therefore, the Jew must join the ranks of the proletariat as that element which strives for the termination of the class struggle. Until now, the Jew was the torchbearer of liberalism, but since the bourgeoisie, which was responsible for Jewish emancipation in the old society, has betrayed its principles, the Jew must become the vanguard of Socialism.

Even prior to the birth of antisemitism, Jews began to join the ranks of the growing socialist movement. The Jewish socialists of Western Europe unfortunately inherited the traditions of the assimilationists and displayed the same lack of self-respect found in the Jewish bourgeoisie, with the only difference that with the former the moral degeneration was revealed more sharply. To Jewish socialists, Socialism meant first of all the discard of Jewishness, just as the liberalism of the Jewish bourgeoisie led to assimilation. And yet, this tendency to deny their Jewishnesss was unnecessary, being prompted by neither socialism nor liberalism. It was a product of the general degeneration and demoralization of the Jews.

Impelled by their Judaism towards the path of revolution, the socialists erred in that they did not guard the purity of their revolt. Instead of emphasizing, in their revolutionary opposition to the class society, their kinship with the most suppressed people of the world, and designating their protest in the first place as specifically Jewish and later raising it to a higher, universal outcry, they acted contrariwise. What is more, they robbed the protest of its Jewish character. They suppressed all reference to their Jewish origin, and thus became merely another type of Jewish assimilationists.

The assimilated bourgeoisie turned away from Judaism. They denied Jewish nationalism because the Jewish people was weak and its conditions unbearable. Jewish Socialists turned away from Judaism, because for them Socialism was not the result of a moral protest against the world of oppressors, but a haven for the Jew whom liberalism had betrayed. Jewish assimilation clothed itself in the mantle of vicarious nationalism, of patriotic fervor for those lands in which Jews resided; Jewish Socialism used internationalism as a cape to cover its nakedness. This negative and honorless attitude towards its Jewish origin was just as little justified by the truth of internationalism as by the illusion of foreign nationalism.

The term "internationalism," because of the poverty of our vocabulary, is a source of unconscious mistakes and conscious falsifications. Two quite diametrically opposed phenomena of life with completely contrary ethical and historic-philosophical values are conceived in the above term, so we must employ criticism and analysis in order to arrive at a clear understanding.

Internationalism, not only in the narrow but also in the cosmopolitan sense, is undoubtedly the ideal to which humanity strives. The confederation of all nations, the creation of one humanity with a common language, territory, and destiny—of which the greatest spirits of all times have dreamed—is undoubtedly one of the greatest concepts of the human mind. Nationalism is always an accidental product, not a rational phenomenon of history. Nationalism is only an historical category and is not absolute. National differences rose in certain historical phases and will disappear in higher historical moments. The characteristic symbol of nationality is neither language, religion nor state, but the consciousness of historic unity.

Socialism will do away with wars, tariffs and the conflicting economic interests among civilized peoples, and will eliminate the possibility of oppression of one nation by the other; on the other hand, commercial and cultural intercourse will increase to create a common base of interest and purposes. This alone will pave the way for internationalism. International developments and solidarity of the civilized peoples will weld them into one humanity. Socialism, with its basic principles of peace, cooperation, and cultural development, bears in itself the seed of realization of the pure internationalism, that is, cosmopolitanism.

Socialism, which proclaimed the holiness of freedom and the right to self-determination, is both in its nature and in its practice the absolute opposite of pseudo-internationalism. Socialism is the opponent of all those conspiring to suppress a people. The socialist movement staunchly supports all attempts of suppressed peoples to free themselves. Each national emancipation movement finds its moral support in Socialist ethics and in socialist concepts of freedom. It was the Internationale which first greeted the Polish revolt against the Czar. Likewise, the Socialist masses of France and Italy reacted favorably toward the Cretes in their revolt against Turkey. At the national and international Socialist congresses the right of every nation to self-determination was proclaimed, since emancipation is an organic part of the ethics of Socialism.

The socialists of most nations have already coordinated their nationalism and socialism. No one can point to socialist leaders who denied their own nationality and preached assimilation with a stronger people. It is the bourgeoisie of oppressed nations who deny nationalism and preach assimilation. They betray their own nation at the first opportunity when it behooves them to do so for more profits. Thus, the Polish bourgeoisie betrayed Poland and was the first to join hands with the enemy. Likewise, the Jewish bourgeoisie adopted assimilation and disposed of the Jewish nationality together with its hopes and aspirations in order that it might lighten itself of the ballast of Jewishness and occupy itself more freely with the stock exchange.

The bearers of national emancipation among all suppressed nations are the intelligentsia, the Socialists, and the proletariat. Only in the case of the Jews among whom everything is topsy-turvy, have the Socialists inherited the assimilation of the bourgeoisie as their spiritual treasure. In this, we recognize the decline in their Socialism.

At one time the Jews did not possess a higher national aspiration, and this was their life tragedy; nevertheless, they were still a separate nation. It was considered by the enemy as such. Robbed of all external national characteristics through dispersion, speaking all languages and jargons, possessing no national property or creative national forces, the Jews were yet a distinct nation whose very existence bore the reason for its being. The existence of the Jews, who for centuries carried on a bitter struggle against the external world, possesses a high significance, since by their existence they represent freedom of conscience. If the suppression of the Jew represented unrighteousness resulting from domination by the strong, then the existence of the Jew was a protest against that injustice. The Jew symbolizes human rights which would be extinguished if he were to vanish. The decline of the Jew must be paralleled by the decline of humanity.

The national suicide of the Jews would be a terrible tragedy for the Jews themselves, and that epoch would be the most tragic in human history. Let us imagine the last Jew surviving when Jewry dies in the midst of the blossoming peoples of the world. The blood which the Jews shed in their struggle for existence, the millions of victims lying strewn over all lands bearing eternal witness to their revolutionary struggle against their oppressors—would appear to him a tragic farce, a lost game. It is the sacred duty of the Jew to live, for he stands for freedom and justice. Schopenhauer once stated that life is an offense because we pay for it with the penalty of death; for the Jew, life is a duty, because to him death is an offense.

In such a time as ours when the large Jewish masses do not and cannot assimilate, when the Jew is surrounded by enemies, when need and misery are the fate of the Jewish people, when the right of the Jew is publicly disregarded, when his honor is tread under foot and his misfortunes mocked at, to justify assimilation would be ironical. To elevate ourselves and give to life a purpose must be the motto of the better type of Jew. Out of the need of the Jew to fight for his existence, there necessarily grows the higher ethical duty of endowing his life with a national content as well as of removing all those barriers which limit the creative genius of the Jewish people.

If Jewish socialism, which claims that it is not only a result of class interests but also of ideological motives, wants to elevate its voice to a sincere and normal protest, then it must accept the Jewish protest as its guiding motive, and proclaim it publicly. The socialism of the Jew must truly become a Jewish socialism.

From the sound of these words, one may perhaps picture a type of reactionary socialism because the word "Jewish" brings to mind the terms Christian, German, National, etc. However, this is not implied, because logically Jewish socialism should be placed on the same level with proletarian socialism, both having their common source in the suppression of human beings and unequal distribution of power.

Where the Jewish proletariat became class-conscious, it also created the true Jewish socialism, free of every slave-like trace of assimilation. The socialism of the Jewish proletariat bears in itself also a special Jewish protest which expresses itself together with its class-consciousness. The peculiar literature, thought and sentiment of the Jewish masses, which give them an outspoken national character differentiating them from other nations, are reflected in Jewish socialism. Free from assimilation and without a tendency toward self-denial, the Jewish proletariat bears in itself, consciously and unconsciously, the specific Jewish protest.

Insofar as the Jewish proletariat had in its early stage nourished itself on the propaganda of the assimilated intelligentsia, thoughts of assimilation entered its ranks, but the healthy consciousness of the proletariat, its self-confidence and self-respect fought and checked this infection. Furthermore, the Jewish class-conscious proletariat greatly influenced the Jewish intelligentsia and aroused it to self-consciousness.

Sooner or later, Jewish socialism will remove all assimilatory tendencies from its ranks, and will loyally and publicly declare itself a huge protest movement of Jews. As a protest movement against Jewish suffering, socialism may become the common possession of all Jews, because Jewish sufferings affect the Jewish proletariat as well as the intelligentsia, the Jewish middle class as well as the upper bourgeoisie.

Antisemitism helps the Jews maintain their national solidarity. As a result of the recognition of their common problem, the Jews may elevate themselves to a nation of honor and respect, and strive for higher goals. However, there must be no mistake of considering the Jewish problem as a desirable means for bringing about their moral elevation, or that antisemitism is a welcomed guest in Jewish ranks. Not the woe of the Jewish masses but a clear understanding of the causes will help solve their problem. Jewish suffering is a result of the unequal distribution of power and therefore will exist as long as there are in the world stronger and weaker forces. This is a truism of social life not influenced by the desires of man.

The example of the Social-Democratic party should illustrate this. This party draws its moral strength from the economic decline of the masses. That, however, does not mean that it desires the economic ruin of the middle class, as reactionary parties maintain. Social-Democracy registers economic fact, diagrams its cause, and transforms it into ammunition for the class struggle.

The socialist movement embodies those political tendencies towards which the Jews are driven. The Jews must accept the socialist movement as their own. The socialist proletarian is the only friend of the Jews and his victory will also end the Jewish suffering.

But as soon as the Jews attained national consciousness, and the Jewish socialists, at the side of economic class struggle, took up the Jewish national protest, there appeared another form of protest which grew out of the peculiar condition of the Jewish people.

Dark clouds hover over the Jewish quarters. The eternal Jew once more takes up his wanderer's staff. Once more walls are erected—"Into the Ghetto!" Need and misery, pain and shame, again become his fate. These sufferings are greater than those of former days because they are accompanied by the knowledge that there is no further escape.

How shall the Jew react?

In the Middle Ages the Jews accepted their fate resignedly and only some individuals amongst them protested against the world. But modern Jewry adopted the rational means of migration. To pave a path for economically driven immigrants, for refined Jews stung by insults, and romantic and orthodox Jews who bewail the deterioration of the people and the destruction of the Temple, to form a rational outlet and raise their individual protest to a general moral protest, to a rebuilding of Jewish life—that is the aim of Zionism, a movement born of Jewish sufferings. Just as Cabet attempted to establish a social republic in Icaria, just as Herzka attempted to undertake the anarchist experiment of a stateless society in Freeland; so does Zionism attempt to create a common territory for the Jewish homeless in Palestine.

A political utopia is that project which goes contrary to the direction of human efforts and experience, or for which there are not present in society any satisfactory motives for its development. Every attempt to turn history forward or backward, contrary to the main tendency of the time, must be considered a political utopia. Thus, for example, it was an utopian experiment when workers and their sympathizers fought the machine during the first days of the industrial revolution. On the other hand, it was an utopia when the socialist, Fourier, sat for many years in his home waiting for a millionaire to come and bring him the necessary capital to develop a socialist state. Even if such a millionaire had come to his aid, the project would not have endured for long. The general social interests of those days were not in harmony with the socialist project which Fourier developed from his ethical and rational convictions. Nevertheless, fantastic experiments are not utopian if they synchronize with the needs of humanity.

Zionism is not utopian, since it derives from the life of the Jews. It is as little utopian as socialism, socialism being the consequence of the social problems produced by the modern class structure. Zionism is justified by existing realities; utopias were the products of individual and rare spirits. Icaria is associated with Cabet, Freeland with Herzka, but the Jewish state is the product of the Jewish nation. The Jewish state answers Jewish needs and Jewish aspirations, and is closely bound up with the old land—Zion.

There is another important difference between the Jewish state and the socialist utopias. With the utopians, the driving force was the idea; with us, the need.

Zionism is a real phenomenon of Jewish life. It has its roots in the economic and social positions of the Jews, in their moral protest, in the idealistic striving to give a better content to their miserable life. It is borne by the active forces of Jewish life. Only cowards and spiritual degenerates may term Zionism an utopia.

All non-Zionist attempts to solve the Jewish problem bear an utopian stamp. For example, when the assimilationists parade about with the hope that Jews will assimilate—it is utopian. Likewise, when some benevolent Jews believe that the Jews can return to agriculture in the land where they reside, and bourgeois Jewry and intelligentsia will lower their living standard—it is also utopian. Furthermore, it is utopian when bourgeois Jewry, feeling its position weakened by Zionism, believes that Zionism will disappear and the Jews will sink to their former resigned state. All these solutions to the Jewish problem are utopian, since they are not in harmony with the striving and feeling of contemporary Jewry.

It is not the utopian element that bars masses of Jews from Zionism, but their subjugation and passiveness which are the result of our centuries-old bondage. Opponents imbibe their opposition to Zionism from various schools of thought, yet it all springs from one source—inner void and spiritual degeneration.

No other class is as morally bankrupt as the bourgeoisie. It lives in an atmosphere of falsehood and fraud. The bourgeois Jews come out openly as the defenders of society and supporters of the State, and yet, deep in their hearts, they greet the revolutionary parties whom they can trust. They are overflowing with patriotism and chauvinism, yet consider the land and the people among whom they live only as objects of exploitation. Outwardly, they parade their love of country and people;

inwardly, they are cynical. Zionism removes the mask and presents them as they are—people without honor and respect, whose sole purpose is the accumulation of money. Zionism arouses the Jews to protest, and enables them to understand their own worthless and miserable existence.

The modern synagogue is partner to the Jewish bourgeoisie. Zionism comes into strong collision with it. At no time in history was the church so pliable to the demands of the ruling class as is the Jewish synagogue of the present time. The synagogue has prostituted itself to the Jewish bourgeoisie. Zionism, which strikes the master, also strikes the servant. Zionism dispels the fable of the Reformed rabbis concerning the Jewish "mission." Therefore, Zionism encounters nowhere so much opposition as in the Reformed synagogue where the Jewish bourgeoisie prays to the almighty dollar.

Opposition to Zionism has also arisen from quarters least expected. It is painful that the Jewish socialist intelligentsia should be hostile to Zionism. How is it possible to derive from the principles of socialism, whose mainstay is equality and self-determination for all nations, opposition to a movement which has no purpose save the creation of a home for the unfortunate persecuted Jewish masses? Through their opposition, the assimilation-socialists best revealed their lack of understanding of the essence of socialism.

Jewish socialists dig up baseless reasons to support their anti-Zionist attitude. When the excuses of internationalism, and the denial of the existence of a Jewish nationality were discarded, they found another argument—that Zionism conflicts with the class struggle. The Jewish people, they maintain, is divided into classes which struggle against each other, while Zionism ignores these economic differences, postulating a so-called unity of the Jewish nation. There can be no more foolish argument than to maintain that the Jewish class struggle conflicts with Zionism. The protagonists of this idea do not grasp the meaning of the class struggle, and create contradictions which do not exist. Why should the Jewish proletariat, which is the first to be helped by Zionism, reject it merely because the other classes of Jewry have also adopted Zionism?

The class struggle does not give vent to all expressions of social life. When a people is endangered, all parties unite to fight the outside enemy, though in normal times the classes fight each other. Similarly, parties unite in elections and form coalitions against internal enemies. Modern parliamentarism is based on this procedure. In every union of men for idealistic purposes the struggle which divides man against man disappears and higher forms of solidarity emerge to the foreground. Class struggle is the main driving force of history, but it is not properly conceived to solve all our social problems. Creative activities are realized not through the class struggle but in spite of it. Zionism is a creative work of the Jews, and is not in contradiction to the class struggle. Moreover, it rises above it. Zionism can be accepted by all Jewry in spite of class differences.

The Jewish proletariat, the poor Jewish masses, the intelligentsia, and the middle class, can justifiably oppose a Jewish state being built on the principles of capitalism. True, the Jewish state, regardless of form, can erase a great number of the Jewish problems, but the modern conscience is so greatly impregnated with social and economic ideals that the Jewish masses will not accept a capitalistic Jewish state.

The *form* of the Jewish state is the only debatable issue involved in Zionism. Zionism must take the opinion of the Jewish masses into consideration, for without them Zionism will be a still-born child. The wheels of the Jewish state cannot be turned if the powerful arms of the Jewish workers are missing. Zionism must take into consideration the socialist aspirations of the Jewish proletariat, without losing sight of the aspirations of the middle class and intelligentsia. Zionism must of necessity fuse with socialism, for socialism is in complete harmony with the wishes and hopes of the Jewish masses.

Any other form of a Jewish state is scientifically and socially unsound.

(1898)

THE TEACHING OF JEWISH HISTORY

by S. M. DUBNOW

JEWISH history possesses the student with the conviction that Jewry at all times, even in the period of political independence, was preeminently a spiritual nation, and a spiritual nation it continues to be in our own days, too. Furthermore, it inspires him with the belief that Jewry, being a spiritual entity, cannot suffer annihilation: the body, the mold, may be destroyed, the spirit is immortal. Bereft of country and dispersed as it is, the Jewish nation lives, and will go on living, because a creative principle permeates it, a principle that is the root of its being and an indigenous product of its history. This principle consists first in a sum of definite religious, moral, or philosophic ideals, whose exponent at all times was the Jewish people, either in its totality, or in the person of its most prominent representatives. Next, this principle consists in a sum of historical memories, recollections of what in the course of many centuries the Jewish people experienced, thought and felt, in the depths of its being. Finally, it consists in the consciousness that true Judaism, which has accomplished great things for humanity in the past, has not yet played out its part, and, therefore, may not perish. In short, the Jewish people lives because it contains a living soul which refuses to separate from its integument, and cannot be forced out of it by heavy trials and misfortunes, such as would unfailingly inflict moral injury upon less sturdy organisms.

This self-consciousness is the source from which the suffering Jewish soul draws comfort. History speaks to it constantly through the mouth of the great apostle who went forth from the midst of Israel eighteen hundred years ago: "Call to remembrance the former days, in which, after ye were enlightened, ye endured a great conflict of sufferings; partly, being made a gazing-stock both by reproaches and afflictions; and partly, becoming partakers with them that were so used. . . . Cast not away therefore your boldness, which hath great recompense of reward" (*Epistle to the Hebrews*, x, 32-34, 35).

Jewish history, moreover, arouses in the Jew the desire to work unceasingly at the task of perfecting himself. To direct his attention to his glorious past, to the resplendent intellectual feats of his ancestors, to their masterly skill in thinking and suffering, does not lull him to sleep, does not awaken a dullard's complacency or hollow self-conceit. On the contrary, it makes exacting demands upon him. Jewish history admonishes the Jews: "Noblesse oblige. The privilege of belonging to a people to whom the honorable title of the 'veteran of history' has been conceded, puts serious responsibilities on your shoulders. You must demonstrate that you are worthy of your heroic past. The descendants of teachers of religion and martyrs of the faith dare not be insignificant, not to say wicked. If the long centuries of wandering and misery have inoculated you with faults, extirpate them in the name of the exalted moral ideals whose bearers you were commissioned to be. If, in the course of time, elements out of harmony with your essential being have fastened upon your mind, cast them out, purify yourselves. In all places and at all times, in joy and in sorrow, you must aim to live for the higher, the spiritual interests. But never may you deem yourselves perfect. If you become faithless to these sacred principles, you sever the bonds that unite you with the most vital elements of your past, with the first cause of your national existence."

The final lesson to be learned is that in the sunny days of mankind's history, in which reason, justice, and philanthropic instinct had the upper hand, the Jews steadfastly made common cause with the other nations. Hand in hand with them, they trod the path leading to perfection. But in the dark days, during the reign of rude force, prejudice, and passion, of which they were the first victims, the Jews retired from the world, withdrew into their shell, to await better days. Union with mankind at large, on the basis of the spiritual and the intellectual, the goal set up by the Jewish Prophets in their sublime vision of the future (*Isaiah,* ch. ii, and *Micah,* ch. iv), is the ultimate ideal of Judaism's noblest votaries. Will their radiant hope ever attain to realization?

If ever it should be realized,—and it is incumbent upon us to believe that it will,—not a slight part of the merits involved will be due to Jewish history. We have adverted to the lofty moral and humanitarian significance of Jewish history in its role as conciliator. With regard to one-half of Jewish history, this conciliatory power is even now a well-established fact. The first part of Jewish history, the Biblical part, is a source from which, for many centuries, millions of human beings belonging to the most diverse denominations have derived instruction, solace, and inspiration. It is read with devotion by Christians in both hemispheres, in their houses and their temples. Its heroes have long ago become types, incarnations of great ideas. The events it relates serve as living ethical formulas. But a time will come—perhaps it is not very far off—when the second half of Jewish history, the record of the two thousand years of the Jewish people's life after the Biblical period will be accorded the same treatment. This latter part of Jewish history is not yet known, and many, in the thrall of prejudice, do not wish to know it. But ere long it will be known and appreciated. For the thinking portion of mankind it will be a source of uplifting moral and philosophical teaching. The thousand years' martyrdom of the Jewish people, its unbroken pilgrimage, its tragic fate, its teachers of religion, its martyrs, philosophers, champions, this whole epic will in days to come sink deep into the memory of men. It will speak to the heart and the conscience of men, not merely to their curious mind. It will secure respect for the silvery hair of the Jewish people, a people of thinkers and sufferers. It will dispense consolation to the afflicted, and by its examples of spiritual steadfastness and self-denial encourage martyrs in their devotion. It is our firm conviction that the time is approaching in which the second half of Jewish history will be to the noblest part of *thinking* humanity what its first half has long been to *believing* humanity, a source of sublime moral truths. In this sense, Jewish history in its entirety is the pledge of the spiritual union between the Jews and the rest of the nations.

(1903)

WORK AND CULTURE

by AARON DAVID GORDON

A PEOPLE wholly detached from nature, imprisoned in walls during thousands of years, such a people, inured to all phases of life except that ultimately natural one of spontaneous work for its own sake, cannot become once more a living, natural, and labouring people without the extreme exertion of its total will. We lack the one thing needful—work. Not compulsory work, but that work with which such a being as man is organically and naturally integrated and through which, in turn, a people is integrated with its earth and that culture which is rooted in the soil and in work. It is true that among other peoples, too, all individuals do not work productively, that many disdain work and seek ways of living by the labour of others. But a truly living people unfolds its activity in a wholly natural way; its work constitutes one of its organic functions and is executed in accordance with its nature. To the majority of any living people work is second nature. It is not so among us. We really disdain work and even the workers among us labour in the constant hope of some day exchanging work for a comfortable life. We must not deceive ourselves; we must come to see clearly how unhappy is our condition in this respect, how estranged our spirit, both individual and national, has become from work. Quite characteristic is the saying, "So long as Israel does God's will, others will work for us." For it is not a mere saying. Consciously or not, this thought has become almost an instinct and almost second nature among us.

Let us now assume that a dense Jewish settlement were to come into being, would this situation change at once? Will a change come over the substance of our soul without some radical healing? Will not our Jews continue to prefer mercantile pursuits, peddling, financial transactions, all the callings in which others work and they assume direction? And even if life were to force a part of them to actual labour, will these people not again choose such urban pursuits as offer the possibilities of attaining wealth and leisure, if they do not, in fact, emigrate to other and wealthier lands? Under these circumstances the land would again be cultivated by others and the essential and organic labour performed by them. Can such be the natural state of a living folk?

Who is there that meditates concerning this matter? Who feels it profoundly? We have no work and no one feels the lack. And we seem not even to feel it when we discuss our national rebirth. We feel the lack of work neither in its aspect of that force which marries man to earth and lets him truly possess it, nor as the chief source from which a creative national culture must arise. We have no land, no living speech or culture—so much at least we feel and seem more or less to recognize, and we seek to do what is necessary or what is possible. Yet if no one among us truly works, what will all else avail us? Let Ivan, John, Mustapha do the work. We will create culture, produce national values, and seek to bring about the reign of absolute justice on earth.

Now what is the character of this "culture" which after long and stubborn conflicts has finally been agreed upon within our movement?

It consists in what, among us, is known as a requickening of the spirit. But this spirit which we want to bring back to life is in itself no loving spirit; it neither penetrates nor quickens the body nor does it draw life from the body; it is quite abstract, and its glory is to be found only in the innermost cells of the brain. In brief, this whole culture is nothing but a group of opinions. And when it is a question of mere opinions or views, one individual can select those of Hermann Struck or the Rabbi of Lida, and another those of Marx and Engels.

Under such barren aspects are we accustomed to regard culture and even to speak of its reflourishing in the dispersion. "Spirit" and "opinions"—such things take up no room in space and it is hard to say whether they are either in harmony with the time or genuinely rooted in the folk. But the truth is that in the diaspora we can have no living culture which must be nourished by life itself and develop from it. And the reason is this, that in the diaspora we have no life of our own; the life that we live in the diaspora is not our life. What we have in the diaspora are certain inherited cultural goods which at need we have refashioned according to the spirit of the time and land in which we are. We have had, that is, to bring them in harmony with the life which the will of others forces us to live and with the wind of the spirit that blows in the world of those others. In the Galuth we have developed thus an adaptability to remold the products of an alien life according to our spirit and to fashion of the fruit of alien work tidbits that suit our taste. Beyond that we have nothing but the knowledge and conviction that we possess a huge minus. In this unnatural condition our only real sharing of civilization is in the realms of ideas, literature, poetry. Here we have produced much that is new and have even exhibited some creative ability. But that does not suffice for a living culture.

A living culture embraces the whole of life. Everything that life creates for life's necessities, that is culture—digging the earth, building houses and roads; such work, such labour, such activity is culture, or, rather, the basis and substance of culture. The order and manner and way according to which these things are done produce the form of a national culture. All that the workers feel and do and experience working or resting, and the relations which arise the while with that nature which is alive in each—this it is that creates civilization. From this the highest culture—science, art, philosophy, poetry, ethics, religion—draws its nourishment. These high and sublimated aspects of culture which alone those have in mind who speak of culture among us are only the cream at the top of a national culture in the widest sense. But can he produce cream who has no milk? Or is it possible to skim one's own cream from a stranger's milk?

What is it that we seek in Palestine, if not just this thing that we have nowhere else—the living milk of culture? What we need today in our great poverty is not an academic culture, but a culture of life itself, in the cells and atoms of which that academic culture is embedded—a culture of life itself which, given time and conditions, will gather at its top, to keep our simile, the natural cream of its higher manifestations. We need to create the philosophy of life as well as its art, its poetry, its ethics, its religion. Nor must we forget to build a bridge of life, a living bridge, between our present and our past. Living we need to create our own life, conformable to our spirit and our kind. And at this point I must add a few words to make the matter even clearer, though it should be clear enough even so. We are the children of God who created the universe by the word of His mouth. And when I speak of "creating" I mean to make the strict comparison and to say that by heeding a simple word we can create what we need. Therefore the matter may be formulated quite simply thus: All that we desire in Palestine comes to this, that we create with our own hands all that constitutes life; that with our own hands we perform all the work and labour that is needed from the highest and most complicated and easiest down to the coarsest and hardest and most contemptible, and that we thus come to feel and think and experience all that labouring human beings in the performance of all these varied tasks can come to feel and think and experience. Only when we do that will we possess a culture because only thus will we have a life of our own.

But among us it is possible that people come together from all the lands of the dispersion and even from Palestine and take council concerning what must be done for our rebirth and our redemption and that we talk about a living culture without its occurring to anyone to speak of the ultimate foundation of all culture, of the essential thing that we lack—namely, work.

(1911)

THE SOLUTION OF THE JEWISH PROBLEM

by LOUIS D. BRANDEIS

WHY is it that liberalism has failed to eliminate the anti-Jewish prejudice? It is because the liberal movement has not yet brought *full* liberty. Enlightened countries grant to the individual equality before the law; but they fail still to recognize the equality of whole peoples or nationalities. We seek to protect as individuals those constituting a minority; but we fail to realize that protection cannot be complete unless group equality also is recognized.

Deeply imbedded in every people is the desire for full development —the longing, as Mazzini phrased it "to elaborate and express their idea, to contribute their stone also to the pyramid of history." Nationality like democracy has been one of the potent forces making for man's advance during the past hundred years. The assertion of nationality has infused whole people with hope, manhood and self-respect. It has ennobled and made purposeful millions of lives. It offered them a future, and in doing so revived and capitalized all that was valuable in their past. The assertion of nationality raised Ireland from the slough of despondency. It roused Southern Slavs to heroic deeds. It created gallant Belgium. It freed Greece. It gave us united Italy. It manifested itself even among free peoples—like the Welsh who had no grievance, but who gave expression to their nationality through the revival of the old Cymric tongue. Each of these peoples developed because, as Mazzini said, they were enabled to proclaim "to the world that they also live, think, love and labor for the benefit of all."

In the past it has been generally assumed that the full development of one people necessarily involved its domination over others. Strong nationalities are apt to become convinced that by such domination only, does civilization advance. Strong nationalities assume their own superiority, and come to believe that they possess the divine right to subject other peoples to their sway. Soon the belief in the existence of such a right becomes converted into a conviction that a duty exists to enforce it. Wars of aggrandizement follow as a natural result of this belief.

This attitude of certain nationalities is the exact correlative of the position which was generally assumed by the strong in respect to other individuals before democracy became a common possession. The struggles of the eighteenth and nineteenth centuries both in peace and in war were devoted largely to overcoming that position as to individuals. In establishing the equal right of every person to development, it became clear that equal opportunity for all involves this necessary limitation: Each man may develop himself so far, but only so far, as his doing so will not interfere with the exercise of a like right by all others. Thus liberty came to mean the right to enjoy life, to acquire property, to pursue happiness in such manner and to such extent as the exercise of the right in each is consistent with the exercise of a like right by every other of our fellow citizens. Liberty thus defined underlies twentieth century democracy. Liberty thus defined exists in a large part of the western world. And even where this equal right of each individual has not yet been accepted as a political right, its ethical claim is gaining recognition. Democracy rejected the proposal of the superman who should rise through sacrifice of the many. It insists that the full development of each individual is not only a right, but a duty to society; and that our best hope for civilization lies not in uniformity, but in wide differentiation.

The movements of the last century have proved that whole peoples have individuality no less marked than that of the single person; that the individuality of a people is irrepressible, and that the misnamed internationalism which seeks the obliteration of nationalities or peoples is unattainable. The new nationalism proclaims that each race or people, like each individual, has a right and duty to develop, and that only through such differentiated development will high civilization be attained. Not until these principles of nationalism, like those of democracy, are generally accepted, will liberty be fully attained, and minorities be secure in their rights. But there is ground for hope that the establishment of these principles will come as one of the compensations of the present war; and with it, the solution of the Jewish problem.

The difference between a nation and a nationality is clear; but it is not always observed. Likeness between members is the essence of nationality; but the members of a nation may be very different. A nation may be composed of many nationalities, as some of the most successful nations are. An instance of this is the British nation, with its division into English, Scotch, Welsh, and Irish at home; with the French in Canada; and, throughout the Empire, scores of other nationalities. Other examples are furnished by the Swiss nation with its German, French and Italian sections; by the Belgian nation composed of Flemings and Walloons; and by the American nation which comprises nearly all the white nationalities. The unity of a nationality is a fact of nature. The unity into a nation is largely the work of man. The false doctrine that nation and nationality must be made co-extensive is the cause of some of our greatest tragedies. It is, in large part, the cause also of the present war. It has led, on the one hand, to cruel, futile attempts at enforced assimilation, like the Russianizing of Finland and Poland, and the Prussianizing of Posen, Schleswig-Holstein, and Alsace-Lorraine. It has led, on the other hand, to those Panistic movements which are a cloak for territorial ambitions. As a nation may thrive though composed of many nationalities, so a nationality may thrive though forming parts of several nations. The essential in either case is recognition of the equal rights of each nationality.

W. Allison Phillips recently defined nationality as "an extensive aggregate of persons, conscious of a community of sentiments, experiences, or qualities which make them feel themselves a distinct people." And he adds: "If we examine the composition of the several nationalities we find these elements: Race, language, religion, common habitat, common conditions, mode of life and manners, political association. The elements are, however, never all present at the same time, and none of them is essential. . . . A common habitat and common conditions are doubtless powerful influences at times in determining nationality; but what part do they play in that of the Jews or the Greeks, or the Irish in dispersion?"

See how this high authority assumes without question that the Jews are, despite their dispersion, a distinct nationality; and he groups us with the Greeks or the Irish—two other people of marked individuality. Can it be doubted that we Jews—aggregating 14,000,000 people—are "an extensive aggregate of persons"; that we are "conscious of a community of sentiments, experiences and qualities which make us *feel* ourselves a distinct people," whether we admit it or not?

It is no answer to this evidence of nationality to declare that the Jews are not an absolutely pure race. There has, of course, been some intermixture of foreign blood in the 3,000 years which constitute our historic period. But, owing to persecution and prejudice, the intermarriages with non-Jews which occurred, have resulted merely in taking away many from the Jewish community. Intermarriage has brought few additions. Therefore the percentage of foreign blood in the Jews of today is very low. Probably no important European race is as pure.

But common race is only one of the elements which determine nationality. Conscious community of sentiments, common experiences, common qualities are equally, perhaps more, important. Religion, traditions and customs bound us together though scattered throughout the world. The similarity of experiences tended to produce similarity of qualities and community of sentiments. Common suffering so intensified the feeling of brotherhood as to overcome largely all the influences making for diversification. The segregation of the Jews was so general, so complete, and so long continued as to intensify our "peculiarities" and make them almost ineradicable.

We recognize that with each child the aim of education should be to develop his own individuality, not to make him an imitator, not to assimilate him to others. Shall we fail to recognize this truth when applied to whole peoples? And what people in the world has shown greater individuality than the Jews? Has any a nobler past? Does any possess common ideas better worth expressing? Has any marked traits worthier of development? Of all the people in the world those of two tiny states stand preeminent as contributors to our present civilization,—the Greeks and the Jews. The Jews gave to the world its three greatest religions, reverence for law, and the highest conceptions of morality. Never before has the value of our contribution been so generally recognized. Our teaching of brotherhood and righteousness has, under the name of democracy and social justice, become the twentieth century striving of America and of western Europe. Our conception of law is embodied in the American constitutions which proclaim this to be a "government of laws and not of men." And for the triumph of our other great teaching—the doctrine of peace—this cruel war is paving the way.

While every other people is striving for development by asserting its nationality, and a great war is making clear the value of small nations, shall we voluntarily yield to antisemitism, and instead of solving our "problem" end it by ignoble suicide? Surely this is no time for Jews to despair. Let us make clear to the world that we too are a nationality clamoring for equal rights to life and to self-expression. That this should be our course has been recently expressed by high non-Jewish authority. Thus Seton-Watson, speaking of the probable results of the war, said:

"There are good grounds for hoping that it (the war) will also give a new and healthy impetus to Jewish national policy, grant freer play to their splendid qualities, and enable them to shake off the false shame which has led men who ought to be proud of their Jewish race to assume so many alien disguises and to accuse of antisemitism those who refuse to be deceived by mere appearances. It is high time that the Jews should realize that few things do more to foster antisemitic feeling than this very tendency to sail under false colors and conceal their true identity. The Zionists and the orthodox Jewish Nationalists have long ago won the respect and admiration of the world. No race has ever defied assimilation so stubbornly and so successfully; and the modern tendency of individual Jews to repudiate what is one of their chief glories suggests an almost comic resolve to fight against the course of nature."

Standing upon this broad foundation of nationality, Zionism aims to give it full development. Let us bear clearly in mind what Zionism is, or rather what it is not.

It is not a movement to remove all the Jews of the world compulsorily to Palestine. In the first place there are 14,000,000 Jews, and Palestine would not accommodate more than one-fifth of that number. In the second place, it is not a movement to compel anyone to go to Palestine. It is essentially a movement to give to the Jew more, not less freedom,— it aims to enable the Jews to exercise the same right now exercised by practically every other people in the world: To live at their option either in the land of their fathers or in some other country; a right which members of small nations as well as of large,—which Irish, Greek, Bulgarian, Servian, or Belgian, may now exercise as fully as Germans or English.

Zionism seeks to establish in Palestine, for such Jews as choose to go and remain there, and for their descendants, a legally secured home, where they may live together and lead a Jewish life; where they may expect ultimately to constitute a majority of the population, and may look forward to what we should call home rule. The Zionists seek to establish this home in Palestine because they are convinced that the undying longing of Jews for Palestine is a fact of deepest significance; that it is a manifestation in the struggle for existence by an ancient people which had established its right to live—a people whose three thousand years of civilization has produced a faith, culture, and individuality which enable them to contribute largely in the future, as they had in the past, to the advance of civilization; and that it is not a right merely, but a duty of the Jewish nationality to survive and develop. They believe that there only can Jewish life be fully protected from the forces of disintegration; that there alone can the Jewish spirit reach its full and natural development; and that by securing for those Jews who wish to settle in Palestine the opportunity to do so, not only those Jews, but all other Jews will be benefited and that the long perplexing Jewish Problem will, at last, find solution.

Our Jewish Pilgrim Fathers have laid the foundation. It remains for us to build the superstructure.

Let no American imagine that Zionism is inconsistent with Patriotism. Multiple loyalties are objectionable only if they are inconsistent. A man is a better citizen of the United States for being also a loyal citizen of his state, and of his city; for being loyal to his family, and to his profession or trade; for being loyal to his college or his lodge. Every Irish American who contributed towards advancing home rule was a better man and a better American for the sacrifice he made. Every American Jew who aids in advancing the Jewish settlement in Palestine, though he feels that neither he nor his descendants will ever live there, will likewise be a better man and a better American for doing so.

Note what Seton-Watson says:

"America is full of nationalities which, while accepting with enthusiasm their new American citizenship, nevertheless look to some centre in the old world as the source and inspiration of their national culture and traditions. The most typical instance is the feeling of the American Jew for Palestine which may well become a focus for his *declasse* kinsmen in other parts of the world."

There is no inconsistency between loyalty to America and loyalty to Jewry. The Jewish spirit, the product of our religion and experiences, is essentially modern and essentially American. Not since the destruction of the Temple have the Jews in spirit and in ideals been so fully in harmony with the noblest aspirations of the country in which they lived.

America's fundamental law seeks to make real the brotherhood of man. That brotherhood became the Jewish fundamental law more than twenty-five hundred years ago. America's insistent demand in the twentieth century is for social justice. That also has been the Jews' striving for ages. Their affliction as well as their religion has prepared the Jews for effective democracy. Persecution broadened their sympathies; it trained them in patient endurance, in self-control, and in sacrifice. It made them think as well as suffer. It deepened the passion for righteousness.

Indeed, loyalty to America demands rather that each American Jew become a Zionist. For only through the ennobling effect of its strivings can we develop the best that is in us and give to this country the full benefit of our great inheritance. The Jewish spirit, so long preserved, the character developed by so many centuries of sacrifice, should be preserved and developed further, so that in America as elsewhere the sons of the race may in future live lives and do deeds worthy of their ancestors.

(1915)

THE TENETS OF ZIONISM

by MAX NORDAU

THERE is nothing vague or hazy about the tenets of Zionism. It is easy to state them clearly and tersely, as follows:

The Jews form not merely a religious community but also a nation.

There are Jews who sever their national bonds and tend towards the dissolution of the people of Israel in their non-Jewish surroundings. But the large majority of Jews, chiefly in Eastern Europe, desire ardently to preserve their Jewish national identity. Zionism has no meaning for Jews who favour the melting pot theory. It is the ideal of those who feel themselves to belong to a Jewish nation.

These latter are convinced that in order to work out their possibilities of progress in civilization, to develop their character, to realize their hereditary notions of morals, justice, and brotherhood, and to escape the blighting influence of hatred and persecution, they must be redeemed from their Dispersion, be gathered together, and settle in a country of their own, where they may live a natural life as tillers of the soil.

The only country answering this purpose is Palestine, the historic home of their forefathers, which for nearly two thousand years has never ceased to be the object of their yearning.

Zionism does not pretend to lead back to the Holy Land of their ancestors all the Jews of the globe. The return of those who cling with all their heart to the country of their birth and of their citizenship is out of the question. Only those will set out for the East who feel that there and nowhere else has life moral and material satisfaction and happiness in store for them.

Zionism has not the ambition of founding an independent Jewish State, be it kingdom or a republic. All it desires is that its adherents should be allowed to immigrate without any restraint into Palestine, to buy there as much land as they can obtain for their money, to enjoy autonomy of local administration, and not to be hampered in their earnest efforts to create culture and prosperity. It goes without saying that Zionistic Jews pledge themselves to observe the most scrupulous, most generous loyalty towards the Power under whose sovereignty Palestine is placed.

This is the case for Zionism, fully and sincerely, though shortly, expounded.

The necessity of Zionism, the only practical scheme for putting an end to twenty centuries of unutterable sufferings of millions of highly gifted human beings artificially kept down to a low state of development, is superabundantly proved by present events. At this moment, some five hundred thousand Jewish soldiers, rather more than less, part of them under the military law of their country, but others from their own free will, fight in the ranks of the armies of all the nations at war, suffer cruel hardships, shed their blood, sacrifice their life, inscribe heroic deeds of arms in the annals of glory, and yet see offending doubt cast on their patriotism, feel themselves surrounded by an atmosphere of suspicion and hostility, hear often the contemptuous words "foreigners" and "cosmopolitans" muttered behind their back or even roughly hurled in their face, not to speak of the atrocities committed against millions of Jewish victims in the war area of Russia. There is only one way of avoiding a recurrence of these horrors, and that is by giving these "foreigners" and "cosmopolitans" a home of their own, which is what Zionism is striving for.

To those inclined to treat our aspirations as a dream, we can show most promising beginnings of Jewish colonization in Palestine, with tens of thousands of acres of beautiful cornfields, vineyards, orange, almond, and olive-groves; with neat, clean, thriving villages, and Hebrew schools, where a generation of bright and healthy children receive an excellent education in the sacred language of the Prophets. These colonies, it is true, are at present gravely imperilled by the War. It is our immediate duty to do all in our power to pilot them through the gale of the hour. Once peace is re-established, they will convince the world, and even sceptical Jews, of our capacity as agriculturists, wine-growers, and cattle-breeders.

I have confined myself within the limits of prosaic matter-of-fact. I avoid adding even one word about the beauty and loftiness of the Zionist ideal.

Whoever wishes for a future for Judaism and believes in it must realize that nothing can ensure it but Zionism.

(1916)

THE SPIRITUAL PATTERN OF JUDAISM

by MARTIN BUBER

IT is a fundamental fact of psychical dynamics that the manifoldness of the soul is constantly perceived by man as a dualism. Since in fact consciousness does not differentiate between appearance and reality it may be said that the soul tends constantly to assume a dualistic form. Man, in brief, experiences the fullness of inner realities and possibilities as a substance that tends toward two opposite poles; he experiences his inner way as a pilgrimage from crossroads to crossroads. The two poles or contradictories which attract the soul may change content and name; the decision at the crossroads of choice may be perceived as a personal decision or as a necessity imposed from without or even as accident. The pattern remains the same. And this pattern is one of the decisive ultimates of human life; it is perhaps the most essential of all, since it bodies forth the mystery of the original twofold nature of the psyche which determines its nature and meaning. Now this pattern or fundamental form is in no human type so powerful a determinant or so central as in the Jew both of the past and of the present. In no other type has it assumed a reality so pure and so complete nor affected so decisively both character and fate. Nowhere else has this determinant created anything so extraordinary or paradoxical or heroic or in the nature of a marvel as the striving of the Jew after unity. And it is this striving after unity that makes of Judaism a human phenomenon and makes the Jewish problem to be a problem of all mankind.

This is neither the place nor the moment to explain the origin or development of this extxreme consciousness of duality in Judaism. But whoever knows how to interpret history will not fail to find it again

and again from the earliest records on to the present day. Its most powerful expression in the primordial period is the myth of the fall of man
as it was incorporated in the book of Genesis. This myth, of which
the autochthonous character is not denied even by the pan-Babylonians,
establishes the elements of good and of evil, the clearest and most telling of all the contents of man's inner duality, with consummate power
and clearness. It represents man's task as being in the nature of a
choice, of a decision, and represents the whole future as dependent upon
this decision. It speaks for man who is torn between the poles of a dualism. Let us not be deceived into thinking the dualism of the ancient
Persians at all analogous to this. Persian dualism has reference to the
objective world, not to the world of the soul. It is cosmological, not psy-
chological. Persian dualism is a description of reality, not a confession of
guilt. According to it man *is* divided even as the cosmos is. According
to the antique Jew the world was not divided, nor was man divided.
No, man separated himself; he fell and failed and became unlike the
Divine. The world as object remained homogeneous, and Satan a servant
of the Lord. It is the soul that is riven in two, and the world only so far
as it is a symbol of the soul. . . .

I have taken the classical example of the myth of the fall of man
and cannot stop to analyse others. But open the great record of Jewish
antiquity wherever you please; read in the historical books the tales of the
apostasy from Yahveh or read in the prophetical books the call to the
conquest of injustice, or in Job the expression of insight into the necessity of inner dualism, which the pure will cannot master nor he who
fights for his integrity escape, but only redemption can lead him forth
from it; or hear in the *Psalms* the ever-returning cry for cleansing through
God—and in all these passages you will find the experience of inner
division and everywhere the striving after oneness.

The striving after oneness. After oneness in the soul of the individual. After oneness between faction and faction of a people, between
people and people, between humanity and all other living things. Between God and the world.

And this God Himself had come forth out of that striving after
oneness, out of that dark, impassioned striving after oneness. He had been
evoked not from nature, but from the soul of man. The believing Jew
"asked not concerning the heavens or the earth, if he had but Him,"
because he had brought Him forth not from reality, but from his own
yearning, because he had not seen Him in heaven or on earth, but had
conceived Him as the Oneness above his own duality and as the salva-

tion of his own suffering spirit. The believing Jew (and the believing Jew was the Jew entire of nature) found his integrity in his God; through Him he took his redeeming flight into that primordial childlike mythic age of undivided being in which, as Job says, "God's mystery was above my hut"; through Him he fled into the Messianic future of re-integration, of wholeness; in Him he was redeemed from all duality.

For just as the idea of inner twoness is a Jewish idea, so is the idea of redemption therefrom Jewish. The Hindu idea of redemption is doubtless purer and more absolute; but its goal is not redemption from the duality of the soul but from all implication with the world. The Hindu redemption means an awakening, the Jewish a conversion; the one aims after liberation from illusion, the other a grasping of truth; thus the one is a negation and the other an affirmation; the Brahmin floats into the "intense inane"; the Jew seeks the pathway of humanity. Like all historical ideas, the Jewish idea is less sharply definable but far more stirring. It speaks through Job's "I know that my Redeemer liveth," and in the Psalmist's "Create a new spirit within me." In it no less was rooted the idea of redemption of the Jew Jesus. And when Jewish mysticism altered the original character of the idea of God and carried a dualistic notion into the very conception of Him, then the Jewish notion of redemption rose to the heights of the Indic itself: it became the idea of the redemption of God Himself through the reuniting of the God-being, far removed from the world of things, with the God-glory or emanation which wanders, exiled, in that phenomenal world; it became the idea of the redemption of God through his creature: By each soul's rising from its twoness to oneness, by each soul's growing to be at one within itself, God reattains His Oneness.

It is the striving after unity that has rendered the Jew creative. Struggling out of the division of the "I" after oneness, he created the idea of the God Who is One; striving after unity out of the cleavage in twain of human society, he created the idea of universal justice; seeking to bring union out of the division of all living things, he created the idea of universal love; striving to unify a riven world, he created the Messianic ideal, which a far later age, largely under the guidance of Jews, dwarfed and trivialized and called socialism.

In order to comprehend what the fundamental change which I am advocating could effect, it is necessary to recall to ourselves the nature of that profound Judaism of which we desire the rebirth. You touch only the coarsest externals of organizational form when you speak of it as a religious persuasion; you touch a deeper reality when you speak of a folk and its ways. But it is necessary to peer still deeper in order to discover its innermost character.

Judaism is an intellectual and spiritual process which manifests itself in the inner history of the Jewish people and in the works of its great representatives. To identify this process, as both Lazarus and Achad Ha'Am do (each in his own language), with the doctrine of unity or the spirit of the Prophets is still to limit it unduly. The doctrine of unity is but a single element, and the spirit of the Prophets but a single stage in that great process which is to be called Judaism. And only he who grasps this process in all its magnitude, in all the fullness of its constituent elements and in the manifold transformations of its revelation through history, can comprehend the significance of that which I call renewal here.

The spiritual process of Judaism effectuates itself historically as the striving after an ever more perfect realization (embodiment in concrete vital terms) of three interdependent ideas: The idea of Unity, the idea of Action, the idea of the Future. When I speak of ideas I do not, evidently, mean abstract concepts, but natural tendencies in the national character, which manifest themselves so powerfully and so enduringly as to produce that complex or web of spiritual works and values which may be fairly pronounced to be the *absolute life of the people Israel.*

Now every people of strong specific gifts has similar tendencies peculiar to itself and a whole world of works and values which are the creative expressions of these tendencies, so that it may be said to live a twofold life—the one fugitive and relative in the succession of its mortal days, in the arising and fading of its generations, the other life (strictly simultaneous with the first) an abiding and absolute life in the world of the wandering and seeking spirit of man. And though in that first or relative living all things seem accidental and often desperately meaningless, yet are there revealed in that other or absolute life, with more and more of clearness, the great and radiant lines of both meaning and necessity.

The relative life of a people remains the possession of its folk-consciousness; its absolute life enters immediately or mediately into the consciousness of mankind. But there is none among the peoples of earth in which this constant begetting of an absolute life, in which the characteristic spiritual process of its nationality is so visible and so strongly marked as in the Jewish people. In its relative life, in that aspect even which is commonly called history, as well as in the common day of every present, there is the confusion of finite purpose and haste and desire and pain. But from this confusion arise evermore, radiant and magnificent, the eternal aims and write their indestructible signs across the heaven of the abiding. And to the eye that penetrates through the relative to the absolute life of our people, it is revealed that the former with all its busy confusion exists only to beget the latter and that the latter is the ultimate reality and the former only the many-coloured, manifold and fugitive appearance. The proof of this can be tested more clearly and unequivocally in the life of the Jewish people than in any other way, and it is for this reason that I dared to call Judaism a spiritual process.

(1917)

THE JEWISH RELIGION

by C. G. MONTEFIORE

THE non-nationalist, or purely religious, Jew regards the Jews as a religious community. So far as they are anything more, in his eyes, that more is of small value whether for themselves or for the world. If the Jews have anything to give, if they have any spiritual function or task, it must be in the sphere of religion, though religion must not be so narrowly defined as to exclude morality, more especially in its relation to religion. The non-nationalist, or purely religious, Jew assumes the continued existence of Jews as a distinct religious community, among the various nations of European descent, and it is the groups of Jews in these various countries rather than the Jews of Palestine, who, it is hoped, may render some religious service to Europe, though if Palestinian Jews help in that service, so much the better.

It is, perhaps, most straightforward to make at once the simple statement that the faith of this second division of Jews is that Jews and Judaism may yet have some service to render to the cause of Theism, as they conceive and interpret Theism. It is, it must be confessed, a presumptuous faith, involving as it does, at first, a belief that Jewish Theism has special and peculiar aspects of value and truth, and secondly, a belief that the tiny minority of Jews may exercise some religious influence outside their own borders. And it must be admitted that these beliefs are rash and strange.

It has been said that all argument must be avoided, and all attempts at rejoinder to very obvious and very pertinent objections. Yet to this rule one exception has to be made, for it would not be easy to get on and make things clear without it. It may, then, be justifiably asked by the critics of Judaism: 'What contribution did Judaism make to Theism and its development between A.D. 300 and the present day? What direct re. ligious influence has it had in the last sixteen hundred years? Christian. ity has had its own history since Constantine made it the dominant religion of the Roman Empire. What have the Jews done to affect that history? If Jewish Theism is somehow distinctive and valuable, is there (apart from the Jews themselves) more of it than there would have been if the Jews in the year A.D. 326 had been entirely exterminated? Is it more widely accepted and believed in?' Some answers to these questions are to be found in previous chapters, but I want to speak, not of the past, but of the future.

Religious faith takes very long views; it thinks of Him in whose sight a thousand years are but as yesterday when it is passed, or as a watch in the night. So thinking, it can, and does, become yet more daring and presumptuous. Strange visions pass before the Jewish mind, nor could even the genius of a Browning in *Holy Cross Day* interpret them quite faithfully. It is not an Ibn Gabirol or a Maimonides, still less a Spinoza, who fulfilled the Jewish mission most truly, or rendered the greatest service to the Jewish cause. No. It was the many little obscure Jewish communities through the ages, persecuted and despised, who kept alive the flame of purest Monotheism and the supremacy and divineness of the Moral Law. The imageless synagogue was perhaps squalid; the services within it were often crude and undignified; there were certainly several untenable beliefs and also much superstition. But, withal, at the root there was something which has yet to come by its own, something very pure, something which at once can satisfy reason and transcends reason, something that is the seed of a future, preserved, it may be, in an uncouth and unattractive husk. Jewish faith is not perturbed if the witnessing was silent and passive, if the messengers have made, and still make, little stir, and have produced visible results that seem but small. Only let them hold fast, only let the 'witnesses' and the 'servants' remain faithful, in prosperity as in adversity, in new environments as in old, in freedom as in servitude, and the promise shall yet be fulfilled. The Lord's hand is not shortened that it cannot save. . . .

But a dream as to the future, in answer to searching and inconvenient questions as to the present, may seem fantastical. Let us return to the present, before we touch again upon the future.

If compelled to translate dreams, visions, and faith into baldest words, they who hold this faith, see these visions, and dream these dreams, would, I suppose, say that now and henceforward, when and where there is free intercourse between Jew and Gentile, when and where artificial barriers are broken down, and when and where unfettered interchange of thought and discussion is the rule, Judaism may exercise a more direct influence upon the world's religious future than it has done in the last sixteen hundred years. It is, for those who hold this view, an article of faith that their form of Theism, together with their conception of the relation of morality to religion and to God, has in it elements of value and of truth which will ultimately prevail, or which, at any rate, in various modes and forms and embodiments, will be more and more widely accepted by mankind. This faith does not mean—at all events to Liberal Jews, of whose dreams and visions and beliefs I know most, because I know them from within—that the Jewish conception of God and of His relations to the world and to man has reached its term or limit of development. It does not mean that this Jewish conception cannot, and will not, expand and deepen. It does not mean that it contains all truth, or that it has not its own special difficulties and rough edges which the future will have to tackle and to overcome. But it does mean that this conception is believed to be fundamentally true and pure, with little to abandon and with much to keep. To set forth that conception in detail and fullness this is not the place, though incidentally, a word or two has to be said of it. Meanwhile, it has to be confessed that the Jewish view of what Israel has yet to give to the world is exceedingly daring and presumptuous, for it is nothing less than a faith that Israel has still something to say and to do as regards the world's attitude towards that which comes first and comes last in human thought, towards that on which all action and character do ultimately depend: the belief in God and in His relation to human righteousness and duty. If any part of this faith were to be fulfilled, how superb would be the Epilogue! It would put much of the past "Legacy" into the shade. For this would be indeed a gift of value unassessable.

Once more, however, let me come down from these vague and shadowy hopes and anticipations, which none beyond Israel can fully share, and few even can adequately appreciate, to something more restricted and, perhaps, more generally approvable. Among the nations of Europe and among their descendants in the new worlds of America and Australia, Theism is accepted by many, and is held in several forms. Even within the Christian limits God is conceived in more ways than one, and greater emphasis is laid, here upon one aspect of His Being, there upon another. But, while Theism is the accepted faith of many, it is also being attacked, and perhaps, above all, it is being forgotten. It has its antagonists, from Pantheists on the one side to Atheists on the other, while there are many more to whom it seldom makes an effective appeal. Now, if only there could be enkindled a religious revival among the Jews, so that they took their religious mission and function more seriously, if only the flame of faith in Judaism and religion burnt more brightly and keenly, so that the drift towards indifferentism and agnosticism could be wholly stopped (I do not know—I have no adequate information—how serious or insignificant the drift may be), if one could count upon ten millions or more of eager and impassioned Theists in Europe and its offshoots, would not such a force for the cause of Theism be worth having? Would not even those who conceive the nature of God somewhat differently from Israel consider that such a band of allies would not be entirely negligible?

The matter may also be put thus: the Jewish conception of God and of His relation to man, the Jewish conception of the relation of religion to morality, are akin to Christian conceptions dealing with these same high themes. Yet while akin, they are not identical with them. In some respects the two sets of conceptions can be regarded as not so much antagonistic as complementary. And it may, perhaps, be truly said that the maintenance of these complementary conceptions (where the many-sided truth is too hard for man to grasp in its fullness) may be of value to mankind. The concurrent existence of certain one-sidednesses may tend to safety. They may enrich civilization instead of impoverishing it. Thus one can imagine a philosophic Christian recognizing that Israel may still have something to give, as an ally in an age-old struggle, and as clinging to and pressing, even if with some exaggeration, certain important aspects of an exceedingly complex whole.

It was stated that it would be impossible and out of place to give any portrayal here of Jewish Theism. But yet, in close connexion with the last paragraph, just this must be said. On the one hand, Jewish Theism is very independent of historical criticism; the results of critical investigation upon the Old and the New Testaments will hardly affect it. Again, it is, as Jews think, a very pure Theism; as non-Jews think, a very severe and abstract Theism, which, by rejecting the doctrine of the Incarnation, too utterly separates man from God and God from man, and makes relations between them impossible. On the other hand, Jewish Theism is a very simple Theism, or, as some would say, a very unphilosophic Theism. Its God is both far and near, without and within. It clings to two aspects of God, summed up in the twofold metaphor, which, though a metaphor, yet, as Judaism insists, describes a reality, 'Our Father, our King.' *Abhinu, malkenu.* So Judaism addresses its God, and it refuses to let go either term, either metaphor. What do the two metaphors imply? Do they show that the Jewish conception of God, if, by its rejection of the Incarnation dogma, not anthropomorphic enough on the one hand, is yet, by its insistence upon the divine Kingship and Fatherhood, too anthropomorphic upon the other? I do not know. But may it not also be said that the anthropomorphism, and the rejection of anthropormorphism, are both needed in our conception of God, and may it not be that Judaism, which has its own special acceptances, and its own special rejections, of anthropomorphism, may, for that very reason, be of abiding value as a complement and an ally?

Or, yet again, may the matter be put thus? It is, I gather, often surmised that the least inadequate conception of God is one which most fully and harmoniously combines what is called the immanent and the transcendent aspects of Deity. Now there are times and eras when the one or other of these aspects is more in fashion, or is more heavily stressed. At present, it is the aspect of immanence which is to the fore. It consorts with various ideas that are pleasing to, or favoured by, our thoughts and our emotions, and it would appear as if the stress on immanence were likely to continue for an indefinite time. It harmonizes with certain mystical leanings and yearnings, on the one hand; it harmonizes also with a tendency to emphasize the 'divineness' of man, upon the other. And it harmonizes too with the tendency to insist on autonomous morality to a degree and to an intensity that makes morality something which has come to efflorescence in man, and is unknown beyond and outside him. Judaism is often said to overstress the transcendent aspect of Deity: if it does so, it maybe that it provides and maintains a useful corrective, and that it errs (if indeed it errs) in good company. For that the conception of Deity in Mark, Matthew, and Luke is prevailingly transcendent can hardly be denied. The Gospel hero certainly accepted the 'Father and King' conception of God, and it may be part of the function and gift of Judaism to preserve this conception, in its childlike simplicity and purity, through the ages. It may be that the conception is one-sided and inadequate; but, perhaps, no one religion can either *do* everything or *possess* everything.

There is another connected point, which touches morality and its relation to religion. People decry the 'barren' transcendence of the Jewish God, and with that barren transcendence they connect that terrible bugbear—terrible more especially to Lutheran theologians—of Jewish legalism. Well, Jewish legalism, in the sense of belief in a perfect and divine code identified with the Pentateuch, must pass away. That belief is dissolved by historical criticism. If Judaism depended upon, and were inseparable from, *that* belief, it could, indeed, have no gift to render, no function to fulfill. It must then dwindle and die. The Pentateuchal Code is not Mosaic, homogeneous and perfect; nor is it God-given and divine, in the sense in which all generations of orthodox Jews from the first to the twentieth century A.D. undoubtedly believed it to be. Judaism can emerge, and has emerged, from the narrowing shackles and bondage of this belief into a larger and freer air. Yet with this deliverance and freedom the conception of law in religion has not been entirely abandoned. Judaism still holds that whatever the human history and development of morality may be, morality has not arisen and developed by chance, nor are righteousness and love merely human creations. They have come to be in man because, before man was, they were in God. God is their Author and Source, God is their condition and guarantee. Moreover, man, mysteriously developed from the animal, and, risen above the animal into a kinship with the divine, strives towards, but can never reach, the perfect autonomy of God. Man ever needs an Ought and a Must; the acceptance and acknowledgement of a Law,—'Thou shalt' and 'thou shalt not,'—is at once his limitation and his privilege. The Law is both within him and without him. He discovers it, and it is revealed to him. He accepts it as the law of his own being; he bows down before it as the law of God. It is his own and not his own: it is more and more to be made one with him, but it is to be ever recognized as greater and older and diviner than he. The old covenant and the new covenant are not inconsistent opposites: so far as man is concerned, he needs them both. Both are glorious and sublime. To the freedom of God—the new covenant in its perfection, autonomy in its perfection—he can never attain. For he is man and not God. And though he must strive towards that freedom, it remains his joy and privilege to recognize his *servitude*—he need not fear the word, for in that servitude is joy. Indeed the two covenants tend to merge into one. For the more man recognizes and joyously fulfils the Moral Law, the more he admits the fitness and glory of the old covenant; the more he acknowledges the propriety and grandeur of the Law without—God's law and his law in one—the more joyously and freely he admits and bows down before it in homage and reverence, the nearer has he drawn to the New Covenant, the closer has he come to the purest and the fullest self-realization and autonomy. And if it be said that 'Thy service is perfect freedom' is a Christian maxim, then the reply must be, first, that such Christianity is the purest Judaism, and secondly, that such Christianity is surely somewhat enfeebled at the present time, and that many tendencies and beliefs, now in fashion, appear to oppose and contradict it. Here Israel may surely have something to give, not as antagonist, but as friend, and as a not quite insignificant ally.

> But all, in their unlikeness, blend
> Confederate to one golden end—
> Beauty: the vision whereunto,
> In joy, with pantings, from afar,
> Through sound and odour, form and hue,
> And mind and clay, and worm and star—
> Now touching goal, now backward hurled—
> Toils the indomitable world.[1]

(1927)

OF THE JEWISH RELIGION

by ALBERT EINSTEIN

THERE is, in my opinion, no Jewish view of life in the philosophic sense. Judaism appears to me to be almost exclusively concerned with the moral attitude in and toward life.

Judaism I believe to be rather the content of the life-approach of the Jewish people than the contents of the laws laid down in the Torah and interpreted in the Talmud. Torah and Talmud are for me only the most weighty evidence of the governing concepts of Jewish life in earlier times.

The essence of the Jewish concept of life seems to me to be the affirmation of life for all creatures. For the life of the individual has meaning only in the service of enhancing and ennobling the life of every living thing. Life is holy; i.e., it is the highest worth on which all other values depend. The sanctification of the life which transcends the indi-

[1] William Watson.

vidual brings with it reverence for the spiritual, a peculiarly characteristic trait of Jewish tradition.

Judaism is not a faith. The Jewish God is but a negation of superstition and an imaginative result of its elimination. He also represents an attempt to ground morality in fear—a deplorable, discreditable attempt. Yet it seems to me that the powerful moral tradition in the Jewish people has, in great measure, released itself from this fear. Moreover it is clear that "to serve God" is equivalent to serving "every living thing." It is for this that the best among the Jewish people, especially the Prophets including Jesus, ceaselessly battled. Thus Judaism is not a transcendental religion. It is concerned only with the tangible experiences of life, and with nothing else. Therefore it seems to me to be questionable whether it may be termed a "religion" in the customary sense of the word, especially since no "creed" is demanded of Jews, but only the sanctification of life in its all-inclusive sense.

There remains, however, something more in the Jewish tradition, so gloriously revealed in certain of the psalms; namely, a kind of drunken joy and surprise at the beauty and incomprehensible sublimity of this world, of which man can attain but a faint intimation. It is the feeling from which genuine research draws its intellectual strength, but which also seems to manifest itself in the song of birds. This appears to me to be the loftiest content of the God-idea.

Is this, then, characteristic of Judaism? And does it exist elsewhere under other names? In *pure form* it exists nowhere, not even in Judaism, where too much literalism obscures the pure doctrine. But, nevertheless, I see in Judaism one of its most vital and pure realizations. This is especially true of its fundamental principle of the sanctification of life.

It is noteworthy that in the commandment to keep the Sabbath holy the animals were also expressly included—so strongly was felt as an ideal the demand for the solidarity of all living things. Far more strongly yet is expressed the demand for the solidarity of all humankind; and it is no accident that the socialistic demands for the most part emanated from Jews.

To how great an extent the consciousness of the sanctity of life is alive in the Jewish people is beautifully illustrated by a remark once made to me by Walter Rathenau: "When a Jew says he takes pleasure in the hunt, he lies." It is impossible to express more simply the consciousness of the sanctity and the unity of all life as it exists in the Jewish people.

(1932)

TORAH AS A WAY OF LIFE

by MORDECAI M. KAPLAN

IF the Jews regarded themselves as more qualified for salvation than the rest of mankind, it was not because they believed that they possessed intrinsically superior mental and moral traits. Very few representative teachers or thinkers entertained such a belief. The predominant teaching has been that the Jewish people owed the prerogative of salvation entirely to the particular way of life to which it had dedicated itself. In Jewish tradition that particular way of life is regarded as set forth in the Torah. The term "Torah" not only refers to the particular corpus of writings which include the Bible and the rabbinic literature, but also assigns a position of pre-eminence and authority to these writings. Upon them the Jewish consciousness has been riveted for the last two millennia. If the continuity of that consciousness depends, as was said above, not so much upon retaining its beliefs unchanged as upon maintaining a live interest in certain specific *sancta,* then the Torah, or the sacred and authoritative writings designated by that term, should be accorded a position of primacy alongside the ideas of God and Israel. There can be nothing more paradoxical than a Torah-less Judaism. A Jewish life whose entire stream of consciousness from one end of the year to the next does not receive a single idea or impression directly from the Jewish writings which embody the great Jewish tradition would indeed be anomalous. It is, of course, impossible any longer to expect Jews to devote to those writings anything like the amount of time and attention their forebears were wont to spend. Present-day life is far too crowded to render that feasible. But so long as there is to be found any room in the contemporary scene for Jewish life, the knowledge of Torah must figure in it, or that life will be anything but Jewish.

In spite, however, of the obvious indispensability of such knowledge, the present apathy will continue so long as there prevails the assumption that the only way to know Torah is to know it in the traditional spirit, or not at all. The majority of thinking men and women, finding it impossible to approach the Jewish writings in the traditional spirit, neglect them altogether. It is therefore imperative deliberately to break down that assumption, and to promulgate the principle that *the primary requisite for the continuity of Jewish consciousness is not blind acceptance of the traditional beliefs, but a vital interest in the objects upon which those beliefs were centered.* If for the maintenance of interest in those objects it is necessary to abandon the traditional view concerning them, Jews should not hesitate to do so, and to replace those beliefs with whatever type of ideas is likely to sustain their interest.

This is what has actually been happening with the function of Torah in the life of the Jews during the last century. The Jewish consciousness has been gradually evolving a method whereby its interest in the Torah might be made compatible with the modern approach to reality. The rewriting of Jewish history in systematic and objective fashion is, in effect, a reinterpretation of the career of Israel as presented by the Torah. The Jewish scholars who belong to the Historical School, beginning with Nahman Krochmal, did not merely write history. By making accessible and intelligible numerous facts which seemed to have relevance only in the traditional setting, by furnishing the modern Jew with a connected and plausible account of the Jewish past, they have revitalized the ancient texts and have made possible the retention of the Torah in its widest sense as an object of Jewish consciousness. It is unfortunate that they contributed comparatively little to the scientific and objective study of the Bible, which is basic to a genuine understanding of the first stages of Judaism. The auspicious beginning made by Mendelssohn and the Biurists in the elucidation of the text of the Bible has not been followed up. That lack, however, has been made good by the vast range of biblical research pursued by Christian scholars during the last century. Jews should not allow the Christological hypotheses and theological prejudices which often vitiate this scholarship to stand in the way of utilizing whatever genuine light it sheds upon the Bible, its authorship and the historic background of its various books. It is highly important that the rabbinic texts should be subjected to the same kind of study as has revolutionized our appreciation of the Bible. It will then be possible to envisage the inner life of the Jewish people during the weary centuries of exile and persecution, in its struggle not merely for existence but for salvation. All this material should then be made available in popular form, to forestall the excuse of the Jewish layman that he has no time to wade through a mass of technical facts in order to acquire an appreciable knowledge of the Jewish past and its literature.

But of even greater importance for the reordering of Jewish life than the study of the sacred writings, is the fostering of a mode of life that will be animated by whatever in the traditional attitude toward the

Torah is of incontestable worth. By analyzing the rationale which the Jewish consciousness has formulated to account for the position of pre-eminence and authority it assigned to the Bible and the rabbinic writings, we shall arrive at a knowledge of some of the important implications in the traditional attitude toward the Torah. That rationale contains beliefs which reflect the limited knowledge of the ancients about the manner in which human beings came upon new ideas and plans, and derived the urge and wisdom to execute them. These crude notions are responsible for the literalness with which they assumed the supernatural origin of the Torah. But included also in the rationale are implications which are still relevant, and which in their explicit form should be made part of a modern Jewish ideology.

In the first place, it is evident that when the ancients spoke of Torah they were very far from being as book-minded about it as we are. *We come nearest to experienceing how they felt about Torah when we realize that Torah was to them, in effect, the hypostasis of the civilization of the Jewish people. The writings, as visible objects, were important chiefly as symbols of that civilization, in the same way as the Temple and Ark were important as symbols of the reality and presence of God.* The sense of supreme advantage the Jews felt in possessing the Torah can best be understood if interpreted as equivalent to the belief that theirs was the only true civilization. The apotheosis of the Torah, which one encounters so frequently in the rabbinic literature, loses its bizarre character when read in the light of this equivalence of Torah to civilization. When the Sages say, "God created the world for the sake of the Torah," they say in their way that civilization gives meaning to reality. Or when they state that God in constructing the world followed the plan of the Torah in the same way as an architect follows his blueprints, they imply that God made the nature of the physical environment congenial to civilization. This apotheosis of Torah and the equating of it with civilization *par excellence* did not originate with the Sages. This attitude is expressed even in the Pentateuch where we read: "Observe therefore and do them; for this is your wisdom and your understanding in the sight of the peoples, that, when they hear all these statutes, shall say: 'Surely this great nation is a wise and understanding people.' "

Moreover, the admiration of the Jews for the Torah, unbounded as it was, was not blind and unreasoned. The traditional belief that the Torah came directly from God might have given rise merely to a feeling of awe that would elicit obedience. But the glorification of the Torah, which we find expressed everywhere in traditional literature, is undoubtedly motivated by some other virtue which the Torah is supposed to possess. It is the inherent power of conferring life abundant, or salvation, upon those who order their conduct in accordance with its precepts. The claim to the possession of this power is reiterated throughout the Scriptures, from the standpoint of life in this world, and throughout rabbinic literature, from the standpoint of life in the world to come.

The functional method of reinterpretation, as applied to the God-idea and to the Israel-idea, has been shown to consist largely in disengaging from the context of the ancient world-outlook those elements which answer to permanent postulates of human nature and integrating them into the Jewish ideology that is in the making. By applying the same method to the traditional attitude toward the Torah-idea, we infer from it a number of significant corollaries.

We discern in the concept "Torah" the first attempt on the part of a people to detach itself mentally from its regimen of conduct, and to contemplate it as something more than a matter of chance or accident, like the landscape one is born into. That regimen, it is implied, should not be treated as something arbitrary to which we must submit because we cannot do otherwise, but as inherently right and good which we should accept as an act of free choice. This is what entitles the social system of customs, laws and standards to be considered Torah, the law of God, or as the modern man would put it, a civilization or civilizing agency. Once a people can achieve such detachment from its routine, there is some likelihood of that routine undergoing modification as soon as it fails to keep up with the growing complexity of life. No doubt there will always be resistance to change, but so long as it is recognized that the way of life has to be accepted as a matter of free choice, the forces of intelligence and idealism will ultimately succeed in bringing that way of life in line with man's highest needs and capacities.

The concept "Torah" furthermore, by implication accentuates the highly important truth that human societies should differ from sub-human herds in having their bond of unity based not upon the blind forces of instinct or of consanguinity, but upon their common purpose to work out a way of life to which each member might conform as a free agent. In a sense, the church adopted that principle of organization when it made the basis of its unity a common faith instead of common race or common political interests. But with the organization of modern nations, there has been a return to the sub-human principle of the herd. The pretense of scientific plausibility is nowadays made for the theory of race as the chief determinant of the social life of man. The inevitable consequence of such a theory is a recrudescence of barbarism. This is tragically being demonstrated in the contemporary scene. A whole nation, which has hitherto been regarded as highly cultured, is suffering a moral relapse and is threatening the peace of the world as a result of having perverted the race theory into a claim to world-hegemony.

Finally, there is implied in the idea of Torah the crucial test of the value of a civilization. A civilization fulfills its function only when the people that lives by it, helps its individual men and women to achieve life abundant or salvation. All laws, customs, institutions and social arrangements that hinder the complete self-development of the individual are not civilization, but barbarization, and the peoples that uphold them are not civilized nations in the true sense of the term. To deserve the status of a civilized nation, a people must so order its way of life that all the possibilities in the natural and social environment which make for the complete self-realization of the individual shall be fully utilized.

It is not, however, the traditional Torah, or the Jewish civilization as it has come down from the past, that can any longer elicit the attitude that it is of supreme worth to the Jew and his people. The tradiitonal Torah must be reinterpreted and reconstructed so that it become synonymous with the whole of a civilization necessary to civilize or humanize the individual. Individual self-fulfillment is possible only through affirmative and creative adjustments to a series of concentric and overlapping relationships within the human world, supplemented by a similar adjustment to the world as a whole. All relationships of the individual to his family, to the opposite sex, to friends, to community, to nation, to mankind and to the world as a whole, are potentially capable of evoking affirmative and creative adjustments. This process in every relationship that applies to a Jew is the career of Torah, or the career of the Jewish civilization.

Torah should mean to the Jew nothing less than a civilization which enables the individual to effect affirmative and creative adjustments in his living relationships with reality. Any partial conception of Torah is false to the forces that have made for Judaism's development and survival. Torah means a complete Jewish civilization. But to the Jew in the diaspora it must, in addition, spell the duty of beholding in the non-Jewish civilization by which he lives a potential instrument of salvation. He must help to render that civilization capable of enhancing human life as the Torah enhanced the life of Israel. If, like the Torah, it is to be worthy of fervent devotion, those whose lives it fashions must be convinced of its intrinsic righteousness.

The survival of Judaism in the diaspora depends upon whether the Jews outside Palestine will live Judaism as a civilization to the maximum degree compatible with their physical, economic and mental powers, as well as with the national spirit of the countries in which they live. With the infinite diversity of temperament, training, beliefs, callings and interests, and with their wide range of ideas about life, the universe and God, which prevail among Jews, the most pressing problem of Jewish life is how to render it sufficiently rich in opportunities for Jewish self-expression.

Not even under the most favorable circumstances can Jewish life in the diaspora create that rich variety in content which Judaism requires. All the constituents of Jewish civilization—language, literature, the arts, social standards and values—will be able to thrive creatively mainly in the Jewish National Home. But the Jews in the diaspora cannot afford to wait passively for whatever new values will be evolved in Palestine. Some degree of Jewish life and activity must be counted on as possible also in the diaspora, and with it a certain degree of creativity. Jews everywhere must deliberately strive to enlarge the scope of Jewish thought, increase the sphere of communal and intercommunal action, and widen the range of creative achievement. The future of Judaism is contingent upon its coming to possess an abundant, diversified and spiritually satisfying content. With that end in view, Jewish life in the diaspora must undergo considerable reconstruction in its folkways, in its ethics and in its educational postulates.

(1934)

BIOGRAPHICAL NOTES

ABRAHAM IBN DAUD was born at Toledo about 1110 and died about 1180. He was the first Aristotelian of the medieval Jewish thinkers, but he was more popularly known for his polemical work, *The Book of Tradition*. The selection included here, translated by Harry A. Wolfson, is reprinted from Hebrew Union College Jubilee Volume (1925 pp. 314-315).

ABRAHAM IBN EZRA was born in Toledo, Spain, in 1093 and died in 1167. He traveled widely during the last twenty years of his life, leaving the impress of his character and scholarship on many communities. He wrote a little library of religious and secular works, and, as a poet, he ranks with the best of his contemporaries.

ISAAC ABRAVANEL was born in Lisbon in 1437 and died in Venice in 1509. He served as finance minister in the courts of Alfonso V of Portugal and Ferdinand of Castile. When the Jews were expelled from Spain in 1492, he fled to Italy, and after much distress he was given a diplomatic post in Venice in 1503 where he passed his remaining years. He wrote extensively on philosophy, the Talmud and the Bible. His extensive commentary on the Bible from which the selection included is taken (reprinted from B. Halper, *Post-Biblical Hebrew Literature*), is quite modern in its treatment of the subject.

URIEL ACOSTA was born at Oporto in 1590 of a Marrano family, and died in Amsterdam in 1640. He emigrated to Holland with his family in 1618 and there embraced Judaism. The dramatic story of his life is told in his brief autobiography (here included in abridged form) *Exemplar Humanae Vitae*, which was written shortly after he was publicly disgraced and just before he shot himself. He is the central figure of Gutzkow's popular tragedy, *Uriel Acosta*, and Zangwill portrayed him in *Dreamers of the Ghetto*.

SAMUEL JOSEPH AGNON, one of the most talented of contemporary Hebrew writers, was born in Buczacz, Galicia, in 1888. Here he soaked himself in Jewish learning and the rich ghetto lore that became the subject matter of his subsequent literary productions. He spent six years in Palestine until 1913 when he went to Germany; in 1924 he returned to Palestine where he has made his permanent residence. He has undertaken to record, in a prose that is as sensitive and epic as its subject, the whole panorama of the passing Jewish order. He has written, in addition to numerous short stories, a two-volume picaresque novel, *The Bridal Canopy* (English version by I. M. Lask, New York, 1937). In 1922 an edition of his collected writings in four volumes was published. Agnon was the recipient of the Bialik Prize for Hebrew Literature in 1934.

AHAD HAAM (real name Asher Ginzberg) was born in Russia of Hasidic parentage and died in Palestine in 1927. He received an extensive Jewish as well as general education. He earned his livelihood as a tea merchant but devoted his energies to the advancement of Hebrew literature and of the Zionist movement. He occupies a pre-eminent place as a philosopher of modern Jewish nationalism. During the last five years of his life he lived in Palestine. Some of his essays have been translated into English by Leon Simon: *Essays on Zionism and Judaism* (London, 1922) and *Selected Essays* (Phila., 1911) from which the essay included is reprinted.

JOSEPH ALBO was born about 1380 and died in 1444. He was an important preacher and theologian and his work *Principles (Ikkarim)* attained wide popularity. The selection included here is reputed from the English translation by Isaac Husik (Phila., 1930, vol. 3, pp. 217-229). It is possible that the discussion has some relation to the religious disputation at Tortosa (1413-1414) which Albo attended.

JUDAH ALHARIZI lived in the 11th and 12th centuries and died about 1230. He was born in Spain and traveled considerably on the Continent and in the Near East. His observations on men and manners, expressed with subtle irony and humor, comprise his notable poetic work, *Tahkemoni* ("A Sage Teacher"). The poem included here is reprinted from *Poems of Emma Lazarus* (vol. 2, pp. 204-205).

SOLOMON ALKABEZ was born in Safed, Palestine, and flourished there during the first half of the 16th century. He was a kabbalist and liturgical poet of note and made a deep impression upon his contemporaries. The most famous of his poems is his hymn for the Sabbath Eve service, *Come my Beloved,* here included. It is part of the ritual, and was translated into German by both Herder and Heine.

S. ANSKY (real name S. J. Rappaport) was born in Russia in 1863, and died in Warsaw in 1920. He worked at several trades as a youth, and later served as correspondent in Western Europe for several Russian publications. He also wrote stories of Jewish life, composed *The Oath,* a poem which was adopted by the Jewish workers' organizations as their hymn, and headed the Baron Horace Ginsburg Expedition for the collection and study of Jewish folklore. Based upon such materials (which were published in *Dos Yiddishe Etnografische Program* in St. Petersburg, 1915) was his famous play, *The Dybbuk,* which won acclaim on the stages of Europe, America and Palestine. The selection here included, *The Trial,* is taken from the English translation by Henry G. Alsberg and Winifred Katzen (New York, 1926).

SHOLEM ASCH was born in Poland in 1880. He attended Jewish schools and was initiated into general culture by his wife. He wrote stories in both Hebrew and Yiddish and with the publication of *The Village* he quickly won high rank among the younger writers. Subsequently he lived in New York and Paris and produced an extraordinary array of plays, stories and novels which have made him pre-eminent in contemporary Yiddish literature. Among his best-known works, which have been translated into English and for which he has received wide recognition, are: *Mottke the Thief, The Mother, Three Cities, Salvation* and *The War Goes On.* The play included here, *The Sinner,* is reprinted from *East and West.*

ISAAC BABEL, one of the most distinguished contemporary Russian writers, was born in Odessa in 1894. Although his father was a tradesman, he was given a thorough Jewish education and attended the commercial High School where he came under the influence of a French instructor and began to write stories in French. He served with the Cossacks in their campaign against the Whites and the Poles. He has published little besides two famous books, *Odessa Tales* (stories of Jewish life in Odessa) and *Red Cavalry* (episodes from the war between Poland and the Soviet armies), but both are considered to be masterpieces. *My Pidgeon-House,* here included, was translated from the Russian by John Cournos.

BAHYA IBN PAKUDA lived in the eleventh century. He wrote the first systematic treatise on Jewish ethics and his book, *The Inner Duties of the Heart,* from which the selection included is taken (Part I, chapter 2), has been called "the most inspired book written by a Jew in the Middle Ages." A translation of Part One was made by Moses Hyamson (New York, 1925).

S. N. BEHRMAN was born in Worcester, Mass., in 1893. He studied at Clark, Columbia and Harvard Universities, and it was in Professor G. P. Baker's 47 Workshop at Harvard that he served his apprenticeship as a playwright. His plays on Broadway and scenarios for Hollywood have achieved uncommon success. Among his well-known plays are: *Meteor, Brief Moment, Biography, End of Summer* and *Rain from Heaven* from which the piece, here included, is taken.

ISAAC DOB BERKOWITZ was born in Russia in 1885. He made his literary debut in 1903 and in 1905 he emigrated to New York. Unable to orient himself in the American Jewish environment he recrossed the Atlantic and sojourned in a number of European capitals where he contributed to the Hebrew and Yiddish press. During the World War he returned to New York where a number of his plays were successfully produced. Afterwards he left America to take up permanent residence in Palestine. Berkowitz belongs to the realistic school of fiction. He translated into Hebrew the works of his father-in-law, Sholom Aleichem.

HAYYIM NAHMAN BIALIK was born in Russia in 1873 and was buried in Palestine in 1934. He passed his boyhood in severe poverty, attended Jewish schools, wandered considerably, and while engaged in various occupations, mastered secular culture. He is generally acknowledged to be the outstanding figure in contemporary Hebrew letters. Bialik's poetry was one of the spiritual factors helping to shape the Zionist movement. In recognition of his preeminence in Hebrew literature, an annual "Bialik Prize for Hebrew Literature" has been established in Palestine, where he spent the last years of his life. Some of his poetry has been translated into English in two small volumes by Maurice Samuel and L. V. Snowman.

JEAN-RICHARD BLOCH was born in Paris fifty-one years ago. He is generally regarded as one of the outstanding men of letters in France today. A highly inquisitive man and blessed with an acute mind and alert sensibilities he has accumulated a vast culture which overflows into his writings. He is constantly raising provocative and social problems. Some of his outstanding works are: "— & Company," from which the story included is taken, Kurdish Night, and Sybilla (novels); Cocoanuts and Bananas (travel essays); The Last Emperor, and Forces of the World (plays); Lévy (collection of short stories); and Fate of the Century (criticism).

LOUIS DEMBITZ BRANDEIS was born in Louisville, Kentucky, in 1856. He studied abroad, made a brilliant record at the Harvard Law School and by his espousal of public causes came to be known as "The People's Attorney." In 1916 he was appointed an Associate Justice of the Supreme Court of the United States by President Wilson. Between 1913 and 1921 he was a leader of the Zionist movement. The selection, here included, is from The Jewish Problem: How to Solve It (1915). Further material may be found in Louis Dembitz Brandeis by Jacob de Haas (1929).

MYRON BRINIG was born in Minneapolis in 1900, and spent his childhood in Butte, Montana. He studied at New York University and the University of Pennsylvania, worked at many random jobs, spent some time on the Continent and finally buckled down to writing. He contributed stories to numerous periodicals but it was his autobiographical novel Singermann (from which Rachel and the Child is selected) that won for him recognition and popularity. Other novels: Anthony in the Nude, Wide Open Town, This Man is My Brother (sequel to Singermann), Flutter of an Eyelid and Three Sisters.

MAX BROD was born in Prague in 1884. He has an intensely Jewish and Zionistic background and these influences have colored all of his writings. After he received his doctorate in philosophy at the University of Prague he became a government official but soon turned to journalism and a literary career. He finally assumed the editorial direction of the Prager Tageblatt, which he still continues. Some of his best-known works for which he has received wide recognition are: The Book of Love (verse), Arnold Beer, The Destiny of a Jew, David Reubeni, The Blessed Land, Jewesses, The Kingdom of Love, Tycho Brahe's Way to God, The Life of Heinrich Heine, and The Woman Who Never Disappoints.

MARTIN BUBER was born in Vienna in 1878. As a youth he lived in Galicia, where he came into close touch with Hasidic life and lore. He studied at the universities in Vienna, Berlin, Leipzig and Zurich and has taught at the universities of Frankfort and the Hebrew University in Jerusalem. He is one of the intellectual leaders of the Zionist movement and the most ardent advocate of Neo-Hasidism, winning into his circle of disciples such men as Max Brod and Franz Werfel. Among his important literary works are an epoch-making German translation of the Bible (in collaboration with Franz Rosenzweig) and many volumes of Hasidic lore. The essay included is reprinted from Lewisohn's *Rebirth*. A volume of his essays on Hasidism and stories of Israel Baalshem, translated by Lucy Cohen, *Jewish Mysticism*, was published in 1931.

JOSEPH COTLER was born in Russia in 1896 and died in 1935 as a result of an automobile accident. He came to New York at the age of fifteen and studied at the National Academy of Art. In 1921, upon the advice of Moishe Nadir, he began to write light, whimsical verse and stories which he illustrated himself. His poetry, folk tales and children's stories are unique in Yiddish literature. He conducted a column in the New York *Freiheit,* and was the director of the noted Madjacot Schpiel, the Yiddish marionette theater.

JOHN COURNOS was born in a Russian village in 1881. He came to America when he was ten and, resident in Philadelphia, he worked at various jobs. He decided upon a literary career at the age of thirty-one, visited England "to learn English on English soil," and within the last fifteen years has established himself as novelist, translator, editor, critic and playwright. *Shylock's Choice,* the play here included, has been produced both in England and America. Some of his outstanding books are: *In Exile* (poetry); *Sport of the Gods* (play); *The Mask, Babel, New Candida, The Devil Is an English Gentleman* (novels); *Autobiography* (1936).

DAVID BEN JESSE was born in Bethlehem, Palestine, about 1040 B.C. and died in Jerusalem about 970 B.C. The story of David's rise from minstrel and armor-bearer in the court of Saul to King of Israel is told unforgettably in the books of *Samuel* and *Kings,* and is known to every school child. Even though only a few fragments of his own poems are extant, they indicate that he was a not inconsiderable poet. David is a central figure in Jewish tradition and legend.

BABETTE DEUTSCH was born in New York City in 1895. She was graduated from Barnard College in 1917. She has contributed verse and criticism to numerous periodicals. She won the *Nation* Poetry Prize in 1926 and was Phi Beta Kappa poet at Columbia University in 1926. In this volume she appears both as poet and translator. Among her outstanding books are: *Banners, Honey Out of the Rock, Epistle to Prometheus, Fire for the Night* (verse); *Potable Gold* (criticism); *A Brittle Heaven, In Such a Night* (novels); *Modern Russian Poetry, Russian Poetry, Contemporary German Poetry* (anthologies in collaboration with her husband, Avraham Yarmolinsky). *Psalm: 1933* appeared in *Opinion* (July, 1933).

SIMON MAKOWOWITCH DUBNOW was born in Molulev, Russia, in 1860. He is the most influential living Jewish historian. His various writings cover a vast array of subjects, but his reconstruction and interpretation of the history of the Jews of Central and Eastern Europe have revised our perspective of modern Jewish history. Dubnow is also an influential publicist, having advocated diaspora nationalism and the establishment of minority rights for Jews long before they were granted in the Versailles Treaty. (See Friedlander, *Dubnow's Theory of Jewish Nationalism*). His *chef d'oeuvre* is a ten volume history of the Jews. Among his writings that are available in English are: *Jewish History* (an essay from which the selection included is taken) and *History of the Jews in Russia and Poland*.

ILYA EHRENBOURG, one of the most talented of contemporary Russian writers, was born in Moscow forty-four years ago. His literary vogue is extensive both among the proletarian masses as well as among the intellectuals in the Soviet Union. His writing is distinguished by a sensitive simplicity and a highly subtle realism, devoid of any attempt to shock or to impress his readers but calculated to arouse on the one hand the broadest and most active sympathies within them towards the exploited and the oppressed, and on the other hand a feeling of bitter resentment against their oppressors. His best-known works in English translation are: *The Second Day* (novel); *The Visa of Time* (essays); *The Life of Oracchus Babeuf* (biography); *The Dream Factory* (on the cinema); *Spain* (social-political study); and *The Extraordinary Adventures of Julio Jurenito and His Disciples*. The story included, translated by Leon Dennen, is reprinted from *Opinion*.

ALBERT EINSTEIN was born in Ulm, Germany, in 1879. He studied physics and mathematics in Zurich and soon became the most eminent living physicist. He became interested in Jewish life in 1921, took an active part in the Zionist movement and the development of the Hebrew University in Palestine. When the Nazis compelled him to leave Germany, he accepted an invitation to teach at Princeton where he now resides. The essay, here included, first appeared in *Opinion* (Sept. 1932). For additional essays on related subjects, see *On Zionism* (New York, 1931) and *Cosmic Religion* (New York, 1931).

MARTIN FEINSTEIN was born in New York City in 1892 and died there in 1934. He was educated at the College of William and Mary and the University of Michigan where he taught rhetoric for several years. He served in the A.E.F. during the World War, receiving wounds which ultimately led to his death. He contributed verse to numerous American magazines and was awarded the *Nation* Poetry prize in 1922. Especially noteworthy are his poems on Jewish life, which appeared for many years in the *Menorah Journal*. The poem, here included, is reprinted from his volume, *In Memoriam*.

EDNA FERBER was born in Kalamazoo, Michigan, where she attended the public schools. She began her career as a newspaper woman and gradually turned to writing fiction, chiefly of Middle West life and characters. She has written more than twenty volumes of novels, plays and short stories, several of which (*The Girls, So Big, Show Boat, Cimarron*) were best sellers and were made into films. The story included here is taken from an early autobiographical novel, *Fanny Herself*.

LION FEUCHTWANGER, the son of a prosperous Jewish manufacturer, was born in Munich in 1884. He studied at the Universities of Berlin and Munich and received the degree of Doctor of Philosophy at the latter institution. He instantaneously achieved a literary as well as a popular success with his works. More than any other writer of our time he has developed "the political novel" to its greatest satiric effectiveness. His lampooning of Hitler and the Nazis in the novels *Success* and *the Oppermanns* have brought upon him the hatred and vengeance of the present rulers of Germany. He has been obliged to flee for his life to Southern France where he now resides. Some of his other well-known works in English translation are: *Power, Josephus, The Ugly Duchess, Success, The Jew of Rome, The Oppermanns* (novels); and *Julia Farnese* (drama).

IRVING FINEMAN was born in New York City in 1893. He studied at the Massachusetts Institute of Technology and Harvard, taught engineering at the University of Illinois, and is now a lecturer in literature at Bennington College. During the war he served in the U. S. Navy as an engineer officer. His first novel, *This Pure Young Man,* was awarded the Longmans Green prize of $7,500 in 1930. An interest in the problems of the modern Jew led him to write *Hear, Ye Sons,* a chronicle of Jewish life in the nineteenth century. The story included here, *How Many Angels . . . ,* first appeared in *The Menorah Journal* (Feb., 1929).

EDMOND FLEG was born in Geneva in 1874. He studied at various European universities, saw service at the front in the French Army during the war for which he was awarded the Croix de Guerre, and since then has devoted himself chiefly to literary pursuits. He and André Spire are the creators of a renascence of Jewish letters among the new generation of Jewish writers in France. Fleg has excelled as critic, playwright and translator. Among his outstanding works that have been translated into English are: *Why I am a Jew, The Life of Moses, The Life of Solomon, The Jewish Anthology* (abridged), *The Land of Promise,* and *Jesus.* The poem included is reprinted from *The Wall of Weeping* (1929).

KARL EMIL FRANZOZ was born in Podolia in 1848 and died in Berlin in 1904. He studied law and medicine at the universities of Gratz and Vienna, traveled through Europe and Asia Minor, and finally settled in Berlin. While he held various government positions he wrote travel memoirs, literary criticism, novels and numerous short stories. His fame, however, has been achieved chiefly by his stories of Jewish life in the Galician ghettos. *The Jews of Barnow,* from which the story included is chosen, has been translated into many European tongues.

DAVID FREEDMAN was born in New York City in 1898 and died there in 1936. He studied at the College of the City of New York. After editing several trade journals, he began to write humorous stories of Jewish life which, like *Mendel Marantz,* here included, won wide popularity. Later he became a "gag-writer" for many comedians and wrote humorous skits for the moving pictures. He collaborated with Eddie Cantor in writing two books, *My Life Is in Your Hands* and *Ziegfeld, the Great Glorifier.*

DAVID FRISHMAN was born of wealthy parents in Zgierz, Poland, in 1863 and died in Poland in 1922. He received a good Jewish and secular education and for almost forty-five years exercised a widespread critical influence upon Hebrew literature. He has written in both Yiddish and Hebrew, verse, fiction and criticism, but is widely known for his feuilletons and his translations into Hebrew of Andersen, Eliot, Tagore, Nietzsche, Wilde, Shakespeare and a score of other European masters. A complete edition of his Hebrew and Yiddish works was published in 1927.

SIMEON SAMUEL FRUG was born in Russia in 1860, and died there in 1916. He wrote verse in Hebrew, Russian and Yiddish. The subject matter of his poetry was rooted in Jewish lore. Among the Russified Jews and Russians he was regarded as the Jewish national poet. *The Golden Key,* here included, first appeared in the *Jewish Quarterly Review* (First Series, vol. IV).

ABRAHAM GEIGER was born in Frankfort-on-the-Main in 1810 and died in Berlin in 1874. He studied at the Universities of Heidelberg and Bonn and occupied several important pulpits in Germany. He was the outstanding protagonist of Reform Judaism during his time. The essay included is selected from his Lectures on *Judaism and Its History* (1864). It is revised from the translation of M. Mayer (New York, 1865).

GLÜCKEL OF HAMELN was born in Hamburg in 1646 and died in Metz in 1724. Her autobiography, which together with those of Uriel Acosta and Solomon Mainmon are unique in Jewish literature until modern times, is a fascinating record of her varied experiences and of the tempo of Jewish life during her times. The selection included was translated from the original Judeo-German by Beth-Zion Lask. A complete translation has been made by Marvin Lowenthal: *The Memoirs of Glückel of Hameln.*

SAMUEL GLUSBERG was born in Buenos Aires in 1902. His parents are Jews born in Eastern Europe. In his early twenties, he had already established himself as a creative force in the cultural life of his country. He founded and edited the publishing house known as "Babel" (Biblioteca Argentina de Buenas Ediciones Literarias) which soon gathered together the élite of Argentinian and South American writers, including such classic figures as Leopoldo Lugones and many of the youngest radical writers. In addition, he edited *La Vida Literaria,* a magazine devoted to literary news, and when that was discontinued he founded *Trapalanda,* in which work by pre-eminent European and American masters is translated. In addition to innumerable essays, Señor Glusberg (who has now assumed the nom de plume "Enrique Espinoza") has published volumes of stories: *La Levita Gris* and *Ruth y Noemi,* which reveal his close and sensitive connection with the Jewish life of the new world.

MICHAEL GOLD was born in New York City in 1896, of poverty-stricken parents. He attended public school, worked at a variety of random jobs, and when he was twenty allied himself with the I. W. W. He contributed to radical newspapers and magazines (writing, among other things, some notable stories on proletarian Jewish life), and in 1929 founded with Hugo Gellert the *New Masses,* a communist weekly, of which he is still an editor. He conducts a virile column in *The Daily Worker,* and writes: "I now believe that writing is the one way in which I, as an individual, can best contribute to the world revolutionary movement." Of his four published volumes, *Jews Without Money,* an autobiographical novel, received wide popularity.

LOUIS GOLDING was born in Manchester, England, in 1895. He was educated at the Manchester Grammar School and Oxford University, served with the English army during the War, and has traveled as widely as any living author. He began to write at the age of nine and his uncommon talent has sought expression in verse, prose and fiction. His novel, *Magnolia Street,* was a best seller in England and America, helping to gain for him the large audience he deserves. Among his other important works are: *Prophet and Fool* (verse); *Those Ancient Lands* (travel); *Forward from Babylon, Day of Atonement, The Miracle Boy* (novels); and *This Wanderer* (short stories) from which the story included here is reprinted.

MEIR ARON GOLDSCHMIDT was born in Vordingborg, Denmark, in 1819 and died in Copenhagen in 1887. Educated in Danish schools but unable to take a degree because he was a Jew, he launched upon a career of vigorous political journalism for which he was frequently fined and sentenced to prison. After 1862 he devoted himself exclusively to fiction, and produced many notable novels and short stories, especially of Jewish life, which won him wide acclaim. Several of his works have been translated into Yiddish, Hebrew and other European languages. The story here included was translated from the Danish by J. B. C. Watkins.

AARON DAVID GORDON was born in a Russian village in 1856 and died in Palestine in 1922. He was largely self-educated. When he was forty-eight years old, he emigrated to Palestine to become an agricultural laborer in the Jewish settlements. Later he became a member of Dagania, the oldest collective, and lived and wrote there until his death. He was one of the intellectual leaders of the labor movement in Palestine and his writings, permeated with the thought of Tolstoi and Carpenter, still are regarded with reverence. His writings were published in four volumes (Hebrew). The selection here included is reprinted from Lewisohn's *Rebirth.*

LEON GORDON (also Judah Loeb Gordon) was born in Wilna, Russia, in 1831 and died in St. Petersburg in 1892. He was educated in the Rabbinical Seminary at Wilna, engaged in educative and communal work for which he received special recognition from the Russian Government. For a brief time Gordon was regarded as a political criminal and thrown into prison and exiled. He contributed essays, criticism, fiction and verse to numerous Hebrew periodicals and was considered the most influential poet of his time. For his life and work see *Leon Gordon,* by A. B. Rhine (1910).

URI ZWI GREENBERG was born in Poland in 1890. He went to Palestine in 1920 and soon established himself as a publicist and poet. Like his Palestinian contemporaries, Shlonsky, Lamdan and Carni, his poetry breathes the new spirit of the country and of postwar expressionism. He is at present a contributor to the *Doar Hayom*.

JUDAH HALEVI was born about 1085 in Toledo, Spain, and died in the Near East after 1140. He received a Jewish education at the school of Isaac Alfasi, a great scholar, and studied medicine. He practiced in several cities in Spain and finally succumbed to an irresistible urge to see Palestine. Halevi occupies a unique place in Jewish history both as philosopher and poet. Among his writings that are available in English are: *Judah Halevi's Kitab Al Khazari* (London, 1930); *Selected Poems of Jehudah Halevi,* by Nina Salaman (Phila., 1924).

ALBERT HALPER was born in Chicago in 1904. He attended the public schools and Northwestern University, and worked at a large variety of jobs. He became a frequent contributor of stories and essays to numerous literary journals, and with the publication of his *Union Square* and *On the Shore,* he quickly won high rank among the younger novelists. The simplicity and graphic vigor of his prose as well as his able portraiture are exhibited in the story included here, which is reprinted from *On the Shore*. Other novels: *The Foundry* and *The Chute* (1937).

HAYYIM HAZAZ was born in 1898 in the Ukraine. Here he was educated, witnessed the Bolshevik revolution, but left to live in Paris and the East, and in 1921 settled in Palestine. He is one of the most original of the new generation of Hebrew writers. His novelettes on Jewish village life in Russia during the revolution and his short stories on biblical episodes as well as those on present-day Palestinian life have enriched modern Hebrew prose with a quality of magnificence and have won for him high rank among contemporary Hebrew writers. *The Account,* here included, was translated from the Hebrew by I. M. Lask.

BEN HECHT was born in New York City in 1893. He attended public schools in Racine, Wisconsin, and, after working at various jobs, became a reporter on the *Chicago Daily News*. His vivacious cynicism and brilliant conversation made him the center of the "Chicago Group" of intellectuals. Of his numerous novels, stories and plays, many of which were acclaimed on Broadway and the cinema, some of the outstanding are: *Erik Dorn, 1001 Afternoons in Chicago, Humpty Dumpty, Count Bruga, A Jew in Love, Front Page, The Wonder Hat*. The story included here is reprinted from *The Champion from Far Away* (stories).

HEINRICH HEINE was born in Düsseldorf, Germany, in 1797, and died in Paris in 1856. After failing in business, he studied at Bonn, Göttingen and Berlin, where he joined a group of Jewish and non-Jewish intellectuals. He was "baptized but not converted" in order to secure a livelihood but, disillusioned, he repudiated the act and in 1831 made his home in Paris. Seized with a chronic illness in 1847, he never arose from his "mattress grave." Heine is one of the unique geniuses of modern times. His observations on Jews and Judaism, which have been gathered into one volume (*Confessio Judaica*, 1925), are as profound as they are acrid. Selections from his poetry have been translated into English by Emma Lazarus (1881) and Louis Untermeyer (1917).

THEODOR HERZL was born in Budapest in 1860 and died in Vienna in 1904. He studied law but soon turned to journalism and literature, and in his day was one of the most influential journalists in Vienna. Herzl was the organizer and leader of the Zionist movement. He stated his viewpoint in *The Jewish State* (1896) from which the selection included is taken. One of his associates, Jacob de Haas, wrote a full-length biography, *Theodor Herzl* (2 vols., 1927), and an abridged translation of his *Diaries* was made by Maurice Samuel (*Theodor Herzl: A Memorial*, 1929).

MOSES HESS was born in Bonn, Germany, in 1812 and died in Paris in 1875. He was self-educated. He was a leader in the Social-Democratic movement, being closely associated for some years with Marx and Engels. The Damascus affair (1840) reawakened his interest in Jewish life and in numerous writings he laid the basis of Jewish nationalism. His chief work on this question, *Rome and Jerusalem* (1863), proposed the Jewish colonization of Palestine. The selections included here are reprinted from the above book translated by Meyer Waxman (Bloch, 1918).

SAMSON RAPHAEL HIRSCH was born in Hamburg, Germany, in 1808, and died in Frankfort-on-the-Main in 1888. He received a Jewish education under eminent teachers and he also studied at the University of Bonn. He was the chief rabbi of many communities in Germany, but distinguished himself chiefly as the defender and interpreter of orthodox Judaism. Of his numerous writings, the most popular is *The Nineteen Letters of Ben Uziel*, from which the selection included is taken (revised from the translation of B. Drachman, New York, 1899).

PEREZ HIRSHBEIN was born in 1880 in a Russian village, where he spent the better part of his early years, and attended elementary schools. In 1902 his lyrics appeared in a number of Hebrew journals and in 1905 he published his first play, *Miriam*. Two years later he took an active part in the development of the Yiddish theater by organizing a stage troupe in Odessa. In 1911 he wrote the play, *The Idle Inn*, one of his better works, and at the end of the same year he emigrated to America, where his plays had been popular with dramatic groups and, subsequently, with the Jewish Art Theater. Hirshbein represents the modern Yiddish drama at its best. He has published many books of plays, travel and fiction. The play included is reprinted from *East and West*.

ISAIAH BEN AMOZ was born about 760 B.C. in Jerusalem and died there after 701 B.C. He was a man of profound religious and political insight, one of the greatest of the Hebrew prophets and poets. His writings and a few biographical details have been preserved in chapters 1-39 of the book of *Isaiah*.

JEREMIAH BEN HILKIAH was born of a priestly family in Anathoth, Palestine, about 650 B.C. and died in Egypt after 586 B.C. His career as a statesman-prophet extended from 626 B.C. until after the destruction of the Temple, when he was compelled to leave his country by a group of refugees. The Biblical book of *Jeremiah* is highly autobiographical in character, and the prophecies contain passages that have won a place in world literature. No prophet has had a greater influence upon the history of Judaism and of Christianity.

JACOB KAHAN was born in 1881 in Slutzk, and was educated at the University of Bern in Switzerland. He began to write Hebrew poetry when he was a youth and has contributed considerably to periodical literature. He was a founder and served as secretary of the Society for Hebrew Language and Culture in Berlin, which played an important role in the renascence of Hebrew literature. At present he serves as instructor in modern Hebrew literature in the Warsaw Institute for the Science of Judaism and is one of the leaders of the Revisionist party. The poems included here are reprinted from Fleg's *Jewish Anthology*.

ELEAZAR BEN KALIR lived in the eighth or ninth centuries. He was the most popular of the earliest group of liturgical poets including his master, Jannai and Jose ben Jose. Although much of his poetry is didactic versifying, some of it is of high merit.

MORDECAI MENAHEM KAPLAN was born in Lithuania in 1881. He was educated in the United States, has taught in the Jewish Theological Seminary since 1910 and is the founder and leader of the Society for the Advancement of Judaism in New York. He is one of the few religious thinkers that American Jewry has produced. His essay is selected from his *chef d'oeuvre*, *Judaism as a Civilization* (1934). Other works: *Judaism in Transition* (1936); *The Meaning of God in Modern Jewish Religion* (1937).

ISAAC KIPNIS was born in Russia in 1896. He attended heder and later worked in various tanneries. About 1920 his trade union sent him to study in Kiev, where he was admitted to the Yiddish literary circles. Since 1922 he has published stories in important Yiddish anthologies circulating in the Soviet Union and attained prominence with the publication of his book, *Months and Days: A Chronicle* (1926). Kipnis is one of the most promising writers in contemporary Soviet-Yiddish literature. The story included was translated by Samuel Kreiter.

ABRAHAM M. KLEIN was born in 1909 in Canada, where he attended the public schools and received a Jewish education. He was graduated from McGill University in 1930, took a degree in law from the Université de Montreal in '33, and is now practicing law in Montreal. He has been associated with the Zionist organization in numerous capacities. His poetry has been published in *The American Caravan, Canadian Forum, Menorah Journal, Poetry* and other periodicals. Ludwig Lewisohn regards Klein as "the first contributor of authentic Jewish poetry to the English language." *Haggadah,* here included, is from his *Selected Poems* (Behrman, 1937).

ARTHUR KOBER was born in New York City in 1900. He was educated in the public schools and worked at many random jobs before he turned to writing. He has utilized Jewish life in the Bronx to create a folk saga. His humor is deft and free from traditional sentimentality. The stories about the Gross family which originally appeared in the *New Yorker* were collected and published in *Thunder Over the Bronx* (1935). His play, *Having a Wonderful Time,* which was a Broadway success, won the Roi Cooper Megrue Prize for 1937.

LEON KOBRIN was born in Russia in 1872. He came to the United States in 1892, worked in sweatshops and began his literary career with translations and adaptations from Russian literature. During the last forty years he has written a large number of plays, stories and novels in Yiddish, which have won for him a high rank in Yiddish letters. The story included is out of his novel, *A Lithuanian Village,* which appeared in English in 1920.

SICHA LANDAU was born in Poland in 1889, and died in New York in 1937. He came to America in 1906, and soon afterwards began to write verse and edit Yiddish literary magazines. He was one of the leaders of the *Junge* movement which gave a new direction to Yiddish literature. Several volumes of his poetry have been published, and he compiled an anthology of Yiddish poetry.

I. M. LASK was born in London in 1905, and was educated in Birkbeck College, London University. He has contributed verse, stories and criticism to numerous English and American periodicals, and has translated into English the writings of many Hebrew authors, especially contemporary Palestinians. He had made Palestine his permanent home. He is at present on the staff of *Hadar,* in Tel Aviv. The poem included appeared with twelve other poems in the *Menorah Journal* (October-December, 1936).

ELSE LASKER-SCHÜLER was born at Elberfeld in 1876. She lived in Berlin and was a member of a circle of modernist writers and artists, but had to leave Germany after the inception of the Nazi regime. She is one of the great lyric poets of modern times. *My People,* here included, is selected from *Hebraische Balladen.* Unfortunately, not one of her numerous volumes of plays, novels, essays and poetry has been translated into English. She lives in Switzerland and has just published a travel book on Palestine (*Das Hebräerland,* Zurich, 1937).

MANE LAYB (BRAHINSKY) was born in Russia in 1884. He participated in the revolutionary movement there, and after the 1905 uprisings came to New York. He began to write lyrics at an early age, and has contributed verse to Yiddish newspapers and magazines both here and abroad. He holds high rank as a poet in modern Yiddish literature. The poem included here first appeared in an article on *American Yiddish Poetry* by Marie Syrkin (*Reflex,* Sept., 1927).

EMMA LAZARUS was born of Sephardic stock in New York City in 1849 and died there in 1887. She began to publish verse in her youth, and made the acquaintance of most of the important literati, particularly Emerson, in America. The persecution of Jews in Russia in the 1880's brought her into the fold of her people and gave a new verve to her poetry. Her translations of de Musset, Petrarch, Heine and the medieval Hebrew poets are among the best. Her poem, *The New Colossus,* is inscribed on the Statue of Liberty, and a bronze tablet commemorative of her rests in the pedestal of the Statue. Her writings have been published in two volumes, *Poems of Emma Lazarus* (1888).

MICAH JOSEPH LEBENSOHN was born in Wilna, Russia, in 1828, and died there in 1852. He was the son of a noted poet, and at a very early age began to write Hebrew verse. Afflicted with tuberculosis, he went to Berlin and several watering places in Europe, but finally returned to his native city, doomed to die. A complete edition of his poetry and translations, from which the poem included was selected, was published in Berlin in 1924.

MEYER LEVIN was born in Chicago in 1905. He was educated at the University of Chicago and studied art in Paris. He started newspaper work on the Chicago *Daily News,* conducted experimental marionette theaters in Chicago and New York, worked as a pioneer in a Palestinian commune, and at present is an assistant editor of *Esquire.* He has contributed noteworthy stories of Jewish life to the *Menorah Journal,* and in addition to three novels, *Reporter, Frankie and Johnny* and *Yehuda,* has retold some of the most fascinating Hasidic tales in *The Golden Mountain.* The story included is out of his latest novel, *The Old Bunch* (1937).

LUDWIG LEWISOHN was born in Berlin on May 30, 1882. In 1890 his parents brought him to America. He received his education largely at the College of Charleston and at Columbia University. At first he was a publisher's reader and then a magazine writer. But in 1910 he began his academic career at the University of Wisconsin as an instructor in the German language and literature, and in 1911 he was appointed a professor in that subject at Ohio State University. Later, due largely to his resentment of campus antisemitism, he left the University and joined the staff of *The Nation,* first as dramatic critic and then as an associate editor. In the meantime he had achieved an imposing position in American letters as critic and as novelist. In recent years his reconversion to Judaism and his enthusiastic espousal of the Zionist cause have given his writings a new direction and verve. Some of his best-known works are: *Upstream, Israel, The Island Within, Last Days of Shylock, Expression in America, A Book of Modern Criticism* and *Creative America, Trumpet of Jubilee.*

S. LIEBEN (real name Israel Hurwitz) was born in Russia in 1872. Twenty years later he emigrated to New York by way of London, and earned his livelihood as a shopworker and newsboy. His first literary efforts were published in Yiddish labor journals; after the split in the ranks of the Socialist party he allied himself with the writers on *Der Vorwarts,* a daily with which he is still associated. Lieben is one of the pioneers of realism in Yiddish fiction. His descriptions of the sweatshop and immigrant life of the New York ghetto three decades ago are honest, simple and touching. He is the author of several volumes of short stories.

MARVIN LOWENTHAL was born in Bradford, Pennsylvania, in 1890. He was graduated from the University of Wisconsin and Harvard University. For some years he made his home in Paris and, as foreign correspondent of the *Menorah Journal,* he traveled widely on the Continent and in Mediterranean countries. His diversified writings are unique in American literature. The selection included here, *Our Fathers That Begat Us,* which first appeared in the *Menorah Journal* (1925-1926), is a permanent contribution to modern Jewish literature. His published books: *The Memoirs of Glückel of Hameln* (translation); *A World Passed By* (Art and History); *The Autobiography of Montaigne; The Jews of Germany* (History).

SAMUEL DAVID LUZZATTO was born in Trieste, Italy, in 1800 and died in Padua in 1865. He received an extensive Jewish and general education and in 1829 was appointed a professor in the Rabbinical College of Padua. He wrote extensively, both in Hebrew and Italian, on philosophy, Biblical and Talmudic subjects and composed a large number of poems. Luzzatto defended traditional Judaism against his contemporary opponents and earlier philosophers like Spinoza, Abraham ibn Ezra and Maimonides. The selection here included is reprinted from Shalom Spiegel's *Hebrew Reborn* (pp. 87-89).

SOLOMON MAIMON was born in Lithuania in 1754 and died in Berlin in 1800. He received a Talmudic education and finally worked his way to Berlin. There he associated with Moses Mendelssohn's circle of intellectuals and made real contributions to philosophy; but because of his cynicism and sharp criticism, he was ostracized by his associates. In 1793 he published his autobiography under the title, *Salomon Maimon's Lebensgeschichte,* from which *On to Berlin* is a selection.

KARL MARX was born in Treves, Germany, in 1818, and died in London in 1883. When he was six years of age, his father, an attorney, adopted Christianity. He was educated at the Universities of Bonn and Berlin, and then turned to journalism and politics. His materialistic interpretation of history and economic theory have influenced the whole modern world. Together with Friedrich Engels, he helped to organize the workers of various countries into an international unit. His last and greatest work was *The Capital.* The selection here included is part of an essay he wrote in 1844 in the *Rheinische Zeitung* (see Marx, *Collected Essays,* London, 1930).

ANDRÉ MAUROIS (real name Emile Herzog) was born in 1885 in Elboeuf, France, and educated at the lycée at Rouen. He was a manager of textile mills and until the 20's he divided his time between literature and business. He won a distinguished place in modern letters as novelist and biographer. The story, here included, is reprinted from *Yisroel* (London, 1933). Among his outstanding books are: *The Life of Shelley, The Life of Disraeli, Byron* (biography), *Bernard Quesnay, Atmosphere of Love, Weigher of Souls* (novels), *Aspects of Biography, The Miracle of England, An Essay on Silence* (criticism and travel).

MEIR OF ROTHENBURG was born of a distinguished family at about 1215 and died in the fortress of Ensisheim, Alsace, in 1293. He was a brilliant Talmudic scholar, a man of noble character and the recognized leader of Franco-German Jewry during his time. Because he was unwilling that the Jews pay an exorbitant ransom for him, he remained in prison from 1286 until his death. Meir was also a liturgical poet. The poem included here is reprinted from *Songs of Exile,* by Nina Davis (Phila., 1901).

MENDELE MOCHER SEFORIM (real name Sholem Jacob Abromovitch) was born in Russia in 1836, and died in 1917. He wrote both in Hebrew and Yiddish, and even though he created a new style in both languages, his Yiddish writings became most popular. He is known as "the grandfather" of Yiddish literature. His books not only gave a true portrayal of ghetto life, but also brought to light the social and economic roots of poverty and ignorance. On his seventy-fifth birthday, his collected writings were issued in seventeen volumes; the hundredth anniversary of his birth in 1936 was commemorated throughout the Jewish world. Available in English are: *The Travels of Benjamin the Third (Menorah Journal,* Aug.-Nov., 1936), from which the selection included is taken, and *Fishke the Lame,* translated by A. S. Rappoport (London, 1928).

MOSES MENDELSSOHN was born in Dessau in 1728 and died in Berlin in 1786. He received a Jewish education in his native town and then went to Berlin, where he earned his livelihood by tutoring and later as a bookkeeper in a silk factory. He became a dominant force in the intellectual revival in Frederick's Berlin, being a bosom friend of Lessing, who immortalized Mendelssohn in *Nathan the Wise.* Gifted with a philosophic mind and literary taste of a high order, he brought Western culture into the Jewish community through his commentary on the Bible and translation of the Pentateuch into German. His chief works (*Jerusalem, Phaedo,* etc.) have been translated into English by M. Samuels (London, 1838) and in the *Hebrew Review* (vol. 1, London, 1834).

SARAH GERTRUDE MILLIN was born in England in 1892. Her parents took her to South Africa when she was six months old, and there she began to contribute to periodicals at an early age. She is regarded as one of the significant contemporary novelists. Among her books: *The Dark River* (1920); *Adam's Rest* (1922); *God's Stepchildren* (1924); *The Coming of the Lord* from which the story here included is taken (1928), and *Rhodes: A Life* (1933).

CLAUDE GOLDSMID MONTEFIORE was born of a distinguished family in London in 1858. He was educated at Balliol College, Oxford, and the University of Berlin. He has devoted his life to study and public service. Montefiore is perhaps the outstanding representative of Liberal Judaism. He has defended liberal Judea in a vast army of books and pamphlets and is a vehement opponent of Jewish nationalism. Among his important works are: *The Origin of Religion as Illustrated by the Ancient Hebrews* (1892); *Bible for Home Reading* (1890); *Rabbinic Literature and Gospel Teaching* (1927); *The Synoptic Gospels* (1930). The essay here included is reprinted from *The Legacy of Israel* (New York, 1927, pp. 514-522).

RACHEL MORPURGO was born in Trieste of a noted Italian-Jewish family in 1790 and died there in 1871. She began to write Hebrew poetry at an early age and continued, with increasing power, until her death. In 1890 a complete edition of her Hebrew poetry and letters was published under the title *The Harp of Rachel*. An appreciation of her work may be found in *Rachel Morpurgo and Contemporary Hebrew Poets of Italy,* by Nina Salaman (1924). *Song* is reprinted from *Songs of Many Days,* by Nina Salaman.

MOSES BEN MAIMON (also Maimonides and Rambam) was born in Cordova in 1135 and died in Cairo in 1204. He came of a distinguished family and received a broad secular as well as religious education. When he was thirteen years old, he fled from his native land with his family because of persecution and lived under stress for some years in Northern Africa, Palestine and finally in Egypt. He excelled in philosophy, medicine, law and literature and is usually regarded as the greatest Jew of the Middle Ages. Of his numerous writings, the two most important works are: *The Guide of the Perplexed,* from which the selection included is taken (pp. 219-220; 225-227 in the Friedländer edition) and his code of Jewish law, *Mishneh Torah*. See Abrahams and Yellin, *Maimonides* (London, 1935), and *A Bibliography of Maimonides,* by Joseph I. Gorfinkle, New York, 1932.

MOSES IBN EZRA was born in Granada, Spain, about 1070 and died after 1138. He was one of the intellectual leaders of medieval Spanish Jewry. His writings comprise philosophy, literary criticism and poetry. Ibn Ezra's poetry achieved considerable popularity and his *Tahḳemoni* is considered one of the masterpieces of Jewish literature. The poems included are reprinted from *The Poems of Emma Lazarus* (vol. 2). See also *Selected Poems of Moses ibn Ezra,* translated by Solomon Solis-Cohen (Phila., 1934).

NAHUM was a liturgical poet who lived about 1300. Nothing is known of his life beyond that he probably lived in southern Spain.

ISRAEL NAJARA was born in Damascus about 1550 and died in Gaza or Adrianople about a half century later. His thinking was deeply colored by contemporary Jewish mysticism and Spanish-Turkish poetry. The erotic element in his religious poetry is so strong that it evoked the condemnation of the rabbis, but Luria declared that his hymns were heard in heaven with joy. The poem here included is selected from *Songs of Exile,* by Salaman (p. 60).

ROBERT NATHAN was born in New York City in 1894. He received his education at private schools, both here and abroad, and at Harvard University. He first worked in an advertising agency and later devoted himself entirely to writing. His poetry and fiction are permeated with subtle phantasy and satire. Among his books: *Youth Grows Old, A Cedar Box, Selected Poems* (verse); *Peter Kindred, Don Quixote, the Woodcutter's House, There Is Another Heaven, Jonah, The Orchid, Road of Ages* (novels).

MAX NORDAU (real name Suedfeld) was born in Budapest in 1849 and died in Paris in 1923. He studied medicine and his books, *Conventional Lies, Diseases of the Century* and *Degeneration,* made him internationally famous. He wrote considerably on philosophical and historical subjects. During Herzl's leadership of the Zionist movement, Nordau was his chief lieutenant and spokesman. His essay, *The Tenets of Zionism,* is reprinted from *Zionism,* edited by Goodman and Lewis (1916).

JOSEPH OPATOSHU (real name Opatovsky) was born in 1887 in Poland. After the failure of the Russian Revolution in 1905, in which he participated, he left for Paris. He studied engineering in the Polytechnic Institute at Nancy. He emigrated to America in 1907 and worked as a newsboy, factory laborer and Hebrew teacher. In 1914 he became an engineer and followed this calling for a short time. Then he decided on a literary career. Opatoshu began to contribute short stories to Yiddish literary periodicals and newspapers and founded and edited himself several such journals. He is regarded as one of the outstanding of contemporary Yiddish writers. He is the author of novels, plays and numerous short stories, some of which have been translated into Polish, German and English. Much of his work, like his noteworthy *Poilische Velder,* is concerned with the delineation of human conflicts caused by brutal, primitive passions. The story included was translated by Samuel Kieiter.

ISAAC LOEB PEREZ was born in Zamascz, Poland, in 1852, and died in Warsaw in 1915. He received religious and secular instruction, saturated himself in Polish, German and French literature, and became in turn Hebrew teacher, brewery manager, flour-mill operator and lawyer before he decided to devote himself to writing. Stirred by the brutal wave of antisemitism that swept over Russia in the eighties, he became an advocate of social reform, espoused the cause of the workers, and began to write exclusively in Yiddish, the worker's language. Perez is one of the notable figures of modern Yiddish literature. His genius found expression in poetry, drama, journalism and particularly short stories, which have won general acclaim. The story here included, translated by Samuel P. Rudens, appeared in *Yiddish Short Stories,* edited by Isaac Goldberg. Many of his stories and plays have appeared in Anglo-Jewish magazines. For a study, see A. A. Roback, *Peretz, Psychologist of Literature.* There are also two volumes of short stories in English: *Stories and Pictures,* translated by Helena Frank, and *Bontche the Silent,* translated by A. S. Rappoport.

PHILO OF ALEXANDRIA (also "Philo Judaeus") was born in Alexandria, Egypt, about 20 B.C. and died after 45 C.E. He was a leader of the Jewish community and in 40 headed a delegation to Emperor Caligula to ask protection from the attacks of the Greeks. He was a prolific writer, most of his works taking the form of commentaries on The Pentateuch. As a philosopher, he advocated a synthesis between stoicism and Judaism. The selection here included is from the Loeb Classical Library edition of *Philo* (vol. I, pp. 21-27; IV, pp. 33-43).

DAVID PINSKI was born in Russia in 1872. When he came to the United States in 1899, at the invitation of a New York labor newspaper, he had already established his reputation as a journalist and short story writer. The Kishinev pogrom in 1905 aroused him to action. In several labor-Zionist journals which he edited, he fought against the dominance of reactionaries and yellow journalism in American-Jewish life. Pinski's novels and plays, which portray the worker in the class struggle and the plight of the individual in a system of oppression, are of high artistic value. *The Treasure* was produced by the Theater Guild. Among his writings that have been translated are: *Temptations* (short stories); *Arnold Levenberg* (novel); *King David and His Wives,* from which *Michal* is reprinted, *Ten Plays,* and *The Treasure* (drama).

HARRY ALAN POTAMKIN was born in New York City in 1900 and died there in 1933. He was educated at the University of Pennsylvania, and worked in experimental education and cinema criticism. He contributed verse and prose to numerous magazines. *Süsskind of Trimberg* first appeared in the *Menorah Journal* (June, 1925).

RACHEL (surname BLUWSTEIN) was born in Russia in 1890 and died in Palestine in 1931. She was the most notable of a group of women Hebrew poets in Palestine, and her poems, largely written while suffering from tuberculosis during the last years of her life, have achieved wide popularity. All of her verse, published in two slender volumes, is marked by a tender lyricism and Biblical simplicity. Some of them have been set to music.

ABRAHAM RAISEN was born in Russia in 1876. He received the conventional Jewish education and in his early youth was initiated into European culture. He is one of the most distinguished figures in modern Yiddish literature. Influenced by the Russian lyricists and encouraged by Sholom Aleichem, his poetry and stories soon won a large audience among the Yiddish reading masses. He influenced both Yiddish literature and the younger writers by the publication of several journals of literature and criticism in Europe and the United States, where he now lives. He has also been a vigorous protagonist for the acceptance of Yiddish as the national language of the Jewish people.

DAVID REUBENI was born in Arabia about 1490, and died in Llerena, Spain, after 1535. He claimed to represent his brother Joseph, who ruled over a Jewish kingdom in Arabia and wanted the help of Christian rulers to defeat the Turk in the Holy Land. His striking appearance and romantic tale made a deep impression both upon Pope Clement VII and King John III of Portugal. Reubeni and his fellow-adventurer, Solomon Molko, were burned at the stake at the command of Emperor Charles V. Reubeni's diary, describing his travels and experiences, was translated into English by Elkan Adler in *Jewish Travellers,* from which the selection included is reprinted.

CHARLES REZNIKOFF was born in Brooklyn, N. Y., in 1894. He attended the University of Missouri and New York University and while writing, earned his living writing as a legal researcher. He has contributed prose and verse to numerous periodicals. A number of his significant poems, stories and plays about Jewish life and history appeared in the *Menorah Journal*, from which *Uriel Acosta* (Feb., 1925) is reprinted. Published books: *By the Waters of Manhattan, Testimony* and *The Tale of a Needle Worker* (novels); *Nine Plays, Five Groups of Verse, Jerusalem the Golden, "In Memoriam: 1933"* (poetry).

ISAAC ROSENBERG was born at Bristol, England, in 1890 and was killed in action in April, 1918. He attended schools in London, where at an early age he exhibited extraordinary talents for drawing and writing. He was one of the most gifted poets of those who lost their lives in the war, and the first (after Emma Lazarus) of a group of young poets writing in English whose verse is saturated with a Hebraic spirit. *Poems,* a volume of his verse and letters edited by Gordon Bottomley with a memoir by Lawrence Binyon, was published in 1922 (Heineman, London).

MORRIS ROSENFELD was born in Russia in 1862, and died in New York in 1923. His life was a story of incredible suffering and unhappiness. He worked as a tailor in factories and sweatshops, and his poetry burns with protest and despair. He won international recognition when Leo Wiener of Harvard introduced his poetry to the English-reading public. He translated some of Rosenfeld's poems, which comprise the book, *Songs from the Ghetto* (1898). Between 1898 and 1903 he lectured widely both here and abroad, and in 1914 a second volume of poems appeared in English, *Songs of Labor and Other Poems*.

LEONARD Q. Ross (real name Leo Rosten) was born in Chicago in 1908, and was educated at the University of Chicago and on the Continent. He has contributed to numerous literary journals. His Kaplan stories, one of which is here included, are based upon his experience as a teacher of Americanization classes in a night school for adults, which are, he suggests, "the most complete melting pots that our country has ever had. The Kaplans, the Caravellos, the Mitnicks and the Moskowitzes taught me more than I taught them." These unique stories which appeared in the *New Yorker* during 1936-37 have been issued under the title *The Education of* H*Y*M*A*N K*A*P*L*A*N.

HENRY ROTH was born in Austria in 1906 and was brought to New York by his parents when he was eighteen months old. He is a graduate of the College of the City of New York. His first novel, *Call It Sleep* (1934), from which the story here included is taken, won immediate acclaim and stamped him as one of the most promising of the new vintage of American novelists.

HARRY SACKLER was born in Galicia, Poland, in 1883. He came to New York in 1902 and began to contribute to the New York *Vorwartz* in 1907. He has written extensively in the Hebrew, Yiddish and Anglo-Jewish presses. As an artist, he has his roots in the past; his writing is permeated with Jewish history and lore. Among his works that have appeared in English are: *The Legend of Luz (Menorah Journal,* vol. 10), *The Seer Looks at His Bride,* reprinted here from the *Reflex* (July, 1927), *The Zaddik's Journey* (*Reflex*, Nov., 1927), and a novel, *Festival at Meron* (1935).

SOLOMON SCHECHTER was born in Roumania in 1847 and died in New York City in 1915. He received a Jewish education from eminent teachers and attended the University of Vienna. Later he served as lecturer in Talmud at the University of Cambridge and president of the Jewish Theological Seminary in New York City. Schechter was not only a great scholar but an essayist of high caliber. Although he wrote no systematic philosophy of Judaism, he was the ablest advocate and interpreter of so-called Conservative Judaism. Among his well-known works are: *Studies in Judaism* (3 vols.) and *Aspects of Rabbinic Theology*.

ZALMAN SCHNAIUR was born of a notable Hasidic family in Shklov, Russia, in 1887. He received a traditional Jewish education and gave signs of his ability to write at an early age. He is one of the major figures in modern Hebrew and Yiddish literatures. Schnaiur has written verse, prose, drama and fiction. The poems here included are reprinted from *The Jewish Anthology* (Fleg). One of his novels, *Noah Pandre,* translated by Joseph Leftwich, introduced him to the English reading public.

ISIDOR SCHNEIDER was born in Horodenko, Poland, in 1896 and was brought to New York as a young child. He studied in the public schools on the East Side and attended the College of the City of New York. For some years he was engaged in the publishing business and wrote during leisure time. Schneider's contributions have appeared in numerous periodicals and among his outstanding books are: *The Temptation of St. Anthony and Other Poems; Dr. Transit* and *The Kingdom of Necessity* (novels). He was awarded a Guggenheim Fellowship in 1936, which has enabled him to study and write abroad at present.

ARTHUR SCHNITZLER was born in Vienna in 1862 and died there in 1931. He studied medicine at the University of Vienna but devoted his life to literature. His knowledge of medicine and psychology has deeply influenced his writing. Schnitzler is regarded as one of the masters of modern European literature. His plays dominated the Vienna stage for some years. He dealt with the Jewish problem in *Professor Bernhardi,* here included, and *The Road to the Open.* A large number of his books have been translated into English.

EDWIN SEAVER was born in Washington, D. C., in 1900. He was educated at Worcester Academy and Harvard College ('22). In collaboration with his wife, he edited and publish *1924,* a magazine of the arts, presenting the work of the more advanced writings of the time. He has been on the staff of the New York *Evening Post* and *Sun,* contributed to numerous periodicals and anthologies and at present is literary editor of the *Sunday Worker.* He has published two novels, *The Company* (1930) and *Between the Hammer and the Anvil* (1937), and a third will be issued in 1938 by Scribner's.

LOEB SHAPIRO was born in Russia in 1878 and received traditional Jewish education. He began to contribute stories to well-known almanacs which were edited by Perez and Raisin. In 1906 he emigrated to America and wrote for various literary magazines. His progrom stories, written in the heat of the Kishevev massacre, have made a singularly strong impression upon his readers. Three years later he returned to Warsaw. There he worked on newspapers and also translated a number of continental and English novels. Then he left for Switzerland and from there again for America, where he has lived since. In 1912 he retired from writing and has been working on a scientific discovery. *The Kiss* is reprinted from *East and West*.

DAVID SHIMONOWITZ was born in Russia in 1886. He settled in Palestine before the War. As a Hebrew poet, he ranks close to Bialik, Tchernihovsky and Schnaiur. His idylls are among the best poetic descriptions of the land of Israel in the making, and he has produced a considerable number of verse fables of very high order. One of his ballads was included in *The Jewish Caravan* (1935).

ABRAHAM SHLONSKY was born in 1900 in Krüllow, Russia, and in his youth made his home in Palestine, where he soon became recognized as one of the important Hebrew poets. He has been the editor of an important Hebrew literary periodical and has published several volumes of verse which have won wide acclaim. He has translated into Hebrew the works of many European masters, including Gogol, Hugo and Bulwer Lytton.

SIMEON BEN SIRA (Greek form, Jesus ben Sirach) lived in Palestine about 200 B.C. He was the author of *Ecclesiasticus,* perhaps the most important of the Apocryphal books. In 1896 Solomon Schechter discovered thirty-nine chapters of the original Hebrew which had been lost since ancient times.

SHOLOM ALEICHEM (real name Sholem Rabinowitz) was born in Russia in 1859 and died in New York in 1916. With Mendele and Perez, he stands out as one of the pillars of modern Yiddish literature. Beginning his literary career as a youth with a Yiddish adaptation of *Robinson Crusoe,* he early made notable contributions to Hebrew and Yiddish periodicals and became pre-eminent as humorist, critic and playwright. During his years of affluence, he assisted indigent colleagues, published anthologies and was the first editor of a Yiddish periodical to provide adequate honoraria for writers. His numerous books and stories, such as *Menahem Mendel* and *Tevye the Dairyman,* are among the classics of Yiddish literature. Several of his stories have been published in collections and in Anglo-Jewish magazines. Available in English also are: *Stempenyu* (novel) and *Jewish Children* (short stories), both translated by Hannah Berman.

I. J. SINGER was born in Poland in 1893. Believing his early stories immature, he destroyed them. A novelette, *Perl,* which was published in 1921, attracted considerable attention, and he became a regular contributor to the New York *Vorwartz*. The dramatization of his novel, *Yoshe Kalb* (*The Sinner,* 1933) by Maurice Schwartz made a profound impression upon theatergoers, and his novel, *The Brothers Ashkenazi* (1936), won for him high rank among contemporary novelists. He lives in New York City.

Moses Smilansky was born in Russia in 1874, emigrated to Palestine in 1891 and has lived there ever since. He was one of the young agricultural pioneers of his day and now as one of the wealthiest orange growers is president of the Farmers Association. He has achieved a reputation as a Hebrew journalist and a short story writer. In his stories he relates the experiences of the struggles of his generation in Palestine, and tells of Arab life in villages and tents, always with sympathy and understanding. The story included here, translated by I. M. Lask, is reprinted from *The Palestine Caravan* (London, 1935).

Solomon ibn Gabirol was born in Malaga, Spain, about 1021 and died in Valencia about 1058. Biographical details are wanting. Gabirol was one of the most original philosophic minds in the Middle Ages and his poetry, both religious and secular, ranks with the best of world poetry. The poems included are reprinted from *The Poems of Emma Lazarus* (vol. 2). Works available in English translation: *A Choice of Pearls,* translated by Ascher; *The Improvement of the Moral Qualities,* by S. S. Wise (1901); *Selected Religious Poems of Solomon ibn Gabirol,* by Zangwill-Davidson (1923).

Baruch Spinoza was born in Amsterdam in 1632 and died in 1677. He received a Jewish education and was expected to be a rabbi. A knowledge of contemporary thought led him to reject the traditional Jewish ideology and in 1656 he was excommunicated by the Amsterdam rabbis. For the remainder of his life he earned his livelihood by polishing lenses, rejecting various offers, including a chair in philosophy at Heidelberg. He is regarded as one of the greatest minds of modern times. Among his epoch-making works are: *Ethics, The Improvement of the Understanding, Theological-Political Treatise,* from which the selection included is taken (chapter 3, Elwes' translation). For the Jewish background of Spinoza's thought, see *Philosophy of Spinoza,* by H. A. Wolfson (2 vols., Cambridge, 1934).

André Spire was born of a prominent family in Nancy, France, in 1868. He was educated in the University of Nancy, where his literary career began, and the Ecole de Droit de Paris. He was deeply influenced by the Dreyfus Case, and a French translation of Zangwill which reawakened his Jewish consciousness. A racial spirit dominates his poetry written after 1904. A biographical portrait and a critique of Spire's poetry with forty translations will be found in *André Spire and His Poetry,* by Stanley Burnshaw (1933), from which the poem included is reprinted.

Judah Steinberg was born in Bessarabia in 1861 and died in Odessa in 1908. He was the son of a famous Zaddik, earned a livelihood by instructing children in Hebrew and in 1897, with the publication of a volume of stories, *In City and Country,* attracted the attention of the Hebrew-reading public. Two volumes of his stories, *In Those Days* (1915), from which the story included is taken, and *The Breakfast of the Birds* (1917), have been translated into English. Four volumes of his collected works were published in Berlin in 1910. Together with Perez and Berdyczevski, he is considered the most notable interpreter of Hasidism in stories.

GLADYS BRONWYN STERN was born in London in 1890. She was educated at Notting Hill High School, and has traveled and lived on the Continent. She is one of the most distinguished English novelists. Among her numerous works, many of which deal with her family background, are: *Debatable Ground, The Matriarch, Mosaic, A Deputy Was King, Debonair* and *Petruchio* (novels); *Smoke Rings, Jack A'Manory* and *The Slower Judas* (short stories).

NAHMAN SYRKIN was born in Russia in 1868, and died in New York in 1924. He was educated under Jewish scholars and at the Universities of Berlin and Zurich. He contributed extensively to the Jewish press in Russia, Germany and America, and was known as a brilliant orator. He was one of the earliest and chief exponents of socialist Zionism, advocating the Jewish working masses as the only valid instrument for national rehabilitation. The essay included is reprinted from a booklet of his *Essays on Socialist Zionism* (1935, Young Poale Zion Alliance).

SAUL TCHERNIHOWSKY was born in the Crimea in 1875. He received a secular and Jewish education, and studied medicine at Heidelberg. He is one of the pre-eminent poets of modern Hebrew literature, and a scholar of uncommon attainments. He has translated into Hebrew Plato, Homer, is at work on a Dictionary of Medicine and Natural Science (Hebrew), and his collected works were published in ten volumes in 1932. An appreciation of his poetry with translations may be found in *Tchernichovski and His Poetry*, by L. V. Snowman (London, 1929). He now resides in Palestine.

LOUIS UNTERMEYER was born in New York City in 1885. He attended public schools and was in the jewelry business until 1923, when he decided to devote himself entirely to literature. Untermeyer has established himself as a poet, critic and translator of the first order. His numerous anthologies are used widely in schools and colleges. Some of his outstanding books are: *Challenger, These Times, Roast Leviathan* (from which the poem included here is reprinted), *Burning Bush, Collected Parodies* (verse); *Poems of Heinrich Heine, The Fat of the Cat* (translations); *Modern American Poetry, Modern British Poetry* (anthologies).

JAKOB WASSERMANN was born in Fürth, Germany, in 1873 and died in Austria in 1934. He entered the field of literature against the wishes of his family, and quickly established his reputation as one of the most significant European novelists. The profound urge for justice which permeates all his work, Wassermann ascribed to his Jewish heritage. He discussed this subject at length in his autobiography, *My Life as a German and a Jew.* Among his other outstanding works that have been translated are: *The Dark Pilgrimage,* from which the story included here is taken, *The Maurizius Case, Wedlock* and *The World's Illusion* (novels).

FRANZ WERFEL, the son of a wealthy Jewish merchant, was born in Prague in 1890. During the World War he saw active service in Eastern Galicia as a soldier in the Austrian Army. At first Werfel was an enthusiastic member of Martin Buber's neo-Hasidic coterie in Prague, but due entirely to the temperamental instability of his genius he abandoned this interest soon for socialism and then successively became an adherent of anarchism, idealistic internationalism, Communism and finally even mystic Catholicism. More recently, as a direct result of Fascist persecution of the Jews in Central Europe, he has fled to England and again has become a devout Jew. His spectacle play on the destiny of the Jewish people, *The Eternal Road,* was produced on Broadway by Max Reinhardt in 1936-37. Franz Werfel has been hailed by Romain Rolland as the greatest of living poets and one of the very greatest among novelists and dramatists. Some of his best-known works are: *Goat-Song, Juarez and Maximilien,* and *Schweiger* (plays); *The Pure in Heart, Verdi, The Pascarella Family* and *The Forty Days of Musa Dagh* (novels).

YEHOASH (real name Solomon Bloomgarden) was born in Russia in 1871, and died in New York City in 1927. He came to America in 1890, engaged in business for some years, and, stricken with tuberculosis, went to Denver. There he resumed writing verse in Yiddish, which brought him immediate acclaim. Much of his later poetry and prose is based upon his impressions during travels to the East. The last ten years of his life were devoted to an exquisite translation of the Bible into Yiddish. Among his writings that have been translated into English are: *The Shunamite (Statford Journal,* 1914), *Mishna Abot* (New York, 1921) and *The Feet of the Messinger* (Phila., 1923).

SIMEON YUSHKEVITCH was born in Russia in 1868, and died in Paris in 1927. In Paris he completed the study of medicine. He made his literary debut in 1897 in Russian-Jewish periodicals with stories and novels depicting the disintegration of the old Jewish communal life under the influence of changing economic conditions. He was popular in Russified Jewish intellectual circles. He wrote 25 volumes of novels and plays, some of which have been translated into German and French. The story here included was translated by John Cournos.

ISRAEL ZANGWILL was born in London in 1864 and died at the age of sixty-two in Sussex, England. He attended the Jews Free School in East London and received the B.A. degree with highest honors from London University. Although an eminent novelist, critic and playwright, Zangwill is best known as an interpreter of Jewish life. His *Children of the Ghetto* quickly won the acclaim of English readers and critics, and his subsequent volumes, *Dreamers of the Ghetto, Ghetto Tragedies, Ghetto Comedies* and *The King of Schnorrers* are still widely read in English-speaking countries. Zangwill also played a notable role as a champion of the downtrodden and persecuted. He allied himself with Theodor Herzl, the founder of the Zionist movement, and later organized the Jewish Territorial Organization (JTO) for the purpose of establishing autonomous Jewish countries·for persecuted Jews in various parts of the world. His uncompromising zeal for truth and his devastating tongue and pen made him a prophetic spirit in every cause that he espoused.

ARNOLD ZWEIG was born in Glogau, Silesia, in 1887. Although the son of a harnessmaker he nevertheless acquired an extensive academic training at the Universities of Breslau, Munich, Berlin, Göttingen, Rostick, and Tübingen. He saw active service at the front during 1915-1918. His war experience turned him into a militant pacifist. After the war he devoted himself to writing as a career. He is now a refuge from Nazi Germany and has made Palestine his home. As a leading exponent of the Zionist-Socialist viewpoint, he wrote extensively on Palestine Jewish labor and the Jewish question in general. Among his best-known works are: *The Case of Sergeant Grischa, De Vrient Goes Home, Young Woman of 1914,* and *Claudia* (novels); *Boys and Men, Girls and Women* and *Playthings of Time* from which the story included is taken (collections of short stories), and *Lessing, Kleist and Buchner* (critical literary essays).

STEFAN ZWEIG was born in Vienna in 1881, of wealthy parents. He received a doctor's degree in philosophy at the University of Vienna. Then he decided upon a literary career. It was interrupted, however, by the World War, when his pacifism brought him to Switzerland. Here he attached himself to Romain Rolland and the militant international peace movement. The anti-war play *Jeremiah* (from which the last act is included here), later produced by Max Reinhardt, resulted from this experience. He is now a voluntary exile from Fascist Austria, residing in London. Zweig's literary versatility has been quite extraordinary. He has excelled as biographer, novelist, short story writer, poet, dramatist, literary and theater critic and psychologist. Some of his best-known works which have made him famous throughout the world are: *Amok* (novel); *Conflicts* and *Passion and Pain* and *Kaleidoscope* (collection of short stories); *Joseph Fouche* and *Marie Antoinette* (biography); *Mental Healers* (psychologic studies of Mesmer, Mrs. Eddy, and Freud) and *Adepts in Self-Portraiture* (Casanova, Stendhal, and Tolstoi); *Three Masters* (literary studies of Balzac, Dickens and Dostoievsky); and *Volpone* (a free adaptation of the play by Ben Jonson).

SELECTED BIBLIOGRAPHY

The following books, in addition to those mentioned in preceding pages, will give the curious reader a fuller introduction to the history and development of Jewish literature and a selection of the literature accessible in English translation.

I. GENERAL WORKS

Abrahams, Israel: A History of Jewish Literature, Phila., 1899. A brief survey from 70 C.E. to the 18th century.

Abrahams, Israel: By-Paths in Hebraic Bookland, Phila., 1920. Short essays on Jewish books and authors.

Abrahams, Israel: The Book of Delight and Other Papers, Phila., 1912.

Herder, Johann Gottfried von: The Spirit of Hebrew Poetry, 1883. A superb work on Biblical poetry.

Karpeles, Gustav: Jewish Literature and Other Essays, Phila., 1895.

Judaica: A descriptive bibliography of books of Jewish interest in the Boston Public Library, compiled by Fanny Goldstein, Boston, 1931. Also a supplement for May, 1936.

Oesterley and Box: A Short Survey of the Literature of Rabbinical and Medieval Judaism, London, 1920.

Steinschneider, Moritz: Jewish Literature, London, 1857. A handbook of Jewish literature from the 8th to the 18th centuries by the greatest of Jewish bibliographers.

The Jewish Encyclopaedia: vols. I-XII, New York, 1905. Rich with biographical and bibliographical materials.

The Menorah Journal: vols. I-XXV, New York, 1915—

Waxman, Meyer: A History of Jewish Literature, vols. I-III, New York, 1930-1936. A comprehensive survey of Jewish literature from the close of the Bible to (with the completion of the fourth volume) the present day.

II. BOOKS ON HEBREW LITERATURE

Bloch, Joshua: Modern Hebrew Literature, New York, 1928. (Columbia University Course in Literature, vol. I, pp. 195-201.)

Klausner, Joseph: A History of Modern Hebrew Literature, London, 1932.

Slousch, Nahum: The Renascence of Hebrew Literature, Phila., 1909.

Spiegel, Shalom: Hebrew Reborn, New York, 1930. Essays on currents and outstanding figures in modern Hebrew literature.

III. BOOKS ON YIDDISH LITERATURE

Lieberman, Herman: Yiddish Literature. An essay in voiume VIII of the Columbia University Extension Course in Literature.

Roback, A. A.: Curiosities of Yiddish Literature, Cambridge, Mass., 1933. Contains a valuable "Syllabus of Yiddish Literature."

Wiener, Leo: Yiddish Literature in the Nineteenth Century, New York, 1899. Contains selections with translations.

IV. COLLECTIONS OF TRANSLATIONS FROM HEBREW AND YIDDISH

Abrahams, Israel: Hebrew Ethical Wills, Phila., 1926. A selection (Hebrew and English) of unique testamentary literature, from the Rabbinic period to 1800.

Block, Etta: One-Act Plays from the Yiddish, First Series, Cincinnati, 1923. Second Series, New York, 1929.

Fein, Harry H.: A Harvest of Hebrew Verse, Boston, 1934. Chiefly contemporary.

Fleg, Edmond: The Jewish Anthology, New York, 1925. Translated from the French by Maurice Samuel.

Frank Helena: Yiddish Tales, Phila., 1912. Short stories by representative Yiddish writers.

Goldberg, Isaac: Six Plays of the Yiddish Theatre, First Series, Boston, 1916; Second Series, Boston, 1918. Yiddish Short Stories, Girard, Kansas, 1923. Little Blue Book No. 489.

Halper, H.: Post-Biblical Hebrew Literature, Phila., 1921. Selected translations from 200 B.C. to the end of the 18th century, with a companion volume of Hebrew texts.

Katznelson-Rubashow, Rachel: The Plough Woman, New York, 1932. Records and writings of the pioneer women of modern Palestine, translated from the Hebrew by Maurice Samuel.

Levin, Meyer: The Golden Mountain, New York, 1932. Hasidic tales about Israel Baalshem and the fairy tales of his great-grandson, Nahman of Bratzlav.

Leftwich, Joseph: Yisröel, London, 1933. A compilation of stories by modern Jewish writers, arranged according to countries and language.

Newman, Louis I., and Spitz, Leon: The Hasidic Anthology, New York, 1934. Selected Hasidic parables and tales, arranged according to subject matter.

Rogoff, Harry: East and West, New York, 1916. A magazine devoted to the interpretation and translation of modern Yiddish literature.

Raskin, Philip M.: Anthology of Modern Jewish Poetry, New York, 1927.

Salaman, Nina: Apples and Honey, New York, 1927. Selected literature, designed chiefly for youth.

Zabara, Joseph Ben Meir: The Book of Delight, translated from the Hebrew by Moses Hadas. A classic of medieval folk literature, written by a Spanish-Jewish author of the 12th century.

INDEX OF AUTHORS

Abraham ibn Daud, 669
Abraham ibn Ezra, 582
Abravanel, Isaac, 690
Acosta, Uriel, 293
Agnon, S. J., 355
Albo, Joseph, 693
Alharizi, Judah, 585
Alkabez, Solomon Halevi, 592
Ansky, S., 457
Asch, Sholem, 528
Babel, Isaac, 168
Bahya ibn Pakuda, 670
Behrman, S. N., 537
Berkowitz, I. D., 254
Bialik, Hayyim Nahman, 611
Bloch, Jean-Richard, 138
Brandeis, Louis D., 755
Brinig, Myron, 44
Brod, Max, 271
Buber, Martin, 763
Cotler, Joseph, 350
Cournos, John, 436
David ben Jesse, 547
Deutsch, Babette, 639
Dubnow, S. M., 749
Ehrenbourg, Ilya, 156
Einstein, Albert, 773
Eleazar ben Kalir, 561
Feinstein, Martin, 641
Ferber, Edna, 57
Feuchtwanger, Lion, 283
Fineman, Irving, 12
Fleg, Edmond, 618
Franzos, Karl Emil, 267
Freedman, David, 359
Frishman, David, 600

Frug, S., 603
Geiger, Abraham, 722
Glückel of Hameln, 290
Glusberg, Samuel, 203
Gold, Michael, 20
Golding, Louis, 117
Goldschimdt, Meir Aron, 150
Gordon, Aaron David, 752
Gordon, J. L., 599
Greenberg, Uri Zwi, 642
Haam, Ahad, 730
Halevi, Judah, 577, 679
Halper, Albert, 3
Hazaz, Hayyim, 178
Hecht, Ben, 376
Heine, Heinrich, 233, 595
Herzl, Theodor, 735
Hess, Moses, 718
Hirsch, Samson Raphael, 710
Hirschbein, Perez, 504
Isaiah ben Amoz, 550
Jeremiah ben Hilkiah, 552
Kahan, Jacob, 627
Kaplan, Mordecai M., 775
Kipnis, I., 159
Klein, Abraham M., 649
Kober, Arthur, 389
Kobrin, Leon, 240
Landau, Sicha, 640
Lask, I. M., 648
Lasker-Schüler, Else, 625
Layb, Mane, 636
Lazarus, Emma, 599
Lebensohn, Micah Joseph, 598
Levin, Meyer, 31
Lewisohn, Ludwig, 69

Lieben, S., 28
Lowenthal, Marvin, 76
Luzzatto, S. D., 702
Maimon, Solomon, 278
Marx, Karl, 714
Maurois, André, 135
Meir of Rothenburg, 586
Mendele Mocher Seforim, 332
Mendelssohn, Moses, 703
Millin, Sarah Gertrude, 195
Montefiore, C. G., 767
Morpurgo, Rachel, 595
Moses ben Maimon, 686
Moses ibn Ezra, 572
Nahum, 590
Najara, Israel, 594
Nathan, Robert, 639
Nordau, Max, 761
Opatoshu, J., 237
Perez, Isaac Loeb, 217
Philo of Alexandria, 664
Pinski, David, 401
Potamkin, Harry Alan, 647
Rachel, 644
Raisen, Abraham, 626
Reubeni, David, 303
Reznikoff, Charles, 441
Rosenberg, Isaac, 641
Rosenfeld, Morris, 604
Ross, Leonard Q., 392

Roth, Henry, 38
Sackler, Harry, 514
Schechter, Solomon, 726
Schnaiur, Zalman, 636
Schneider, Isidor, 646
Schnitzler, Arthur, 468
Seaver, Edwin, 54
Shapiro, L., 251
Shiminowitz, David, 187
Shlonsky, Abraham, 643
Simeon ben Sira, 561
Sholem Aleichem, 342
Singer, I. J., 225
Smilansky, Moses, 191
Solomon ibn Gabirol, 564
Spinoza, Baruch, 698
Spire, André, 607
Steinberg, Judah, 260
Stern, G. B., 120
Syrkin, Nahman, 741
Tchernihowsky, Saul, 619
Untermeyer, Louis, 630
Wassermann, Jakob, 129
Werfel, Franz, 426
Yehoash, 609
Yushkevitch, Simeon, 246
Zangwill, Israel, 319
Zweig, Arnold, 126
Zweig, Stefan 411

INDEX OF TITLES

A Herring for My Uncle, 3
A Letter from America, 240
A Passover Eve, 233
A Pot Story, 355
A Tale of Barnow, 267
Aarons, 54
Among the Marranos, 303
Atticism and Judaism, 702
Baby Milly and the Pharaoh, 376
Before I Was Born, 350
Benjamin's First Journey, 332
Bitter Maté, 203
Civil and Religious Autonomy, 703
Divine Manifesto, 655
Egypt, 1937, 31
Emancipation and Judaism, 710
Escapade, 271
From Bodana's Diary, 159
Glass, 254
Heder, 38
How Many Angels . . . , 12
Holy Land, 69
In Defense of the Torah, 693
In Defense of Republics, 690
In the Dark, 504
Israel and the World, 679
Joseph Caro, 237
Judaism and Nationality, 718
Kabbalists, 283
Latifa, 191
Malkah, 225
Manasseh, 28
Meditations of a Sceptic, 658
Mendel Hertz, 150
Mendel Marantz—Housewife, 359
Michal, 401

Military Service, 260
Mrs. Gross Remembers, 389
Mr. Kaplan's So-and-So, 392
My Pigeon-House, 168
Of God and Man, 664
Of Prophecy, 686
Of Race Superiority, 698
Of the First and the Last Things, 672
Of the Jewish Religion, 773
Of Wisdom and Love, 656
On to Berlin, 278
Our Fathers That Begat Us, 76
Passover Fugue, 342
Paul and Gamaliel, 426
Professor Bernhardi, 468
Quest for God, 293
Rachel and Her Child, 44
Safe Harbour, 120
Shylock's Choice, 436
Socialism and Zionism, 741
Some Comfort, 730
The Account, 178
The Apparition, 126
The Case of Agathon Geyer, 129
The Decision, 195
The Emancipation of the Jew, 714
The Everlasting Road, 411
The Fast, 57
The Graves of the Maccabees, 187
The Haunted Cinema, 117
The Interpretation of Judaism, 722
The Jewish Question, 735
The Jewish Religion, 767
The King of Schnorrers, 319
The Kiss, 251
The Law in Judaism, 726

The Outing, 138
The Poor Jews, 135
The Saint of the Umbrella Store, 20
The Sciences and the Aim of Life, 669
The Seer Looks at his Bride, 514
The Sinner, 528
The Solution of the Jewish Problem, 755
The Spiritual Pattern of Judaism, 763
The Teaching of Jewish History, 749

The Tenets of Zionism, 761
The Trial, 457
The Unity of God, 670
The Zaddik, 156
Torah as a Way of Life, 775
They're Leaving . . . , 246
Three Gifts, 217
That Speck, 537
Uriel Acosta, 441
Work and Culture, 752
Zipporah's Wedding, 290

INDEX OF FIRST LINES OF POETRY

A jug of water in the hand, and on 645
A watery waste the sinful world has grown, 581
Ah, vale of woe, of gloom and darkness moulded, 595
Almighty! What is man? 567
And it shall come to pass in the last day, 551
And so we twain must part! Oh, linger yet, 579
And there are times when dreams are vanities. 637
As a signet of carbuncle 561
As a woman who holds me within her spell 643
Ask, is it well, O thou consumed of fire, 586
Behold my country—the carcass of a savage, 643
Bless the Lord, O my soul. 559
Blue and very quiet hour of evening, 636
But yesterday the earth drank like a child 577
By the life of our troth, my love, 579
By the rivers of Babylon 639
Come, my belovèd, to meet the Bride; 592
"Conquer the gloomy night of thy sorrow, for the morning greets thee with
     laughter. 571
Dew, precious dew, unto thy land forlorn! 563
Do you know what the mountains are? 630
Down the long hall she glistens like a star, 599
For our sore-shattered Jewish life 640
Forget thine anguish, 566
Full in her glory, she as Tirzah fair 561
Go to the ant, thou sluggard; 555
Girl, you must not cry: I tell you, you must not cry, 627
Give me free space! For my imprisoned sighs 628
Hark! my beloved! 548
Hear, O Israel! 607
Her blood flows in my blood; 645
Here are the graves. And here is thy grave too. 621
"Ho, everyone that thirsteth, come ye to the waters, 553
How do I love you? I never seek to know 648
I gave them the gold of my spirit, 627
I know that this my crying, like the crying 611

I will sing a song of battle   583
In the blossom-land Japan   609
In the dead of night I heard a sound of storm,   600
In the evening though her garden   595
It may be these things never did occur.   645
Laugh at all my dreams, my dearest;   624
Like an arrow shot   598
Long in the lap of childhood didst thou sleep,   578
Loved of my soul! Father of grace!   594
May has come from out the showers,   604
Moses, from whose loins I sprung,   641
My bowels, my bowels!   552
My help, my hope, my strength shall be,   582
My thoughts impelled me to the resting-place   576
My two-score years and ten are over,   580
Night, and the heavens beam serene with peace,   564
Now the dreary winter's over,   590
Now such am I; as quiet   644
Now will I sing to my wellbeloved   550
O city of the world, with sacred splendor blest,   579
O West, how fragrant breathes thy gentle air,   582
"Old Jews!" Well, David, aren't we?   630
On a wild horse, scattering rage and terror,   599
On with another new love,   627
Once, upon a time far distant,   603
Ophra washeth her garments in the waters   579
Out of the murk of wild and sinister day,   641
Praise ye the Lord for the avenging of Israel,   545
"See'st thou o'er my shoulders falling,   578
Set me as a seal upon thy heart,   549
Süsskind of Trimberg clad his soul in byssus,   647
Sweetheart, kiss the gray   626
That rock is crumbling   625
The Autumn promised, and he keeps   569
The beauty of Israel is slain upon thy high places: 547
The clusters in Thy vinyard turn to gold,   644
The long-closed door, oh, open it again, send me back once more my fawn
    that had fled.   585
The shadow of the houses leave behind,   572
The sky is dotted like th' unleavened bread,   649
The sun o'er the treetops is no longer seen;   617
The sweetest melody   626
There are abandoned corners of our Exile,   612

There be three things which are too wonderful for me,   555
There is a lonely mountain-top,   609
These are the chosen people. He has set   639
To thee I come, O long-abandoned god   619
Two steps from my garden rail   615
Unto the house of prayer my spirit yearns,   574
What is the crown of kings, and what the glory   642
Where is the man who has been tried and found strong and sound?   572
Who is this that darkeneth counsel by words without knowledge?   556
Will night already spread her wings and weave   564
Will the wolves lie down with the lambs and feed them?   618
With heavy groans did I approach my friends,   571
With such a throb does blood   646
"With tears thy grief thou dost bemoan,   570
Would that I had a little boy,   646
You will lift up your eyes to the heavens and know them not,   636

ACKNOWLEDGMENTS

Special thanks are due to the following authors and translators for permission to use their materials in this volume:

Henry C. Alsberg, Louis D. Brandeis, Stanley Burnshaw, John Cournos, Babette Deutsch, Edna Ferber, Irving Fineman, David Freedman, Michael Gold, Albert Halper, Hayyim Hazaz, Mordecai M. Kaplan, Abraham M. Klein, I. M. Lask, Meyer Levin, Paul P. Levertoff, Ludwig Lewisohn, Marvin Lowenthal, Kate Pohli-Macleod, Charles Reznikoff, Henry Roth, Maurice Samuel, Edwin Seaver, Isidor Schneider, G. B. Stern, Marie Syrkin.

And grateful acknowledgment is made to the following holders of copyright and publishers:

Brentano's, New York: for *A Letter from America* from *A Lithuanian* by Leon Kobrin; Covici Friede, Inc., New York: for *Baby Milly and the Pharaoh* from *The Champion from Far Away* by Ben Hecht; E. P. Dutton & Co., New York: for *The End of Sorrow* from *The Wall of Weeping* by Edmond Fleg, translated by Humbert Wolfe; The East and West Publishing Co., New York, and Harry Rogoff: for selections from the *East and West* magazine; Farrar & Rinehart, Inc., and Eric S. Pinker & Adrienne Morrison, Inc., New York: for *The Haunted Cinema* from *This Wanderer* by Louis Golding, and *Rachel and Her Child* from *Singermann* by Myron Brinig; Gilboa Publishing Co., New York: for *Glass* by I. D. Berkowitz and *The Seer Looks at His Bride* by Harry Sackler from *Reflex;* Harper Bros., New York: for selections from *Rebirth* translated by Ludwig Lewisohn; The Hebrew Union College, Cincinnati: for *The Sciences and the Aim of Life* by Abraham ibn Daud, translated by Harry A. Wolfson; John Heritage, London: for *The Poor Jews* by André Maurois from *Yisroel;* Harcourt, Brace and Company, New York: for *Roast Leviathan* from *Roast Leviathan* by Louis Untermeyer; Houghton Mifflin and Company, Boston: for selected translations from *The Poems of Emma Lazarus;* The Jewish Publication Society of America, Philadelphia: for selections from *Ikkarim* by Joseph Albo, translated by Isaac Husik, *Studies in Judaism* by Solomon Schechter, *Selected Essays* by Achad Haam, translated by Leon Simon, *In Those Days* by Jehudah Steinberg and *Post-Biblical Hebrew Literature* by B. Halper; Alfred A. Knopf, New York: for *These Are the Chosen People* from *Selected Poems* by Robert Nathan, and *Escapade* from *Reubeni* by Max Brod; Paul P. Levertoff and A. R. Mowbray & Co., London: for *Paul and Gamaliel* from *Paul Among the Jews* by Franz Werfel; Liveright Publishing Corporation, New York: for *The Case of Agathon Geyer* from *The Dark Pilgrimage* by Jakob Wassermann, *Malkah* from *The Sinner* by I. J. Singer, *The Decision* from *The Coming of the Lord* by Sarah Gertrude Millin, and *The Saint of the Umbrella Store* from *Jews Without Money* by Michael Gold; The Loeb Classical Library and the Harvard University Press, Cambridge, Mass.: for *Of God and Man* from *Philo,* translated by F. H. Colson and G. H. Whitaker; The Macmillan Company, New York: for *The King of Schnorrers* by Israel Zangwill; the *Menorah Journal,* New York: for *Our Fathers That Begat Us* by Marvin Lowenthal, *Uriel Acoste* by Charles Reznikoff, *How Many Angels* . . . by Irving Fineman, *Benjamin's First Trip* by Mendele Mocher Seforim, translated by Yossef Gaer, *Joy of Knowledge* by Isidor Schneider, and *Süsskind of Trimberg* by Harry Alan Potamkin; *The New Yorker* and Maxim Lieber, New York: for *Mr. Kaplan's So-and-So* by Leonard Q. Ross; *Opinion,* New York: for *Of the Jewish Religion* by Albert Einstein and *The Zaddik* by Ilya Ehrenbourg, translated by Leon Dennen; Leonard Parsons, London: for *The Emancipation of the Jew* from *Selected Essays* by Karl Marx, translated by H. J. Stenning; A. D. Peters and G. B. Stern, London: for *Safe Harbour* from *Debatable Ground* by G. B. Stern; Random House, Inc., New York: for *That Speck* from *Rain from Heaven* by S. N. Behrman; Henry Roth and Robert Ballou, publisher, New York: for *Heder* from *Call It Sleep* by Henry Roth; George Rutledge and Sons, London: for *Among the Marranos* from *Jewish Travellers* by Elkan Adler; Simon & Schuster, Inc., New York: for *Mrs. Gross Remembers* from *Thunder Over the Bronx* by Arthur Kober and *The Picnic* from *"— & Company"* by Jean-Richard Bloch; The Viking Press, New York: for *A Herring for My Uncle* from *On the Shore* by Albert Halper, *Michal* from *King David and His Wives* by David Pinski, *Kabbalists* from *Power* by Lion Feuchtwanger, *Egypt, 1937,* from *The Old Bunch* by Meyer Levin, *The Everlasting Road* from *Jeremiah* by Stefan Zweig, and *The Apparition* from *Playthings of Time* by Arnold Zweig.